Chapter 1: Problem Solving

MATH IN ▶ Criminal Investigation

In traditional cops-and-robbers movies, crime fighters use guns and fists to catch criminals, but in real life, more often than not it's brain power that brings the bad guys to justice. That's why the show CSI marked a revolution of sorts when it debuted in October of 2000: it featured scientists fighting crime, not tough guys. Solving a case is intimately tied to the process of problem solving: investigators are presented with a mystery, and use whatever evidence they can find and their reasoning ability to reconstruct the crime. Continue reading about Math in Criminal Investigation on page 3.

Chapter 2: Sets

MATH IN ▶ Demographics

The world certainly has changed a lot in the last fifty years. If you could travel back to the middle of the twentieth century, you'd have an awful hard time finding anyone that would believe that one of the most famous, and richest, people in the world in the early twenty-first century would be a golfer that is part white, part African-American, and part Asian. Our society is becoming more and more diverse every year, to the point where even defining what we mean by "race" isn't so easy anymore. Sorting it all out to get any sort of meaningful picture of what we as Americans look like isn't easy, and the techniques of set theory are very useful tools in trying to do so. Continue reading about Math in Demographics on page 41.

Chapter 3: Logic

MATH IN ▶ The Art of Persuasion

Everywhere you turn in modern society, somebody is trying to convince you of something. "Vote for me!" "Buy my product!" "Lease a car from our dealership!" "Bailing out the auto industry is a bad idea!" "You should go out with me this weekend!" "Join our fraternity!" Logic is sometimes defined as correct thinking or correct reasoning. Some people refer to logic by a more casual name: common sense. Regardless of what you call it, the ability to think logically is crucial for everyone because our lives are inundated daily with advertisements, contracts, product and service warranties, political debates, and news commentaries, to name just a few. Continue reading about Math in the Art of Persuasion on page 91.

Chapter 9: Measurement

MATH IN ▶ Travel

To measure something means to assign a number that represents its size. In fact, measurement might be the most common use of numbers in everyday life. Numbers are used to measure height, weight, distance, grades, weather, size of a home, capacity of bottles and cans, and much more. Even in our monetary system, we use numbers to measure sizes: little ones, like the cost of a candy bar, and big ones, like an annual salary. One obvious application of this skill comes into play when traveling outside the United States. Most countries use the metric system almost exclusively, meaning that to understand various bits of information, you need to be able to interpret measurements in an unfamiliar system. Continue reading about Math in Travel on page 481.

Chapter 10: Geometry

MATH IN > **Home Improvement**

It probably won't surprise you to learn that one of the most common questions that math students ask is "How can I actually use this stuff?" Of course, how math is used in our world is the main theme of this book, and this chapter fits that framework especially well. The ideas presented are commonly used in everyday things like working around the home, so we'll present some actual projects that geometry was used for in the home of one of the authors. **Continue reading about Math in Home Improvement on page 511.**

Chapter 11: Probability and Counting Techniques

MATH IN > **Gambling**

The fact that you're reading this sentence means that you're probably taking a math class right now. But maybe not...you could be an instructor evaluating the book, or maybe an editor looking for mistakes (unsuccessfully, we hope). Still, I would be willing to bet that you're taking a math class. The word "probably" indicates a certain likelihood of something happening, and that basic idea is the topic of this chapter. We call the study of the likelihood of events occurring probability. **Continue reading about Math in Gambling on page 573.**

Chapter 12: Statistics

MATH IN > **Sociology**

Broadly defined, sociology is the study of human behavior within society. One important branch is criminology. This is not about investigating crimes, but rather studying patterns of criminal behavior and their effect on society. The main tool used by sociologists is statistics. This important area of math allows researchers to study patterns of behavior objectively by analyzing information gathered from a mathematical perspective, not a subjective one. **Continue reading about Math in Sociology on page 647.**

MATH
in Our World
Second Edition

David Sobecki
Associate Professor
Miami University Hamilton

Allan G. Bluman
Professor Emeritus
Community College of Allegheny County

Angela Schirck-Matthews
Professor
Broward College

MGF 1106
Liberal Arts Math

Special Edition for
Saint Petersburg College

Boston   Burr Ridge, IL   Dubuque, IA   New York   San Francisco   St. Louis
Bangkok   Bogotá   Caracas   Lisbon   London   Madrid
Mexico City   Milan   New Delhi   Seoul   Singapore   Sydney   Taipei   Toronto

The **McGraw-Hill** Companies

Math in Our World, Second Edition
MGF 1106
Liberal Arts Math
Special Edition for Saint Petersburg College

This book is a McGraw-Hill Learning Solutions textbook and contains select material from *Math in Our World*, Second Edition by Dave Sobecki, Allan G. Bluman and Angela Schirck-Matthews. Copyright © 2011 by The McGraw-Hill Companies, Inc. Reprinted with permission of the publisher. Many custom published texts are modified versions or adaptations of our best-selling textbooks. Some adaptations are printed in black and white to keep prices at a minimum, while others are in color.

1 2 3 4 5 6 7 8 9 0 KNG KNG 12 11 10

ISBN-13: 978-0-07-745350-3
ISBN-10: 0-07-745350-6

Learning Solutions Specialist: Jeff Schmitt
Production Editor: Jessica Portz
Printer/Binder: King Printing

Brief Contents

About the Authors

Dave Sobecki

Dave Sobecki is an associate professor in the Department of Mathematics at Miami University in Hamilton, Ohio. He earned a B.A. in math education from Bowling Green State University before continuing on to earn an M.A. and a Ph.D. in mathematics from Bowling Green State University. He has written or coauthored five journal articles, eleven books, and five interactive CD-ROMs. Dave lives in Fairfield, Ohio, with his wife (Cat) and dogs (Macleod and Tessa).

His passions include Ohio State football, Cleveland Indians baseball, heavy metal music, travel, and home improvement projects.

Dedication: *To two of my biggest supporters: my wife Cat, and my friend Dawn.*

Allan G. Bluman

Allan G. Bluman is a professor emeritus at the Community College of Allegheny County, South Campus, near Pittsburgh, Pennsylvania. He has taught mathematics and statistics for over 35 years. He received an Apple for the Teacher award in recognition of his bringing excellence to the learning environment at South Campus. He has also taught statistics for Penn State University at the Greater Allegheny (McKeesport) Campus and at the Monroeville Center. He received his master's and doctor's degrees from the University of Pittsburgh.

He is the author of two other textbooks, *Elementary Statistics: A Step By Step Approach* and *Elementary Statistics: A Brief Version.* In addition, he is the author of four mathematics books in the McGraw-Hill DeMystified Series. They are *Pre-Algebra, Math Word Problems, Business Math,* and *Probability.*

He is married and has two sons and a granddaughter.

Dedication: *To Betty Bluman, Earl McPeek, and Dr. G. Bradley Seager, Jr.*

Angela Schirck-Matthews

Angela Schirck-Matthews is a Professor of Mathematics at Broward College in Davie, Florida, where she has been teaching mathematics since 1991. Before her employment at Broward College she taught undergraduate mathematics at the University of Miami in Coral Gables, Florida. She is also an alumna of both institutions; Angela earned an Associate of Arts degree in liberal arts at Broward College and went on to earn a Bachelor of Arts degree in mathematics at Florida Atlantic University in Boca Raton, Florida. After graduating from Florida Atlantic University, she continued her education at the University of Miami where she earned a Master of Science degree in mathematics and completed coursework toward a Ph.D. in mathematics.

Angela lives in Hollywood, Florida with her husband, three of her four children, and two dogs.

Dedication: *To my parents Joe and Karen, for their love and encouragement throughout my life.*

Letter from the Authors

Liberal arts math is a challenging course to teach because most of the time, the audience is very different from other college math classes. For most students the course is terminal, and in many cases represents the only math credits the student will take in college. Given this audience, it can often be a great challenge to motivate students and make them see the relevance of math, how math plays a role in our world, and how the thinking and problem-solving strategies that students will learn and practice can be used beyond the classroom.

The first step to gaining interest is to find a way to **engage** students. This is typically done using applications, but too often we rely on the old classics, the applications that we remember from our own education. This is where the two new coauthors come in (Dave and Angie): each is known for making math engaging to students, and together, they bring a fresh, modern approach to the second edition. To fully engage students in the 21st century, we need to think modern, emphasizing applications that show the relevance of math to today's students. We've made every attempt to make that the focus of this edition, from financing a car to figuring out a healthy daily calorie intake to understanding how overwhelming our national debt really is, and what that means to us as citizens. The pizza theme that is carried throughout the book is a constant reminder to students that math isn't a spectator sport, but something that plays an important role in their everyday lives.

No one has ever become stronger by watching someone else lift weights, and our students aren't going to be any better at thinking and problem-solving unless we encourage them to **practice** it on their own. *Math in Our World* includes a plethora of applications and real-world problems for students to hone their skills and give their brains a workout. The critical thinking skills they practice in using this text will serve them well in any future courses whether there is math involved or not. But more important, it will help them to become problem solvers and thinkers beyond the halls of academia.

Once we've drawn your students' attention and offered them plenty of practice, we turn to our ultimate goal in writing this text: helping your students to **succeed.** We're confident that this book offers a fantastic vehicle to drive your classes to higher pass rates because of the pedagogical elements, writing style, and interesting problem sets. Additionally, while no book can prevent the underpreparedness of students in a course like this, we've got you covered there as well with ALEKS Prep. You can read more about it on the back cover and on preface pages x and xi.

Finally, to further emphasize clarity and consistency, we as an author team took it upon ourselves to produce the lecture videos, exercise videos, and solution manuals to accompany *Math in Our World,* allowing our voices to carry throughout these supplements, perfectly complementing the text. We hope that you and your students enjoy using *Math in Our World* as much as we enjoyed writing it and putting all the pieces together. Good luck, and please don't hesitate to contact your local McGraw-Hill representative to let us know what you think!

—*Dave, Al, and Angie*

Engage

Joint experiences in the classroom have helped each of the authors bring a unique perspective to the text, influencing the **writing style** significantly. Both practical and conversational, the writing functions as a tool to guide learning for students outside of the classroom. The goal is to draw in even the most hesitant students by relating to them through the casual, spoken language they regularly use with friends. By doing so, students gain both a firm initial understanding of the basic concepts fundamental to the curriculum and also a greater degree of retention of the long-term implications of those concepts.

● **Chapter Openers** directly engage student interest by immediately tying mathematical concepts to each of their everyday lives. These vignettes introduce concepts by referencing popular topics familiar to a wide variety of students— travel, demographics, the economy, television, and even college football. By taking slower steps to reach the critical topics of a chapter, students are able to more fully grasp how math really does relate to their own world, further solidifying the connections imperative to retention of information.

● Used to clarify concepts and emphasize particularly important points, **Math Notes** provide suggestions for students to keep in mind as they progress through the chapter.

Math Note

We often use the word *nearest* to describe the place value to round to. Instead of saying, "Round to the hundreds place," we might say, "Round to the nearest hundred."

● **Sidelights** contain carefully chosen material highlighting relevant interdisciplinary connections within math to encourage both curiosity and motivation in students who have a wide variety of interests. These include biographic vignettes about famous mathematicians as well as other interesting facts that emphasize the importance of math in areas like weather, photography, music, and health.

Sidelight AN ARBITRARY DISCUSSION

In common usage, the word *arbitrary* is often misinterpreted as a synonym for *random*. When reaching into a bag of potato chips, you make a random selection, and some people would also call this an arbitrary selection. But in math, the word *arbitrary* means something very different. When randomly selecting that chip, you have still chosen a specific chip—it is probably not representative of every chip in the bag. Some chips will be bigger, and others smaller. Still others may have more salt, some less.

When we use *arbitrary* in math, we're referring to a nonspecific item that is able to represent *all* such items. In the series of calculations we looked at above, we could never

be sure that the result will always be 3 [...]
numbers. Why? Because we'd have to try [...]
which is of course impossible. You have [...]
than spend the rest of your life testing nu[...]
The value of performing the calculation [...]
ber *x* is that this one calculation proves [...]
every number you choose. It is absolutely [...]
of mathematics to understand that choo[...]
bers can almost never *prove* a result, be[...]
every number. Instead, we'll rely on usin[...]
and deductive reasoning.

34. Estimate the total cost of the following items for your dorm room:
Loft bed	$159.95
Beanbag chair	$49.95
Storage cubes	$29.95
Lava lamp	$19.95
35. Estimate the time it would take you in a charity bike tour to ride 86 miles at a rate of 11 miles per hour.
36. If a person earns $48,300.00 per year, estimate how

(pie chart: After office hours 9%; Before office hours 25%; Last few office hours 13%; First few working hours 31%; Late morning/early afternoon 22%. Source: USA Today)

47. Estimate the number of people who feel they are most productive outside normal office hours.

● Highly relevant real-world **Application Exercises and Examples** drawn from the experiences and research of the author team further emphasize the importance that *Math in Our World* places upon students' ability to form a distinct connection with the mathematical content. This helps students relate mathematical concepts presented in a section and the real life relevance of something familiar to them, increasing both student interest and motivation—key factors affecting their comprehension. The new edition brings many brand new and updated application exercises to students in each chapter, ranging in topics from **MP3** player usage, college degree majors, elections, relevant business decisions, and scenarios involving popular statistics.

● An **Index of Applications** is located immediately after the Detailed Table of Contents and is organized by discipline to help identify applications relevant to specific fields.

Practice

Implementing the **Step-by-Step Approach** used for years in Allan Bluman's *Elementary Statistics: A Step by Step Approach,* this text seeks to guide even the most hesitant student through the basic concepts fundamental to a liberal arts math curriculum. The authors realize that, in order to do so, students need to be introduced to those concepts through a highly relevant example in the opening vignette of each chapter. Carefully chosen questions immediately follow the opening vignette to help students form a connection between the relevant example and the mathematical concepts of the chapter, easing the transition for them. Using the engaging writing style characteristic of the text, the authors support concepts through abundant examples, helpful practice problems, and rich exercise sets.

● **Worked Example Problems** with detailed solutions help students master key concepts. Where solutions consist of more than one step, a numbered, step-by-step procedure is used to guide students through the problem-solving process. Additionally, each example is titled to highlight relevant learning objectives.

● One of our hallmark features, **Try This One** practice exercises provide immediate reinforcement for students. Designed to naturally follow each example, these practice exercises ask students to solve a similar problem, actively involving them in the learning process. All answers to Try This One exercises can be found just prior to the end-of-section exercise sets for students to complete the problem-solving process by confirming their solutions.

Calculator Guide

If you use a calculator to try the repeated operations in Example 8, you'll need to press ⊟ (scientific calculator) or ENTER (graphing calculator) after every operation, or you'll get the wrong result. Suppose you simply enter the whole string:

Standard Scientific Calculator

12 ➕ 50 ✖ 2 ➖ 12 ✚

Standard Graphing Calculator

12 ➕ 50 ✖ 2 ➖ 12 ENTER

The result is 100, which is incorrect. In Chapter 5, we'll find out why when we study the order of operations.

EXAMPLE 4 Using Inductive Reasoning to Test a Conjecture

Use inductive reasoning to decide if the following conjecture is true: Any four-digit number is divisible by 11 if the difference between the sum of the first and third digits and the sum of the second and fourth digits is divisible by 11.

SOLUTION

Let's make up a few examples. For 1,738, the sum of the first and third digits is $1 + 3 = 4$, and the sum of the second and fourth digits is $7 + 8 = 15$. The difference is $15 - 4 = 11$, so if the conjecture is true, 1,738 should be divisible by 11. To check: $1,738 \div 11 = 158$ (with no remainder).

For 9,273, $9 + 7 = 16$, $2 + 3 = 5$, and $16 - 5 = 11$. So if the conjecture is true, 9,273 should be divisible by 11. To check: $9,273 \div 11 = 843$ (with no remainder).

Let's look at one more example. For 7,161, $7 + 6 = 13$, $1 + 1 = 2$, and $13 - 2 = 11$. Also $7,161 \div 11 = 651$ (with no remainder), so the conjecture is true for this example as well. While we can't be positive based on three examples, inductive reasoning indicates that the conjecture is true.

▼ **Try This One 4**

Use inductive reasoning to decide if the following conjecture is true: If the sum

---

"I think Try This One makes a great addition to the worked examples, and I would definitely integrate them into the classroom lecture process."

—*Marcia Lambert, Pitt Community College*

"Examples are true to life and ones students will relate to."

—*John Ward, Jefferson Community and Technical College*

"The examples and 'Try This One' encourage individual learning."

—*Sam Buckner, North Greenville University*

● Optional **Calculator Guides** are set in the margins to show students how to use a calculator to solve certain examples, enhancing their skill set for solving problems. Keystrokes for both standard scientific calculators as well as standard TI-84 Plus graphing calculators are shown in order to accommodate students with a variety of tools available to them.

The rich variety of problem material found in the **End-of-Section Exercise Sets** helps check student knowledge in a variety of different ways to cater to the varying interests and educational backgrounds of liberal arts math students. In each end-of-section exercise set, there are:

● **Writing Exercises** that nurture the increased emphasis being placed on writing across the curriculum for many schools. These exercises provide an opportunity for students to summarize with words the key mathematical concepts from the section before attempting other exercises, a skill that may come more naturally for your students than computation.

● Traditional **Computational Exercises** provide additional practice for students, reinforcing relevant concepts just learned with increasing levels of difficulty.

● **Critical Thinking Exercises** drive students to take a concept that they have learned in a given section and apply it in a new direction or setting, revealing a deeper level of understanding.

Exercises and activities located in the **End-of-Chapter Material** provide opportunities for students to prepare for success on quizzes or tests. At the conclusion of each chapter, students find critical summary information that helps them pull together each step learned while moving through the chapter. In each end-of-chapter segment, students and instructors will find:

● An **End-of-Chapter Summary,** separated by section, reviews the important terms and ideas students should have learned from the material. Answers to the questions posed in the opening vignette are also provided, ushering students back to the central theme that mathematics is truly ingrained in many aspects of their lives. This brief summary helps students to gather details that may have at first seemed disparate and assemble them in a logical progression.

● **Review Exercises** are also presented by section with a combination of both computational and real-world application exercises similar to those found in the end-of-section exercise sets.

● A **Chapter Test** gives students the opportunity to check their knowledge of the chapter as a whole in order to prepare for classroom quizzes, tests, and other larger assessments.

● **Chapter Projects** encourage more in-depth investigation for students working to summarize key concepts from the entire chapter. These projects are more extensive than any of the review exercises or test questions and are valuable assets for instructors looking for ways that students can work collaboratively.

Succeed

Experience Student Success!

ALEKS ALEKS is a unique online math tool that uses adaptive questioning and artificial intelligence to correctly place, prepare, and remediate students . . . all in one product! Institutional case studies have shown that **ALEKS has improved pass rates by over 20% versus traditional online homework and by over 30% compared to using a text alone.**

By offering each student an individualized learning path, ALEKS directs students to work on the math topics that they are ready to learn. Also, to help students keep pace in their course, instructors can correlate ALEKS to their textbook or syllabus in seconds.

To learn more about how ALEKS can be used to boost student performance, please visit **www.aleks.com/highered/math** or contact your McGraw-Hill representative.

ALEKS Pie
Each student is given his/her own individualized learning path.

Easy Graphing Utility!
Students can answer graphing problems with ease!

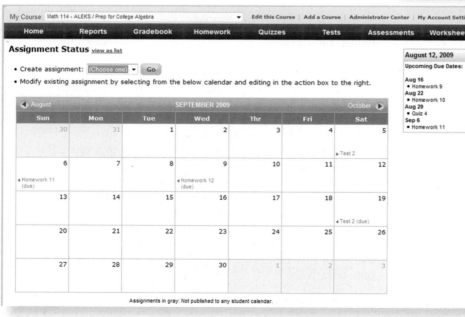

Course Calendar
Instructors can schedule assignments and reminders for students.

New ALEKS Instructor Module
Enhanced Functionality and Streamlined Interface Help to Save Instructor Time

ALEKS® The new ALEKS Instructor Module features enhanced functionality and a streamlined interface based on research with ALEKS instructors and homework management instructors. Paired with powerful assignment driven features, textbook integration, and extensive content flexibility, the new ALEKS Instructor Module simplifies administrative tasks and makes ALEKS more powerful than ever.

Gradebook view for all students

Gradebook view for an individual student

New Gradebook!
Instructors can seamlessly track student scores on automatically graded assignments. They can also easily adjust the weighting and grading scale of each assignment.

Track Student Progress Through Detailed Reporting
Instructors can track student progress through automated reports and robust reporting features.

Automatically Graded Assignments
Instructors can easily assign homework, quizzes, tests, and assessments to all or select students. Deadline extensions can also be created for select students.

Learn more about ALEKS by visiting **www.aleks.com/highered/math** or contact your McGraw-Hill representative.

Supplements

MathZone www.mhhe.com/sobecki. McGraw-Hill's MathZone is a complete online homework system for mathematics and statistics. Instructors can assign textbook-specific content from over 40 McGraw-Hill titles as well as customize the level of feedback students receive, including the ability to have students show their work for any given exercise. Assignable content includes an array of videos and other multimedia along with algorithmic exercises, providing study tools for students with many different learning styles.

MathZone also helps ensure consistent assignment delivery across several sections through a course administration function and makes sharing courses with other instructors easy. In addition, instructors can also take advantage of a virtual whiteboard by setting up a Live Classroom for online office hours or a review session with students.

For more information, visit the book's website www.mhhe.com/sobecki or contact your local McGraw-Hill sales representative www.mhhe.com/rep.

Visual Reporting – The new dashboard-like reports will provide the progress snapshot instructors are looking for to help them make informed decisions about their students.

Item Analysis – Instructors can view detailed statistics on student performance at a learning objective level to understand what students have mastered and where they need additional help.

Managing Assignments for Individual Students – Instructors have greater control over creating individualized assignment parameters for individual students, special populations and groups of students, and for managing specific or ad hoc course events.

New User Interface – Designed by You! Instructors and students will experience a modern, more intuitive layout. Items used most commonly are easily accessible through the menu bar such as assignments, visual reports, and course management options.

Instructor Supplements

- **Computerized Test Bank Online:** Utilizing Brownstone Diploma® algorithm-based testing software, this supplement enables users to create customized exams quickly.
- **Instructor Solutions Manual:** Written by author Angela Schirck-Matthews, the *Instructor Solutions Manual* provides comprehensive, worked-out solutions to all exercises in the text. The methods used to solve the problems in the manual are the same as those used to solve the examples in the textbook. The manual can be found on the Instructor Center at the book's website: www.mhhe.com/sobecki.
- **PowerPoint Slides:** These slides closely follow the textbook, and are completely editable.

Student Supplements

- **Student Solutions Manual:** Written by author Angela Schirck-Matthews, the *Student Solutions Manual* provides comprehensive, worked-out solutions to all of the odd-numbered exercises. The steps shown in the solutions match the style of the worked examples found in the text.
- **Lecture Videos:** Engaging lectures by author Dave Sobecki introduce concepts, definitions, theorems, formulas, and problem solving procedures to help students better comprehend key topics. The videos can be found online at www.mhhe.com/sobecki.
- **Exercise Videos:** Presented by author Angela Schirck-Matthews, these videos work through selected exercises, following the solution methodology found in the text. The videos can be found online at www.mhhe.com/sobecki.

McGraw Hill Tegrity campus

http://tegritycampus.mhhe.com

- Tegrity Campus is a service that makes class time available all the time by automatically capturing every lecture in a searchable format for students to review when they study and complete assignments. With a simple one-click start and stop process, you capture all computer screens and corresponding audio. Students replay any part of any class with easy-to-use browser-based viewing on a PC or Mac.
- Educators know that the more students can see, hear, and experience class resources, the better they learn. With Tegrity Campus, students quickly recall key moments by using Tegrity Campus's unique search feature. This search helps students efficiently find what they need, when they need it across an entire semester of class recordings. Help turn all your students' study time into learning moments immediately supported by your lecture.
- To learn more about Tegrity watch a 2 minute Flash demo at http://tegritycampus.mhhe.com.

ALEKS®

ALEKS (**A**ssessment and **LE**arning in **K**nowledge **S**paces) is a dynamic online learning system for mathematics education, available over the Web 24/7. ALEKS assesses students, accurately determines their knowledge, and then guides them to the material that they are most ready to learn.

With a variety of reports, Textbook Integration Plus, quizzes, and homework assignment capabilities, ALEKS offers flexibility and ease of use for instructors.

- ALEKS uses artificial intelligence to determine exactly what each student knows and is ready to learn. ALEKS remediates student gaps and provides highly efficient learning and improved learning outcomes
- ALEKS is a comprehensive curriculum that aligns with syllabi or specified textbooks. Used in conjunction with McGraw-Hill texts, students also receive links to text-specific videos, multimedia tutorials, and textbook pages.
- ALEKS offers a dynamic classroom management system that enables instructors to monitor and direct student progress toward mastery of course objectives.

ALEKS Prep/Remediation:

- Helps instructors meet the challenge of remediating unequally prepared or improperly placed students.
- Assesses students on their prerequisite knowledge needed for the course they are entering (for example, calculus students are tested on precalculus knowledge) and prescribes unique and efficient learning paths specific to their strengths and weaknesses.
- Students can address prerequisite knowledge gaps outside of class, freeing the instructor to use class time pursuing course outcomes.

Electronic Textbook: CourseSmart is a new way for faculty to find and review e-textbooks. It's also a great option for students who are interested in accessing their course materials digitally and saving money. CourseSmart offers thousands of the most commonly adopted textbooks across hundreds of courses from a wide variety of higher education publishers. It is the only place for faculty to review and compare the full text of a textbook online, providing immediate access without the environmental impact of requesting a print exam copy. At CourseSmart, students can save up to 50 percent off the cost of a print book, reduce their impact on the environment, and gain access to powerful Web tools for learning including full text search, notes and highlighting, and email tools for sharing notes between classmates. To learn more, visit **www.CourseSmart.com.**

Create: Craft your teaching resources to match the way you teach! With McGraw-Hill Create, **www.mcgrawhillcreate.com,** you can easily rearrange chapters, combine material from other content sources, and quickly upload content you have written like your course syllabus or teaching notes. Find the content you need in Create by searching through thousands of leading McGraw-Hill textbooks. Arrange your book to fit your teaching style. Create even allows you to personalize your book's appearance by selecting the cover and adding your name, school, and course information. Order a Create book and you'll receive a complimentary print review copy in 3–5 business days or a complimentary electronic review copy (eComp) via email in about one hour. Go to **www.mcgrawhillcreate.com** today and register. Experience how McGraw-Hill Create empowers you to teach *your* students *your* way.

Design
Based on Student Feedback

The development team at McGraw-Hill Higher Education realizes that there are many elements beyond content that contribute to creation of a student-friendly textbook. After hosting several student focus groups, we have learned a great deal about how students use their books, what pedagogical elements are useful, which elements are distracting and not useful, and general feedback on page layout. As a result of this feedback, we have integrated many of the student suggestions in a manner that is helpful for students, and simultaneously does not detract from instructor use of the text.

The following specific choices in *Math in Our World* have been made to increase student engagement based directly upon this feedback.

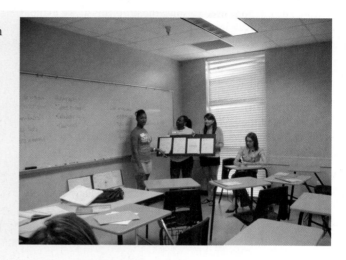

Section 1-1 The Nature of Mathematical Reasoning

Learning Objectives clearly define and set goals for students at the beginning of each section to focus and direct their learning.

LEARNING OBJECTIVES

☐ 1. Identify two types of reasoning.

☐ 2. Use inductive

Part of being an adult is making decisions—every day is full of them, from the simple, like what to eat for breakfast, to the critical, like a choice of major. If you make every decision based on a coin flip, chances are you won't get very far in life. Instead, it's important to be able to analyze a situation and make a decision based on logical thinking. We'll call the process of logical thinking **reasoning.** It doesn't take a lot of imagination to understand how important reasoning is in everyone's life.

EXAMPLE 5   Finding a Counterexample

Find a counterexample that proves the conjecture below is false.
Conjecture: A number is divisible by 3 if the last two digits are divisible by 3.

SOLUTION

We'll pick a few numbers at random whose last two digits are divisible by 3, then divide them by 3, and see if there's a remainder.

1,527: Last two digits, 27, divisible by 3; $1,527 \div 3 = 509$
11,745: Last two digits, 45, divisible by 3; $11,427 \div 3 = 3,809$

At this point, you might start to suspect that the conjecture is true, but you shouldn't! We've only checked two cases.

1,136: Last two digits, 36, divisible by 3; $1,136 \div 3 = 378\frac{2}{3}$

This counterexample shows that the conjecture is false.

Check boxes alert students to the completion of each goal once a learning objective has been completed.

☑ 3. Find a counterexample to disprove a conjecture.

▼ Try This One 5

Find a counterexample to disprove the conjecture that the name of every month in English contains either the letter y or the letter r.

CAUTION

Remember: One counterexample is enough to show that a conjecture is false. But one positive example is *never* enough to show that a conjecture is true.

Making caution boxes red and placing them in the body of the text emphasizes their importance for students and makes them a more useful tool.

Example headings are shaded and pulled out in to the margins to make them easy for students to identify.

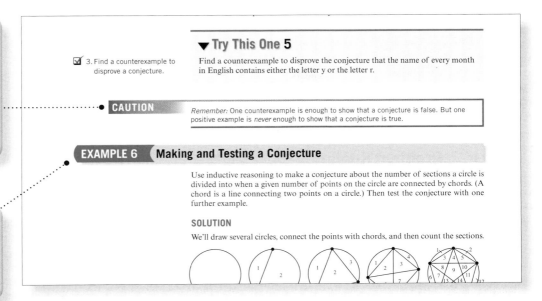

▼ **Try This One 5**

☑ 3. Find a counterexample to disprove a conjecture.

Find a counterexample to disprove the conjecture that the name of every month in English contains either the letter y or the letter r.

CAUTION

Remember: One counterexample is enough to show that a conjecture is false. But one positive example is *never* enough to show that a conjecture is true.

EXAMPLE 6   **Making and Testing a Conjecture**

Use inductive reasoning to make a conjecture about the number of sections a circle is divided into when a given number of points on the circle are connected by chords. (A chord is a line connecting two points on a circle.) Then test the conjecture with one further example.

SOLUTION

We'll draw several circles, connect the points with chords, and then count the sections.

Students said that when they spend a lot of time on the exercise sets, a white background can be hard on their eyes. To help them, we have chosen to use soft colors for both end-of-section and end-of-chapter exercise sets.

EXERCISE SET 1-1

Writing Exercises

1. Explain the difference between inductive and deductive reasoning.
2. What is meant by the term *conjecture?*
3. Give a real-life example of how to use inductive reasoning.
4. What is a counterexample? What are counterexamples used for?
5. Explain why you can never be sure that a conclusion you arrived at using inductive reasoning is true.
6. Explain the difference between an arbitrary number and a number selected at random.

Computational Exercises

For Exercises 7–14, use inductive reasoning to find a pattern, and then make a reasonable conjecture for the next number or item in the sequence.

7. 1   2   4   7   11   16   22   29   __
8. 5   15   45   135   405   1215

11. 100   99   97   94   90   85   79   __
12. 9   12   11   14   13   16   15   18   __

13.

A darker shaded bar runs along all end-of-chapter material to make it easily identifiable for students.

Review Exercises

Section 1-1

For Exercises 1–4, make reasonable conjectures for the next three numbers or letters in the sequence.

1. 3   4   6   7   9   10   12   13   15   16   __ __ __
2. 2   7   4   9   6   11   8   13   __ __ __

For Exercises 5 and 6, make a reasonable conjecture and draw the next figure.

5.

Updated Content

CHAPTER 1 Problem Solving

- Section 1-1 on mathematical reasoning has been expanded from three examples to ten examples.
- New real-world application exercises have been added throughout the chapter to reinforce the real-world relevance of key concepts, particularly in Section 1-1 where the total number of exercises has increased from 23 to 70.
- Sections 1-2 and 1-3 have been rearranged so that estimation is learned first. This allows it to then be used later in the chapter as a tool in problem solving.
- Estimation in particular has many new problems based on real data that will interest modern college students, including more examples than the previous edition.

CHAPTER 2 Sets

- Coverage is greatly increased throughout the chapter, including new sub-sections on cardinality of sets (Section 2-1), set subtraction and Cartesian product (Section 2-2), DeMorgan's laws and cardinality of unions (Section 2-3), and countable and uncountable sets (Section 2-5).
- Eight new applications have been added to Section 2-1, establishing a total of thirty-four questions based on current events and relevant data. Additionally, thirty-six new application exercises have been added to Sections 2-3 and 2-4.
- Two new sidelights on infinite sets in Section 2-5 have been added to increase the interdisciplinary connections students can make to enhance their understanding of key concepts.

CHAPTER 3 Logic

- The coverage of truth tables has been standardized by using the method of building new columns for parts of compound statements as the main presentation. To accommodate a variety of teaching styles, the method of writing truth values underneath connectives is still presented as an alternative method.
- An application of truth tables has been added as a worked example in Section 3-2.
- Content updates include the addition of DeMorgan's laws to Section 3-3 and circular reasoning among common fallacies in Section 3-4.
- A total of thirty-eight new application exercises have been added to Sections 3-2 and 3-3 and the applications in Section 3-4 have been updated to reflect current student interests.

CHAPTER 4 Numeration Systems

- Coverage of tally systems and multiplicative grouping systems has been added and the Chinese system has been expanded from a Sidelight to full coverage in Section 4-1.
- Tools and algorithms in arithmetic, located in Section 4-2, is completely new to the second edition.

CHAPTER 5 The Real Number System

- More worked examples and real-world applications have been created to facilitate student learning, including applications of LCM and GCF (Section 5-1) and arithmetic with integers and order of operations (Section 5-2). Additionally, brand new application exercises have been created in every section, including sixteen new applications in Section 5-5.
- Common "canceling" mistakes are now more prominently featured through a new Sidelight found in Section 5-2.
- Coverage of adding and subtracting of fractions has been increased extensively and the chapter has been rearranged to cover this topic after multiplication and division of fractions to ease the learning progression for students.
- The new presentation of calculator guides for arithmetic with scientific notation are especially helpful in this chapter.

CHAPTER 6 Topics in Algebra

- Formerly Chapter 7, the order of Sections 4 and 5 have been reversed from the previous edition so that ratio, proportion, and variation are now presented directly after applications of solving equations.
- Organization and coverage of topics through much of the chapter has been reevaluated to focus on understanding what it really means to solve an equation. This includes increased coverage of solving linear equations with fractions and three-part inequalities and an introduction to the terms "identity" and "contradiction" in Section 6-2.
- Real-world applications have been added to both worked examples and exercise sets throughout the chapter, including twenty new application exercises in Section 6-2 and a doubling of the number of applications in worked examples in Sections 6-1 to 6-4 from the first edition.

CHAPTER 7 Additional Topics in Algebra

- Formerly Chapter 8, it has been expanded to include a brand new section on solving systems of equations with matrices (Section 7-3). Additionally, coverage of functions has grown to encompass two sections, including a total of thirty new application exercises.
- To provide further reinforcement for critical concepts like basic linear equations, linear systems, and linear inequalities, a total of five new application examples and thirty-one new exercises have been added.
- The second edition presents a more thorough coverage of graphing linear inequalities in two variables before moving on to systems of linear inequalities.

CHAPTER 8 Consumer Mathematics

- Formerly Chapter 9, it has undergone significant changes to content coverage, including new sub-sections on the banker's rule and discounted loans (Section 8-2), a new subsection on fixed installment loans and APR (Section 8-4), and an entirely new section on stocks and bonds (Section 8-6).
- Organizationally, the discussion of interest has been split into two sections, one on simple interest and one on compound interest.
- The coverage of annuities in Section 8-3 has been expanded, and a section formerly focused on markup and markdown has been replaced with a more thorough coverage of percent increase and decrease, including an example on deceptive use of percents in advertising.
- Updates to the discussion of home ownership now reflect current interest rates and trends.

CHAPTER 9 Measurement

- Formerly found only in Appendix A, the discussion of measurement has been expanded into an entirely new chapter.

CHAPTER 10 Geometry

- A new section on non-Euclidean and transformational geometries has been added to the text.
- Expanded coverage is found throughout the chapter, including sections focused on area and volume as well as finding angles in the trigonometry section.
- New applications of parallel lines and transversals using city streets have been added.

CHAPTER 11 Probability and Counting Techniques

- The entire chapter has been completely reorganized and rewritten to include a new section on the binomial theorem. This includes shifting counting techniques to be presented prior to probability and the addition of permutations when some objects are alike.
- Dozens of new application exercises are found throughout the chapter, including comparisons of expected value for common games of chance and real world applications of probability and counting.

CHAPTER 12 Statistics

- Nearly all worked examples and exercises featuring statistics have been replaced with problems featuring newer, more relevant data.
- A table is now included in Section 12-3 to compare the strengths and weaknesses of different measures of average.
- Coverage of the empirical rule can now be found in the discussion of the normal distribution and the discussion of finding area under the normal curve has been streamlined.
- The presentation of correlation is now based on an interesting real-world example of a correlation between MySpace usage and illiteracy and helpful information regarding the use of technology to find correlation coefficients and regression lines has been added.

CHAPTER 13 Other Mathematical Systems

- Formerly Chapter 6, coverage of mathematical systems has been moved to Section 13-1 so that clock and modular arithmetic can be taught in the context of mathematical systems.
- Mathematical systems are now introduced in terms of the familiar example of making turns at intersections and new application exercises in Section 13-1 include the pull chain on a ceiling fan and mixing paint colors.
- Presentation of clock arithmetic now uses the standard clock with numbers from 1 through 12, and also includes clocks with other numbers of hours.
- Congruences in modular arithmetic have been revised so that now all use the $\equiv$ symbol.

CHAPTER 14 Voting Methods

- Formerly Chapter 13, two completely new sections on apportionment and apportionment flaws have been added to the new edition.

CHAPTER 15 Graph Theory

- This is a completely new chapter to the second edition and features an expanded form of the coverage of networks, formerly found in Chapter 10.

Acknowledgements

McGraw-Hill's 360° Development Process is an ongoing, market-oriented approach to building accurate and innovative print and digital products. It is dedicated to continual large-scale and incremental improvement driven by multiple customer feedback loops and checkpoints. This process is initiated during the early planning stages of our new products, intensifies during the development and production stages, and then begins again upon publication, in anticipation of the next edition.

A key principle in the development of any mathematics text is its ability to adapt to teaching specifications in a universal way. The only way to do so is by contacting those universal voices—and learning from their suggestions. We are confident that our book has the most current content the industry has to offer, thus pushing our desire for accuracy to the highest standard possible. In order to accomplish this, we have moved through an arduous road to production. Extensive and open-minded advice is critical in the production of a superior text.

We engaged dozens of instructors and students to provide us with guidance during the development of the second edition. By investing in this extensive endeavor, McGraw-Hill delivers to you a product suite that has been created, refined, tested, and validated to be a successful tool in your course.

The McGraw-Hill mathematics team and the authors wish to thank the following instructors who participated in postpublication reviews of the first edition, the proposed second edition table of contents, and both first and second drafts of the second edition manuscript to give feedback on reworked narrative, design changes, pedagogical enhancements, and organizational changes. This feedback was summarized by the book team and used to guide the direction of the final text.

Gerald Angelichio, *Herkimer County Community College*
Anne Antonippillai, *University of Wisconsin—Stout*
Hamid Attarzadeh, *Jefferson Community and Technical College*
Jon Becker, *Indiana Univ-Northwest-Gary*
Andrew Beiderman, *Community College of Baltimore County Essex*
Laverne Blagmon-Earl, *Univ of Dist of Columbia*
Mike Bosch, *Iowa Lakes Community College*
Caroline Boulis, *Lee University*
Mark Brenneman, *Mesa Community College*
Sam Buckner, *North Greenville University*
Brian Burrell, *University of Massachusetts—Amherst*
Gerald Burton, *Virginia State University*
Fred Butler, *York College of Pennsylvania*

David Capaldi, *Johnson & Wales University*
Blayne Carroll, *Lee University*
Gail Carter, *St. Petersburg College—Tarpon Springs*
Florence Chambers, *Southern Maine Community College*
Kristin Chatas, *Washtenaw Community College*
Sandy Cohen, *Saint Petersburg College*
Lynn Craig, *Baton Rouge Community College*
Karen Crossin, *George Mason University*
Cheryl Davids, *Central Carolina Tech College*
Mark Ellis, *Central Piedmont Comm Coll*
Dan Endres, *University of Central Oklahoma*
Scott Fallstrom, *University of Oregon*
Shurron Farmer, *University of Dist of Columbia*
Nicki Feldman, *Pulaski Technical College*
Scott Garten, *Northwest Missouri State University*

Mahmood Ghamsary, *California State University, Fullerton*
Carrie Goehring, *Jackson State Community College*
John Grant, *Towson University*
Bo Green, *Abilene Christian University*
Sheryl Griffith, *Iowa Central Community College*
Renu Gupta, *Louisiana State University—Alexandria*
Kim Hagens, *Louisiana State University*
Quin Hearn, *Brevard Community College—Cocoa*
Thomas Hoffman, *Coastal Carolina University*
Lori Holdren, *Lake City Community College*
Robert Jajcay, *Indiana State University, Terre Haute*
Maryann Justinger, *Erie Community College South Campus—Orchard Park*
Joseph Kazimir, *East Los Angeles College*
David Keller, *Kirkwood Community College*
Betsy Kiedaisch, *College of Dupage*
Vesna Kilibarda, *Indiana University Northwest*
Bob Koca, *Community College Of Baltimore County, Essex*
Bhaskara Kopparty, *Indiana State University—Terre Haute*
Steve Kristoff, *Ivy Tech Community College of Indiana*
Pamela Krompak, *Owens Community College*
Valerie LaFrance, *Saint Petersburg College*
Marcia Lambert, *Pitt Community College*
Eveline Lapierre, *Johnson & Wales University*
John Lattanzio, *Indiana University of Pennsylvania*
Edith Lester, *Volunteer State Community College*
Antonio Magliaro, *Quinnipiac University*

Barbara Manley, *Jackson State Community College*
Carrie McCammon, *Ivy Tech Community College of Indiana*
Cornelius Nelan, *Quinnipiac University*
Bernard Omolo, *University of South Carolina Upstate*
Eugenia Peterson, *Richard J Daley College*
Becky Pohle, *Ivy Tech Community College of Indiana*
Elaine Previte, *Bristol Community College*
Carolyn Reed, *Austin Community College*
Natalie Rivera, *Estrella Mountain Community College*
Lisa Rombes, *Washtenaw Community College*
Fary Sami, *Harford Community College*
Nancy Schendel, *Iowa Lakes Community College, Estherville*
Mike Skowronski, *University of Wisconsin, Oshkosh*
Zeph Smith, *Salt Lake Community College*
Laura Stapleton, *Marshall University*
Janet Teeguarden, *Ivy Tech Community College of Indiana*
William Thralls, *Johnson & Wales University, North Miami*
David Troidl, *Erie Community College*
John Ward, *Jefferson Community and Technical College*
Susan Warner, *Friends University*
John Weglarz, *Kirkwood Community College*
Ronald White, *Norfolk State University*
Greg Wisloski, *Indiana University of Pennsylvania*
Judith Wood, *Central Florida Community College*

The authors would like to thank the many people who have helped bring the second edition of Math in Our World to life. First and foremost we acknowledge the comments and suggestions we received from all reviewers of the manuscript. Their thoughtful insights allowed us to understand how we can better help their students learn and be engaged by math, and guided us through this substantial revision. We think the result is a truly student-friendly text. Additionally, we thank Cindy Trimble and George Watson whose invaluable contributions have helped us to ensure that we present the most accurate information possible, and Jennifer Siegel of Broward College for providing many application exercises with style and flair.

Finally, at McGraw-Hill Higher Education, we thank John Osgood, Sponsoring Editor; Christina Lane, Developmental Editor; Kevin Ernzen, Marketing Manager; April Southwood, Senior Project Manager; Tara McDermott, Designer; Amber Bettcher, Digital Product Manager; and Sandy Schnee, Senior Media Project Manager. Their expertise helped transform this work from raw manuscript to a finished product we're very proud of.

Detailed Table of Contents

Index of Applications

Automotive

Car accidents, 656
Dealership capacity, 391
Depreciation, 269
Fuel efficiency, 674
Gas mileage, 30, 34
Gas prices, 680
Loans, 447
Purchase price, 307
Stopping distance, 340
Tire life, 698
Used car purchase, 327

Consumer Information

Advertising statements, 115
Airline tickets, 373
ATM banking, 637
Auction sales, 388
Bar codes, 178
Book prices, 373
Cab fare, 355
Cable TV, 208
Candy prices, 373
Car purchase, 307
Cell phone charges, 34
Cell phone equipment, 621
Cell phone minutes, 300
Cell phone plans, 327
Chicken prices, 373
Coffee prices, 372
Computer purchase, 630
Cost of fast food meal, 23
Cost of milk, 25
Credit card balance, 453, 456
Credit card finance charge, 453
Credit card penalty fees, 25
Credit card statement, 457
Credit cards, 424
Discount cards, 426
Discount price, 284
Down payment, 327, 446, 455, 456
Electric bill, 307
Estimating cost of cell phone, 18
Estimating remodeling costs, 19
Estimating total cost, 17, 24, 36
Exchange rate, 490
Existing home sales, 673
Fast food costs, 373
Food costs, 325
Gas prices, 680
Health club membership, 209

Home buying, 419
Home ownership, 457
Housing prices, 53
Identity theft, 52, 657
Installment buying, 446
Internet service, 208
Inventory levels, 393
Laundry detergent, 674
Lightbulb ratings, 674
Loan payoff, 451, 456
Misleading advertising, 426
Monthly payments, 431, 447, 455, 462
Movie tickets, 381
Newspaper advertisements, 358
Nut prices, 381
Online transactions, 638
Paint cost, 317
Party costs, 342
Pizza cost, 356
Pizza toppings, 81
Price reduction percent, 428
Retail sales, 147, 193
Sale prices, 23, 342
Sales tax, 284, 425, 428
School supplies, 381
Television screen size, 529
Thrift store prices, 373
Train fares, 342

Education

Bachelor's degrees, 52
Class scheduling, 80
Class size, 220
Costs, 428
Course selection, 64, 71, 77
Debt after graduation, 638
Degree completion, 388
Enrollment numbers, 318, 359
Extra credit, 36
Financial aid, 80
Grade point average, 36, 648
Grading structure, 392
Graduate school applications, 684
Groups for a project, 208
IQ testing, 685
Levels, 359
Major selection, 663
Majors, 80
Missed tests, 343
Political science class, 209
Quiz grades, 327
Reasons for failure, 80

Saving for college, 445
Scholarship application, 655
Student loans, 436
Study habits, 622
Teacher salaries, 428, 697
Test grades, 327, 328
Test percentiles, 684
Test times, 387
Textbook costs, 400
Textbook inventory, 381
Textbook resales, 81
Textbook sales, 697
True/false questions, 399
Tuition, 307

Finance

Account balances, 214
Actuarial method, 450
Advertising budget, 233
Amortization schedule, 462
Annual percentage rate, 448
Annuities, 441, 445
Average daily balance, 452, 454
Bank balance, 220
Banker's rule, 433
Bonds, 471
Business expansion, 445
Car loan, 447
Certificate of deposit, 272
Checking account balance, 218, 273
Coins, 29
Combined revenue, 307
Commission, 24, 425, 428
Comparing mortgages, 460
Comparison of effective rates, 440
Compound interest, 437
Computing principal, 432
Credit card balance, 453, 456
Credit card finance charge, 453
Credit card penalty fees, 25
Credit card statement, 457
Credit cards, 424
Debt, 269
Depreciation, 269
Discount, 284
Discounted loan, 434, 436
Down payment, 446, 455, 456
Earnings per share, 469, 472
Effective interest, 287, 439
Estate division, 234
Finance charge, 446, 453

xxvi

Problem Solving

Outline

1-1 The Nature of Mathematical Reasoning
1-2 Estimation and Interpreting Graphs

1-3 Problem Solving
Summary

MATH IN Criminal Investigation

In traditional cops-and-robbers movies, crime fighters use guns and fists to catch criminals, but in real life, often it's brain power that brings the bad guys to justice. That's why the TV show *CSI* marked a revolution of sorts when it debuted in October 2000: it featured scientists fighting crime, not tough guys. Solving a case is intimately tied to the process of problem solving: investigators are presented with a mystery, and they use whatever evidence they can find and their reasoning ability to reconstruct the crime. Hopefully, this will lead them to a suspect.

Of course, this isn't limited to just crime fighting. Students in math classes often ask, "When am I going to use what I learn?" The best answer to that question is, "Every day!" Math classes are not only about facts and formulas: they're also about exercising your mind, training your brain to think logically, and learning effective strategies for solving problems. And not just math problems. Every day of our lives, we face a wide variety of problems: they pop up in our jobs, in school, and in our personal lives. Which computer should you buy? What should you do when your car starts making an awful noise? What would be a good topic for a research paper? How can you get all your work done in time to go to that party Friday night?

Chapter 1 of this book is dedicated to the most important topic we'll cover: an introduction to some of the classic techniques of problem solving. These techniques will prove to be useful tools that you can apply in the rest of your education. But more importantly, they can be applied just as well to situations outside the classroom.

And this brings us back to our friends from *CSI*. The logic and reasoning that they use to identify suspects and prove their guilt are largely based on problem-solving skills we'll study in this chapter. By the time you've finished the chapter, you should be able to evaluate the situations below, all based on episodes of *CSI*. In each case, you should identify the type of reasoning that was used and decide whether the conclusion would stand up as proof in a court of law.

- After a violent crime, the investigators identify a recently paroled suspect living in the area who had previously committed three very similar crimes.
- A homeless man is found dead from exposure after being roughed up. His wrists look like he had been handcuffed, and fingerprints on his ID lead them to a local police officer.
- A murder victim grabbed a pager from the killer while being attacked and threw it under the couch. With the suspect identified, the investigators found that his DNA matched DNA found under the victim's fingernails.
- A series of five bodies are found posed like mannequins in public places. The lead suspect is an artist that is found to have sketches matching the poses of all five victims.

For answers, see Math in Criminal Investigation Revisited on page 35

Section 1-1 The Nature of Mathematical Reasoning

LEARNING OBJECTIVES

☐ 1. Identify two types of reasoning.

☐ 2. Use inductive reasoning to form conjectures.

☐ 3. Find a counter-example to disprove a conjecture.

☐ 4. Explain the difference between inductive and deductive reasoning.

☐ 5. Use deductive reasoning to prove a conjecture.

Part of being an adult is making decisions—every day is full of them, from the simple, like what to eat for breakfast, to the critical, like a choice of major. If you make every decision based on a coin flip, chances are you won't get very far in life. Instead, it's important to be able to analyze a situation and make a decision based on logical thinking. We'll call the process of logical thinking **reasoning.** It doesn't take a lot of imagination to understand how important reasoning is in everyone's life.

You may not realize it, but every day in your life, you use two types of reasoning to make decisions and solve problems: *inductive reasoning* or *induction,* and *deductive reasoning* or *deduction*.

Oddsmakers, who set point spreads for sporting events, predict how teams and individual players will do based on their past performance. This is an example of inductive reasoning.

☑ 1. Identify two types of reasoning.

Inductive reasoning is the process of reasoning that arrives at a general conclusion based on the observation of specific examples.

For example, suppose that your instructor gives a surprise quiz every Friday for the first four weeks of your math class. At this point, you might make a **conjecture,** or educated guess, that you'll have a surprise quiz the next Friday as well. As a result, you'd probably study before that class.

This is an example of inductive reasoning. By observing certain events for four *specific* Fridays, you arrive at a general conclusion. Inductive reasoning is useful in everyday life, and it is also useful as a problem-solving tool in math, as shown in Example 1.

EXAMPLE 1   Using Inductive Reasoning to Find a Pattern

Use inductive reasoning to find a pattern, and then find the next three numbers by using that pattern.

$$1, 2, 4, 5, 7, 8, 10, 11, 13, \_\_, \_\_, \_\_$$

SOLUTION

To find the pattern, look at the first number and see how to obtain the second number. Then look at the second number and see how to obtain the third number, etc.

$$1 \underset{+1}{\frown} 2 \underset{+2}{\frown} 4 \underset{+1}{\frown} 5 \underset{+2}{\frown} 7 \underset{+1}{\frown} 8 \underset{+2}{\frown} 10 \underset{+1}{\frown} 11 \underset{+2}{\frown} 13 \underset{+1}{\frown} \_\_ \underset{+2}{\frown} \_\_ \underset{+1}{\frown} \_\_$$

The pattern seems to be to add 1, then add 2, then add 1, then add 2, etc. So a reasonable conjecture for the next three numbers is 14, 16, and 17.

▼ Try This One 1

Use inductive reasoning to find a pattern and make a reasonable conjecture for the next three numbers by using that pattern.

$$1, 4, 2, 5, 3, 6, 4, 7, 5, \_\_, \_\_, \_\_$$

EXAMPLE 2 | Using Inductive Reasoning to Find a Pattern

Make a reasonable conjecture for the next figure in the sequence.

SOLUTION

The flat part of the figure is up, right, down, and then left. There is a solid circle ● in each figure. The sequence then repeats with an open circle ○ in each figure. So we could reasonably expect the next figure to be

Recognizing, describing, and creating patterns are important in many fields. Many types of patterns are used in music such as following an established pattern, altering an established pattern, and producing variations on a familiar pattern.

▼ Try This One 2

Make a reasonable conjecture for the next figure in the sequence.

EXAMPLE 3 | Using Inductive Reasoning to Make a Conjecture

When two odd numbers are added, will the result always be an even number? Use inductive reasoning to determine your answer.

SOLUTION

We will try several specific examples:

$$3 + 7 = 10 \qquad 25 + 5 = 30$$
$$5 + 9 = 14 \qquad 1 + 27 = 28$$
$$19 + 9 = 28 \qquad 21 + 33 = 54$$

Since all the answers are even, it seems reasonable to conclude that the sum of two odd numbers will be an even number.

Note: Since the sum of *every* pair of odd numbers hasn't been tried, we can't be 100% sure that the answer will always be an even number by using inductive reasoning.

2. Use inductive reasoning to form conjectures.

▼ Try This One 3

If two odd numbers are multiplied, is the result always odd, always even, or sometimes odd and sometimes even? Use inductive reasoning to answer.

One number is *divisible* by another number if the remainder is zero after dividing. For example, 16 is divisible by 8 because $16 \div 8$ has remainder zero. And 17 is not divisible by 8 because $17 \div 8$ has remainder 1.

EXAMPLE 4   Using Inductive Reasoning to Test a Conjecture

Use inductive reasoning to decide if the following conjecture is true: Any four-digit number is divisible by 11 if the difference between the sum of the first and third digits and the sum of the second and fourth digits is divisible by 11.

SOLUTION

Let's make up a few examples. For 1,738, the sum of the first and third digits is $1 + 3 = 4$, and the sum of the second and fourth digits is $7 + 8 = 15$. The difference is $15 - 4 = 11$, so if the conjecture is true, 1,738 should be divisible by 11. To check: $1,738 \div 11 = 158$ (with no remainder).

For 9,273, $9 + 7 = 16$, $2 + 3 = 5$, and $16 - 5 = 11$. So if the conjecture is true, 9,273 should be divisible by 11. To check: $9,273 \div 11 = 843$ (with no remainder).

Let's look at one more example. For 7,161, $7 + 6 = 13$, $1 + 1 = 2$, and $13 - 2 + 11$. Also $7,161 \div 11 = 651$ (with no remainder), so the conjecture is true for this example as well. While we can't be positive based on three examples, inductive reasoning indicates that the conjecture is true.

▼ Try This One 4

Use inductive reasoning to decide if the following conjecture is true: If the sum of the digits of a number is divisible by 3, then the number itself is divisible by 3.

Inductive reasoning can definitely be a useful tool in decision making, and we use it very often in our lives. But it has one very obvious drawback: because you can very seldom verify conclusions for every possible case, you can't be positive that the conclusions you're drawing are correct. In the example of the class in which a quiz is given on four consecutive Fridays, even if that continues for 10 more weeks, there's still a chance that there won't be a quiz the following Friday. And if there's even one Friday on which a quiz is not given, then the conjecture that there will be a quiz every Friday proves to be false.

This is a useful observation: while it's not often easy to prove that a conjecture is true, it's much simpler to prove that one is false. All you need is to find one specific example that contradicts the conjecture. This is known as a **counterexample.** In the quiz example, one Friday without a quiz serves as a counterexample: it proves that your conjecture that there would be a quiz every Friday is false. In Example 5, we'll use this idea to prove that a conjecture is false.

EXAMPLE 5   Finding a Counterexample

Find a counterexample that proves the conjecture below is false.
Conjecture: A number is divisible by 3 if the last two digits are divisible by 3.

SOLUTION

We'll pick a few numbers at random whose last two digits are divisible by 3, then divide them by 3, and see if there's a remainder.

1,527:   Last two digits, 27, divisible by 3; $1,527 \div 3 = 509$
11,745:   Last two digits, 45, divisible by 3; $11,427 \div 3 = 3,809$

At this point, you might start to suspect that the conjecture is true, but you shouldn't! We've only checked two cases.

1,136: Last two digits, 36, divisible by 3; $1,136 \div 3 = 378\frac{2}{3}$

This counterexample shows that the conjecture is false.

▼ Try This One 5

☑ 3. Find a counterexample to disprove a conjecture.

Find a counterexample to disprove the conjecture that the name of every month in English contains either the letter y or the letter r.

CAUTION

Remember: One counterexample is enough to show that a conjecture is false. But one positive example is *never* enough to show that a conjecture is true.

EXAMPLE 6   Making and Testing a Conjecture

Use inductive reasoning to make a conjecture about the number of sections a circle is divided into when a given number of points on the circle are connected by chords. (A chord is a line connecting two points on a circle.) Then test the conjecture with one further example.

SOLUTION

We'll draw several circles, connect the points with chords, and then count the sections.

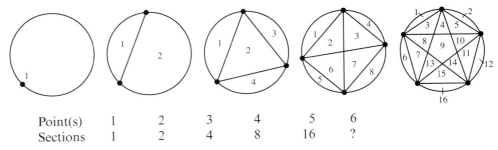

Point(s)	1	2	3	4	5	6
Sections	1	2	4	8	16	?

Looking at the pattern in the number of sections, we see that a logical guess for the next number is 32. In fact, the number appears to be 2 raised to the power of 1 less than the number of points. This will be our conjecture. Let's see how we did by checking with six points.

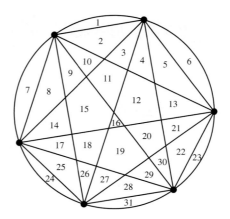

Uh oh . . . there are 31 sections! It looks like our conjecture is not true.

▼ Try This One 6

Given that there are 31 sections with 6 points, guess how many there will be with 7, and then check your answer.

The other method of reasoning that we will study is called *deductive reasoning,* or *deduction.*

Deductive reasoning is the process of reasoning that arrives at a conclusion based on previously accepted general statements. It does not rely on specific examples.

Here's an example of deductive reasoning. At many colleges, a student has to be registered for at least 12 hours to be considered full-time. So we accept the statement "A student is full-time if he or she is registered for at least 12 hours" as true. If we're then told that a particular student has full-time status, we can conclude that she or he is registered for at least 12 hours. The key is that we can be *positive* that

Sidelight   MATH AND WEATHER PREDICTION

Weather involves numerous variables, such as temperatures, wind velocity and direction, type and amount of precipitation, cloud cover, and atmospheric pressures, to name just a few. All these variables use numbers.

To create a weather forecast, the National Weather Service collects information from various sources such as satellites, weather balloons, weather stations, and human observers around the world. The information is then put into a computer and a grid with over 200,000 points is drawn up by the computer showing the weather conditions at each point at the time the data were collected.

From this grid, the computer is able to predict the movement of weather fronts at 10-minute intervals into the future, and a forecast of tomorrow's weather can be generated.

Short-term forecasts are generally accurate, but due to variations in atmospheric conditions, long-range forecasts are at best guesses based on current conditions. Sometimes, however, atmospheric conditions change so rapidly that even short-term forecasts are inaccurate.

☑ 4. Explain the difference between inductive and deductive reasoning.

this is true. This is what separates deductive reasoning from inductive reasoning. Example 7 illustrates the difference between using inductive and deductive reasoning in math.

EXAMPLE 7 **Using Deductive Reasoning to Prove a Conjecture**

Consider the following problem: Think of any number. Multiply that number by 2, then add 6, and divide the result by 2. Next subtract the original number. What is the result?

(a) Use inductive reasoning to make a conjecture for the answer.
(b) Use deductive reasoning to prove your conjecture.

SOLUTION

(a) Inductive reasoning will be helpful in forming a conjecture. We'll choose a few specific numbers at random and perform the given operations to see what the result is.

Number:	12	5	43
Multiply by 2:	$2 \times 12 = 24$	$2 \times 5 = 10$	$2 \times 43 = 86$
Add 6:	$24 + 6 = 30$	$10 + 6 = 16$	$86 + 6 = 92$
Divide by 2:	$30 \div 2 = 15$	$16 \div 2 = 8$	$92 \div 2 = 46$
Subtract the original number:	$15 - 12 = 3$	$8 - 5 = 3$	$46 - 43 = 3$
Result:	3	3	3

At this point, you may be tempted to conclude that the result is always 3. But this is just a conjecture: we've tried only three of infinitely many possible numbers! As usual when using inductive reasoning, we can't be completely sure that our conjecture is always true.

(b) The problem with the inductive approach is that it requires using specific numbers, and we know that we can't check every possible number. Instead, we'll choose an *arbitrary* number and call it x. If we can show that the result is 3 in this case, that will tell us that this is the result for *every* number. Remember, we'll be doing the exact same operations, just on an arbitrary number x.

Number:	x
Multiply by 2:	$2x$
Add 6:	$2x + 6$
Divide by 2:	$\dfrac{2x + 6}{2} = x + 3$
Subtract the original number:	$x + 3 - x = 3$

Now we know for sure that the result will always be 3, and our conjecture is proved.

▼ **Try This One 7**

☑ 5. Use deductive reasoning to prove a conjecture.

Consider the following problem: Think of any number. Multiply that number by 3, then add 30, and divide the result by 3. Next subtract the original number. What is the result?

(a) Use inductive reasoning to make a conjecture for the answer.
(b) Use deductive reasoning to prove your conjecture.

Sidelight AN ARBITRARY DISCUSSION

In common usage, the word *arbitrary* is often misinterpreted as a synonym for *random*. When reaching into a bag of potato chips, you make a random selection, and some people would also call this an arbitrary selection. But in math, the word *arbitrary* means something very different. When randomly selecting that chip, you have still chosen a specific chip—it is probably not representative of every chip in the bag. Some chips will be bigger, and others smaller. Still others may have more salt, some less.

When we use *arbitrary* in math, we're referring to a nonspecific item that is able to represent *all* such items. In the series of calculations we looked at above, we could never be sure that the result will always be 3 by choosing specific numbers. Why? Because we'd have to try it for *every* number, which is of course impossible. You have better things to do than spend the rest of your life testing number after number. The value of performing the calculation on an *arbitrary* number x is that this one calculation proves what will happen for *every* number you choose. It is absolutely crucial in the study of mathematics to understand that choosing specific numbers can almost never *prove* a result, because you can't try every number. Instead, we'll rely on using arbitrary numbers and deductive reasoning.

Let's try another example. Try to focus on the difference between inductive and deductive reasoning, and the fact that inductive reasoning is great for giving you an idea about what the truth might be for a given situation, but deductive reasoning is needed for proof.

EXAMPLE 8 Using Deductive Reasoning to Prove a Conjecture

Use inductive reasoning to arrive at a general conclusion, and then prove your conclusion is true by using deductive reasoning.

Select a number:
Add 50:
Multiply by 2:
Subtract the original number:
Result:

SOLUTION

Approach: Induction

Try a couple different numbers and make a conjecture.

Original number:	12	50
Add 50:	$12 + 50 = 62$	$50 + 50 = 100$
Multiply by 2:	$62 \times 2 = 124$	$100 \times 2 = 200$
Subtract the original number:	$124 - 12 = 112$	$200 - 50 = 150$
Result:	112	150

The conjecture is that the final answer is 100 more than the original number.

Approach:	Deduction
Select a number:	x
Add 50:	$x + 50$
Multiply by 2:	$2(x + 50) = 2x + 100$
Subtract the original number:	$2x + 100 - x$
Result:	$x + 100$

Our conjecture was right: the final answer is always 100 more than the original number.

Calculator Guide

If you use a calculator to try the repeated operations in Example 8, you'll need to press ☐= (scientific calculator) or ENTER (graphing calculator) after every operation, or you'll get the wrong result. Suppose you simply enter the whole string:

Standard Scientific Calculator

12 ☐+ 50 ☐× 2 ☐− 12 ☐=

Standard Graphing Calculator

12 ☐+ 50 ☐× 2 ☐− 12 ENTER

The result is 100, which is incorrect. In Chapter 5, we'll find out why when we study the order of operations.

▼ **Try This One 8**

Arrive at a conclusion by using inductive reasoning, and then try to prove your conclusion by using deductive reasoning.

Select a number:

Add 16:

Multiply by 3:

Add 2:

Subtract twice the original number:

Subtract 50:

Result:

Now that we've seen how inductive and deductive reasoning can be used, let's review by distinguishing between the two types of reasoning in some real-world situations.

EXAMPLE 9   **Comparing Inductive and Deductive Reasoning**

Determine whether the type of reasoning used is inductive or deductive.

The last six times we played our archrival in football, we won, so I know we're going to win on Saturday.

SOLUTION

This conclusion is based on six specific occurrences, not a general rule that we know to be true. Therefore, inductive reasoning was used.

▼ **Try This One 9**

Determine whether the type of reasoning used is inductive or deductive.

There is no mail delivery on holidays. Tomorrow is Thanksgiving, so I know my student loan check won't be delivered.

EXAMPLE 10   **Comparing Inductive and Deductive Reasoning**

Determine whether the type of reasoning used is inductive or deductive.

The syllabus states that any final average between 80 and 90% will result in a B. If I get 78% on my final, my overall average will be 80.1%, so I'll get a B.

SOLUTION

Although we're talking about a specific person's grade, the conclusion that I'll get a B is based on a general rule: all scores in the 80s earn a B. So this is deductive reasoning.

▼ **Try This One 10**

Determine whether the type of reasoning used is inductive or deductive.

Everyone I know in my sorority got a least a 2.5 GPA last semester, so I'm sure I'll get at least a 2.5 this semester.

Remember that both inductive reasoning and deductive reasoning are useful tools for problem solving. But the biggest difference between them is that conclusions drawn from inductive reasoning, no matter how reasonable, are still at least somewhat uncertain. But conclusions drawn by using deductive reasoning can be considered definitely true, as long as the general rules used to draw the conclusion are known to be true.

In addition, it's worth reviewing the fact that to disprove a conjecture, you only need to find one specific example for which it's not true. But to prove a conjecture, you have to show that it's true in *every* possible case.

Answers to Try This One

1 Pattern: Every entry is 1 more than the one that comes two spots before it. The next three numbers are 8, 6, 9.

2 ◺ 2

3 Always odd

4 True

5 June has neither a y nor an r.

6 There are 57.

7 10

8 The result is the original number.

9 Deductive

10 Inductive

EXERCISE SET 1-1

Writing Exercises

1. Explain the difference between inductive and deductive reasoning.
2. What is meant by the term *conjecture?*
3. Give a real-life example of how to use inductive reasoning.
4. What is a counterexample? What are counterexamples used for?
5. Explain why you can never be sure that a conclusion you arrived at using inductive reasoning is true.
6. Explain the difference between an arbitrary number and a number selected at random.

Computational Exercises

For Exercises 7–14, use inductive reasoning to find a pattern, and then make a reasonable conjecture for the next number or item in the sequence.

7. 1   2   4   7   11   16   22   29   __
8. 5   15   45   135   405   1215   __
9. 10   20   11   18   12   16   13   14   14   12   15   __
10. 1   4   9   16   19   24   31   34   39   46   __

11. 100   99   97   94   90   85   79   __
12. 9   12   11   14   13   16   15   18   __

13.

14.

For Exercises 15–18, find a counterexample to show that each statement is false.

15. The sum of any three odd numbers is even.
16. When an even number is added to the product of two odd numbers, the result will be even.
17. When an odd number is squared and divided by 2, the result will be a whole number.
18. When any number is multiplied by 6 and the digits of the answer are added, the sum will be divisible by 6.

For Exercises 19–22, use inductive reasoning to make a conjecture about a rule that relates the number you selected to the final answer. Try to prove your conjecture by using deductive reasoning.

19. Select a number:
    Double it:
    Subtract 20 from the answer:
    Divide by 2:
    Subtract the original number:
    Result:
20. Select a number:
    Multiply it by 9:
    Add 21:
    Divide by 3:
    Subtract three times the original number:
    Result:
21. Select a number:
    Add 50:
    Multiply by 2:
    Subtract 60:
    Divide by 2:
    Subtract the original number:
    Result:
22. Select a number:
    Multiply by 10:
    Subtract 25:
    Divide by 5:
    Subtract the original number:
    Result:

For Exercises 23–32, use inductive reasoning to find a pattern for the answers. Then use the pattern to guess the result of the final calculation, and perform the operation to see if your answer is correct.

23. $12,345,679 \times 9 = 111,111,111$
    $12,345,679 \times 18 = 222,222,222$
    $12,345,679 \times 27 = 333,333,333$
    $\vdots$
    $12,345,679 \times 72 = ?$

24. $0^2 + 1 = 1$
    $1^2 + 3 = 2^2$
    $2^2 + 5 = 3^2$
    $3^2 + 7 = 4^2$
    $4^2 + 9 = 5^2$
    $5^2 + 11 = ?$

25. $999,999 \times 1 = 0,999,999$
    $999,999 \times 2 = 1,999,998$
    $999,999 \times 3 = 2,999,997$
    $\vdots$
    $999,999 \times 9 = ?$

26. $1 = 1^2$
    $1 + 2 + 1 = 2^2$
    $1 + 2 + 3 + 2 + 1 = 3^2$
    $\vdots$
    $1 + 2 + 3 + 4 + 5 + 6 + 7 + 6 + 5 + 4 + 3 + 2 + 1 = ?$

27. $9 \times 9 = 81$
    $99 \times 99 = 9,801$
    $999 \times 999 = 998,001$
    $9,999 \times 9,999 = 99,980,001$
    $99,999 \times 99,999 = ?$

28. $1 \times 8 + 1 = 9$
    $12 \times 8 + 2 = 98$
    $123 \times 8 + 3 = 987$
    $1,234 \times 8 + 4 = 9,876$
    $12,345 \times 8 + 5 = ?$

29. $1 \cdot 1 = 1$
    $11 \cdot 11 = 121$
    $111 \cdot 111 = 12,321$
    $1,111 \cdot 1,111 = 1,234,321$
    $11,111 \cdot 11,111 = ?$

30. $9 \cdot 91 = 819$
    $8 \cdot 91 = 728$
    $7 \cdot 91 = 637$
    $6 \cdot 91 = 546$
    $5 \cdot 91 = ?$

31. Explain what happens when the number 142,857 is multiplied by the numbers 2 through 8.
32. A Greek mathematician named Pythagoras is said to have discovered the following number pattern. Find the next three sums by using inductive reasoning. Don't just add!
    $1 = 1$
    $1 + 3 = 4$
    $1 + 3 + 5 = 9$
    $1 + 3 + 5 + 7 = 16$
    $1 + 3 + 5 + 7 + 9 = ?$
    $1 + 3 + 5 + 7 + 9 + 11 = ?$
    $1 + 3 + 5 + 7 + 9 + 11 + 13 = ?$
33. Select any two-digit number, such as 62. Multiply it by 9: $62 \times 9 = 558$. Then add the digits: $5 + 5 + 8 = 18$. Keep adding the digits in the answer until you get a single answer. In this case, the answer is $1 + 8 = 9$. Try several other numbers. Using inductive reasoning, what can you conjecture about any whole number multiplied by 9?
34. Select any three-digit number in which all digits are different, such as 571. Reverse the digits and subtract the smaller number from the larger number: $571 - 175 = 396$. Reverse the digits in that number and add the new number to the old number:

$396 + 693 = 1,089.$ (*Note:* If an answer has two digits, place a 0 in the hundreds place.) Now select several other three-digit numbers and try the procedure again. By using inductive reasoning, what can you conjecture?

35. Use inductive reasoning to make a conjecture about the next three sums, and then perform the calculations to verify that your conjecture is true.

$$1 + \frac{1}{2} = \frac{3}{2}$$

$$1 + \frac{1}{2} + \frac{1}{2 \cdot 3} = \frac{5}{3}$$

$$1 + \frac{1}{2} + \frac{1}{2 \cdot 3} + \frac{1}{3 \cdot 4} = \frac{7}{4}$$

$$1 + \frac{1}{2} + \frac{1}{2 \cdot 3} + \frac{1}{3 \cdot 4} + \frac{1}{4 \cdot 5} = ?$$

$$1 + \frac{1}{2} + \frac{1}{2 \cdot 3} + \frac{1}{3 \cdot 4} + \frac{1}{4 \cdot 5} + \frac{1}{5 \cdot 6} = ?$$

$$1 + \frac{1}{2} + \frac{1}{2 \cdot 3} + \frac{1}{3 \cdot 4} + \frac{1}{4 \cdot 5} + \frac{1}{5 \cdot 6} + \frac{1}{6 \cdot 7} = ?$$

36. Use inductive reasoning to determine the unknown sum, then perform the calculation to verify your answer.
$2 = 1(2)$
$2 + 4 = 2(3)$
$2 + 4 + 6 = 3(4)$

$2 + 4 + 6 + 8 = 4(5)$
$2 + 4 + 6 + 8 + 10 + 12 + 14 = ?$

In Exercises 37–40, use inductive reasoning to predict the next equation in the pattern.

37. $5 = \dfrac{5(2)}{2}$

$5 + 10 = \dfrac{10(3)}{2}$

$5 + 10 + 15 = \dfrac{15(4)}{2}$

$5 + 10 + 15 + 20 = \dfrac{20(5)}{2}$

38. $50,505 \times 2 = 101,010$
$50,505 \times 4 = 202,020$
$50,505 \times 6 = 303,030$
$50,505 \times 8 = 404,040$

39. $37,037 \times 3 = 111,111$
$37,037 \times 6 = 222,222$
$37,037 \times 9 = 333,333$
$37,037 \times 12 = 444,444$

40. $4 \cdot 1^3 = 1^2 \cdot (2)^2$
$4 \cdot (1^3 + 2^3) = 2^2 \cdot (3)^2$
$4 \cdot (1^3 + 2^3 + 3^3) = 3^2 \cdot (4)^2$

Real-World Applications

In Exercises 41–64, determine whether the type of reasoning used is inductive or deductive reasoning.

41. I am going to be rich some day. I know this because everyone in my family who graduated from college is rich, and I just graduated from college.

42. If a computer tech says it will cost $100 to clear the viruses from my PC, it will actually cost $150. A computer tech told me it would cost $100 to clean up my PC; therefore I can expect it to cost me $150.

43. I know I will have to work a double shift today because I have a migraine and every time I have a migraine I get stuck pulling a double.

44. If class is canceled, I go to the beach with my friends. I did not go to the beach with my friends yesterday; therefore, class was not canceled.

45. On Christmas Day, movie theaters and Chinese restaurants are always open, so this Christmas Day we can go to a movie and get some Chinese takeout.

46. For the first three games this year, the parking lot was packed with tailgaters, so we'll have to leave extra early to find a spot this week.

47. Every time Beth sold back her textbooks, she got a mere fraction of what she paid for them; so this semester she realized it would not be worth the effort to sell back her books at all.

48. Experts say that opening email attachments that come from unknown senders is one way you'll get a virus on your computer. Shauna constantly opens attachments from people she doesn't know, so she'll probably end up with a virus on her system.

49. Whenever Marcie let friends set her up on a blind date, the guy turned out to be a total loser. This time, when a friend offered to fix her up, she decided the guy would be a loser, so she declined.

50. Each time I have moved, something has gone wrong. So now that I am moving again next week, I know something has to go wrong.

51. The professor's policy is that any student whose cell phone goes off during class will be asked to leave. So when Ericka forgot to turn hers off and it rang during a quiz, the professor asked her to leave class.

52. Both times Melanie took her state test for teacher certification, she'd been so nervous she blanked out and failed the test. So when she walked into the testing room this time, her heart started beating faster and her palms were sweaty.

53. Since Josie ate a diet of mostly foods high in saturated fat, she was not surprised when her doctor said her cholesterol levels were too high.

54. In the past, even when Chris followed a recipe, her meal was either burned or underdone. Now her party guests know to eat before they attend her dinners so they won't starve all evening.

55. Tim has already lost three cell phones. He didn't spend a lot of money on his newest cell phone because he knows he'll eventually lose that one too.

56. Marathon runners should eat extra carbs before a big race, and since Mark did not eat enough carbs before the race, he felt sluggish the entire time.

57. Organizing chapter contents in your own words before the test will decrease the amount of study you have to do before a test. When Scott tried this method, he was pleasantly surprised at how fast he was able to study.

58. When the printer runs out of paper, a little light on the LCD display flashes. So when the light was flashing, Frank knew he needed to put more paper into the printer.

59. Few people showed up at the last several fund-raisers, which were not publicized very well. So this time, the organizers of the fund-raisers went all out with advertising the event well before the date to ensure more people would attend.

60. Since it gets dark around 6:00 P.M. during the winter months, Connie made her children come in from playing at 5:30 P.M.

61. The last several network dramas I've followed have been canceled just when I started getting into them. So I'm not going to bother watching the new one they're advertising even though it looks good, because I don't want to be disappointed when it gets canceled.

62. Rollerblading without knee pads and a helmet is said to be dangerous. So when I got my first pair of Rollerblades, I made sure to get a helmet and knee pads.

63. Every time Ralph trusted his girlfriend to return the DVDs to Blockbuster on time, she returned them late and he was stuck with a late charge. So this time, he made sure to drop off the DVDs on his way to work.

64. Whenever Sarah drove over the speed bumps near the dorm too fast, her CD player would skip around like crazy. So this time before she entered the dorm parking lot, she paused the CD.

Critical Thinking

65. When a map is drawn, countries that share a common border are always shaded with different colors. Can you draw a map on a flat surface consisting of five different countries so that five different colors are required to meet this criterion?

66. Find the next three numbers in the sequence.
    (a) 1, 1, 2, 3, 5, 8, 13, 21, . . .
    (b) 1, 4, 9, 16, 25, 36, . . .
    (c) 1, 2, 4, 8, 16, 32, . . .

67. The following figure is called *Pascal's triangle*. It has many uses in mathematics and other disciplines. Some uses will be shown in later chapters. Use inductive reasoning to find the numbers in the last row. (*Hint:* The entries that aren't 1 are obtained by using addition.)

```
              1
           1     1
        1     2     1
     1     3     3     1
   1    4     6     4     1
 1    5    10    10    5    1
1   __   __   __   __   __   1
```

68. The difference of two squares $a^2 - b^2$ can be found by using the pattern illustrated in the following:

$$16^2 - 13^2 = 3(16 + 13) = 3 \cdot 29 = 87$$
$$25^2 - 21^2 = 4(25 + 21) = 4 \cdot 46 = 184$$

Using algebra and deductive reasoning, show that this will always be true.

69. The numbers 1, 3, 6, 10, 15, . . . are called *triangular numbers* since they can be displayed as shown.

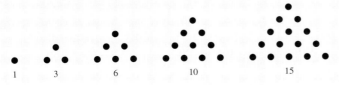

The numbers 1, 4, 9, 16, 25, . . . are called *square numbers* since they can be displayed as shown.

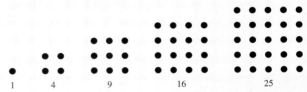

The numbers 1, 5, 12, 22, 35, . . . are called *pentagonal numbers* since they can be displayed as shown.

(a) Using inductive reasoning, find the next three triangular numbers.
(b) Using inductive reasoning, find the next three square numbers.
(c) Using inductive reasoning, find the next three pentagonal numbers.
(d) Using inductive reasoning, find the first four hexagonal numbers.

70. Refer to Exercise 69. The formula for finding triangular numbers is $\dfrac{n[1n - (-1)]}{2}$ or $\dfrac{n(n + 1)}{2}$. The formula for finding square numbers is $\dfrac{n(2n - 0)}{2}$ or n^2. The formula for pentagonal numbers is $\dfrac{n(3n - 1)}{2}$. Find the formula for hexagonal numbers, using inductive reasoning.

Section 1-2 Estimation and Interpreting Graphs

LEARNING OBJECTIVES

☐ 1. Identify some uses for estimation.

☐ 2. Round numbers to a given level of accuracy.

☐ 3. Estimate the answers to real-world problems.

☐ 4. Use estimation to obtain information from graphs.

☑ 1. Identify some uses for estimation.

Math Note

We often use the word *nearest* to describe the place value to round to. Instead of saying, "Round to the hundreds place," we might say, "Round to the nearest hundred."

Everyone likes buying items on sale, so we should all be familiar with the idea of finding a rough approximation for a sale price. If you're looking at a pair of shoes that normally sells for $70 and the store has a 40% off sale, you might figure that the shoes are a little more than half price, which would be $35, so they're probably around $40. We will call the process of finding an approximate answer to a math problem **estimation.** Chances are that you use estimation a lot more than you realize, unless you carry a calculator with you everywhere you go. (Okay, so your cell phone has a calculator, but how often do you use it?)

Estimation comes in handy in a wide variety of settings. When the auto repair shop technicians look over your car to see what's wrong, they can't know for sure what the exact cost will be until they've made the repairs, so they will give you an estimate. When you go to the grocery store and have only $20 to spend, you'll probably keep a rough estimate of the total as you add items to the cart. If you plan on buying carpet for a room, you'd most likely measure the square footage and then estimate the total cost as you looked at different styles of carpet. You could find the exact cost if you really needed to, but often an estimate is good enough for you to make a sound buying decision.

Estimation is also a really useful tool in checking answers to math problems, particularly word problems. Let's say you're planning an outing for a student group you belong to, and lunch is included at $3.95 per person. If 24 people signed up and you were billed $94.80, you could quickly figure that this is a reasonable bill. Since 24 is close to 25, and $3.95 is close to $4.00, the bill should be close to $25 \times \$4.00 = \$100$.

You also use estimation when rounding numbers for simplicity. If someone asks your height and age, you might say $5'11''$ and 20, even if you're actually $5'10\frac{1}{2}''$ (everyone fudges a little) and 20 years, 4 months, and 6 days old.

Since the process of estimating uses rounding, we'll start with a brief review of rounding. Rounding uses the concept of place value. The *place value* of a digit in a number tells the value of the digit in terms of ones, tens, hundreds, etc. For example, in the number 325, the 3 means 3 hundreds or 300 since its place value is hundreds. The 2 means 2 tens, or 20, and the 5 means 5 ones. A place value chart is shown here entitled "Rounding Numbers."

Rounding Numbers

To round numbers, use these rules:

1. Locate the place-value digit of the number that is being rounded. Here is the place-value chart for whole numbers and decimals:

8,	9	8	5,	7	3	0,	2	6	1	.	2	3	5	6	7	5
billions	hundred-millions	ten-millions	millions	hundred-thousands	ten-thousands	thousands	hundreds	tens	ones		tenths	hundredths	thousandths	ten-thousandths	hundred-thousandths	millionths

2a. If the digit to the right of the place-value digit is 0 through 4, then do not change the place-value digit.

2b. If the digit to the right of the place-value digit is 5 through 9, add 1 to the place-value digit.

Note: When you round whole numbers, replace all digits to the right of the digit being rounded with zeros. When you round decimal numbers, drop all digits to the right of the digit that is being rounded.

EXAMPLE 1 **Rounding Numbers**

Round each number to the place value given.

(a) 7,328 (hundreds)
(b) 15,683 (thousands)
(c) 32.4817 (tenths)
(d) 0.047812 (ten-thousandths)

SOLUTION

(a) In the number 7,328, 3 is in the hundreds place, so it's the digit being rounded. Since the digit to the right is 2, the digit 3 remains the same, and the 2 and 8 are replaced by zeros. The rounded number is 7,300.
(b) In the number 15,683, the 5 is the digit to be rounded. Since the digit to the right is 6, 1 is added to the 5 and the digits 6, 8, and 3 are replaced by zeros. The rounded number is 16,000.
(c) In the number 32.4817, the 4 is the digit to be rounded. Since the digit to the right of the 4 is 8, 1 is added to the 4 to get 5 and all digits to the right of the 4 are dropped. The rounded number is 32.5.
(d) In the number 0.047812, the 8 is the digit to be rounded. Since the digit to the right of 8 is 1, the 8 remains the same. The digits 1 and 2 are dropped. The rounded number is 0.0478.

 2. Round numbers to a given level of accuracy.

▼ **Try This One 1**

Round each number to the place value given.

(a) 372,651 (hundreds)
(b) 32.971 (ones)
(c) 0.37056 (thousandths)
(d) 1,465.983 (hundredths)

Estimation

When you estimate answers for numerical calculations, two steps are required.

1. Round the numbers being used to numbers that make the calculation simple.

2. Perform the operation or operations involved.

EXAMPLE 2 **Estimating Total Cost When Shopping**

The owner of an apartment complex needs to buy six refrigerators for a new building. She chooses a model that costs $579.99 per refrigerator. Estimate the total cost of all six.

SOLUTION

Step 1 Round the cost of the refrigerators. In this case, rounding up to $600 will make the calculation easy.

Step 2 Perform the calculation: $600 \times 6 = \$3,600$. Our estimated cost is $3,600. (The actual cost will be a little less than $3,600—note that we rounded the price up, so our estimate will be high.)

Sidelight THE BIGGEST NUMBER IN THE WORLD?

It seems that large numbers are a part of our advancing civilization. Cave people probably relied on their fingers and toes for counting, while large numbers today tend to overwhelm us.

Do you know what the largest number is? A million? A billion? A trillion? Do you know how large a million is? A billion? A trillion?

A million is no longer considered a large number. Many times, we hear the word *billion* being used. Government budgets are in the billions of dollars, the world population is approaching 7 billion, etc. Just how large are these numbers?

If you counted to a million, one number per second with no time off to eat or sleep, it would take you approximately $11\frac{1}{2}$ days. A million pennies would make a stack almost a mile high and a million $1 bills would weigh about a ton.

A million is written as a 1 followed by six zeros (1,000,000). Millions are used for measuring the distance from the earth to the sun, about 93 million miles.

The number 1 followed by nine zeros is called a billion (1,000,000,000). It is equal to 1,000 million.

It would take you 32 years to count to a billion with no rest. A billion dollars in $1 bills would weigh over a thousand tons. The age of the earth is estimated to be almost 4.5 billion years. There are more than 100 billion stars in our galaxy. A billion pennies would make a stack almost 1,000 miles high.

The number 1 followed by 12 zeros is a trillion. It is written as 1,000,000,000,000. Counting to a trillion would take 32 thousand years. The nearest star is 27 trillion miles away.

A quadrillion, a quintillion, and a sextillion are written with 15, 18, and 21 zeros, respectively. The weight of the earth is 6 sextillion, 570 quintillion tons (6.6 sextillion tons). Adding three zeros brings another -illion until a vigintillion is reached. That number has a total of 63 zeros.

Is this the largest number? No. A nine-year-old child invented a number with 100 zeros. It is called a googol. It looks like this:

10,000,000,000,000,000,000,000,000,000,000,
000,000,000,000,000,000,000,000,000,000,000,
000,000,000,000,000,000,000,000,000,000,000

This number is said to be more than the total number of protons in the universe. Yet an even larger number is the googolplex. It is a 1 followed by a googol of zeros. If you tried to write it, it would take a piece of paper larger than the distance from here to the moon.

Ultimately though, any number you can think of can be made larger by simply adding 1.

▼ Try This One 2

At one ballpark, large frosty beverages cost $6.75 each. Estimate the cost of buying one for each member of a group consisting of four couples.

Students often wonder, "How do I know what digit to round to?" There is no exact answer to that question—it depends on the individual numbers. In Example 2, the cost of the refrigerators could have been rounded from $579.99 to $580. Then the cost estimate would be $580 × 6 = $3,480. This is a much closer estimate because we rounded the cost to the nearest dollar, rather than the nearest $100.

Deciding on how much to round is really a tradeoff: ease of calculation versus accuracy. In most cases you'll get a more accurate result if you round less, but the calculation will be a little harder. Since there's no exact rule, it's important to evaluate the situation and use good old-fashioned common sense. And remember, when you are estimating, there is no one correct answer.

EXAMPLE 3   Estimating the Cost of a Cell Phone

You're considering a new cell phone plan where you have to pay $179 up front for the latest phone, but the monthly charge of $39.99 includes unlimited minutes and messaging. Estimate the cost of the phone for 1 year if there are no additional charges.

SOLUTION

Step 1 We can round the cost of the phone to $180 and the monthly charge to $40.

Step 2 The monthly cost estimate for 1 year will be $40 × 12 = $480; add the estimated cost of the phone to get an estimated total cost of $480 + $180 = $660.

▼ Try This One 3

A rental car company charges a rate of $78 per week to rent an economy car. For an up-front fee of $52, you can upgrade to a midsize car. Estimate the cost of renting a midsize car for 3 weeks.

EXAMPLE 4 **Estimating Remodeling Costs**

The Fabeets family plans on remodeling their living room. They will be replacing 21 square yards of carpet at a cost of $23 per yard and having 16 linear feet of wall papered at a cost of $32 per foot. Estimate the total cost of the remodel.

SOLUTION

Step 1 We can round the size and cost of the carpet to 20 square yards and $25 per square yard. We can also round the length and cost of the wall to 15 feet and $30 per foot.

Step 2 The estimated carpet cost is 20 × $25 = $500. The estimated wallpaper cost is 15 × $30 = $450. So our estimate for the total cost is $500 + $450 = $950.

▼ Try This One 4

☑ 3. Estimate the answers to real-world problems.

Estimate the total cost if the Fabeets family decides to remodel a bedroom by installing 16 square yards of carpet at $18 per square yard and having 21 feet of wall painted at a cost of $12 per foot.

Sometimes you will need to overestimate or underestimate an answer. For example, if you were buying groceries and had only $20.00, you would want to overestimate the cost of your groceries so that you would have enough money to pay for them. If you needed to earn money to pay the cost of your college tuition for the next semester, you would want to underestimate how much you could earn each week in order to determine the number of weeks you need to work to pay your tuition.

At times you will need to make estimates from information displayed in various graphs, such as bar graphs, pie graphs, or time series graphs. Examples 5, 6, and 7 illustrate how this can be done.

A **bar graph** is used to compare amounts or percents using either vertical or horizontal bars of various lengths which correspond to the amounts or percents.

EXAMPLE 5 **Obtaining Information from a Bar Graph**

The graph shown represents the percent of electricity generated by nuclear energy in five countries. Find the approximate percent of electricity generated by nuclear energy in France.

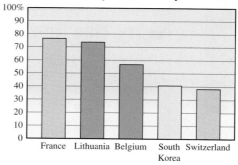

Percent of Electricity Generated by Nuclear Energy

Source: *The World Almanac and Book of Facts*

SOLUTION

The first vertical bar represents the percentage for France. Reading across from the height of the bar to the vertical axis, we see that the height is a little bit more than halfway between 70 and 80%, so we estimate that the answer is about 76%.

▼ **Try This One 5**

Using the graph shown in Example 5, find the approximate percent of electricity generated by nuclear energy for Switzerland.

A **pie chart**, also called a **circle graph**, is constructed by drawing a circle and dividing it into parts called sectors, according to the size of the percentage of each portion in relation to the whole.

EXAMPLE 6 **Obtaining Information from a Pie Chart**

The pie chart shown represents the number of fatal occupational injuries in the United States for a selected year. If the total number of fatal injuries was 5,915 for the year, estimate how many resulted from assaults and violent acts.

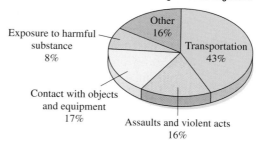

Fatal Occupational Injuries

Source: *The World Almanac and Book of Facts*

SOLUTION

The sector labeled "Assaults and violent acts" indicates that 16% of the total fatal occupational injuries resulted from assaults and violent acts. So we need to find 16% of 5,915. To find a percentage, we multiply the decimal equivalent of the percentage by the total amount. In this case, we get $0.16 \times 5,915 = 946.4$. Since 0.4 fatal injury makes no sense, we round to 946. (*Note:* To change a percent to decimal form, move the decimal point two places to the left and drop the percent sign: 16 percent means "16 per hundred," which is 16/100, or 0.16. We will study percents in detail in Chapter 8.)

▼ Try This One 6

Using the chart shown in Example 6, find the approximate number of fatal occupational injuries that resulted from transportation accidents.

A **time series graph** or **line graph** represents how something varies or changes over a specific time period.

EXAMPLE 7   Obtaining Information from a Line Graph

The graph shown indicates the number of cable systems in the United States from 1960 to 2005. Find the approximate number of cable systems in 1970.

Number of Cable Systems in the United States

Source: National Cable and Telecommunications Association

SOLUTION

Locate the year 1970 on the horizontal axis and move up to the line on the graph. At this point, move horizontally to the point on the vertical axis as shown.

The height is about halfway between 2,000 and 3,000; so there were about 2,500 cable systems in the United States in 1970.

▼ Try This One 7

Using the graph shown in Example 7, find the approximate number of cable systems in the United States for the year 2005.

Distances between two cities can be estimated by using a map and its scale. The procedure is shown in Example 8.

EXAMPLE 8   Estimating Distance by Using a Map

A portion of a map is reproduced below. Fairbanks and Cordova are $2\frac{7}{8}$ inches apart on the map. If the scale is $\frac{1}{4}$ inch = 25 miles, estimate the distance between the cities.

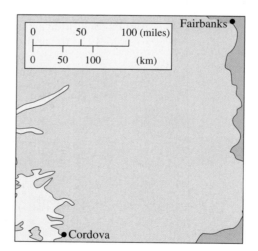

SOLUTION

First, we need to know how many $\frac{1}{4}$-inch units there are in $2\frac{7}{8}$ inches. Three full inches would be 12 quarter-inch units; $2\frac{7}{8}$ is $\frac{1}{8}$ less than 3, which is one-half of a $\frac{1}{4}$-inch unit less than 3. This means that there are $11\frac{1}{2}$ quarter-inch units. (You could also divide $2\frac{7}{8}$ by $\frac{1}{4}$ to get the same result.) Now we multiply: $25 \times 11\frac{1}{2} = 287.5$. So the cities are about 287.5 miles apart.

▼ Try This One 8

4. Use estimation to obtain information from graphs.

Estimate the distance between two cities that are $2\frac{1}{8}$ inches apart on a map if the scale is $\frac{1}{8}$ inch = 50 miles.

Answers to Try This One

1 (a) 372,700
(b) 33
(c) 0.371
(d) 1465.98

2 About $56

3 About $290

4 About $500

5 About 39%

6 About 2,543

7 About 8,000

8 About 850 miles

EXERCISE SET 1-2

Writing Exercises

1. What is estimation? Describe it in your own words.
2. Think of three real-world situations where you could use estimation.
3. Explain why an exact answer to a math problem isn't always necessary.
4. How can estimation be used as a quick check to see if the answer to a math problem is reasonable?
5. Describe the rules for rounding numbers to a given place.
6. Explain why there is never a single, correct answer to a question that asks you to estimate some quantity.

Computational Exercises

For Exercises 7–26, round the number to the place value given.

7. 2,861 (hundreds)
8. 732.6498 (thousandths)
9. 3,261,437 (ten-thousands)
10. 9,347 (tens)
11. 62.67 (ones)
12. 45,371,999 (millions)
13. 218,763 (hundred-thousands)
14. 923 (hundreds)
15. 3.671 (hundredths)
16. 56.3 (ones)
17. 327.146 (tenths)
18. 83,261,000 (millions)
19. 5,462,371 (ten-thousands)
20. 7.123 (hundredths)
21. 272,341 (hundred-thousands)
22. 63.715 (tenths)
23. 264.97348 (ten-thousandths)
24. 1,655,432 (millions)
25. 563.271 (hundredths)
26. 426.861356 (hundred-thousandths)

Real-World Applications

27. Estimate the total cost of eight energy-saving light-bulbs on sale for $16.99 each.
28. Estimate the cost of five espresso machines that cost $39.95 each.
29. Estimate the time it would take you to drive 237 miles at 37 miles per hour.
30. Estimate the distance you can travel in 3 hours 25 minutes if you drive on average 42 miles per hour.
31. Estimate the sale price of a futon you saw on eBay that costs $178.99 and is now on sale for 60% off.
32. Estimate the sale price of a DVD player that costs $42.99, on sale for 15% off.
33. Estimate the total cost of the following meal at McDonald's:
    Quarter pounder with cheese $2.89
    Supersized fries $1.89
    Small shamrock shake $1.29

34. Estimate the total cost of the following items for your dorm room:

Loft bed	$159.95
Beanbag chair	$49.95
Storage cubes	$29.95
Lava lamp	$19.95

35. Estimate the time it would take you in a charity bike tour to ride 86 miles at a rate of 11 miles per hour.

36. If a person earns $48,300.00 per year, estimate how much the person earns per hour. Assume a person works 40 hours per week and 50 weeks per year.

37. If a person earns $8.75 per hour, estimate how much the person would earn per year. Assume a person works 40 hours per week and 50 weeks per year.

38. If a salesperson earns a commission of 12%, estimate how much money the salesperson would earn on an item that sold for $529.85.

39. Estimate the cost of putting up a decorative border in your dorm room if your room is 24 feet long and 18 feet wide and the border costs $5.95 every 10 feet.

40. Estimate the cost of painting a homecoming float if the area to be painted is 12 feet by 16 feet and a quart of paint that covers 53 square feet costs $11.99.

41. Posters for a rock concert cost $4.95 each. Estimate the cost of hanging the maximum number of posters along a 30-foot-long hallway if the posters are each 2 feet wide and there is to be 5 feet between posters.

42. Estimate your cost to live in an apartment for 1 year if the rent is $365.00 per month and utilities are $62.00 per month.

Use the information shown in the graph for Exercises 43–46. The graph gives the areas of various college campuses in acres.

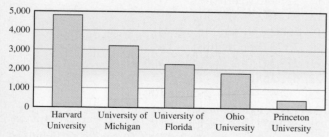

Source: http://colleges.usnews.rankingsandreviews.com

43. Estimate the area of the campus of the University of Michigan.

44. Estimate the area of the campus of Princeton University.

45. Estimate the difference between the largest campus shown and the smallest campus shown.

46. Estimate the areas of the two universities that are approximately the same size.

Use the information shown in the graph for Exercises 47 and 48. The graph represents a survey of 1,385 office workers and shows the percent of people who indicated what time of day is most productive for them.

Source: *USA Today*

47. Estimate the number of people who feel they are most productive outside normal office hours.

48. Estimate the number of people who feel they are most productive before late morning.

Use the information shown in the graph for Exercises 49 and 50. The graph represents a survey of undergraduates enrolled in college in the 2003–2004 school year.

Source: www.acenet.edu

49. Approximately what percentage of students worked more than 21 hours per week?

50. Approximately what percentage of students worked less than 35 hours per week?

Use the information shown in the graph for Exercises 51–54. The graph shows the cigarette consumption (in billions) in the United States for the years 1900 to 2007.

Source: www.infoplease.com

51. Estimate the number of cigarettes smoked in 1950.
52. Estimate the number of cigarettes smoked in 1985.
53. Estimate the year or years in which 200 billion cigarettes were smoked.
54. Estimate the year or years in which 400 billion cigarettes were smoked.
55. In the 2007 atlas distributed by State Farm Insurance, Cincinnati and Columbus are $8\frac{3}{4}$ inches apart. Estimate the distance between the cities if the scale is 1 inch = 11 miles.
56. In the 2007 atlas distributed by State Farm Insurance, Pittsburgh and Johnstown, PA, are $4\frac{7}{8}$ inches apart. Estimate the distance between the cities if the scale is $\frac{1}{2}$ inch = 6 miles.

*Use the information in the graph for Exercises 57–60. The graph shows the average daily reach for the five most visited sites on the Internet for the three-month period ending July 21, 2008. (**Reach** is the percentage of global Internet users who visit a site.)*

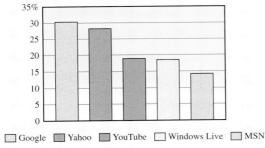

Average Daily Reach for Top Five Websites

☐ Google ■ Yahoo ■ YouTube ☐ Windows Live ☐ MSN

57. Estimate the average daily reach for Yahoo.
58. Estimate the average daily reach for YouTube.
59. Estimate the combined average daily reach for Google and Windows Live.
60. Estimate the difference in average daily reach between the first and fifth most visited sites.

Use the information in the graph for Exercises 61 and 62. The graph shows the number of people who would start over in a completely different career.

Career Change

Yes 51%

No 25%

Maybe 24%

Source: The Konn/Ferry International Survey

61. What percent of people would definitely not choose a different career?
62. The total number of people surveyed was 1,733. Approximately how many would choose a different career?

Use the information in the graph for Exercises 63 and 64. The graph shows the average penalty fees for credit cards for 2002 to 2007.

Average Credit Card Penalty Fees

Source: *USA Today*

63. Estimate the credit card penalty fees for 2004.
64. What was the penalty fee increase from 2002 to 2007?

Critical Thinking

65. Sometimes graphs are drawn in such a way as to support a conclusion that may or may not be true. Look at the graph and see if you can find anything misleading.

Cost of Milk

$1.08

$1.59

MILK   MILK

Fall 1988   Fall 2006

66. The choice of labeling on a graph can have a profound effect on how the information is perceived.

Compare the graph below to the one from Exercises 63 and 64. It contains the same information as the earlier graph. Why does it appear to show a much sharper increase in credit card penalty fees?

Average Credit Card Penalty Fees

67. Find an advertisement for a store that sells consumer electronics, either from a newspaper or on the Internet. Then use it to estimate the cost of a home entertainment center consisting of a 26-inch flat screen TV, a DVD player, a surround sound system, and a cabinet. Does the total amount sound like a good deal to you?

68. Find an advertisement for a store that sells consumer electronics, either from a newspaper or on the Internet. Then use it to estimate the cost of a home computer center consisting of a computer desk, computer, printer, and 20-inch monitor. Does the total amount sound like a good deal to you?

Section 1-3 Problem Solving

LEARNING OBJECTIVES

☐ 1. State the four steps in the basic problem-solving procedure.

☐ 2. Solve problems by using a diagram.

☐ 3. Solve problems by using trial and error.

☐ 4. Solve problems involving money.

☐ 5. Solve problems by using calculation.

☑ 1. State the four steps in the basic problem-solving procedure.

There's a good reason that questions in math classes are usually called *problems:* the study of mathematics is all about learning and applying problem-solving skills and strategies. For most of recorded history, math and problem solving have been intimately connected, and a tremendous amount of effort has gone into using math as a problem-solving tool. In this section, we'll learn about a simple framework for problem solving and practice a number of useful strategies.

A Hungarian mathematician named George Polya did a lot of research on the nature of problem solving in the first half of the 20th century. His biggest contribution to the field was an attempt to identify a series of steps that were fundamental to problem-solving strategies used by great thinkers throughout human history. One of his books, published in 1945 (and still a big seller on Amazon!), set forth these basic steps. *How to Solve It* is so widely read that it has been translated into at least 17 languages.

Polya's strategy is not necessarily earth-shattering: its brilliance lies in its simplicity. It provides four basic steps that can be used as a framework for problem solving in any area, from mathematics to home improvements.

Polya's Four-Step Problem-Solving Procedure

Step 1 *Understand the problem.* An excellent way to start is to write down information given in a problem as you come to it. Especially with lengthy problems, if you read the whole thing all at once, you may get a bit overwhelmed and intimidated. If you read the problem slowly and carefully, and you write down information as it's provided, you will always have a head start. It is equally important to carefully note exactly what it is that you are being asked to find, since this will guide you to the next step. You should probably read a problem more than once to make sure you understand what information you are given and what you are asked to find.

Step 2 *Devise a plan to solve the problem.* There are many ways to solve problems. It may be helpful to draw a picture. You could make an organized list. You may be able to solve it by trial and error. You might be able to find a similar problem that has already been solved and apply the technique to the problem that you are trying to solve. You may be able to solve the problem by using the arithmetic operations of addition, subtraction, multiplication, or division. You may be able to solve the problem by using algebraic equations or geometric formulas.

Step 3 *Carry out the plan to solve the problem.* After you have devised a plan, try it out. If you can't get the answer, try a different strategy. Also be advised that sometimes there are several ways to solve a problem, so different students can arrive at the correct answer by different methods.

Step 4 *Check the answer.* Some problems can be checked by using mathematical methods. Sometimes you may have to ask yourself if the answer is reasonable, and sometimes the problem can be checked by using a different method. Finally, you might be able to use estimation to approximate the answer. (See Section 1–2.)

In each of the examples in this section, we'll illustrate the use of Polya's four-step procedure.

EXAMPLE 1 **Solving a Problem by Using a Diagram**

A gardener is asked to plant eight tomato plants that are 18 inches tall in a straight line with 2 feet between each plant. How much space is needed between the first plant and the last one?

SOLUTION

Be careful—what seems like an obvious solution is not always correct! You might be tempted to just multiply 8 by 2, but instead we will use Polya's method.

Step 1 *Understand the problem.* In this case, the key information given is that there will be eight plants in a line, with 2 feet between each. We are asked to find the total distance from the first to the last.

Step 2 *Devise a plan to solve the problem.* When a situation is described that you can draw a picture of, it's often helpful to do so.

Step 3 *Carry out the plan to solve the problem.* The figure would look like this:

Now we can use the picture to add up the distances:

$$2 + 2 + 2 + 2 + 2 + 2 + 2 = 14 \text{ feet}$$

Step 4 *Check the answer.* There are eight plants, but only seven spaces of 2 feet between them. So $7 \times 2 = 14$ feet is right.

Math Note

Sometimes problems will contain extraneous information. In Example 1, the height of the plants is immaterial to the distance between them, so you can (and should) ignore that information. Students sometimes get into trouble by trying to incorporate *all* the information provided without considering relevance.

▼ Try This One 1

Suppose you want to cut a 4-foot party sub into 10 pieces. How many cuts do you need to make?

Sidelight   GEORGE POLYA (1887–1985)

Born in Hungary, George Polya received his Ph.D. from the University of Budapest in 1912. He studied law and literature before turning his interests to mathematics. He came to the United States in 1940 and taught at Brown University. In 1942, he moved to Stanford University. His most famous book entitled *How to Solve It* was published in 1945 by Princeton University Press.

This book explained his method of problem solving, which consisted of four major steps.

1. Understand the problem.
2. Devise a plan.
3. Carry out the plan.
4. Look back.

Over 1 million copies of the book have been sold, and it is still being published today.

His four-step process is used as a blueprint for solving problems not only in mathematics but in other areas of study as well. The book has been translated into at least 17 languages and is sold worldwide.

In addition to his famous book, Polya has written over 200 articles, nine other books, and numerous other papers.

EXAMPLE 2   **Solving a Perimeter Problem**

Scientists and inventors often use sketches to organize their thoughts as Leonardo da Vinci did. He wrote backward in Latin to protect his work.

A campus group is setting up a rectangular area for a tailgate bash. They have 100 feet between two roads to use as width and 440 feet of fence to use. What length will use up the total amount of fence and enclose the biggest space?

SOLUTION

Step 1 *Understand the problem.* We're asked to consider a rectangular area, so there will be four sides. We're told that the width is 100 feet and that the four sides add up to 440 feet. (That is, the perimeter is 440 feet.) We're asked to find the length.

Step 2 *Devise a plan to solve the problem.* This is a classic example of a problem where a diagram will be useful. This should help us to figure out all the dimensions.

Step 3 *Carry out the plan to solve the problem.* Our diagram looks like this:

100 feet ▭ 100 feet

(Since the area is rectangular, the opposite sides have the same length.) Of the 440 feet of fence, 200 feet is accounted for in our diagram. That leaves $440 - 200 = 240$ feet to be divided among the remaining two sides. Each has length 120 feet.

Step 4 *Check the answer.* If there are two sides with width 100 feet and two others with length 120 feet, the perimeter is $100 + 100 + 120 + 120 = 440$ feet.

☑ 2. Solve problems by using a diagram.

▼ Try This One 2

A rectangular poster promoting the tailgate bash in Example 2 is restricted to 10 inches in width to fit bulletin board restrictions. The printer suggests a perimeter of 56 inches for maximum savings in terms of setup. How tall will the posters be?

EXAMPLE 3 **Solving a Problem by Using Trial and Error**

Math Note

The trial-and-error method works nicely in Example 3, but for many problems, there are just too many possible answers to try. It's not a strategy that you should rely on for solving every problem.

Suppose that you have 10 coins consisting of quarters and dimes. If you have a total of $1.90, find the number of each type of coin.

SOLUTION

Step 1 *Understand the problem.* We're told that we have a total of 10 coins and that some are dimes (worth $0.10 each) and the rest are quarters (worth $0.25 each). The total value is $1.90. The problem is to find how many quarters and dimes together are worth $1.90.

Step 2 *Devise a plan to solve the problem.* One strategy that can be used is to make an organized list of possible combinations of 10 total quarters and dimes and see if the sum is $1.90. For example, you may try one quarter and nine dimes. This gives $1 \times \$0.25 + 9 \times \$0.10 = \$1.15$.

Quarters	Dimes	Amount
1	9	$1.15

Step 3 *Carry out the plan.* Since one quarter and nine dimes is wrong, try two quarters and eight dimes.

Quarters	Dimes	Amount
2	8	$1.30

This doesn't work either. We'll continue until we get the correct answer.

Quarters	Dimes	Amount
1	9	$1.15
2	8	$1.30
3	7	$1.45
4	6	$1.60
5	5	$1.75
6	4	$1.90 ◄——— Correct

Answer: six quarters and four dimes.

Step 4 *Check the answer.* In this case, our answer can be checked by working out the amounts: $6 \times \$0.25 + 4 \times \$0.10 = \$1.90$.

▼ **Try This One 3**

☑ 3. Solve problems by using trial and error.

Michelle bought some 42-cent stamps and some 59-cent stamps. If she bought a total of seven stamps and spent a total of $3.45, how many of each kind did she buy?

EXAMPLE 4 **Solving a Problem Involving Salary**

So you've graduated from college and you're ready for that first real job. In fact, you have two offers! One pays an hourly wage of $19.20 per hour, with a 40-hour work week. You work for 50 weeks and get 2 weeks' paid vacation. The second offer is a salaried position, offering $41,000 per year. Which job will pay more?

SOLUTION

Step 1 *Understand the problem.* The important information is that the hourly job pays $19.20 per hour for 40 hours each week, and that you will be paid for 52 weeks per year. We are asked to decide if that will work out to be more or less than $41,000 per year.

Step 2 *Devise a plan to solve the problem.* We can use multiplication to figure out how much you would be paid each week and then multiply again to get the yearly amount. Then we can compare to the salaried position.

Step 3 *Carry out the plan to solve the problem.* Multiply the hourly wage by 40 hours; this shows that the weekly earnings will be $19.20 \times 40 = 768. Now we multiply by 52 weeks: $768 \times 52 = $39,936$. The salaried position, at $41,000 per year, pays more.

Step 4 *Check the answer.* We can figure out the hourly wage of the job that pays $41,000 per year. We divide by 52 to get a weekly salary of $788.46. Then we divide by 40 to get an hourly wage of $19.71. Again, this job pays more.

☑ 4. Solve problems involving money.

▼ Try This One 4

A condo on the water in Myrtle Beach can be rented for $280 per day, with a nonrefundable application fee of $50. Another one down the beach can be rented for $2,100 per week. Which condo costs less for a week's stay?

EXAMPLE 5   Solving a Problem by Using Calculation

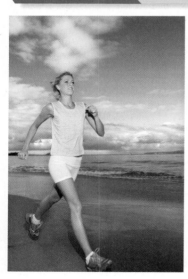

A 150-pound person walking briskly for 1 mile can burn about 100 calories. How many miles per day would the person have to walk to lose 1 pound in 1 week? It is necessary to burn 3,500 calories to lose 1 pound.

SOLUTION

Step 1 *Understand the problem.* A 150-pound person burns 100 calories per 1 mile and needs to burn 3,500 calories in 7 days to lose 1 pound. The problem asks how many miles per day the person has to walk to lose 1 pound in 1 week.

Step 2 *Devise a plan to solve the problem.* We will calculate how many calories need to be burned per day and then divide by 100 to see how many miles need to be walked.

Step 3 *Carry out the plan.* Since 3,500 calories need to be expended in 7 days, divide 3,500 by 7 to get 500 calories per day. Then divide 500 by 100 to get 5 miles. It is necessary to walk briskly 5 miles per day to lose 1 pound in a week.

Step 4 *Check the answer.* Multiply 5 miles per day by 100 calories per mile by 7 days to get 3,500 calories.

▼ Try This One 5

Megan's car gets 28 miles per gallon on long trips. She leaves home, bound for a friend's house 370 miles away. If she makes the drive in 6 hours, how many gallons of gas per hour is the car burning?

Sidelight A LEGENDARY PROBLEM SOLVER

Archimedes is considered by some to be the greatest mathematician of the ancient world. But he is best known for a famous problem he solved in the bathtub.

King Hieron II of Syracuse ordered a solid gold crown from a goldsmith sometime around 250 BCE. He suspected that the crown was not really solid gold, but he didn't want to have it melted down to check, because of course that would ruin it. He asked his friend Archimedes if he could figure out a way to determine whether the crown really was pure gold without destroying it.

After some serious thought, Archimedes decided to relax by taking a bath. While sitting in the tub, he saw that the water level rose in proportion to his weight. Suddenly, he realized that he had discovered the solution to his problem. By placing the crown in a full tub of water, he could tell how much of it was gold by weighing the amount of water that overflowed. Legend has it that Archimedes was so excited by this burst of inspiration that he forgot to clothe himself and ran naked through the streets of Syracuse, shouting "Eureka" ("I have found it!"), a performance that would most likely get him arrested, or maybe institutionalized, today.

It turns out that the crown was not solid gold, and the goldsmith either was placed in jail or had his head removed from his shoulders, depending on which account you believe. The moral of this story is that you never know where inspiration in solving a problem might come from.

EXAMPLE 6   Solving a Problem by Using Calculation

For a date party at a certain restaurant there is a flat fee of $125 to rent the banquet room plus a charge of $18 per person attending. How much will the date party cost if 104 people attend?

SOLUTION

Step 1 *Understand the problem.* We are asked to find the cost of the party. We are given that there is a flat rate of $125 and a per-person charge of $18.

Step 2 *Devise a plan to solve the problem.* To find the total cost, we should add all the costs involved—the flat rate plus the per-person charge. The flat rate is $125, and the per-person charge is 18×104.

Step 3 *Carry out the plan.* Add: $125 + $18(104) = $125 + $1,872 = $1,997$. So it will cost $1,997 for the date party.

Step 4 *Check the answer.* Here we will use estimation to see if the answer makes sense. The cost of the party is about $125 + $20(100) = $2,125$. So our answer appears to be reasonable.

☑ 5. Solve problems by using calculation.

▼ Try This One 6

If it costs $35.00 per day and $0.25 per mile to rent a car, how much will it cost a person to rent a car for a 2-day, 300-mile round trip?

Strategies for Understanding a Problem

One reason that problem solving is challenging is that every problem can be a little different. But here are some suggestions for helping to understand a problem and devise a strategy for solving.

- If the problem describes something that can be diagrammed, a drawing almost always helps.

- Write down all the numeric information in the problem. This often helps to organize your thoughts.

- Sometimes making a chart to organize information is helpful, especially when you're trying to use trial and error.

- Don't expect that you'll know exactly how to solve a problem after reading it once! Most often you'll need to read through a problem several times, and even then you may need to just try some approaches before finding one that works.

Answers to Try This One

1 Nine

2 18 inches

3 Four $0.42 stamps and three $0.59 stamps

4 The condo for $280 per day costs less for a week.

5 About 2.2 gallons per hour

6 $145.00

EXERCISE SET 1-3

Writing Exercises

1. List and describe the four steps in problem solving.
2. Discuss what you should do first when given a word problem to solve.
3. Discuss different ways you might be able to check your answer to a problem.
4. Why is trial and error not always a good problem-solving strategy?

Computational Exercises

5. One number is 6 more than another number, and their sum is 22. Find the numbers.
6. One number is 7 more than another number. Their sum is 23. Find the numbers.
7. The sum of the digits of a two-digit number is 7. If 9 is subtracted from the number, the answer will be the number with the digits reversed. Find the number.
8. A mother is 4 times as old as her daughter. In 18 years, the mother will be twice as old as her daughter. Find their present ages.
9. In 28 years, Mark will be 5 times as old as he is now. Find his present age.
10. Pete is twice as old as Lashanna. In 5 years, the sum of their ages will be 37. Find their present ages.
11. A piece of rope is 48 inches long and is cut so that one piece is twice as long as the other. Find the length of each piece.
12. At the dog park, there are several dogs with their owners. Counting heads, there are 12; counting legs, there are 38. How many dogs and owners are there?

Real-World Applications

13. Fred has $5.05 worth of coins floating around in his backpack, all of which are quarters and dimes. If there are 5 more dimes than quarters, how many coins of each are there?

14. A tip jar contains twice as many quarters as dollar bills. If it has a total of $12 in it, how many quarters and how many dollar bills does it contain?

15. A fraternity charged $2.00 admission for guys and $1.00 admission for gals to their finals week bash. The fraternity made $75 and sold 55 tickets. How many gals attended the party?

16. While sitting in the quad on central campus, I counted 9 students riding 2-wheeled mopeds or 3-wheeled scooters, which made a total of 21 wheels. How many mopeds and how many scooters passed by me?

17. Jane has 10 phone cards worth either $20 or $15. How many of each does she have if the phone cards total $180?

18. May receives $87 for working one 8-hour day. One day she had to stop after working 5 hours because of a doctor's appointment. How much did she make that day?

19. The manager of the new campus Internet café wants to put six PCs on each table with 3 feet between the PCs and 2 feet on each end. The PCs measure $1\frac{1}{2}$ feet wide and 21 inches high. What length of tables should the Internet café order?

20. Bob is building a deck that is 32 feet long, and he has posts that are 6 inches square to use to build the railing. If he puts the posts 4 feet apart with one on each end, how many posts will he use?

21. Suzie hangs 10 pictures that each measure $8\frac{1}{2}$ inches wide on a wall. She spaces them 6 inches apart with 2 inches on each end, so that they fit perfectly on the wall. How wide is the wall?

22. You want to cut a width of mat board to frame pictures so you can fit six pictures that have a width of 6 inches each with 2 inches between them and a 1-inch border. How wide should you cut the mat board?

23. The campus athletic department is building a new pool that is 60 feet long, and there is enough tile for a 220-foot border. How wide should the pool be to ensure that all tiles are used?

24. If the length of the campus quad is double its width and there's a short retaining wall around the perimeter that measures 300 feet, what are the length and width of the quad?

25. If you have enough caulk to seal 380 feet of window casings, and each window measures 2 feet by 3 feet, how many windows can you caulk?

26. For the Spring Fling gala, Felicia has 500 feet of lights to hang. If the width of the room is 70 feet, what is the length of the room if she can hang all the lights so that they go around the room exactly once?

27. Two students are paid a total of $60 for leading a campus tour at freshman orientation. The tour lasts approximately 2 hours. If Sam works for $1\frac{1}{2}$ hours, Pete works $\frac{1}{2}$ hour, and each makes the same hourly wage, how much does each receive?

28. You have one-half of an energy drink left. If you drink one-half of that, how much of your energy drink do you have left?

29. At the campus bookstore, a stocker has to move three laptops in bags that weigh 6 pounds each and six backpacks that weigh 8 pounds each. If she lifts them all at once to move them out of the way, how much weight does she lift?

30. A small beverage company has 832 bottles of water to ship. If there are 6 bottles per case, how many cases are needed and how many bottles will be left over?

31. A person's monthly budget includes $256 for food, $125 for gasoline, and $150 for utilities. If this person earns $1,624 per month after taxes, how much money is left for other expenses?

32. One protein bar has 15 grams of carbs. If a runner wanted to eat 300 grams of carbs the week before a big marathon, how many protein bars would she have to eat?

33. A bag of pretzels contains 1,650 calories. If a person purchased 26 bags of pretzels for a picnic, how many calories would be consumed if all the bags were eaten?

34. An automobile travels 527 miles on 12.8 gallons of gasoline. How many miles per gallon did the car get?

35. If a family borrows $12,381 for an addition to their home, and the loan is to be paid off in monthly payments over a period of 5 years, how much should each payment be? (Interest has been included in the total amount borrowed.)

36. Assuming that you could average driving 55 miles per hour, how long would it take you to drive from one city to another if the distance was 327 miles?

37. Ticketmaster is selling tickets for an upcoming concert. They are charging $32 for floor seats, $25 for pavilion seats, and $20 for lawn seats (not including the huge handling fee). A group of students purchases 5 floor tickets, 8 pavilion tickets, and 3 lawn tickets. What is the total cost of all the concert tickets purchased by the group of students?

38. Four friends decide to rent an apartment. Because each will be using it for different lengths of time, Mary will pay $\frac{1}{2}$ of the monthly rent, Jean will pay $\frac{1}{4}$ of the monthly rent, Claire will pay $\frac{1}{8}$ of the monthly rent, and Margie will pay the rest. If the monthly rent is $2,375, how much will each person pay?

39. The Campus Pizza Shack pays its employees 46.5 cents per mile if they use their own cars for

deliveries. In one month, Jenny racked up 106 miles delivering pizzas on campus. How much will she be paid for her mileage?

40. Harry fills up his Jeep with gasoline and notes that the odometer reading is 23,568.7 miles. The next time he fills up his Jeep, he pays for 12.6 gallons of gasoline. He notes his odometer reading is 23,706.3 miles. How many miles per gallon did he get?

41. A clerk earns $9.50 per hour and is paid time and a half for any hours worked over 40. Find the clerk's pay if he worked 46 hours during a specific week.

42. A cell phone company charges 35 cents per minute during the daytime and 10 cents per minute during the evening for those who go over their allotted monthly minutes. If Sally went 32 minutes over her monthly minutes, find out how much she'd save if she went 32 minutes over her monthly minutes during the evening compared to during the daytime.

Critical Thinking

43. With a power mower, Phil can cut a large lawn in 3 hours. His younger brother can cut the same lawn in 6 hours. If both worked together, using two power mowers, how long would it take them to cut the lawn?

44. A king decided to pay a knight one piece of gold for each day's protection on a 6-day trip. The king took a gold bar 6 inches long and paid the knight at the end of each day; however, he made only two cuts. How did he do this?

45. At the finals of the campuswide Brainbowl League Tournament, your team was asked to measure out exactly 1 gallon of water using only a 5-gallon and a 3-gallon container, without wasting any water. Your team completed the task. How did they do it?

46. What is the smallest number of cars that can tailgate in a straight line at a football game so that one car is in front of two cars, one car is behind two cars, and one car is between two cars?

47. A college student with a part-time job budgets $\frac{1}{5}$ of her income for clothes, $\frac{2}{5}$ for living expenses (including food and rent), $\frac{1}{10}$ for entertainment, and $\frac{1}{2}$ of the remainder for savings. If she saves $1,200 per year, what is her yearly income?

48. To purchase a computer for the Student Activities office, the freshman class decides to raise $\frac{1}{3}$ of the money, and the sophomore class decides to raise $\frac{1}{2}$ of the money. The Student Government Association agrees to contribute the rest, which amounted to $400. What was the cost of the computer?

CHAPTER **1** **Summary**

Section	Important Terms	Important Ideas
1-1	Inductive reasoning Deductive reasoning Conjecture Counterexample	**In mathematics,** two types of reasoning can be used. They are inductive and deductive reasoning. Inductive reasoning is the process of arriving at a general conclusion based on the observation of specific examples. Deductive reasoning is the process of reasoning that arrives at a conclusion based on previously accepted statements.
1-2	Estimation Bar graph Pie chart Time series graph	**In many** cases, it is not necessary to find the exact answer to a problem. When only an approximate answer is needed, you can use estimation. This is often accomplished by rounding the numbers used in the problem and then performing the necessary operation or operations.
1-3	Polya's four-step problem-solving procedure	**A mathematician** named George Polya devised a procedure to solve mathematical problems. The steps of his procedure are (1) understand the problem, (2) devise a plan to solve the problem, (3) carry out the plan to solve the problem, and (4) check the answer.

MATH IN ⟩ **Criminal Investigation REVISITED**

1. The suspect was identified by specific incidents in the past, which makes this inductive reasoning that would not hold up in court without further evidence.

2. Fingerprints positively identify the officer as having had contact with the victim. This is deductive reasoning and would be useful in court.

3. Like fingerprints, DNA can positively show that the suspect had physical contact with the victim. This evidence, based on deductive reasoning, would hurt the suspect badly in court.

4. While this is compelling evidence, it's based on assuming that those five drawings indicate the artist is the killer. While unlikely, it could be a coincidence based on five drawings, so this is inductive reasoning. It might impress a jury to some extent, but wouldn't be sufficient for a conviction.

Review Exercises

Section 1-1

For Exercises 1–4, make reasonable conjectures for the next three numbers or letters in the sequence.

1. 3   4   6   7   9   10   12   13   15   16   __ __ __
2. 2   7   4   9   6   11   8   13   __ __ __
3. 4   z   16   w   64   t   256   __ __ __
4. 20   A   18   B   16   C   __ __ __

For Exercises 5 and 6, make a reasonable conjecture and draw the next figure.

5.

6.

For Exercises 7 and 8, find a counterexample to show that each statement is false.

7. The product of three odd numbers will always be even.

8. The sum of three multiples of 5 will always end in a 5.

For Exercises 9 and 10, use inductive reasoning to find a rule that relates the number selected to the final answer, and then try to prove your conjecture, using deductive reasoning.

9. Select an even number.

   Add 6:
   Divide the answer by 2:
   Add 10:
   Result:

10. Select a number.

    Multiply it by 9:
    Add 18 to the number:
    Divide by 3:
    Subtract 6:
    Result:

In Exercises 11 and 12, use inductive reasoning to find the next two equations in the pattern:

11. $337 \times 3 = 1,011$
    $337 \times 6 = 2,022$
    $337 \times 9 = 3,033$

12. $33 \times 33 = 1,089$
    $333 \times 333 = 110,889$
    $3333 \times 3333 = 11,108,889$

13. Use inductive reasoning to solve the last equation.

    $\sqrt{1} = 1$
    $\sqrt{1 + 3} = 2$
    $\sqrt{1 + 3 + 5} = 3$
    $\sqrt{1 + 3 + 5 + 7} = 4$
    $\sqrt{1 + 3 + 5 + 7 + 9 + 11 + 13 + 15 + 17} = ?$

14. Take the number 153, cube each digit, and add the cubes. What is the result? Now cube the digits of the result and add the cubes. What is the result? Use inductive reasoning to determine the result if the procedure is repeated 10 times.

In Exercises 15–18, decide whether inductive or deductive reasoning was used.

15. My professor has given extra credit to his students for contributing canned goods to a food pantry during finals week for the last 5 years, so I know I'll get a chance for some easy extra credit on my final.

16. A GPA of 3.5 is required to make the dean's list. I checked with all my teachers to see what my final grades will be, and my GPA works out to be 3.72, so I'll be on the dean's list this semester.

17. To qualify for bowl games, college football teams have to win at least six games. Our team finished 5–7, so they won't be playing in a bowl game this year.

18. The fastest time that I've ever made it to class from my apartment is 8 minutes, and class starts in 7 minutes, so I'll be late today.

Section 1-2

For Exercises 19–23, round each number to the place value given.

19. 132,356 (thousands)
20. 186.75 (ones)
21. 14.63157 (ten-thousandths)
22. 0.6314 (tenths)
23. 3,725.63 (tens)
24. Estimate the cost of four lawn mowers if each one costs $329.95.
25. Estimate the cost of five textbooks if they cost $115.60, $89.95, $29.95, $62.50, and $43.10.
26. A car averages 14 miles per gallon of gas. Estimate how far the car can travel on 19 gallons of gas.
27. A family of six consists of four people older than 12 and two people 12 or under. Tickets into an amusement park are $57.95 for those over 12 and $53.95 for those 12 and under. Estimate how much it would cost the family to go to the amusement park.
28. At M.T. Wallatts University, it costs a student $689 per credit-hour to attend.

    (a) Estimate the cost for a student to attend one semester if he registers for 9 credit-hours.
    (b) If a student makes $11 an hour at her part-time job (after taxes) and works 30 hours a week, approximately how many weeks will she have to work to afford one semester with 9 credit-hours?

29. A video store sells used DVDs for $8.95, tax included. About how many could you buy with the $130 you got for selling your textbooks back?

Use the information shown in the pie chart for Exercises 30 and 31. The pie chart shows the percent of the pollutants released into the environment for a specific year.

Pollutant Releases in the United States

Source: *The World Almanac and Book of Facts*

30. If the total amount of pollutants released is 1,953 million pounds, find the amount of pollutant released in the air.
31. If the total amount of pollutants released is 1,953 million pounds, find the amount of pollutants released in surface water.

Use the information shown in the graph for Exercises 32 and 33. The graph shows the average weekly salary (in dollars) for U.S. production workers from 1970 to 2005.

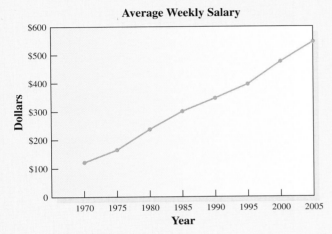

Average Weekly Salary

Source: *World Almanac and Book of Facts*

32. Estimate the weekly salary in 1988.
33. Estimate the weekly salary in 2003.
34. Estimate the distance between two cities that are 8 inches apart on a map if the scale is 2 inches = 15 miles.

Section 1-3

35. Cindy has 32 flyers about a campus symposium on environmental issues that she is organizing. She gave away all but 9. How many did she have left?
36. A tennis team played 40 matches. The team won 20 more matches than they lost. How many matches did the team lose?
37. If a person weighs 110 pounds when standing on one foot on a scale, how much will that person weigh when he stands on a scale with both feet?
38. A small mocha latte and biscotti together cost $3.40. If the mocha latte cost $0.40 more than the biscotti, how much did each cost?
39. Harry is 10 years old, and his brother Bill is twice as old. When Harry is 20, how old will Bill be?
40. Mary got $80 in tips last night for her waitressing job at the campus café. She spent $8.00 downloading songs online to her MP3 player and then spent $\frac{1}{3}$ of the remainder on tickets for the spring dance on Saturday. How much did she have left?

41. Your science textbook and its accompanying lab packet cost $120. If the textbook costs twice as much as the lab packet, how much did the lab packet cost?
42. Fill in the squares with digits to complete the problem. There are several correct answers.

43. In 10 years, Harriet will be 3 times as old as she was 10 years ago. How old is she now?
44. At times during the summer in Alaska, the day is 18 hours longer than the night. How long is each?
45. Babs is 9 years older than Debbie, and Jack is 7 years younger than Babs. The sum of their ages is 20. How old is Debbie?
46. Using $+$, $-$, and $\times$, make a true equation. Do not change the order of the digits.

$$2 \quad 9 \quad 6 \quad 7 \quad = \quad 17$$

47. Tina and Joe are doing homework problems together for their math class. Joe says to Tina, "If I do one more problem, then we'll have both done the same number of problems." Tina says to Joe, "If I do one more problem, than I will have done twice the number you have!" How many problems has each one done so far?
48. Can you divide a pie into 11 pieces with four straight cuts? The cuts must go from rim to rim but not necessarily through the center. The pieces need not be identical.
49. How many triangles are in the figure shown here?

50. In 20 years, Charles will be 3 times as old as he is now. How old is he now?
51. The sum of two numbers is 20 and the difference is 5. Find the numbers.
52. A health food store charges $2.00 per pound for high-protein nature mix and $2.75 for low-carb soy medley. If 10 pounds of the two items mixed together costs $24.50, find the amount of each type in the mixture.
53. Taylor had $1,000 to invest. He invested part of it at 8% and part of it at 6%. If his total simple interest was $76.00, find how much he invested for 1 year at each rate.

Chapter Test

For Exercises 1 and 2, make reasonable conjectures for the next three numbers in the sequence.

1. 2 4 3 6 5 9 8 __ __ __
2. 5 10 20 40 80 __ __ __
3. Use inductive reasoning to find the solution to the problem; then check it by performing the calculation.

$$0 \cdot 9 + 8 = 8$$
$$9 \cdot 9 + 7 = 88$$
$$98 \cdot 9 + 6 = 888$$
$$987 \cdot 9 + 5 = 8,888$$
$$\vdots$$
$$9,876,543 \cdot 9 + 1 = ?$$

4. Use inductive reasoning to find the solution to the problem; then check it by performing the calculation.

$$6 \times 7 = 42$$
$$66 \times 67 = 4,422$$
$$666 \times 667 = 444,222$$
$$6,666 \times 6,667 = ?$$

5. Use inductive reasoning to find a rule that relates the number you selected to the final answer, and try to prove your conjecture.

   Select a number:
   Add 10 to the number:
   Multiply the answer by 5:
   Add 15 to the answer:
   Divide the answer by 5:
   Result:

6. There were 12 students in line to register for the Underwater Basketweaving 101 course. All but 2 changed their minds. How many remained in line?
7. For a job, a worker receives a salary that doubles each day. After 10 days of work, the job is finished and the person receives $100.00 for the final day's work. On which day did the worker receive $25.00?
8. What are the next two letters in the sequence O, T, T, F, F, S, S, ... ? (*Hint:* It has something to do with numbers.)
9. By moving just one coin, make two lines, each three coins long.

10. A ship is docked in harbor with a rope ladder hanging over the edge, and 9 feet of the ladder is above the waterline. The tide is rising at 8 inches per hour. After 6 hours, how much of the ladder remains above the waterline?
11. The problem here was written by the famous mathematician Diophantus. Can you find the solution?

    The boyhood of a man lasted $\frac{1}{6}$ of his life; his beard grew after $\frac{1}{12}$ more; after $\frac{1}{7}$ more he married; 5 years later his son was born; the son lived to one-half the father's age; and the father died 4 years after the son. How old was the father when he died?

12. A number divided by 3 less than itself gives a quotient of $\frac{8}{5}$. Find the number.
13. The sum of $\frac{1}{2}$ of a number and $\frac{1}{3}$ of the same number is 10. Find the number.
14. Add five lines to the square to make three squares and two triangles.

15. One person works for 3 hours and another person works for 2 hours. They are given a total of $60.00. How should it be divided up so that each person receives a fair share?
16. The sum of the reciprocals of two numbers is $\frac{5}{6}$ and the difference is $\frac{1}{6}$. Find the numbers. (*Hint:* The reciprocal of a number n is $\frac{1}{n}$.)
17. If Sam scored 87% on his first exam, what score would he need on his second exam to bring his average up to 90%?
18. Mt. McKinley is about 20,300 feet above sea level, and Death Valley is 280 feet below sea level. Find the vertical distance from the top of Mt. McKinley to the bottom of Death Valley.
19. The depth of the ocean near the island of Mindanao is about 36,400 feet. The height of Mt. Everest is about 29,000 feet. Find the vertical distance from the top of Mt. Everest to the floor of the ocean near the island of Mindanao.
20. A person is drawing a map and using a scale of 2 inches = 500 miles. How far apart on the map will two cities be located if they are 1,800 miles apart?
21. Mark's mother is 32 years older than Mark. The sum of their ages is 66 years. How old is each?
22. Round 1,674,253 to the nearest hundred-thousand.
23. Round 1.3752 to the nearest hundredth.
24. Estimate the cost of Stuart's new wardrobe for his campus interview if a blazer costs $69.95, a new tie costs $32.54, and new pants cost $42.99.

25. Using the graph, estimate the average number of hours per week U.S. production workers worked in 1980 and 2005.

Average Hours Worked

Source: *World Almanac and Book of Facts*

26. Using the pie chart, of the 3,646 students surveyed at 7 universities, estimate the number of students surveyed who do not live in a residence hall.

Residence

Source: http://www.acha-ncha.org/data/DEMOGF06.html

27. For a specific year, the number of homicides reported for selected cities is shown here. Estimate the number of homicides in Baltimore and the difference between the number of homicides in Chicago and Atlanta.

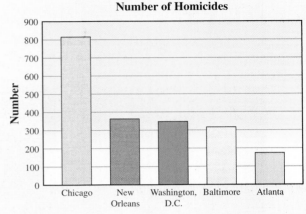

Number of Homicides

Source: *USA Today*

28. Estimate the distance between two cities that are 4 inches apart if the scale on a map is $\frac{1}{2}$ inch = 8 miles.

Projects

1. In Section 1-3, we solved some problems by using algebraic equations. For more complicated situations, more than one equation might be required. When this is the case, it's not uncommon for there to be more than one correct solution. Can you solve the following problem?

   Darla went to Costco and spent $100 for 100 items. She bought 6-packs of bottled water, 20-oz bottles of Diet Pepsi, and 10-pack pouches of Kool-Aid mix. Each 6-pack of water cost $3.00, each bottle of Diet Pepsi cost $1.00, and each pouch of Kool-Aid mix cost $0.50. How many of each item did Darla buy?

2. One reason that Polya's method has stood the test of time is that it is used not just in math, but also for any problem needing to be solved. For each of the problems listed, write a paragraph explaining how each of the steps in Polya's method could be applied.

   (a) A homeowner has a small set of stairs leading from his back door down to a featureless backyard. He would like to have a place for outdoor parties during the summer.

   (b) Your car has been making a really funny noise whenever you go over 50 miles per hour.

   (c) You've balanced your checkbook and found out that you won't have enough money to pay for tuition and books next semester.

   (d) One of your friends heard something you said about him behind his back, and now he is very upset with you.

Sets

Outline

MATH IN Demographics

The world certainly has changed a lot in the last 50 years. If you could travel back to the middle of the 20th century, you'd have an awful hard time finding anyone who would believe that one of the most famous, and richest, people in the world in the early 21st century would be a golfer who is part white, part African-American, *and* part Asian. Our society is becoming more and more diverse every year, to the point where even defining what we mean by *race* isn't so easy anymore. The most common racial groups referred to in population statistics are white, black, Asian, and Hispanic, but many people fall into more than one category (including the President of the United States!). But it's even more confusing than that: *Hispanic* isn't really a race, but rather an ethnic group, and many Hispanics also report themselves as either white or black.

Sorting it all out to get any sort of meaningful picture of what we as Americans look like isn't easy, and the techniques of set theory are very useful tools in trying to do so. In this chapter, we'll define what we mean by sets, and we'll study sets and how they can be used to organize information in an increasingly complex world. The concept of sets has been used extensively since people began studying mathematics, but it wasn't until the late 1800s that the theory of sets was studied as a specific branch of math. One of the major tools that we will use to study sets—the Venn diagram—was introduced in an 1880 paper by a man named John Venn. These diagrams allow us to picture complicated relationships between sets of objects, like people of certain races.

Because race and ethnicity are self-reported in a variety of different ways, it's very difficult to find detailed data on the breakdown of races, but there are some reasonable estimates out there. The following estimates were cobbled together from a number of different sources. In a group of 1,000 randomly selected Americans, 777 would self-report as white, 139 as black, and 149 as Hispanic. In addition, 19 would self-report as black and white, 18 as black and Hispanic, and 85 as white and Hispanic. Finally, 7 would self-report as all three. Based on these estimates, after completing this chapter, you should be able to answer the following questions:

1. How many of the original 1,000 report as white only, black only, and Hispanic only?
2. How many report as Hispanic and black, but not white?
3. How many report as either Hispanic or black?
4. How many report as none of white, black, or Hispanic?

For answers, see Math in Demographics Revisited on page 87

41

Section 2-1 The Nature of Sets

Groups of people, categories of items in stores, laws that apply to traffic—our world is divided into groups of things, or sets. So studying sets from a mathematical standpoint is a good opportunity to study how math is used in our world.

Basic Concepts

We will begin with a basic definition of sets.

LEARNING OBJECTIVES

☐ 1. Define set.

☐ 2. Write sets in three different ways.

☐ 3. Classify sets as finite or infinite.

☐ 4. Define the empty set.

☐ 5. Find the cardinality of a set.

☐ 6. Decide if two sets are equal or equivalent.

☑ 1. Define set.

> A **set** is a well-defined collection of objects.

By *well-defined* we mean that given any object, we can definitely decide whether it is or is not in the set. For example, the set "letters of the English alphabet" is well-defined since it consists of the 26 symbols we use to make up our alphabet, and no other objects. The set "tall people in your class" is not well-defined because who exactly belongs to that set is open to interpretation.

Each object in a set is called an **element** or a **member** of the set. One method of designating a set is called the **roster method,** in which elements are listed between braces, with commas between the elements. The order in which we list elements isn't important: $\{2, 5, 7\}$ and $\{5, 2, 7\}$ are the same set. Often, we will name sets by using a capital letter.

Laws that specify who can vote in a specific election determine a well-defined set of people. There are many other laws that might affect certain sets, like the set of businesses in a certain industry. These laws need to clearly define the set the law applies to—if that set were not well-defined, it would be almost impossible to enforce the law.

EXAMPLE 1　　**Listing the Elements in a Set**

Math Note

The commas make it clear that it is the words, not the letters, that are the elements of the set.

Write the set of months of the year that begin with the letter M.

SOLUTION

The months that begin with M are March and May. So, the answer can be written in set notation as

$$M = \{\text{March, May}\}$$

Each element in the set is separated by a comma.

▼ Try This One 1

Write the set of the Great Lakes.

In math, the set of *counting numbers* or **natural numbers** is defined as $N = \{1, 2, 3, 4, \ldots\}$. (When we are designating sets, the three dots, or *ellipsis,* mean that the list of elements continues indefinitely in the same pattern.)

EXAMPLE 2 | **Writing Sets Using the Roster Method**

Math Note

You can list an element of a set more than once if it means a lot to you, but it's common to choose not to list repeats. For example, the set of letters in the word *letters* is written as $\{l, e, t, r, s\}$.

Use the roster method to do the following:

(a) Write the set of natural numbers less than 6.
(b) Write the set of natural numbers greater than 4.

SOLUTION

(a) $\{1, 2, 3, 4, 5\}$
(b) $\{5, 6, 7, 8, \ldots\}$

▼ **Try This One 2**

Write each set, using the roster method.

(a) The set of even natural numbers from 80 to 90.
(b) The set of odd natural numbers greater than 10.

The 2008 U.S. Olympic team is a set of athletes. Swimmer Michael Phelps is an element of that set.

The symbol $\in$ is used to show that an object is a member or element of a set. For example, let set $A = \{2, 3, 5, 7, 11\}$. Since 2 is a member of set A, it can be written as

$$2 \in \{2, 3, 5, 7, 11\} \qquad \text{or} \qquad 2 \in A$$

Likewise,

$$5 \in \{2, 3, 5, 7, 11\} \qquad \text{or} \qquad 5 \in A$$

When an object is not a member of a set, the symbol $\notin$ is used. Because 4 is not an element of set A, this fact is written as

$$4 \notin \{2, 3, 5, 7, 11\} \qquad \text{or} \qquad 4 \notin A$$

EXAMPLE 3 | **Understanding Set Notation**

Math Note

Be sure to use correct symbols when you show membership in a set. For example, the notation $\{6\} \in \{2, 4, 6\}$ is incorrect since the set $\{6\}$ is not a member of this set: the number 6 is.

Decide whether each statement is true or false.

(a) Oregon $\in A$, where A is the set of states west of the Mississippi River.
(b) $27 \in \{1, 5, 9, 13, 17, \ldots\}$
(c) $z \notin \{v, w, x, y, z\}$

SOLUTION

(a) Oregon is west of the Mississippi, so Oregon is an element of A. The statement is true.
(b) The pattern shows that each element is 4 more than the previous element. So the next three elements are 21, 25, and 29; this shows that 27 is not in the set. The statement is false.
(c) The letter z is an element of the set, so the statement is false.

▼ Try This One 3

Decide whether each statement is true or false.

(a) July $\in A$, where A is the set of months between Memorial Day and Labor Day.
(b) $21 \in \{2, 5, 8, 11, \ldots\}$
(c) map $\notin \{m, a, p\}$

There are three common ways to designate sets:

1. The *list* or *roster* method.
2. The *descriptive* method.
3. *Set-builder* notation.

We already know a lot about using the list or roster method; the elements of the set are listed in braces and are separated by commas, as in Examples 1 through 3. The **descriptive method** uses a short statement to describe the set.

EXAMPLE 4   Describing a Set in Words

Use the descriptive method to describe the set E containing $2, 4, 6, 8, \ldots$.

SOLUTION

The elements in the set are called the even natural numbers. The set E is the set of even natural numbers.

▼ Try This One 4

Use the descriptive method to describe the set A containing $-3, -2, -1, 0, 1, 2, 3$.

Math Note

When you hear *variable*, you might automatically think *letter*, like *x* or *y*. But you should think about what the word *variable* really means: something that can change, or vary. A variable is just a symbol that represents some number or object that can change.

The third method of designating a set is **set-builder notation,** and this method uses *variables*.

A **variable** is a symbol (usually a letter) that can represent different elements of a set.

Set-builder notation uses a variable, braces, and a vertical bar | that is read as "such that." For example, the set $\{1, 2, 3, 4, 5, 6\}$ can be written in set-builder notation as $\{x \mid x \in N$ and $x < 7\}$. It is read as "the set of elements x such that x is a natural number and x is less than 7." We can use any letter or symbol for the variable, but it's common to use x.

EXAMPLE 5   Writing a Set Using Set-Builder Notation

Use set-builder notation to designate each set, then write how your answer would be read aloud.

(a) The set R contains the elements 2, 4, and 6.
(b) The set W contains the elements red, yellow, and blue.

Math Note

Recall from Example 4 that E represents the set of even natural numbers. Also, you should note that there could be more than one way to write a set in set-builder notation. In Example 5, we could have written $W = \{x \mid x$ is a color in the flag of Colombia$\}$.

SOLUTION

(a) $R = \{x \mid x \in E$ and $x < 7\}$, the set of all x such that x is an even natural number and x is less than 7.

(b) $W = \{x \mid x$ is a primary color$\}$, the set of all x such that x is a primary color.

▼ **Try This One 5**

Use set-builder notation to designate each set; then write how your answer would be read aloud.

(a) The set K contains the elements $10, 12, 14, 16, 18$.

(b) The set W contains the elements Democratic and Republican.

EXAMPLE 6   Using Different Set Notations

Designate the set S with elements $32, 33, 34, 35, \ldots$ using

(a) The roster method.

(b) The descriptive method.

(c) Set-builder notation.

SOLUTION

(a) $\{32, 33, 34, 35, \ldots\}$

(b) The set S is the set of natural numbers greater than 31.

(c) $\{x \mid x \in N$ and $x > 31\}$

▼ **Try This One 6**

Designate the set with elements $11, 13, 15, 17, \ldots$ using

(a) The roster method.

(b) The descriptive method.

(c) Set-builder notation.

If a set contains many elements, we can again use an ellipsis to represent the missing elements. For example, the set $\{1, 2, 3, \ldots, 99, 100\}$ includes all the natural numbers from 1 to 100. Likewise, the set $\{a, b, c, \ldots, x, y, z\}$ includes all the letters of the alphabet.

EXAMPLE 7   Writing a Set Using an Ellipsis

Using the roster method, write the set containing all even natural numbers between 99 and 201.

SOLUTION

$\{100, 102, 104, \ldots, 198, 200\}$

▼ **Try This One 7**

2. Write sets in three different ways.

Using the roster method, write the set of odd natural numbers between 50 and 500.

Finite and Infinite Sets

Sets can be classified as *finite* or *infinite*.

If a set has no elements or a specific natural number of elements, then it is called a **finite set.** A set that is not a finite set is called an **infinite set.**

The set {p, q, r, s} is called an finite set since it has four members: p, q, r, and s. The set $\{10, 20, 30, \ldots\}$ is called an infinite set since it has an unlimited number of elements: the natural numbers that are multiples of 10.

EXAMPLE 8   Classifying Sets as Finite or Infinite

Classify each set as finite or infinite.

(a) $\{x \mid x \in N \text{ and } x < 100\}$
(b) Set R is the set of letters used to make Roman numerals.
(c) $\{100, 102, 104, 106, \ldots\}$
(d) Set M is the set of people in your immediate family.
(e) Set S is the set of songs that can be written.

SOLUTION

(a) The set is finite since there are 99 natural numbers that are less than 100.
(b) The set is finite since the letters used are C, D, I, L, M, V, and X.
(c) The set is infinite since it consists of an unlimited number of elements.
(d) The set is finite since there is a specific number of people in your immediate family.
(e) The set is infinite because an unlimited number of songs can be written.

▼ **Try This One 8**

3. Classify sets as finite or infinite.

Classify each set as finite or infinite.

(a) Set P is the set of numbers that are multiples of 6.
(b) $\{x \mid x \text{ is a member of the U.S. Senate}\}$.
(c) $\{3, 6, 9, \ldots, 24\}$.

There are some situations in which it is necessary to define a set with no elements. For example, the set of female Presidents of the United States would contain no people, so it would have no elements.

A set with no elements is called an *empty set* or **null set.** The symbols used to represent the null set are { } or $\varnothing$.

EXAMPLE 9 **Identifying Empty Sets**

Which of the following sets are empty?

(a) The set of woolly mammoth fossils in museums.
(b) $\{x \mid x$ is a living woolly mammoth$\}$
(c) $\{\varnothing\}$
(d) $\{x \mid x$ is a natural number between 1 and 2$\}$

SOLUTION

(a) There is certainly at least one woolly mammoth fossil in a museum somewhere, so the set is not empty.
(b) Woolly mammoths have been extinct for almost 8,000 years, so this set is most definitely empty.
(c) Be careful! Each instance of $\{ \ \}$ and $\varnothing$ represents the empty set, but $\{\varnothing\}$ is a set with one element: $\varnothing$.
(d) This set is empty because there are no natural numbers between 1 and 2.

▼ **Try This One 9**

Which of the following sets are empty sets?

(a) $\{x \mid x$ is a natural number divisible by 7$\}$
(b) $\{x \mid x$ is a human being living on Mars$\}$
(c) $\{+, -, \times, \div\}$
(d) The set Z consists of the living people on earth who are over 200 years old.

CAUTION

Don't write the empty set as $\{\varnothing\}$. This is the set *containing* the empty set.

☑ 4. Define the empty set.

Cardinal Number of a Set

The number of elements in a set is called the *cardinal number* of a set. For example, the set $R = \{2, 4, 6, 8, 10\}$ has a cardinal number of 5 since it has 5 elements. This could also be stated by saying the **cardinality** of set R is 5. Formally defined,

The **cardinal number** of a finite set is the number of elements in the set. For a set A the symbol for the cardinality is $n(A)$, which is read as "n of A."

EXAMPLE 10 **Finding the Cardinality of a Set**

Find the cardinal number of each set.

(a) $A = \{5, 10, 15, 20, 25, 30\}$
(b) $B = \{10, 12, 14, \ldots, 28, 30\}$
(c) $C = \{16\}$
(d) $\varnothing$

SOLUTION

(a) $n(A) = 6$ since set A has 6 elements
(b) $n(B) = 11$ since set B has 11 elements
(c) $n(C) = 1$ since set C has 1 element
(d) $n(\varnothing) = 0$ since there are no elements in an empty set

☑ 5. Find the cardinality of a set.

▼ Try This One 10

Find the cardinal number of each set.

(a) $A = \{z, y, x, w, v\}$

(b) $B = \{1, 3, 5, 7, \ldots, 27, 29\}$

(c) $C = \{Chevrolet\}$

> **Math Note**
>
> All equal sets are equivalent since both sets will have the same number of members, but not all equivalent sets are equal. For example, the sets {x, y, z} and {10, 20, 30} have three members, but in this case, the members of the sets are not identical. The two sets are equivalent but not equal.

Equal and Equivalent Sets

In set theory, it is important to understand the concepts of *equal* sets and *equivalent* sets.

> Two sets A and B are **equal** (written $A = B$) if they have exactly the same members or elements. Two finite sets A and B are said to be **equivalent** (written $A \cong B$) if they have the same number of elements: that is, $n(A) = n(B)$.

For example, the two sets {a, b, c} and {c, b, a} are equal since they have exactly the same members, a, b, and c. Also the set {4, 5, 6} is equal to the set {4, 4, 5, 6} since 4 need not be written twice in the second set. The set $C = \{x, y, z\}$ is equivalent to the set $D = \{10, 20, 30\}$ (i.e., $C \cong D$) since both sets have three elements, but the sets are not equal.

EXAMPLE 11 | **Deciding If Sets Are Equal or Equivalent**

State whether each pair of sets is equal, equivalent, or neither.

(a) {p, q, r, s}; {a, b, c, d}

(b) {8, 10, 12}; {12, 8, 10}

(c) {213}; {2, 1, 3}

(d) {1, 2, 10, 20}; {2, 1, 20, 11}

(e) {even natural numbers less than 10}; {2, 4, 6, 8}

SOLUTION

(a) Equivalent

(b) Equal and equivalent

(c) Neither

(d) Equivalent

(e) Equal and equivalent

Two sets of basketball teams on the court have a one-to-one correspondence. (Assuming each has five healthy players!)

▼ Try This One 11

State whether each pair of sets is equal, equivalent, or neither.

(a) {d, o, g}; {c, a, t}

(b) {run}; {r, u, n}

(c) {t, o, p}; {p, o, t}

(d) {10, 20, 30}; {1, 3, 5}

The elements of two equivalent sets can be paired in such a way that they are said to have a *one-to-one correspondence* between them.

Two sets have a **one-to-one correspondence** of elements if each element in the first set can be paired with exactly one element of the second set and each element of the second set can be paired with exactly one element of the first set.

EXAMPLE 12 Putting Sets in One-to-One Correspondence

Show that (a) the sets {8,16, 24, 32} and {s, t, u, v} have a one-to-one correspondence and (b) the sets {x, y, z} and {5, 10} do not have a one-to-one correspondence.

SOLUTION

(a) We need to demonstrate that each element of one set can be paired with one and only one element of the second set. One possible way to show a one-to-one correspondence is this:

$$\{8, \ 16, \ 24, \ 32\}$$
$$\updownarrow \ \ \updownarrow \ \ \updownarrow \ \ \updownarrow$$
$$\{s, \ \ t, \ \ u, \ \ v\}$$

(b) The elements of the sets {x, y, z} and {5, 10} can't be put in one-to-one correspondence. No matter how we try, there will be an element in the first set that doesn't correspond to any element in the second set.

▼ Try This One 12

Show that the sets {North, South, East, West} and {sun, rain, snow, sleet} have a one-to-one correspondence.

Using one-to-one correspondence, we can decide if two sets are equivalent without actually counting the elements. This can come in handy for large sets, and *really* handy for infinite sets!

Correspondence and Equivalent Sets

Two sets are

- Equivalent if you can put their elements in one-to-one correspondence.
- Not equivalent if you cannot put their elements in one-to-one correspondence.

☑ 6. Decide if two sets are equal or equivalent.

In this section, we defined sets and some other basic terms. In Section 2-2, subsets and set operations will be explained.

Answers to Try This One

1 {Ontario, Erie, Huron, Michigan, Superior}

2 (a) {80, 82, 84, 86, 88, 90}
(b) {11, 13, 15, 17, . . .}

3 (a) True   (b) False   (c) True

4 The set of integers from −3 to 3

5 (a) $K = \{x | x \in E, x > 9,$ and $x < 19\}$, the set of all x such that x is an even natural number, x is greater than 9, and x is less than 19.

(b) $W = \{x | x$ is a major American political party$\}$, the set of all x such that x is a major American political party.

6 (a) $\{11, 13, 15, 17, \ldots\}$
(b) The set of odd natural numbers greater than 10
(c) $\{x | x \in N, x$ is odd, and $x > 10\}$

7 $\{51, 53, 55, \ldots, 497, 499\}$

8 (a) Infinite   (b) Finite   (c) Finite

9 (b) and (d)

10 (a) 5   (b) 15   (c) 1

11 (a) Equivalent   (c) Equal and equivalent
(b) Neither   (d) Equivalent

12
North	South	East	West
↕	↕	↕	↕
Sun	Rain	Snow	Sleet

EXERCISE SET   2-1

Writing Exercises

1. Explain what a set is.
2. List three ways to write sets.
3. What is the difference between equal and equivalent sets?
4. Explain the difference between a finite and an infinite set.
5. What is meant by "one-to-one correspondence between two sets"?
6. Define the empty set and give two examples of an empty set.

Computational Exercises

For Exercises 7–20, write each set, using roster notation. Do not include repeats.

7. S is the set of letters in the word *stress*.
8. A is the set of letters in the word *Alabama*.
9. P is the set of natural numbers between 50 and 60.
10. R is the set of even natural numbers between 10 and 40.
11. Q is the set of odd natural numbers less than 15.
12. M is the set of even natural numbers less than 8.
13. $G = \{x | x \in N$ and $x > 10\}$
14. B is the set of natural numbers greater than 100.
15. Y is the set of natural numbers between 2,000 and 3,000.
16. $Z = \{x | x \in N$ and $500 < x < 6,000\}$
17. W is the set of days in the week.
18. C is the set of colors in a U.S. flag.
19. D is the set of suits in a deck of cards.
20. F is the set of face cards in a deck of cards.

For Exercises 21–28, write each set, using the descriptive method.

21. $\{2, 4, 6, 8, \ldots\}$
22. $\{1, 3, 5, 7, \ldots\}$
23. $\{9, 18, 27, 36\}$
24. $\{5, 10, 15, 20\}$
25. $\{m, a, r, y\}$
26. $\{t, h, o, m, a, s\}$
27. $\{100, 101, 102, \ldots, 199\}$
28. $\{21, 22, 23, \ldots, 29, 30\}$

For Exercises 29–34, write each set, using set-builder notation.

29. $\{10, 20, 30, 40, \ldots\}$
30. $\{55, 65, 75, 85\}$
31. X is the set of natural numbers greater than 20.
32. Z is the set of even natural numbers less than 12.
33. $\{1, 3, 5, 7, 9\}$
34. $\{18, 21, 24, 27, 30\}$

For Exercises 35–40, list the elements in each set.

35. H is the set of natural numbers less than 0.
36. $\{x | x \in N$ and $70 < x < 80\}$
37. $\{7, 14, 21, \ldots, 63\}$
38. $\{5, 12, 19, \ldots, 40\}$
39. $\{x | x$ is an even natural number between 100 and 120$\}$
40. $\{x | x$ is an odd natural number between 90 and 100$\}$

For Exercises 41–48, state whether each collection is well-defined or not well-defined.

41. J is the set of seasons in the year.
42. $\{x \mid x \in N\}$
43. $\{x \mid x$ is an excellent instructor$\}$
44. $\{10, 15, 20\}$
45. $\{1, 2, 3, \ldots, 100\}$
46. $\{x \mid x$ is a good professional golfer$\}$
47. $\{100, \ldots\}$
48. W is the set of days of the week.

For Exercises 49–54, state whether each is true or false.

Let $A = \{$Saturday, Sunday$\}$
$\quad B = \{1, 2, 3, 4, 5\}$
$\quad C = \{p, q, r, s, t\}$

49. $3 \in B$
50. $a \in C$
51. Wednesday $\notin A$
52. $7 \notin B$
53. $r \in C$
54. $q \in B$

For Exercises 55–62, state whether each set is infinite or finite.

55. $\{x \mid x \in N$ and x is even$\}$
56. $\{1, 2, 3, \ldots, 999, 1{,}000\}$
57. K is the set of letters of the English alphabet.
58. $\{x \mid x \in$ years in which the past Presidents of the United States were born$\}$
59. $\{3, 6, 9, 12, \ldots\}$
60. $\varnothing$
61. $\{x \mid x$ is a current television program$\}$
62. $\{x \mid x$ is a fraction$\}$

For Exercises 63–70, state whether each pair of sets is equal, equivalent, or neither.

63. $\{6, 12, 18, 20\}$ and $\{20, 12, 6, 18\}$
64. $\{p, q, r, s, t\}$ and $\{5, 3, 4, 2, 1\}$
65. $\{2, 3, 7, 8\}$ and $\{1, 4, 5\}$
66. $\{2, 4, 6, 8\}$ and $\{2, 4, 6, 8, \ldots\}$
67. $\{1, 2, 3, \ldots, 99, 100\}$ and $\{1{,}001, 1{,}002, 1{,}003, \ldots, 1{,}100\}$
68. $\{s, t, o, p\}$ and $\{p, o, t, s\}$
69. $\{x \mid x$ is a three-digit number$\}$ and $\{1, 2, 3, \ldots, 100\}$
70. $\{$January, June, July$\}$ and $\{x \mid x$ is a month that begins with J$\}$

For Exercises 71–74, show that each pair of sets is equivalent by using a one-to-one correspondence.

71. $\{10, 20, 30, 40\}$ and $\{40, 10, 20, 30\}$
72. $\{w, x, y, z\}$ and $\{1, 2, 3, 4\}$
73. $\{1, 2, 3, \ldots, 25, 26\}$ and $\{a, b, c, \ldots, x, y, z\}$
74. $\{x \mid x$ is an odd natural number less than 11$\}$ and $\{x \mid x$ is an even natural number less than 12$\}$

For Exercises 75–82, find the cardinal number for each set.

75. $A = \{18, 24, 32, 63, 48\}$
76. $B = \{1, 2, 5, 7, \ldots, 37\}$
77. $C = \{x \mid x$ is a day of the week$\}$
78. $D = \{x \mid x$ is a month of the year$\}$
79. $E = \{$three$\}$
80. $F = \{t, h, r, e, e\}$
81. $G = \{x \mid x \in N$ and x is negative$\}$
82. $H = \varnothing$

For Exercises 83–90, determine whether each statement is true or false.

83. $\{1, 3, 5\} = \{3, 1, 5\}$
84. $\{2, 4, 6\} \neq \{1, 3, 5\}$
85. All equal sets are equivalent.
86. No equivalent sets are equal.
87. $\varnothing = \{\varnothing\}$
88. $\{2, 6, 10, 12\} = \{2, 6, 10\}$
89. $n\{\varnothing\} = 0$
90. $E = \{2, 4, 6, 8, \ldots\}$ is a finite set

Real-World Applications

91. The table below shows the top 10 states in number of immigrants in 2006.

State	Number of Immigrants	% of Total Immigrants to United States
California	264,677	20.9
New York	180,165	14.2
Florida	155,996	12.3
Texas	89,037	7.0
New Jersey	65,934	5.2
Illinois	52,459	4.1
Virginia	38,488	3.0
Massachusetts	35,560	2.8
Georgia	32,202	2.5
Maryland	30,204	2.4

Source: *The World Almanac and Book of Facts*, 2008.

(a) List the set of states with more than 100,000 immigrants.
(b) List the set of states in the top 10 with fewer than 50,000 immigrants.
(c) List $\{x \mid x$ is a state with at least 5% of the immigrant total$\}$.
(d) List $\{x \mid x$ is a state with between 3% and 9% of the immigrant total$\}$.

92. There is a relatively young workforce in the U.S. information technology industry. The percentage of people by age group working at Internet service providers (ISPs), Web search portals, and data processing companies in 2006 is shown in the table on the next page:

Age Group	Percentage Working at ISPs, Web Search Portals, and Data Processing Companies
16–19	1.1
20–24	10.1
25–34	26.8
35–44	31.8
45–54	19.6
55–64	7.8
65 and older	2.2

Source: http://www.bls.gov/oco/cg/cgs055.htm

(a) List the set of age groups of those whose percentages are over 18%. What can you conclude?
(b) List the set of age groups of those whose percentages are less than 10%. What can you conclude?
(c) List the set of percentages of those who are between 20 and 44 years old.
(d) Find $\{x \mid x$ is the age group with the largest percentage in the industry$\}$.
(e) Find $\{x \mid x$ is the percentage in the industry for those between ages 45 and 64$\}$.
(f) Find $\{x \mid x$ is the percentage in the industry for those under age 16$\}$.

93. Excessive alcohol consumption by those aged 18–24 affects nearly all U.S. college students, whether they choose to drink or not. The consequences of excessive drinking are listed below.

Consequence	Average Number of College Students Aged 18–24 Affected per Year
Death	1,700
Injury	599,000
Assault	696,000
Sexual abuse	97,000
Unsafe sex	500,000
Health problems	150,000
Drunk driving	2,100,000

Source: http://www.collegedrinkingprevention.gov/StatsSummaries/snapshot.aspx

(a) List the set of the three consequences with the most students affected by excessive alcohol consumption.
(b) List the set of consequences that affect between 100,000 and 600,000 college students each year.
(c) Find the set $\{x \mid x$ is a consequence of which over a half million students are affected$\}$.
(d) Find the set $\{x \mid x$ is the average number of college students affected by sexual abuse, death, or health problems$\}$.
(e) Find a set of three elements that do not belong in the set $\{x \mid x$ is a consequence of excessive drinking to college students ages 18–24$\}$.

94. The number of bachelor's degrees awarded by degree-granting institutions in the United States in different years is shown below.

Major	1991	1998	2005
Business	249,200	232,100	311,600
Social sciences	125,100	125,000	156,900
Education	110,800	105,800	105,500
Psychology	58,700	74,100	85,600
Health professions	59,900	86,800	80,700
Engineering	79,800	78,700	78,600
Communications	51,700	49,400	72,700
Computers	25,200	27,800	54,100
Physical sciences	16,300	19,400	18,900
Mathematics	14,400	11,800	14,400
Philosophy	7,400	8,400	11,600

Source: http://nces.ed.gov/programs/coe/2007/section5/table.asp?tableID=739

(a) List the set of majors that increased in popularity every year listed.
(b) List the set of majors that did not increase in popularity from 1998 to 2005.
(c) List the set of majors that had between 50,000 and 110,000 degrees awarded in 1998.
(d) Find the set $\{x \mid x$ increased in popularity between 1991 and 1998$\}$.
(e) Find the set $\{x \mid x$ is a major that starts with the letter M, P, or E$\}$.
(f) To find the percent increase P between an original amount O and a new amount N, use the following formula: $P = (N - O)/O$. Calculate the percent increase for any major that saw an increase in degrees awarded between 1998 and 2005. List the set of majors that increased at least 30%.

95. Identity theft is the fastest-growing crime in the United States, and college students aged 18–24 are the most affected. Of the 675,000 identity theft complaints in 2005 to the Federal Trade Commission, 29% were made by college students in this age group. The following charts show types of identity theft fraud reported in 2005 and the percentage of victims by age.

Types of Identity Theft Fraud Reported in 2005

Percentage of Victims by Age

(a) List the set of the two types of identity fraud with the lowest percentage of reported crimes.
(b) List the set of age groups that are above 18%.
(c) List the set of identity fraud types that have more than 17% of reported crimes.
(d) Find the set $\{x|x$ is a percentage of those 40 and over who are victims of identity fraud$\}$.
(e) Find the set $\{x|x$ is a type of fraud that has between 10% and 20% of reported crimes$\}$.

96. Many people are now using MP3 players on their cell phones rather than a separate MP3 player to listen to music. The chart below shows age groups for those who have phones with MP3 players, those who listened to music using an MP3 player on a phone in the last 12 months, and those who downloaded music to an MP3 on their phone in the last 12 months.

Source: http://www.cellular-news.com/story/20124.php

(a) List the set of age groups of those in which at least 20% listened to an MP3 via cell phone in the last year.
(b) List the set of age groups of those in which less than 10% downloaded music to their phones in the last year.
(c) Find the set $\{x|x$ is an age group in which at least 30% had a phone with an MP3 player$\}$.
(d) Find the set $\{x|x$ is a percentage for those aged 35–44 who have a phone with an MP3 player and listened to MP3 via phone in the last 12 months$\}$.

97. The rising cost of medical care has become one of the biggest burdens on working families in the last 10 years. The graph below represents the average prescription drug price in dollars for the years 2000 to 2006.

Average Prescription Drug Price ($)

(a) Find the set of years when the average prescription drug price was less than $60.
(b) Find the set of years when the average prescription drug price was between $50 and $68.
(c) Find $\{x|x$ is a year in which the average prescription drug price was greater than $50\}$.
(d) Find $\{x|x$ is a year in which the average prescription drug price was less than $60\}$.

98. Housing prices have been in the news a lot in recent years, as the boom that began in 2004 has given way to the bust just a few years later. The graph below displays the median housing prices for all houses sold in the United States between 2003 and 2008.

Median Home Prices in the United States

(a) List the set of years in which the median price was above $200,000.
(b) List the set of years in which the median price was between $175,000 and $200,000.
(c) Find $\{x|x$ is a year in which the median price increased from the year before$\}$.
(d) Find $\{x|x$ is a year in which the median price decreased from the year before$\}$.

Critical Thinking

99. If $A \cong B$ and $A \cong C$, is $B \cong C$? Explain your answer.

100. Is {0} equivalent to $\varnothing$? Explain your answer.

101. The set of people who attend college is not well-defined. How could you alter the definition to make this set well-defined?

102. The set of students in your math class has many subsets. Think of three subsets of this set.

103. Think of two sets of popular songs that are equivalent. Think of a third set of popular songs that is not equivalent to either of the first two sets.

104. Think of two sets of four elements each that have a one-to-one correspondence.

Section 2-2 Subsets and Set Operations

LEARNING OBJECTIVES

☐ 1. Define the complement of a set.

☐ 2. Find all subsets of a set.

☐ 3. Use subset notation.

☐ 4. Find the number of subsets for a set.

☐ 5. Find intersections, unions, and differences of sets.

☐ 6. Find the Cartesian product of two sets.

Math Note

The complement of the universal set is the empty set: $U' = \varnothing$. The complement of the empty set is the universal set: $\varnothing' = U$.

When we classify things in the real world, sets often have relationships with one another. For example, you are a member of both the set of college students and the set of students taking a college math course. You could be in the set of sophomores or the set of juniors, but not in both. You might be in the set of students living off campus and the set of students who walk to class. In this section, we'll be studying relationships between sets.

To begin, we need to consider a new concept called a *universal set*.

A **universal set,** symbolized by U, is the set of all potential elements under consideration for a specific situation.

In the examples above, a reasonable choice of U would be the set of all college students, since all the elements under consideration are college students. Once we define a universal set in a given setting, we are restricted to considering only elements from that set. If $U = \{1, 2, 3, 4, 5, 6, 7, 8\}$, then the only elements we can use to define other sets in this setting are the integers from 1 to 8.

In the remainder of this chapter, we'll use a clever method for visualizing sets and their relationships called a *Venn diagram* (so named because it was developed by a man named John Venn in the 1800s). Figure 2-1 shows an example.

You can get a lot of information from this simple diagram. A set called A is being defined. The universal set from which elements of A can be chosen is $U = \{1, 2, 3, 4, 5, 6, 7, 8\}$. The set A is $\{2, 4, 6, 8\}$, and the elements not in A are $\{1, 3, 5, 7\}$. We will call the elements in U that are not in A the *complement* of A, and denote it A'.

The **complement** of a set A, symbolized A', is the set of elements contained in the universal set that are *not* in A. Using set-builder notation, the complement of A is $A' = \{x \mid x \in U \text{ and } x \notin A\}$.

In a Venn diagram, the complement of a set A is all the things inside the rectangle that are not inside the circle representing set A. This is shown in Figure 2-2.

Figure 2-1

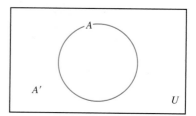

Figure 2-2

EXAMPLE 1 **Finding the Complement of a Set**

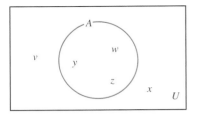

Figure 2-3

Let $U = \{v, w, x, y, z\}$ and $A = \{w, y, z\}$. Find A' and draw a Venn diagram that illustrates these sets.

SOLUTION

Using the list of elements in U, we just have to cross out the ones that are also in A. The elements left over are in A'.

$$U = \{v, \cancel{w}, x, \cancel{y}, \cancel{z}\} \qquad A' = \{v, x\}$$

The Venn diagram is shown in Figure 2-3.

☑ 1. Define the complement of a set.

▼ Try This One 1

Let $U = \{10, 20, 30, 40, 50, 60, 70, 80, 90\}$ and $A = \{10, 30, 50\}$. Find A' and draw a Venn diagram that illustrates these sets.

Subsets

At the beginning of the section, we pointed out that you're in both the set of college students and the set of students taking a college math course. Notice that everyone in the second set is automatically in the first one. We could say that the set of students taking a college math course is contained in the set of all college students. When one set is contained in a second set, we call the smaller set a *subset* of the larger one.

> If every element of a set A is also an element of a set B, then A is called a **subset** of B. The symbol $\subseteq$ is used to designate a subset; in this case, we write $A \subseteq B$.

There are many subsets of this set of spring breakers: the subset of female students, the subset of sophomores, the subset of students who had their fake I.D. confiscated by the police, and so on.

An alternate definition is that A is a subset of B if there are no elements in A that are not also in B.

Here are a couple of observations about subsets.

- Every set is a subset of itself. Every element of a set A is of course an element of set A, so $A \subseteq A$.

- The empty set is a subset of every set. The empty set has no elements, so for any set A, you can't find an element of $\varnothing$ that is not also in A.

If we start with the set $\{x, y, z\}$, let's look at how many subsets we can form:

Number of Elements in Subset	Subsets with That Number of Elements	
3	$\{x, y, z\}$	(One subset)
2	$\{x, y\}, \{x, z\}, \{y, z\}$	(Three subsets)
1	$\{x\}, \{y\}, \{z\}$	(Three subsets)
0	$\varnothing$	(One subset)

So for a set with three elements, we can form eight subsets.

EXAMPLE 2　Finding All Subsets of a Set

Find all subsets of $A = \{American\ Idol,\ Survivor\}$.

SOLUTION

The subsets are

$\{American\ Idol,\ Survivor\}$
$\{American\ Idol\}$
$\{Survivor\}$
$\varnothing$

Note that a set with 2 elements has 4 subsets.

▼ Try This One 2

Find all subsets of $B = \{Verizon,\ Nextel,\ AT\&T\}$.

To indicate that a set is not a subset of another set, the symbol $\not\subseteq$ is used. For example, $\{1, 3\} \not\subseteq \{0, 3, 5, 7\}$ since $1 \notin \{0, 3, 5, 7\}$.

Of the four subsets in Example 2, only one is equal to the original set. We will call the remaining three *proper subsets* of A. The Venn diagram for a proper subset is shown in Figure 2-4. In this case, $U = \{1, 2, 3, 4, 5\}$, $A = \{1, 3, 5\}$, and $B = \{1, 3\}$.

Figure 2-4 $A \subset B$

If a set A is a subset of a set B and is not equal to B, then we call A a **proper subset** of B, and write $A \subset B$.

EXAMPLE 3　Finding Proper Subsets of a Set

Find all proper subsets of $\{x, y, z\}$.

SOLUTION

$\{x, y\}\quad \{x, z\}\quad \{y, z\}$
$\{x\}\quad \{y\}\quad \{z\}$
$\varnothing$

▼ Try This One 3

Find all proper subsets of $\{\blacklozenge, \heartsuit, \spadesuit, \clubsuit\}$.

☑ 2. Find all subsets of a set.

The symbol $\not\subset$ is used to indicate that the set is not a proper subset. For example, $\{1, 3\} \subset \{1, 3, 5\}$, but $\{1, 3, 5\} \not\subset \{1, 3, 5\}$.

EXAMPLE 4　Understanding Subset Notation

State whether each statement is true or false.

(a) $\{1, 3, 5\} \subseteq \{1, 3, 5, 7\}$

(b) $\{a, b\} \subset \{a, b\}$

Math Note

It is important not to confuse the concept of subsets with the concept of elements. For example, the statement $6 \in \{2, 4, 6\}$ is true since 6 is an element of the set $\{2, 4, 6\}$, but the statement $\{6\} \in \{2, 4, 6\}$ is false since it states that the set containing the element 6 is an element of the set containing 2, 4, and 6. However, it *is* correct to say that $\{6\} \subseteq \{2, 4, 6\}$, or that $\{6\} \subset \{2, 4, 6\}$.

(c) $\{x \mid x \in N \text{ and } x > 10\} \subset N$
(d) $\{2, 10\} \nsubseteq \{2, 4, 6, 8, 10\}$
(e) $\{r, s, t\} \not\subset \{t, s, r\}$
(f) $\{\text{Lake Erie, Lake Huron}\} \subset$ The set of Great Lakes

SOLUTION

(a) All of 1, 3, and 5 are in the second set, so $\{1, 3, 5\}$ is a subset of $\{1, 3, 5, 7\}$. The statement is true.
(b) Even though $\{a, b\}$ is a subset of $\{a, b\}$, it is not a proper subset, so the statement is false.
(c) Every element in the first set is a natural number, but not all natural numbers are in the set, so that set is a proper subset of the natural numbers. The statement is true.
(d) Both 2 and 10 are elements of the second set, so $\{2, 10\}$ is a subset, and the statement is false.
(e) The two sets are identical, so $\{r, s, t\}$ is not a proper subset of $\{t, s, r\}$. The statement is true.
(f) Lake Erie and Lake Huron are both Great Lakes, so the statement is true.

▼ Try This One 4

State whether each statement is true or false.

(a) $\{8\} \subseteq \{x \mid x$ is an even natural number$\}$
(b) $\{6\} \subseteq \{1, 3, 5, 7, \ldots\}$
(c) $\{2, 3\} \subseteq \{x \mid x \in N\}$
(d) $\{a, b, c\} \subset \{\text{letters of the alphabet}\}$
(e) $\varnothing \in \{x, y, z\}$

EXAMPLE 5 **Understanding Subset Notation**

State whether each statement is true or false.

(a) $\varnothing \subset \{5, 10, 15\}$
(b) $\{u, v, w, x\} \subseteq \{x, w, u\}$
(c) $\{0\} \subseteq \varnothing$
(d) $\varnothing \subset \varnothing$

SOLUTION

(a) True: the empty set is a proper subset of every set.
(b) False: v is an element of $\{u, v, w, x\}$ but not $\{x, w, u\}$.
(c) The set on the left has one element, 0. The empty set has no elements, so the statement is false.
(d) The empty set is a subset of itself (as well as every other set), but not a proper subset of itself. The statement is false.

▼ Try This One 5

State whether each statement is true or false.

(a) $\varnothing \subseteq \{\text{red, yellow, blue}\}$
(b) $\varnothing \subseteq \varnothing$
(c) $\{100, 200, 300, 400\} \subset \{200, 300, 400\}$
(d) $\{\varnothing\} \subseteq \varnothing$

 3. Use subset notation.

A set with one element has two subsets—itself and the empty set. We have seen that if a set has two elements, there are four subsets, and if a set has three elements, there are eight subsets. This is an excellent opportunity to use the inductive reasoning that we practiced in Chapter 1!

Number of elements	0	1	2	3
Number of subsets	1	2	4	8

Based on this pattern, it's reasonable to conjecture that a set with 4 elements will have 16 subsets, a set with 5 elements will have 32 subsets, and so forth. (Notice that the number of subsets in each case is 2 raised to the number of elements.) It turns out that this is always the case. We also know that the number of proper subsets of a set is always 1 less than the total number of subsets, since only the set itself is excluded when forming proper subsets. We conclude:

The Number of Subsets for a Finite Set

If a finite set has n elements, then the set has 2^n subsets and $2^n - 1$ proper subsets.

EXAMPLE 6   Finding the Number of Subsets of a Set

Find the number of subsets and proper subsets of the set $\{1, 3, 5, 7, 9, 11\}$.

SOLUTION

The set has $n = 6$ elements, so there are 2^n, or $2^6 = 64$, subsets. Of these, $2^n - 1$, or 63, are proper.

▼ Try This One 6

Find the number of subsets and proper subsets of the set $\{OSU, USC, KSU, MSU, UND, PSU, UT, FSU\}$.

4. Find the number of subsets for a set.

Accounts Manager, requires strong management skills, good at working as part of a team and has at least 5-years experience with a similar project. P. O. Box No. 5474

...D Manager strong

The advertisement is looking for people in the *intersection* of three sets of potential employees.

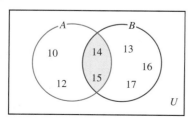

Figure 2-5 $A \cap B = \{14, 15\}$

Intersection and Union of Sets

At the beginning of the section, we pointed out that you might be in both the set of students living off campus and the set of students who walk to class. We will identify objects that are common to two or more sets by using the term *intersection*.

The **intersection** of two sets A and B, symbolized by $A \cap B$, is the set of all elements that are in both sets. In set-builder notation, $A \cap B = \{x \mid x \in A \text{ and } x \in B\}$.

For example, if $A = \{10, 12, 14, 15\}$ and $B = \{13, 14, 15, 16, 17\}$, then the intersection $A \cap B = \{14, 15\}$, since 14 and 15 are the elements that are common to both sets. The Venn diagram for $A \cap B$ is shown in Figure 2-5. Notice that the elements of A are placed inside the circle for set A, and the elements of B are inside the circle for set B. The elements in the intersection are placed into the portion where the circles overlap: $A \cap B$ is the shaded portion.

Intersection is an example of a **set operation**—a rule for combining two or more sets to form a new set. The intersection of three or more sets consists of the set of elements that are in every single set. Note that the word *and* is sometimes used to indicate intersection; $A \cap B$ is the set of elements in A and B.

EXAMPLE 7   Finding Intersections

If $A = \{5, 10, 15, 20, 25\}$, $B = \{0, 10, 20, 30, 40\}$, and $C = \{30, 50, 70, 90\}$, find

(a) $A \cap B$ (b) $B \cap C$ (c) $A \cap C$

SOLUTION

(a) The elements 10 and 20 are in both sets A and B, so $A \cap B = \{10, 20\}$.
(b) The only member of both sets B and C is 30, so $B \cap C = \{30\}$.
(c) There are no elements common to sets A and C, so $A \cap C = \varnothing$.

▼ **Try This One 7**

If $A = \{$Cleveland, Indianapolis, Chicago, Des Moines, Detroit$\}$, $B = \{$New York, Los Angeles, Chicago, Detroit$\}$, and $C = \{$Seattle, Los Angeles, San Diego$\}$, find $A \cap B$, $B \cap C$, and $A \cap C$.

Figure 2-6 $A \cap B = \varnothing$

When the intersection of two sets is the empty set, the sets are said to be *disjoint*. For example, the set of students who stop attending class midway through a term and the set of students earning A's are disjoint, because you can't be a member of both sets. The Venn diagram for a pair of disjoint sets A and B is shown in Figure 2-6. If the sets have no elements in common, the circles representing them don't overlap at all.

Another way of combining sets to form a new set is called *union*.

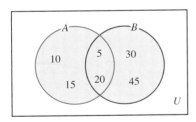

Figure 2-7 $A \cup B$

The **union** of two sets A and B, symbolized by $A \cup B$, is the set of all elements that are in either set A or set B (or both). In set-builder notation,

$$A \cup B = \{x \mid x \in A \quad \text{or} \quad x \in B\}$$

For example, if $A = \{5, 10, 15, 20\}$ and $B = \{5, 20, 30, 45\}$, then the union $A \cup B = \{5, 10, 15, 20, 30, 45\}$. Even though 5 and 20 are in both sets, we list them only once in the union. The Venn diagram for $A \cup B$ is shown in Figure 2-7. The set $A \cup B$ is the shaded area consisting of all elements in either set.

EXAMPLE 8   Finding Unions

If $A = \{0, 1, 2, 3, 4, 5\}$, $B = \{2, 4, 6, 8, 10\}$, and $C = \{1, 3, 5, 7\}$, find each.

(a) $A \cup B$ (b) $A \cup C$ (c) $B \cup C$

SOLUTION

To find a union, just make a list of all the elements in either set without writing repeats.

(a) $A \cup B = \{0, 1, 2, 3, 4, 5, 6, 8, 10\}$
(b) $A \cup C = \{0, 1, 2, 3, 4, 5, 7\}$
(c) $B \cup C = \{1, 2, 3, 4, 5, 6, 7, 8, 10\}$

▼ Try This One 8

If $A = \{a, b, c, d, e\}$, $B = \{a, c, e, g, i\}$, and $C = \{b, d, f, h, j\}$, find $A \cup B$, $A \cup C$, and $B \cup C$.

What about operations involving more than two sets? Just like with operations involving numbers, we use parentheses to indicate an order of operations. This is illustrated in Example 9.

EXAMPLE 9   Performing Set Operations

Let $A = \{l, m, n, o, p\}$, $B = \{o, p, q, r\}$, and $C = \{r, s, t, u\}$. Find each.

(a) $(A \cup B) \cap C$ (b) $A \cap (B \cup C)$ (c) $(A \cap B) \cup C$

SOLUTION

(a) First find $A \cup B$: $A \cup B = \{l, m, n, o, p, q, r\}$. Then intersect this set with set C; the only common element is r, so $(A \cup B) \cap C = \{r\}$.
(b) First find $B \cup C$: $B \cup C = \{o, p, q, r, s, t, u\}$. Then intersect this set with set A to get $\{o, p\}$.
(c) First find $A \cap B$: $A \cap B = \{o, p\}$. Then find the union of this set with set C to get $\{o, p, r, s, t, u\}$.

▼ Try This One 9

If $A = \{2, 3, 4, 5, 6, 7\}$, $B = \{7, 8, 9, 10\}$, and $C = \{0, 5, 10, 15, 20\}$, find $A \cup (B \cap C)$, $(A \cap B) \cup C$, and $A \cap (B \cup C)$.

CAUTION

When combining union and intersection with complements, we'll have to be extra careful. Pay particular attention to the parentheses and to whether the complement symbol is inside or outside the parentheses.

EXAMPLE 10   Performing Set Operations

If $U = \{10, 20, 30, 40, 50, 60, 70, 80\}$, $A = \{10, 30, 50, 70\}$, $B = \{40, 50, 60, 70\}$, and $C = \{20, 40, 60\}$, find each.

(a) $A' \cap C'$ (b) $(A \cap B)' \cap C$ (c) $B' \cup (A \cap C')$

SOLUTION

(a) First, write A' and C': $A' = \{20, 40, 60, 80\}$ and $C' = \{10, 30, 50, 70, 80\}$. Now note that 80 is the only element common to both: $A' \cap C' = \{80\}$.
(b) The parentheses tell us that we should find $A \cap B$ first: $A \cap B = \{50, 70\}$. Next we find the complement: $(A \cap B)' = \{10, 20, 30, 40, 60, 80\}$. Finally, we find the intersection of this set and C: $(A \cap B)' \cap C = \{20, 40, 60\}$.
(c) First, find $A \cap C'$: $C' = \{10, 30, 50, 70, 80\}$, and all but 80 are also in A, so $A \cap C' = \{10, 30, 50, 70\}$. Next note that $B' = \{10, 20, 30, 80\}$. Now form the union: $B' \cup (A \cap C') = \{10, 20, 30, 50, 70, 80\}$.

▼ Try This One 10

Let $U = \{1, 2, 3, 4, 5, 6, 7, 8\}$, $A = \{1, 3, 5, 7\}$, $B = \{2, 4, 6, 8\}$, and $C = \{2, 3, 5, 7\}$. Find each.

(a) C' (b) $(A \cup B)'$ (c) $A' \cap C'$ (d) $(A \cup B) \cap C'$

The union and intersection of sets are commonly used in real life—it's just that you might not have thought of it in those terms. For example, the intersection of the set of U.S. citizens older than 17 and the set of U.S. citizens who are not convicted felons makes up the set of those eligible to vote. The union of the set of your mom's parents and your dad's parents forms the set of your grandparents.

Set Subtraction

The third set operation we'll study is called the *difference* of sets. We also call it *set subtraction* and use a minus sign to represent it.

> The **difference** of set A and set B is the set of elements in set A that are *not* in set B. In set-builder notation, $A - B = \{x \mid x \in A \text{ and } x \notin B\}$.

EXAMPLE 11   Finding the Difference of Two Sets

Let $U = \{2, 4, 6, 8, 10, 12\}$, $A = \{4, 6, 8, 10\}$, $B = \{2, 6, 12\}$, $C = \{8, 10\}$

Find each.

(a) $A - B$ (b) $A - C$ (c) $B - C$

SOLUTION

(a) Start with the elements in set A and take out the elements in set B that are also in set A. In this case, only 6 is removed, and $A - B = \{4, 8, 10\}$.
(b) Start with the elements in set A and remove the elements in set C that are also in set A. In this case, 8 and 10 are removed, and $A - C = \{4, 6\}$.
(c) Start with the elements in set B and take out the elements in set C that are also in set B. In this case, none of the elements in B are also in C. So $B - C = \{2, 6, 12\}$.

Math Note

Sometimes operations can be written in terms of other operations. For example, $3 - 5$ is also $3 + (-5)$. Can you think of a way to write $A - B$ using intersection and complement? Drawing a Venn diagram might help.

▼ Try This One 11

Let $L = \{p, q, r, s, t, u, v, w\}$, $M = \{p, s, t, u, y, z\}$, and $N = \{u, v, w, z\}$. Find

(a) $L - M$ (b) $L - N$ (c) $M - N$

☑ 5. Find intersections, unions, and differences of sets.

Cartesian Products

The fourth set operation we'll study is called the *Cartesian product* or *cross product*. To define it, we need to first define an *ordered pair*. An ordered pair is a pair of numbers or objects that are associated by writing them together in a set of parentheses, like (3, 5). In this ordered pair, 3 is called the *first component* and 5 is called the *second component*.

As indicated by the term *ordered pair,* the order in which numbers are written is important: (3, 5) is not the same ordered pair as (5, 3).

Math Note

The Cartesian product $A \times B$ is usually read aloud as "A cross B."

The **Cartesian product** (denoted $A \times B$) of two sets A and B is formed by writing all possible ordered pairs in which the first component is an element of A and the second component is an element of B. Using set-builder notation, $A \times B = \{(x, y) \mid x \in A \text{ and } y \in B\}$.

EXAMPLE 12   Finding Cartesian Products

Math Note

It's important to note that the Cartesian product of two sets is also a set, so it should be enclosed within braces.

If $A = \{1, 3, 5\}$ and $B = \{2, 4\}$, find $A \times B$ and $B \times A$.

SOLUTION

To form $A \times B$, first form ordered pairs with first component 1: (1, 2) and (1, 4). Then form pairs with first component 3: (3, 2) and (3, 4). Finally, use 5 as the first component: (5, 2) and (5, 4). $A \times B = \{(1, 2), (1, 4), (3, 2), (3, 4), (5, 2), (5, 4)\}$. For $B \times A$, form all possible ordered pairs with first components from B and second components from A: $B \times A = \{(2, 1), (2, 3), (2, 5), (4, 1), (4, 3), (4, 5)\}$.

▼ **Try This One 12**

If $R = \{c, d, e\}$ and $S = \{g, h\}$, find $R \times S$, $S \times R$, and $S \times S$.

☑ 6. Find the Cartesian product of two sets.

CAUTION

Even though we use a multiplication sign for Cartesian product, it has nothing to do with multiplying elements!

In this section, we defined subsets, Venn diagrams, and four basic operations for combining sets: intersection, union, subtraction, and Cartesian product. In the next section, we'll examine how Venn diagrams can be used to study set operations in greater depth.

Answers to Try This One

1 $A' = \{20, 40, 60, 70, 80, 90\}$

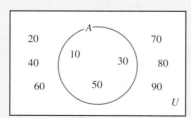

2   {Verizon, Nextel, AT&T}, {Verizon, Nextel}, {Verizon, AT&T}, {Nextel, AT&T}, {Verizon}, {Nextel}, {AT&T}, $\varnothing$

3   {♦,♥,♠}, {♦,♥,♣}, {♦,♠,♣}, {♥,♠,♣}, {♦,♥}, {♦,♠}, {♦,♣}, {♥,♠}, {♥,♣}, {♠,♣}, {♦}, {♥}, {♠}, {♣}, $\varnothing$

4   (a) True   (c) True   (e) True
      (b) False   (d) True

5   (a) True   (b) True   (c) False   (d) False

6   Subsets: $2^8 = 256$; proper subsets: 255

7 $A \cap B = \{\text{Chicago, Detroit}\}$;
      $B \cap C = \{\text{Los Angeles}\}$; $A \cap C = \varnothing$

8 $A \cup B = \{a, b, c, d, e, g, i\}$;
$A \cup C = \{a, b, c, d, e, f, h, j\}$;
$B \cup C = \{a, b, c, d, e, f, g, h, i, j\}$

9 $A \cup (B \cap C) = \{2, 3, 4, 5, 6, 7, 10\}$
$(A \cap B) \cup C = \{0, 5, 7, 10, 15, 20\}$
$A \cap (B \cup C) = \{5, 7\}$

10 (a) $\{1, 4, 6, 8\}$ (c) $\{4, 6, 8\}$
(b) $\varnothing$ (d) $\{1, 4, 6, 8\}$

11 (a) $\{q, r, v, w\}$ (b) $\{p, q, r, s, t\}$ (c) $\{p, s, t, y\}$

12 $R \times S = \{(c, g), (c, h), (d, g), (d, h), (e, g), (e, h)\}$
$S \times R = \{(g, c), (g, d), (g, e), (h, c), (h, d), (h, e)\}$
$S \times S = \{(g, g), (g, h), (h, g), (h, h)\}$

EXERCISE SET 2-2

Writing Exercises

1. What is a subset?
2. Explain the difference between a subset and a proper subset.
3. Explain the difference between a subset and an element of a set.
4. Explain why the empty set is a subset, but not a proper subset, of itself.
5. Explain the difference between the union and intersection of two sets.
6. When are two sets said to be disjoint?
7. What is a universal set?
8. What is the complement of a set?
9. Write an example from real life that represents the union of sets and explain why it represents union.
10. Write an example from real life that represents the difference of sets and explain why it represents difference.

Computational Exercises

For Exercises 11–14, let $U = \{2, 3, 5, 7, 11, 13, 17, 19\}$, $A = \{5, 7, 11, 13\}$, $B = \{2\}$, $C = \{13, 17, 19\}$, *and* $D = \{2, 3, 5\}$. *Find each set.*

11. A'
12. B'
13. C'
14. D'

For Exercises 15–22, find all subsets of each set.

15. $\{r, s, t\}$
16. $\{2, 5, 7\}$
17. $\{1, 3\}$
18. $\{p, q\}$
19. $\{\ \}$
20. $\varnothing$
21. $\{5, 12, 13, 14\}$
22. $\{m, o, r, e\}$

For Exercises 23–28, find all proper subsets of each set.

23. $\{1, 10, 20\}$
24. $\{March, April, May\}$
25. $\{6\}$
26. $\{t\}$
27. $\varnothing$
28. $\{\ \}$

For Exercises 29–38, state whether each is true or false.

29. $\{3\} \subseteq \{1, 3, 5\}$
30. $\{a, b, c\} \subset \{c, b, a\}$
31. $\{1, 2, 3\} \subseteq \{123\}$
32. $\varnothing \subset \varnothing$
33. $\varnothing \in \{\ \}$
34. $\{Mars, Venus, Sun\} \subset \{planets\ in\ our\ solar\ system\}$
35. $\{3\} \in \{1, 3, 5, 7, \ldots\}$

36. $\{x \mid x \in N \text{ and } x > 10\} \subseteq \{x \mid x \in N \text{ and } x \geq 10\}$
37. $\varnothing \subset \{a, b, c\}$
38. $\varnothing \in \{r, s, t, u\}$

For Exercises 39–44, find the number of subsets and proper subsets each set has. Do not list the subsets.

39. $\{25, 50, 75\}$
40. $\{1, 2, 3, 4, 5, 6, 7, 8, 9, 10\}$
41. $\varnothing$
42. $\{0\}$
43. $\{x, y\}$
44. $\{a, b, c, d, e\}$

For Exercises 45–54, use the Venn diagram and find the elements in each set.

45. U
46. A
47. B
48. $A \cap B$
49. $A \cup B$
50. A'
51. B'
52. $(A \cup B)'$
53. $(A \cap B)'$
54. $A \cap B'$

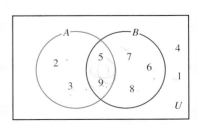

For Exercises 55–64, let

$U = \{10, 20, 30, 40, 50, 60, 70, 80, 90, 100\}$
$A = \{10, 30, 50, 70, 90\}$
$B = \{20, 40, 60, 80, 100\}$
$C = \{30, 40, 50, 60\}$

Find each set.

55. $A \cup C$
56. $A \cap B$
57. A'
58. $(A \cap B) \cup C$
59. $A' \cap (B \cup C)$

60. $(A \cap B) \cap C$
61. $(A \cup B)' \cap C$
62. $A \cap B'$
63. $(B \cup C) \cap A'$
64. $(A' \cup B)' \cup C'$

For Exercises 65–74, let

$U = \{a, b, c, d, e, f, g, h\}$
$P = \{b, d, f, g\}$
$Q = \{a, b, c, d\}$
$R = \{e, f, g\}$

Find each set.

65. $P \cap Q$
66. $Q \cup R$
67. P'
68. Q'
69. $R' \cap P'$

70. $P \cup (Q \cap R)$
71. $(Q \cup P)' \cap R$
72. $P \cap (Q \cap R)$
73. $(P \cup Q) \cap (P \cup R)$
74. $Q' \cup R'$

For Exercises 75–84, let

$U = \{1, 2, 3, 4, 5, 6, 7, 8, 9, 10, 11, 12\}$
$W = \{2, 4, 6, 8, 10, 12\}$
$X = \{1, 3, 5, 7, 9, 11\}$
$Y = \{1, 2, 3, 4, 5, 6\}$
$Z = \{2, 5, 6, 8, 10, 11, 12\}$

Find each set.

75. $W \cap Y$
76. $X \cup Z$
77. $W \cup X$
78. $(X \cap Y) \cap Z$
79. $W \cap X$

80. $(Y \cup Z)'$
81. $(X \cup Y) \cap Z$
82. $(Z \cap Y) \cup W$
83. $W' \cap X'$
84. $(Z \cup X)' \cap Y$

For Exercises 85–88, let

$U = \{1, 2, 3, \ldots\}$
$A = \{3, 6, 9, 12, \ldots\}$
$B = \{9, 18, 27, 36, \ldots\}$
$C = \{2, 4, 6, 8, \ldots\}$

Find each set.

85. $A \cap B$
86. $A' \cap C$

87. $A \cap (B \cup C)'$
88. $A \cup B$

For Exercises 89–94, let

$U = \{20, 40, 60, 80, 100, 110\}$
$A = \{20, 60, 100, 110\}$
$B = \{60, 80, 100\}$
$C = \{80, 100, 110\}$

Find each set.

89. $A - B$
90. $A - C$

91. $B - C$
92. $B - A$

93. $C \cap B'$
94. $A \cap C'$

For Exercises 95–100, let

$U = \{p, q, r, s, t, u, v, w\}$
$A = \{p, q, r, s, t\}$
$B = \{r, s, t, u, v\}$
$C = \{p, r, t, v\}$

Find each set.

95. $C - B$
96. $A - C$

97. $B - C$
98. $B - A$

99. $B \cap C'$
100. $C \cap A'$

For Exercises 101–104, let

$A = \{9, 12, 18\}$
$B = \{1, 2, 3\}$

Find each set.

101. $A \times B$ 102. $B \times A$ 103. $A \times A$ 104. $B \times B$

For Exercises 105–108, let

$A = \{1, 2, 4, 8\}$
$B = \{1, 3\}$

Find each set.

105. $A \times B$ 106. $B \times A$ 107. $B \times B$ 108. $A \times A$

Real-World Applications

109. A student can have a cell phone, a laptop, and an iPod while hanging out on campus between classes. List all the sets of different communication options a student can select, considering all, some, or none of these technologies.

110. If a person is dealt five cards and has a chance of discarding any number including 0, how many choices will the person have?

111. A college freshman can choose one, some, or all of the following classes for her first semester: an English class, a math class, a foreign language class, a science class, a philosophy class, a physical education class, and a history class. How many different possibilities does she have for her new schedule?

112. Since the student union is being remodeled, there is a limited choice of foods and drinks a student can buy for a snack between classes. Students can choose none, some, or all of these items: pizza, fries, big soft pretzels, Coke, Diet Coke, and Hawaiian Punch. How many different selections can be made?

113. Suzie is buying a new laptop for school and can select none, some, or all of the following choices

of peripherals: a laser mouse, a DVD burner, a Web cam, or a jump drive. How many different selections of peripherals are possible for her laptop?

114. To integrate aerobics into her exercise program, Claire can select one, some, or all of these machines: treadmill, cycle, and stair stepper. List all possibilities for her aerobics selection.

Critical Thinking

115. Can you find two sets whose union and intersection are the same set?
116. Write a short paragraph listing five things you admire about your role model and five things you like about yourself. Find the union of the two sets. Find the intersection of the two sets.
117. Select two medications and find a resource on the Internet that lists the possible side effects of each. Find the intersection of the sets.

118. Select two possible careers you may pursue and write the job responsibilities you would have with each one. What responsibilities do the jobs have in common? If you could combine these careers somehow, what would your new job responsibilities be?

Section 2-3 Using Venn Diagrams to Study Set Operations

LEARNING OBJECTIVES

☐ 1. Illustrate set statements involving two sets with Venn diagrams.

☐ 2. Illustrate set statements involving three sets with Venn diagrams.

☐ 3. Use DeMorgan's laws.

☐ 4. Use Venn diagrams to decide if two sets are equal.

☐ 5. Use the formula for the cardinality of a union.

The world we live in is a pretty complicated place. Everywhere you look, there are interactions between sets of people, businesses, products, objects—we could go on, but you probably get the picture. The more complicated these interactions are, the more challenging it can be to sort them out. One good way to get a handle on a complicated situation is to diagram it. When we are dealing with sets, Venn diagrams will be our tool of choice.

In this section, we'll develop a method for drawing Venn diagrams that will help us to illustrate set operations. We'll start with diagrams involving interactions between two sets, as in Figure 2-8. Notice that there are four distinct regions in a Venn diagram illustrating two sets A and B. Let's label these regions with Roman numerals to designate that they represent regions and not elements in the sets.

The procedure that we will use to illustrate set statements, found in the box below, is demonstrated in Examples 1 and 2.

Illustrating a Set Statement with a Venn Diagram

Step 1   Draw a diagram for the sets, with Roman numerals in each region.

Step 2   Using the Roman numerals, list the regions for each set.

Step 3   Find the set of numerals that correspond to the set given in the set statement.

Step 4   Shade the area corresponding to the set of numerals found in step 3.

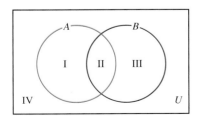

Figure 2-8

Region I represents the elements in set A that are not in set B.
Region II represents the elements in both sets A and B.
Region III represents the elements in set B that are not in set A.
Region IV represents the elements in the universal set that are in neither set A nor set B.

EXAMPLE 1   **Drawing a Venn Diagram**

Draw a Venn diagram to illustrate the set $(A \cup B)'$.

SOLUTION

Step 1 Draw the diagram and label each area.

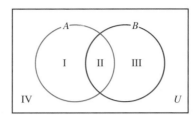

Step 2 From the diagram, list the regions that make up each set.

$U = \{$I, II, II, IV$\}$
$A = \{$I, II$\}$
$B = \{$II, III$\}$

Step 3 Using the sets in step 2, find $(A \cup B)'$.

First, all of I, II, and III are in either A or B, so $A \cup B = \{$I, II, II$\}$. The complement is $(A \cup B)' = \{$IV$\}$.

Step 4 Shade region IV to illustrate $(A \cup B)'$.

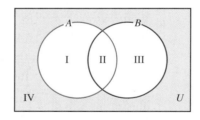

▼ Try This One 1

Draw a Venn diagram to illustrate the set $A' \cap B$.

EXAMPLE 2   **Drawing a Venn Diagram**

Draw a Venn diagram to illustrate the set $A \cup B'$.

SOLUTION

Step 1 Draw the diagram and label each area. This will be the same diagram as in Example 1.

Step 2 From the diagram, list the regions that make up each set.

$U = \{$I, II, II, IV$\}$
$A = \{$I, II$\}$
$B = \{$II, III$\}$

Step 3 Using the sets in step 2, find $A \cap B'$.

First, regions I and IV are outside of set B. Of these two regions, I is also in set A, so $A \cap B' = \{I\}$.

Step 4 Shade region I to illustrate $A \cap B'$.

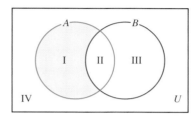

▼ Try This One 2

Draw a Venn diagram to illustrate the set $A' \cup B$.

☑ 1. Illustrate set statements involving two sets with Venn diagrams.

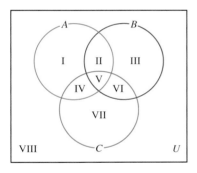

Figure 2-9

A similar procedure can be used to illustrate set statements involving three or more sets. The Venn diagram for three sets is shown in Figure 2-9.

Region I represents the elements in set A but not in set B or set C.
Region II represents the elements in set A and set B but not in set C.
Region III represents the elements in set B but not in set A or set C.
Region IV represents the elements in sets A and C but not in set B.
Region V represents the elements in sets A, B, and C.
Region VI represents the elements in sets B and C but not in set A.
Region VII represents the elements in set C but not in set A or set B.
Region VIII represents the elements in the universal set U, but not in set A, B, or C.

We can use the same four-step procedure (see page 65) to illustrate operations involving three sets. The process is demonstrated in Example 3.

EXAMPLE 3 Drawing a Venn Diagram with Three Sets

Draw a Venn diagram to illustrate the set $A \cap (B \cap C)'$.

SOLUTION

Step 1 Draw and label the diagram as in Figure 2-9.

Step 2 From the diagram, list the regions that make up each set.

$$U = \{I, II, III, IV, V, VI, VII, VIII\}$$
$$A = \{I, II, IV, V\}$$
$$B = \{II, III, V, VI\}$$
$$C = \{IV, V, VI, VII\}$$

Step 3 Using the sets in step 2, find $A \cap (B \cap C)'$.

First, find $B \cap C$: $B \cap C = \{V, VI\}$. The complement is $(B \cap C)' = \{I, II, III, IV, VII, VIII\}$. Regions I, II, and IV are also part of A, so $A \cap (B \cap C)' = \{I, II, IV\}$.

Step 4 Shade regions I, II, and IV to illustrate $A \cap (B \cap C)'$.

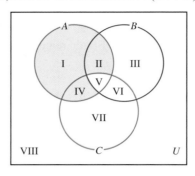

▼ Try This One 3

☑ 2. Illustrate set statements involving three sets with Venn diagrams.

Draw a Venn diagram to illustrate the set $(A \cap B') \cup C$.

De Morgan's Laws

There are two very well-known formulas that are useful in simplifying some set operations. They're named in honor of a 19th-century mathematician named Augustus De Morgan.

First, we'll write the formulas and illustrate each with an example. Then we'll see how Venn diagrams can be used to prove the formulas.

De Morgan's Laws

For any two sets A and B,

$(A \cup B)' = A' \cap B'$

$(A \cap B)' = A' \cup B'$

The first law states that the complement of the union of two sets will always be equal to the intersection of the complements of each set.

EXAMPLE 4   Using De Morgan's Laws

If $U = \{a, b, c, d, e, f, g, h\}$, $A = \{a, c, e, g\}$, and $B = \{b, c, d, e\}$, find $(A \cup B)'$ and $A' \cap B'$.

SOLUTION

$$A \cup B = \{a, b, c, d, e, g\} \qquad \text{and} \qquad (A \cup B)' = \{f, h\}$$

$$A' = \{b, d, f, h\} \qquad B' = \{a, f, g, h\} \qquad \text{and} \qquad A' \cap B' = \{f, h\}$$

Notice that $(A \cup B)'$ and $A' \cap B'$ are equal, illustrating the first of De Morgan's laws.

▼ Try This One 4

If $U = \{15, 30, 45, 60, 75, 90, 105\}$, $A = \{30, 60, 90\}$, and $B = \{15, 45, 75, 90\}$, find $(A \cup B)'$ and $A' \cap B'$.

Sidelight **NOW AND VENN**

Venn diagrams are generally credited to the British mathematician John Venn, who introduced them in an 1880 paper as they are used today. That makes it sound like a pretty old concept, but the general idea can be traced back much further. The great mathematician Leonhard Euler used similar diagrams in the 1700s, and other figures like them can be traced as far back as the 1200s!

The second law states that the complement of the intersection of two sets will equal the union of the complements of the sets.

EXAMPLE 5 **Using De Morgan's Laws**

If $U = \{10, 11, 12, 13, 14, 15, 16\}$, $A = \{10, 11, 12, 13\}$, and $B = \{12, 13, 14, 15\}$, find $(A \cap B)'$ and $A' \cup B'$.

SOLUTION

$$A \cap B = \{12, 13\} \quad \text{and} \quad (A \cap B)' = \{10, 11, 14, 15, 16\}$$
$$A' = \{14, 15, 16\} \quad B' = \{10, 11, 16\}; \quad A' \cup B' = \{10, 11, 14, 15, 16\}$$

Notice that $(A \cap B)'$ and $A' \cup B'$ are equal, illustrating the second of De Morgan's laws.

▼ **Try This One 5**

3. Use De Morgan's laws.

If $U = \{ABC, NBC, CBS, Fox, USA, TBS, TNT, MTV\}$, $A = \{NBC, Fox, USA, TBS\}$, and $B = \{ABC, NBC, CBS, Fox\}$, find $(A \cap B)'$ and $A' \cup B'$.

Venn diagrams can be used to show the equality of two set statements. To do this, we draw a Venn diagram for the set statement on each side of the equation. If the same regions are shaded, then the equation is true. The next example shows how to verify the first of De Morgan's laws by using Venn diagrams. We'll leave the second for you to try.

EXAMPLE 6 **Using a Venn Diagram to Show Equality of Sets**

Use Venn diagrams to show that $(A \cup B)' = A' \cap B'$.

SOLUTION

Start by drawing the Venn diagram for $(A \cup B)'$.

Step 1 Draw the figure (as shown in Step 4).

Step 2 Set U contains regions I, II, III, and IV. Set A contains regions I and II, and B contains regions II and III.

Step 3 $A \cup B = \{I, II, II\}$, so $(A \cup B)' = \{IV\}$.

Step 4 Shade region IV to illustrate $(A \cup B)'$.

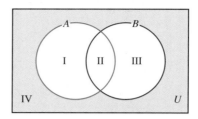

Next draw the Venn diagram for $A' \cap B'$. Steps 1 and 2 are the same as above.

Step 3 $A' = \{$III, IV$\}$ and $B' = \{$I, IV$\}$, so $A' \cap B' = \{$IV$\}$.

Step 4 Shade region IV to illustrate $A' \cap B'$.

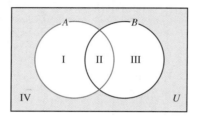

Since the diagrams for each side are identical, we use deductive reasoning to conclude that $(A \cup B)' = A' \cap B'$.

▼ Try This One 6

Use Venn diagrams to show that $(A \cap B)' = A' \cup B'$.

Here's an example using three sets.

EXAMPLE 7 **Using Venn Diagrams to Decide If Two Sets Are Equal**

Determine if the two sets are equal by using Venn diagrams: $(A \cup B) \cap C$ and $(A \cap C) \cup (B \cap C)$.

SOLUTION

The set $A \cup B$ consists of regions I through VI. Of these, IV, V, and VI are also in C, so $(A \cup B) \cap C$ consists of regions IV, V, and VI.

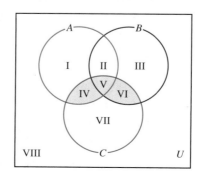

The set $A \cap C$ consists of regions IV and V, and the set $B \cap C$ consists of regions V and VI. Their union is regions IV, V, and VI.

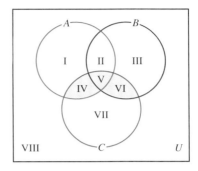

Since the shaded areas are the same, the two sets are equal.

☑ 4. Use Venn diagrams to decide if two sets are equal.

▼ Try This One 7

Determine if the two sets are equal by using Venn diagrams: $B \cup (A \cap C)$ and $(A \cup B) \cap (B \cup C)$.

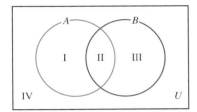

Figure 2-10

The Cardinal Number of a Union

For two sets A and B, how many elements would you guess are in $A \cup B$? Many students guess the number of elements in A plus the number of elements in B, and those students are incorrect when they do. This is an area that Venn diagrams can help us with.

As we can see in Figure 2-10, if we start with the number of elements in A, we're counting all the members in regions I and II. When we add the number of elements in B, we're counting all the members in regions II and III. Do you see the issue? The elements in region II get counted twice. We can fix that by subtracting the number of elements in region II. Since region II represents $A \cap B$, we get the following useful formula:

Math Note

In words, the formula to the right says that to find the number of elements in the union of A and B, you add the number of elements in A and B and then subtract the number of elements in the intersection of A and B.

The Cardinality of a Union

If $n(A)$ represents the cardinal number of set A, then for any two finite sets A and B, $n(A \cup B) = n(A) + n(B) - n(A \cap B)$.

Next, we'll see how this formula can be used in an applied situation.

EXAMPLE 8   Using the Formula for Cardinality of a Union

In a survey of 100 randomly selected freshmen walking across campus, it turns out that 42 are taking a math class, 51 are taking an English class, and 12 are taking both. How many students are taking either a math class or an English class?

SOLUTION

If we call the set of students taking a math class A and the set of students taking an English class B, we're asked to find $n(A \cup B)$. We're told that $n(A) = 42$, $n(B) = 51$, and $n(A \cap B) = 12$. So

$$n(A \cup B) = n(A) + n(B) - n(A \cap B) = 42 + 51 - 12 = 81$$

☑ 5. Use the formula for the cardinality of a union.

▼ Try This One 8

A telephone poll of 200 registered Democrats during the 2008 primary season found that 94 supported Barack Obama, 85 supported Hillary Clinton, and 20 supported both. How many supported either Obama or Clinton?

In this section, we saw how Venn diagrams can be used to illustrate sets, prove equality of two sets, and solve problems. We'll explore the problem-solving aspect of Venn diagrams further in Section 2-4.

Answers to Try This One

1

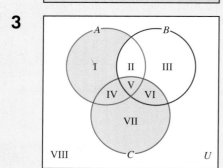

2

3

4   Both are {105}.

5   Both are {ABC, CBS, USA, TBS, TNT, MTV}.

6   Both diagrams are

7   Both diagrams are

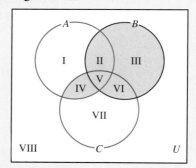

8   159

EXERCISE SET 2-3

Writing Exercises

1. Explain in your own words how to draw a Venn diagram representing the set $A \cup B$.
2. Explain in your own words how to draw a Venn diagram representing the set $A \cap B$.
3. Describe in your own words what De Morgan's laws say.
4. Describe in your own words how to find the cardinal number of the union of two sets.

Computational Exercises

For Exercises 5–28, draw a Venn diagram and shade the sections representing each set.

5. $A \cup B'$
6. $(A \cup B)'$
7. $A' \cup B'$
8. $A' \cup B$
9. $A' \cap B'$
10. $A \cap B'$
11. $A \cup (B \cap C)$
12. $A \cap (B \cup C)$
13. $(A \cup B) \cup (A \cap C)$
14. $(A \cup B) \cap C$
15. $(A \cup B) \cap (A \cup C)$
16. $(A \cap B) \cup C$
17. $(A \cap B)' \cup C$
18. $(A \cup B) \cup C'$
19. $A \cap (B \cup C)'$
20. $A' \cap (B' \cup C')$
21. $(A' \cup B') \cap C$
22. $A \cap (B \cap C)'$
23. $(A \cup B)' \cap (A \cup C)$
24. $(B \cup C) \cup C'$
25. $A' \cap (B' \cap C')$
26. $(A \cup B)' \cap C'$
27. $A' \cap (B \cup C)'$
28. $(A \cup B) \cap (A \cap C)$

For Exercises 29–36, determine whether the two sets are equal by using Venn diagrams.

29. $(A \cap B)'$ and $A' \cup B'$
30. $(A \cup B)'$ and $A' \cup B'$
31. $(A \cup B) \cup C$ and $A \cup (B \cup C)$
32. $A \cap (B \cup C)$ and $(A \cap B) \cup (A \cap C)$
33. $A' \cup (B \cap C')$ and $(A' \cup B) \cap C'$
34. $(A \cap B) \cup C'$ and $(A \cap B) \cup (B \cap C')$
35. $(A \cap B)' \cup C$ and $(A' \cup B') \cap C$
36. $(A' \cup B') \cup C$ and $(A \cap B)' \cap C'$

For Exercises 37–46, use the following Venn diagram to find each set.

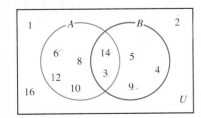

37. $n(A)$
38. $n(B)$
39. $n(A \cap B)$
40. $n(A \cup B)$
41. $n(A')$
42. $n(B')$
43. $n(A' \cap B')$
44. $n(A' \cup B')$
45. $n(A - B)$
46. $n(B - A)$

For Exercises 47–56, use the following information:

$$U = \{x \mid x \text{ is a natural number} < 13\}$$
$$A = \{x \mid x \text{ is an odd natural number}\}$$
$$B = \{x \mid x \text{ is a prime number}\}$$

(*Hint:* The prime numbers less than 13 are 2, 3, 5, 7, and 11.) *Find each.*

47. $n(A)$
48. $n(B)$
49. $n(A \cap B)$
50. $n(A \cup B)$
51. $n(A \cap B')$
52. $n(A' \cup B)$
53. $n(A')$
54. $n(B')$
55. $n(A - B)$
56. $n(B' - A)$

In Exercises 57–60, $A = \{$people who drive an SUV$\}$ and $B = \{$people who drive a hybrid vehicle$\}$. Draw a Venn diagram of the following, and write a sentence describing what the set represents.

57. $A \cup B$
58. $A \cap B$
59. A'
60. $(A \cap B)'$

In Exercises 61–64, $O = \{$students in online courses$\}$, $B = \{$students in blended courses$\}$, and $T = \{$students in traditional courses$\}$. Draw a Venn diagram of the following, and write a sentence describing what the set represents.

61. $O \cap (T \cup B)$
62. $B \cup (O \cap T)$
63. $B \cap O \cap T$
64. $(B \cup O) \cap (T \cup O)$

In Exercises 65–68, $D = \{$students voting Democrat$\}$, $R = \{$students voting Republican$\}$, and $I = \{$students voting Independent$\}$. Draw a Venn diagram of the following, and write a sentence describing what the set represents.

65. $D' \cup R$
66. $D' \cap I'$
67. $(D \cup R) \cap I'$
68. $I - (D \cup R)$

In Exercises 69–72, $G = \{$people who regularly use Google$\}$, $Y = \{$people who regularly use Yahoo!$\}$, and $M = \{$people who regularly use MSN Live$\}$. Draw a Venn diagram of the following, and write a sentence describing what the set represents.

69. $G - Y$
70. $G - (Y \cap M)$
71. $G' \cap Y' \cap M'$
72. $(Y \cap M) \cup (Y \cap G)$

The table and Venn diagram below are to be used for Exercises 73–78. The table shows the four baseball teams that made the playoffs in the American League from 2005 to 2007. For each exercise, write the region(s) of the Venn diagram that would include the team listed.

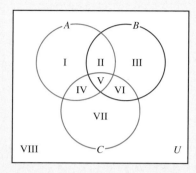

Year	2005	2006	2007
Teams	Boston Red Sox	Detroit Tigers	Boston Red Sox
	Chicago White Sox	Minnesota Twins	Cleveland Indians
	Los Angeles Angels	New York Yankees	Los Angeles Angels
	New York Yankees	Oakland A's	New York Yankees

Note: set A represents 2005 playoff teams, set B represents 2006 playoff teams, and set C represents 2007 playoff teams.

73. Boston Red Sox
74. Los Angeles Angels
75. Cleveland Indians

76. Minnesota Twins
77. New York Yankees
78. Oakland A's

Critical Thinking

79. For two finite sets A and B, is $n(A - B)$ equal to $n(A) - n(B)$? If not, can you find a formula for $n(A - B)$?

80. Can you find a formula for $n(A \cap B)$ in terms of only $n(A)$ and $n(B)$? Why or why not? See if you can find a formula for $n(A \cap B)$ using any sets you like.

81. Make a conjecture about another form for the set $(A \cup B \cup C)'$ based on the first of De Morgan's laws. Check out your conjecture by using a Venn diagram.

82. Make a conjecture about another form for the set $(A \cap B \cap C)'$ based on the second of De Morgan's laws. Check out your conjecture by using a Venn diagram.

Section 2-4 Using Sets to Solve Problems

LEARNING OBJECTIVE

☐ 1. Solve problems by using Venn diagrams.

We live in the information age—every time you turn around, somebody somewhere is trying to gather information about you, your opinions, and (most commonly) your spending habits. Surveys are conducted by the thousands every day, and every person, pet, pastime, and product are classified. Some of the things we've learned about sets can be very helpful in interpreting information from surveys and classifications, and that will be the focus of this section.

When things are classified into two distinct sets, we can use a two-set Venn diagram to interpret the information. This is illustrated in Example 1.

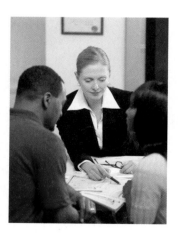

EXAMPLE 1	Solving a Problem by Using a Venn Diagram

In 2008, there were 36 states that had some form of casino gambling in the state, 42 states that sold lottery tickets of some kind, and 34 states that had both casinos and lotteries. Draw a Venn diagram to represent the survey results, and find how many states have only casino gambling, how many states have only lotteries, and how many states have neither.

SOLUTION

Step 1 Draw a Venn diagram with circles for casino gambling and lotteries, labeling the regions as usual.

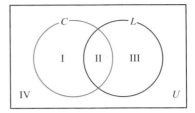

Step 2 Thirty-four states have both, so put 34 in the intersection of C and L, which is region II.

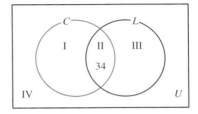

Step 3 Since 36 states have casino gambling and 34 have both, there must be 2 that have only casino gambling. Put 2 in region I. Since 42 states have lotteries and 34 have both, there are 8 that have only lotteries. Put 8 in region III.

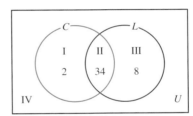

Step 4 Now 44 states are accounted for, so there must be 6 left to put in region IV.

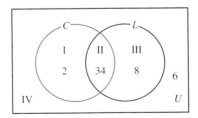

Now we can answer the questions easily. There are only two states that have casino gambling but no lottery (Nevada and Wyoming, in case you're wondering). There are eight states that have lotteries but no casino gambling (region III), and just six states that have neither (region IV).

▼ **Try This One 1**

In an average year, Columbus, Ohio, has 163 days with some rain, 63 days with some snow, and 24 days with both. Draw a Venn diagram to represent these averages, and find how many days have only rain, only snow, and neither.

We can use the results of Example 1 to write a general procedure for using a Venn diagram to interpret information that can be divided into two sets.

Using Venn Diagrams with Two Sets

Step 1 Find the number of elements that are common to both sets and write that number in region II.

Step 2 Find the number of elements that are in set A and not set B by subtracting the number in region II from the total number of elements in A. Then write that number in region I. Repeat for the elements in B but not in region II, and write in region III.

Step 3 Find the number of elements in U that are not in either A or B, and write it in region IV.

Step 4 Use the diagram to answer specific questions about the situation.

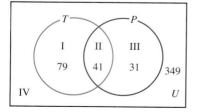

Many news websites include daily surveys, like this one from cnn.com.

One of the most useful applications of Venn diagrams is for studying the results of surveys. Whether they are for business-related research or just to satisfy curiosity, surveys seem to be everywhere these days, especially online. Example 2 analyzes the results of a survey on tattoos and body piercings.

EXAMPLE 2   Solving a Problem by Using a Venn Diagram

In a survey published in the *Journal of the American Academy of Dermatologists*, 500 people were polled by random telephone dialing. Of these, 120 reported having a tattoo, 72 reported having a body piercing, and 41 had both. Draw a Venn diagram to represent these results, and find out how many respondents have only tattoos, only body piercings, and neither.

SOLUTION

In this example, we'll insert just one diagram at the end, and we will refer to it as we go.

Step 1 Place the number of respondents with both tattoos and body piercings (41) in region II.

Step 2 There are 120 people with tattoos and 41 with both, so there are $120 - 41$, or 79, people with only tattoos. This goes in region I. By the same logic, there are $72 - 41$, or 31, people with only piercings. This goes in region III.

Step 3 We now have $41 + 79 + 31 = 151$ of the 500 people accounted for, so $500 - 151 = 349$ goes in region IV.

Step 4 There are 79 people with only tattoos, 31 with only piercings, and 349 with neither.

▼ Try This One 2

According to an online survey on Howstuffworks.com, 12,595 people gave their thoughts on Coke versus Pepsi. Of these, 7,642 drink Coke, 5,619 drink Pepsi, and 1,856 drink both. Draw a Venn diagram to represent these results, and find out how many respondents drink only Coke, only Pepsi, and neither.

Sidelight **HOW MUCH IS YOUR OPINION WORTH?**

Communication in our society is becoming cheaper, easier, and more effective all the time. In the age of cell phones and Internet communication, businesses are finding it simpler than ever to contact people for their opinions, and more and more people are finding out that companies are willing to pay to hear what they have to say. There are literally hundreds of companies in the United States today whose main function is to gather opinions on everything from political candidates to potato chips. In fact, over \$6 *billion* is spent on market research in the United States each year. Maybe you'll think twice the next time somebody asks you for your opinion for free.

When a classification problem or a survey consists of three sets, a similar procedure is followed, using a Venn diagram with three sets. We just have more work to do since there are now eight regions instead of four.

EXAMPLE 3 **Solving a Problem by Using a Venn Diagram**

A survey of 300 first-year students at a large midwestern university was conducted to aid in scheduling for the following year. Responses indicated that 194 were taking a math class, 210 were taking an English class, and 170 were taking a speech course. In addition, 142 were taking both math and English, 111 were taking both English and speech, 91 were taking both math and speech, and 45 were taking all three. Draw a Venn diagram to represent these survey results, and find the number of students taking

(a) Only English.
(b) Math and speech but not English.
(c) Math or English.
(d) None of these three subjects.

SOLUTION

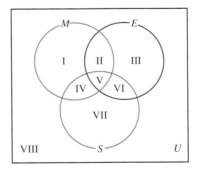

Step 1 The only region we know for sure from the given information is region V—the number of students taking all three classes. So we begin by putting 45 in region V.

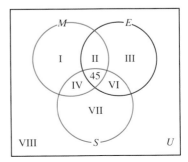

Step 2 There are 142 students taking both math and English, but we must subtract the number in all three classes to find the number in region II: $142 - 45 = 97$. In the same way, we get $91 - 45 = 46$ in region IV (both math and speech) and $111 - 45 = 66$ in region VI (both English and speech).

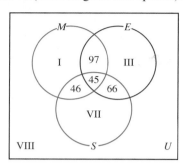

Step 3 Now we can find the number of elements in regions I, III, and VII. There are 194 students in math classes, but $97 + 45 + 46 = 188$ are already accounted for in the diagram, so that leaves 6 in region I. Of the 210 students in English classes, $97 + 45 + 66 = 208$ are already accounted for, leaving just 2 in region III. There are 170 students in speech classes, with $46 + 45 + 66 = 157$ already accounted for. This leaves 13 in region VII.

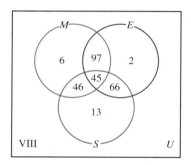

Step 4 Adding up all the numbers in the diagram so far, we get 275. That leaves 25 in region VIII.

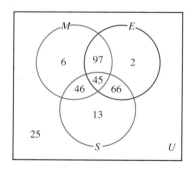

Math Note

Notice that in filling in the Venn diagram in Example 3, we started with the number of elements in the innermost region and worked our way outward.

Step 5 Now that we have the diagram completed, we turn our attention to the questions.

(a) Students taking only English are represented by region III—there are only 2.

(b) Math and speech but not English is region IV, so there are 46 students.

(c) Students taking math or English are represented by all but regions VII and VIII. So there are only 38 students not taking either math or English, and $300 - 38 = 262$ who are.

(d) There are 25 students outside of the regions for all of math, English, and speech.

☑ 1. Solve problems by using Venn diagrams.

▼ Try This One 3

An online music service surveyed 500 customers and found that 270 listen to hip-hop music, 320 listen to rock, and 160 listen to country. In addition, 140 listen to both rock and hip-hop, 120 listen to rock and country, and 80 listen to hip-hop and country. Finally, 50 listen to all three. Draw a Venn diagram to represent the results of the survey and find the number of customers who

(a) Listen to only hip-hop.
(b) Listen to rock and country but not hip-hop.
(c) Don't listen to any of these three types of music.
(d) Don't listen to country music.

We can use the results of Example 3 to write a general procedure for using a Venn diagram to interpret information that can be divided into three sets.

Using Venn Diagrams with Three Sets

Step 1   Put the number of elements common to all three sets in region V.

Step 2   Find the number of elements in $A \cap B$, $A \cap C$, and $B \cap C$. Subtract the number of elements in all three, and place these numbers in regions II, IV, and VI.

Step 3   Subtract the number of elements you now have inside each large set from the total number you were given for each set: these will be the numbers you put in regions I, III, and VII.

Step 4   Add all the numbers inside the circles and subtract that from the total number of elements in U to get the number in region VIII.

Step 5   Use the completed diagram to answer specific questions.

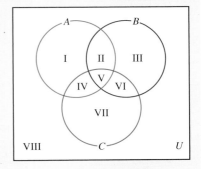

We've come a pretty long way from simply defining what sets and elements are! In this section, we've seen that Venn diagrams can be effectively used to sort out some pretty complicated real-world situations. And the better you are at interpreting information, the better equipped you'll be to survive and thrive in the information age.

Answers to Try This One

1   Only rain: 139; only snow: 39; neither: 163 (assuming it's not leap year!)

2   Only Coke: 5,786; only Pepsi: 3,763; neither: 1,190

3   (a) 100   (b) 70
       (c) 40   (d) 340

EXERCISE SET 2-4

Real-World Applications

1. In a survey of 40 students, 20 use myspace.com, 25 use facebook.com, and 7 use both myspace.com and facebook.com.

   (a) How many use myspace.com only?
   (b) How many use facebook.com only?
   (c) How many use neither myspace.com nor facebook.com?

2. In a class of 25 students, 18 were mathematics majors, 12 were computer science majors, and 7 were dual majors in mathematics and computer science.

   (a) How many students were majoring in mathematics only?
   (b) How many students were not majoring in computer science?
   (c) How many students were not mathematics or computer science majors?

3. There were 16 recycling bins in the student union. Eight of them contained only paper, five contained only plastic, and three contained paper and plastic.

   (a) How many contained only paper?
   (b) How many contained only plastic?
   (c) How many contained neither paper nor plastic?

4. In the cafeteria, 25 students were seated at tables. Fifteen were enrolled in psychology, nine were enrolled in physics, and four were enrolled in both psychology and physics.

   (a) How many students were enrolled in psychology only?
   (b) How many students were not enrolled in physics?
   (c) How many students were enrolled in at least one of these courses?

5. The financial aid department at a college surveyed 70 students, asking if they receive any type of financial aid. The results of the survey are summarized in the table below.

Financial Aid	Number of Students
Scholarships	16
Student loans	24
Private grants	20
Scholarships and loans	9
Loans and grants	11
Scholarships and grants	7
Scholarships, loans, and grants	2

   (a) How many students got only scholarships?
   (b) How many got loans and private grants but not scholarships?
   (c) How many didn't get any of these types of financial aid?

6. The manager of a campus gym is planning the schedule of fitness classes for a new school year, and will decide how often to hold certain classes based on the interests of students. She polls 47 students at various times of day, asking what type of classes they'd be interested in attending. The results are summarized in the table below.

Type of Class	Students Interested
Yoga	17
Pilates	13
Spinning	12
Yoga and pilates	9
Pilates and spinning	3
Yoga and spinning	5
All three	2

   (a) How many students are interested in yoga or spinning, but not pilates?
   (b) How many are interested in exactly two of the three classes?
   (c) How many are interested in yoga but not pilates?

7. One semester in a chemistry class, 14 students failed due to a poor attendance, 23 failed due to not studying, 15 failed because they did not turn in assignments, 9 failed because of poor attendance and not studying, 8 failed because of not studying and not turning in assignments, 5 failed because of poor attendance and not turning in assignments, and 2 failed because of all three of these reasons.

   (a) How many failed for exactly two of the three reasons?
   (b) How many failed because of poor attendance and not studying but not because of not turning in assignments?
   (c) How many failed because of exactly one of the three reasons?
   (d) How many failed because of poor attendance and not turning in assignments but not because of not studying?

8. Last Super Bowl weekend, there were 109 pizzas ordered for the sophomore dorm. That weekend

32 customers ordered their pizza with just pepperoni, 40 ordered their pizza with just sausage, 18 ordered theirs with just onions, 13 ordered theirs with pepperoni and sausage, 10 ordered theirs with sausage and onions, 9 ordered theirs with pepperoni and onions, and 7 ordered theirs with all three items.

(a) How many customers ordered their pizza with pepperoni or sausage (or both)?
(b) How many customers ordered their pizza with sausage or onions (or both)?
(c) How many customers ordered a pizza without pepperoni, sausage, or onions?

9. There were 70 students in line at the campus bookstore to sell back their textbooks after finals: 19 had history books to return, 21 had business books to return, and 19 had math books to return. Nine were selling back both history and business books, eight were selling back both business and math books, five were selling back history and math books, and three were selling back history, business, and math books.

(a) How many students were selling back at most two of these three types of books?
(b) How many students were selling back history and math books but not business books?
(c) How many were selling back neither history nor math books?

10. A survey of 96 students on campus showed that 29 read the *Campus Observer* student newspaper that morning, 24 read the news via the Internet that morning, and 20 read the local city paper that morning. Eight read the *Campus Observer* and the Internet news that morning, while four read the Internet news and the local paper, seven read the *Campus Observer* and the local city paper, and one person read the *Campus Observer,* the Internet news, and the local paper.

(a) How many read the Internet news or local paper but not both?
(b) How many read the Internet news and the local paper but not the *Campus Observer?*
(c) How many read the Internet news or the *Campus Observer?* (*Note: Or* means one or the other or both.)

11. Sixty-one students in an art class were surveyed about their musical tastes. Of those asked, 20 liked alternative, 26 liked hip-hop, 20 liked techno, 9 liked alternative and hip-hop, 15 liked hip-hop and techno, 6 liked alternative and techno, and 3 liked all three types of music.

(a) How many liked none of these three types?

(b) How many liked exactly three of these types?
(c) How many liked exactly one of these types?

12. In a survey of 200 college students, 128 watched at least one reality show on television each week, 131 watched at least one video on MTV each week, 114 watched a national news show on CNN each week, 75 watched a reality show and a video, 59 watched a video and a news show, 81 watched a reality show and a news show, and 33 watched a reality show, a video, and a news show each week.

(a) How many watched exactly two of these?
(b) How many watched only one of these?
(c) How many did not watch a reality show?

13. In a survey of 121 students, 39 belonged to a club on campus, 51 regularly attended a campus sporting event, and 26 belonged to a professional organization. Furthermore, 25 regularly attended campus sporting events and belonged to a campus club, 14 belonged to a professional organization and attended campus sporting events, 18 belonged to a professional organization and a campus club, and 10 were involved in all three.

(a) How many students did exactly one of these?
(b) How many students regularly attended a sporting event, but did not belong to a professional organization?
(c) How many students did not regularly attend a campus sporting event or belong to a professional organization?

14. Out of 20 students taking a midterm exam, 15 answered the first of two bonus questions, 13 answered the second bonus question, and 2 answered neither bonus question. How many students answered both bonus questions?

15. In a group of 34 people waiting in line at the local java house, 18 wanted to order a cappuccino, 20 wanted to order a latte, and 2 wanted to order neither of these drinks. How many wanted to order both a cappuccino and a latte?

16. An entertainment magazine conducted an online poll of 230 college students who watch late-night TV, asking what shows they watch regularly. There were 119 who watch David Letterman, 101 who watch Conan O'Brien, and 75 who watch Jimmy Fallon. In addition, 69 watch Letterman and O'Brien, 48 watch Letterman and Fallon, 38 watch Fallon and O'Brien, and 28 watch all three.

(a) How many don't watch any of these three shows?
(b) How many watch only one of the three shows?
(c) How many watch exactly two of the three shows?

Critical Thinking

17. A researcher was hired to examine the drinking habits of energy drink consumers. Explain why he was fired when he published the results below, from a survey of 40 such consumers:

    23 said they drink Red Bull.
    18 said they drink Monster.
    19 said they drink G2.
    12 said they drink Red Bull and Monster.
    6 said they drink Monster and G2.
    7 said they drink Red Bull and G2.
    2 said they drink all three (not at the same time, hopefully).
    2 said they don't drink any of the three brands.

18. The marketing research firm of OUWant12 designed and sent three spam advertisements to 40 e-mail accounts. The first one was an ad for hair removal cream, the second was an ad for Botox treatments, and the third was an ad for a new all lima bean diet. Explain why, when the following results occurred, the sponsors discontinued their services.

    23 recipients deleted the ad for hair removal cream without looking at it.
    18 recipients deleted the ad for Botox treatments.
    19 recipients deleted the ad for the all lima bean diet.
    12 recipients deleted the ads for hair removal cream and Botox treatments.
    6 recipients deleted the ads for Botox treatments and the all lima bean diet.
    7 recipients deleted the ads for the hair removal cream and the all lima bean diet.
    2 recipients deleted all three ads.

Section 2-5 Infinite Sets

LEARNING OBJECTIVES

☐ 1. Formally define infinite sets.

☐ 2. Show that a set is infinite.

☐ 3. Find a general term of an infinite set.

☐ 4. Define countable and uncountable sets.

The night sky may look infinite, but have you ever thought about what that really means?

Infinity is a concept that's tremendously difficult for us human beings to wrap our minds around. Because our thoughts are shaped by experiences in a physical world with finite dimensions, things that are infinitely large always seem just out of our grasp. Whether you're a believer in the Big Bang theory or creationism, you probably think that one or the other must be true because the alternative is too far beyond our experience: that time didn't have a beginning at all, but extends infinitely far in each direction. Some philosophers feel that human beings are fundamentally incapable of grasping the concept of something infinitely large at all!

The study of infinity and infinite sets from a mathematical standpoint is a relatively young one compared to the history of math in general. For at least a couple of thousand years, the nature of infinity so confounded the greatest human minds that they chose to not deal with it at all. And yet in working with a set as simple as the natural numbers, we deal with infinite sets in math all the time. It's an interesting paradox.

A Definition of Infinite Sets

Recall from Section 2-1 that a set is considered to be finite if the number of elements is either zero or a natural number. Otherwise, it is considered to be an infinite set. For example, the set $\{10, 20, 30, 40\}$ is finite because the number of elements (four) is a natural number. But the set $\{10, 20, 30, 40, \ldots\}$ is infinite because the number of elements is unlimited, and therefore not a natural number.

You might recognize an infinite set when you see one, but it's not necessarily easy to make a precise definition of what it means for a set to be infinite (other than the obvious definition, "not finite"). The German mathematician Georg Cantor, widely regarded as the father of set theory, is famous for his 19th-century study of infinite sets. (Sadly his work was not highly regarded in his lifetime, and he died in a mental institution.) Cantor's simple and elegant definition of an infinite set is as follows:

A set is **infinite** if it can be placed into a one-to-one correspondence with a proper subset of itself.

☑ 1. Formally define infinite sets.

First, notice that a finite set definitely does not meet the condition in this definition: if a set has some finite number of elements, let's say 10, then any proper subset has at most 9 elements, and an attempt at one-to-one correspondence will always leave out at least one member.

The trickier thing is to understand how an infinite set can meet this definition. We'll illustrate with an infinite set we know well, the set of natural numbers $\{1, 2, 3, 4, \ldots\}$. The set of even natural numbers $\{2, 4, 6, 8, \ldots\}$ is of course a proper subset: every even number is also a natural number, but there are natural numbers that are not even numbers. Now we demonstrate the clever way to put these two sets in one-to-one correspondence: match each natural number with its double.

$$1 \leftrightarrow 2, \qquad 2 \leftrightarrow 4, \qquad 3 \leftrightarrow 6, \qquad 4 \leftrightarrow 8, \ldots$$

In general, we can define our correspondence as matching any n from the set of natural numbers with a corresponding even number $2n$. This is a one-to-one correspondence because every natural number has a match (its double), and every even number has a match (its half). So we've put the natural numbers into one-to-one correspondence with a proper subset, and they are an infinite set.

Let's try another example.

EXAMPLE 1 Showing That a Set Is Infinite

Show that the set $\{5, 10, 15, 20, 25, \ldots\}$ is an infinite set.

SOLUTION

A simple way to put this set in correspondence with a proper subset of itself is to match every element n with its double $2n$:

$$\{5, \ 10, \ 15, \ 20, \ 25, \ldots\}$$
$$\updownarrow \ \updownarrow \ \updownarrow \ \updownarrow \ \updownarrow$$
$$\{10, \ 20, \ 30, \ 40, \ 50, \ldots\}$$

The second set, $\{10, 20, 30, 40, 50, \ldots\}$ is a proper subset of the first, and the two are in one-to-one correspondence, so $\{5, 10, 15, 20, 25, \ldots\}$ is an infinite set.

▼ Try This One 1

☑ 2. Show that a set is infinite.

Show that the set $\{-1, -2, -3, -4, -5, \ldots\}$ is an infinite set.

A General Term of an Infinite Set

One consequence of the way we showed that the set of natural numbers is infinite is that we can find a generic formula for the set of even numbers: $2n$, where n is the set $\{1, 2, 3, 4, \ldots\}$. We will call $2n$ in this case a **general term** of the set of even numbers. Notice that we said "a general term," not "the general term." There are other general terms we could write for this set: $2n - 6$, where n is the set $\{4, 5, 6, 7, \ldots\}$, is another possibility. But in most cases the simplest general term is the one where the first listed number is obtained from substituting in 1 for n, and that's the one we'll typically find.

Sidelight THE INFINITE HOTEL

Suppose a hotel in some far-off galaxy was so immense that it actually had infinitely many rooms, numbered 1, 2, 3, 4, ... There's a big convention of creepy alien creatures in town, so every room is filled. A weary traveler drags into the lobby and asks for a room, and when he's informed that the hotel is full, he protests that the hotel can most definitely accommodate him. Do you agree? Can they find a room for him without kicking someone out?

People tend to be split on this question about half and half: half think they can't accommodate him because all the rooms are full, and half think they can because there are infinitely many rooms. In fact, the traveler is correct—it just takes inconveniencing every other guest! If the manager asks every guest to move into the room whose number is 1 higher than his or her current room, everyone that was originally in a room still has one, and our traveler can rest his weary body in room 1.

This clever little mind exercise is a consequence of the fact that the natural numbers form an infinite set—they can be put in one-to-one correspondence with a proper subset of themselves by corresponding any n with $n + 1$.

EXAMPLE 2   Finding a General Term for an Infinite Set

Find a general term for the set $\{4, 7, 10, 13, 16, \ldots\}$.

SOLUTION

We should always begin by trying to recognize a pattern in the numbers of the set. In this case, the pattern is that the numbers increase by 3. When this is the case, $3n$ is a good choice, because as n increases by 1, $3n$ increases by 3. But simply using $3n$ will give us the set $\{3, 6, 9, 12, \ldots\}$, which is not quite what we want. We remedy that by adding 1 to our general term, to get $3n + 1$. (We encourage you to check that answer by substituting in $1, 2, 3, \ldots$ for n to see that it generates the set $\{4, 7, 10, 13, 16, \ldots\}$.)

Math Note

Finding a general term for a set is not always easy. In some cases, it can be very difficult or even impossible. You may need to do some trial and error before finding a formula that works.

▼ **Try This One 2**

Find a general term for the set $\{2, 8, 14, 20, 26, \ldots\}$.

3. Find a general term of an infinite set.

Different Kinds of Infinity?

Quick, which set is bigger, the set of natural numbers or the set of real numbers? You probably answered the set of real numbers. But both sets are infinitely large, so aren't they the same size? Cantor attacked this problem in the late 1800s. He defined a set to be **countable** if it is finite or can be placed into one-to-one correspondence with the natural numbers and an infinite set to be **uncountable** if it cannot. He used the symbol $\aleph_0$, pronounced aleph-null or aleph-naught (aleph is the first letter of the Hebrew alphabet), to represent the cardinality of a countable set.

4. Define countable and uncountable sets.

One of Cantor's greatest achievements was to show that the set of real numbers is not countable. So in this case, your intuition was correct: there *are* more real numbers than natural numbers. But the study of infinite sets is a strange and interesting one, with unexpected results at nearly every turn. For example, it can be shown that the cardinality of the set of numbers between 0 and 1 is the same as the cardinality of the entire set of real numbers! If you're interested in learning about a *really* unusual infinite set, do an Internet search for "Cantor set."

Answers to Try This One

1 Can be done in many ways: one choice is to correspond -1 with -2, -2 with -4, and in general $-n$ with $-2n$.

2 $6n - 4$

EXERCISE SET 2-5

Writing Exercises

1. Define an infinite set, both in your own words and by using Cantor's definition.
2. What is meant by a general term for an infinite set?
3. What does it mean for a set to be countable?

4. Explain how you can tell that the set of natural numbers and the set of even numbers have the same cardinality.

Computational Exercises

For Exercises 5–20, find a general term for the set.

5. $\{7, 14, 21, 28, 35, \ldots\}$
6. $\{1, 8, 27, 64, 125, \ldots\}$
7. $\{4, 16, 64, 256, 1{,}024, \ldots\}$
8. $\{1, 4, 9, 16, 25, \ldots\}$
9. $\{-3, -6, -9, -12, -15, \ldots\}$
10. $\{22, 44, 66, 88, 110, \ldots\}$
11. $\left\{\frac{1}{2}, \frac{1}{3}, \frac{1}{4}, \frac{1}{5}, \frac{1}{6}, \ldots\right\}$
12. $\left\{\frac{1}{3}, \frac{2}{3}, \frac{3}{3}, \frac{4}{3}, \frac{5}{3}, \ldots\right\}$
13. $\{2, 6, 10, 14, 18, \ldots\}$
14. $\{1, 4, 7, 10, 13, \ldots\}$
15. $\left\{\frac{2}{3}, \frac{3}{4}, \frac{4}{5}, \frac{5}{6}, \frac{6}{7}, \ldots\right\}$
16. $\left\{\frac{1}{1}, \frac{1}{4}, \frac{1}{9}, \frac{1}{16}, \frac{1}{25}, \ldots\right\}$
17. $\{100, 200, 300, 400, 500, \ldots\}$
18. $\{50, 100, 150, 200, 250, \ldots\}$
19. $\{-4, -7, -10, -13, -16, \ldots\}$
20. $\{-3, -5, -7, -9, -11, \ldots\}$

For Exercises 21–30, show each set is an infinite set.

21. $\{3, 6, 9, 12, 15, \ldots\}$
22. $\{10, 15, 20, 25, 30, \ldots\}$
23. $\{9, 18, 27, 36, 45, \ldots\}$
24. $\{4, 10, 16, 22, 28, \ldots\}$
25. $\{2, 5, 8, 11, 14, \ldots\}$
26. $\{20, 24, 28, 32, 36, \ldots\}$
27. $\{10, 100, 1{,}000, 10{,}000, \ldots\}$
28. $\{100, 200, 300, 400, 500, \ldots\}$
29. $\left\{\frac{5}{1}, \frac{5}{2}, \frac{5}{3}, \frac{5}{4}, \frac{5}{5}, \ldots\right\}$
30. $\left\{\frac{1}{2}, \frac{1}{4}, \frac{1}{8}, \frac{1}{16}, \ldots\right\}$

Critical Thinking

31. Recall that $\aleph_0$ is the cardinality of the natural numbers (and any other countable set). What do you think $\aleph_0 + 1$ should be? What about $\aleph_0 + \aleph_0$?
32. Can you think of a one-to-one correspondence that will show that the set of integers is countable? (The set of integers consists of the natural numbers, their negatives, and zero.)

33. The set of rational numbers is the set of all possible fractions that have integer numerators and denominators. Intuitively, do you think there are more rational numbers than natural numbers? Why? Do you think that the set of rational numbers is countable?
34. Can you think of any set of tangible objects that is infinite? Why or why not?

CHAPTER **2** **Summary**

Section	Important Terms	Important Ideas
2-1	Set Roster method Element Well-defined Natural numbers Descriptive method Set-builder notation Variable Finite set Infinite set Cardinal number Null set Equal sets Equivalent sets One-to-one correspondence	**A set** is a well-defined collection of objects. Each object is called an element or member of the set. We use three ways to identify sets. They are the roster method, the descriptive method, and set-builder notation. Sets can be finite or infinite. A finite set contains a specific number of elements, while an infinite set contains an unlimited number of elements. If a set has no elements, it is called an empty set or a null set. Two sets are equal if they have the same elements, and two finite sets are equivalent if they have the same number of elements. Two sets are said to have a one-to-one correspondence if it is possible to pair the elements of one set with the elements of the other set in such a way that for each element in the first set there exists one and only one element in the second set, and for each element in the second set there exists one and only one element of the first set.
2-2	Universal set Complement Subset Proper subset Intersection Union Subtraction Cartesian product	**The universal** set is the set of all elements used for a specific problem or situation. The complement of a specific set is a set that consists of all elements in the universal set that are not in the specific set. If every element of one set is also an element of another set, then the first set is said to be a subset of the second set. A subset A of a set B is a proper subset if A is not equal to B. The union of two sets is a set containing all elements of one set or the other set, while the intersection of two sets is a set that contains the elements that both sets have in common. The difference of set A and set B, denoted $A - B$, is the set of elements in set A but not in set B. The Cartesian product of two sets A and B is $A \times B = \{(x, y) \mid x \in A \text{ and } y \in B\}$.
2-3	Venn diagram	**A mathematician** named John Venn devised a way to represent sets pictorially. His method uses overlapping circles to represent the sets. De Morgan's laws for two sets A and B are $(A \cup B)' = A' \cap B'$ and $(A \cap B)' = A' \cup B'$. For any two finite sets A and B, $n(A \cup B) = n(A) + n(B) - n(A \cap B)$.
2-4		**Venn diagrams** can be used to solve real-world problems involving surveys and classifications.
2-5	Infinite set Countable set Uncountable set General term	**An infinite** set can be placed in a one-to-one correspondence with a proper subset of itself. A set is called countable if it is finite or if there is a one-to-one correspondence between the set and the set of natural numbers. A set is called uncountable if it is not countable.

MATH IN › **Demographics REVISITED**

The Venn diagram shown to the right is based on the given demographic estimates:

1. White only: 680; black only: 109; Hispanic only: 53

2. Hispanic and black, but not white: 11
3. Hispanic or black: 270
4. None of white, black, or Hispanic: 50

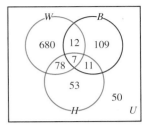

Review Exercises

Section 2-1

For Exercises 1–8, write each set in roster notation.

1. The set D is the set of even numbers between 50 and 60.
2. The set F is the set of odd numbers between 3 and 40.
3. The set L is the set of letters in the word *letter*.
4. The set A is the set of letters in the word *Arkansas*.
5. The set B is $\{x \mid x \in N \text{ and } x > 500\}$.
6. The set C is the set of natural numbers between 5 and 12.
7. The set M is the set of months in the year that begin with the letter P.
8. The set G is the set of days in the week that end with the letter e.

For Exercises 9–12, write each set by using set-builder notation.

9. $\{18, 20, 22, 24\}$
10. $\{5, 10, 15, 20\}$
11. $\{101, 103, 105, 107, \ldots\}$
12. $\{8, 16, 24, \ldots 72\}$

For Exercises 13–18, state whether the set is finite or infinite.

13. $\{x \mid x \in N \text{ and } x \geq 9\}$
14. $\{4, 8, 12, 16, \ldots\}$
15. $\{x, y, z\}$
16. $\{3, 7, 9, 12\}$
17. $\varnothing$
18. {people who have naturally red hair}

Section 2-2

For Exercises 19–22, decide if the statement is true or false.

19. $\{80, 100, 120, \ldots\} \subseteq \{40, 80, 120, \ldots\}$
20. $\{6\} \subset \{6, 12, 18\}$ ← only compare subsets
21. $\{5, 6, 7\} \subseteq \{5, 7\}$

22. $\{a, b, c\} \subset \{a, b, c\}$
23. Find all subsets of $\{r, s, t\}$.
24. Find all subsets of $\{m, n, o\}$.
25. How many subsets and proper subsets does the set $\{p, q, r, s, t\}$ have?
26. How many subsets and proper subsets does the set $\{a, e, i, o, u, y\}$ have?

For Exercises 27–38, let $U = \{p, q, r, s, t, u, v, w, x, y, z\}$, $A = \{p, r, t, u, v\}$, $B = \{t, u, v, x, y\}$, and $C = \{s, w, z\}$. Find each.

27. $A \cap B$
28. $B \cup C$
29. $(A \cap B) \cap C$
30. B'
31. $A - B$
32. $B - A$
33. $(A \cup B)' \cap C$
34. $B' \cap C'$
35. $(B \cup C) \cap A'$
36. $(A \cup B) \cap C'$
37. $(B' \cap C') \cup A'$
38. $(A' \cap B) \cup C$

For Exercises 39–42, let $M = \{s, t, u\}$ and $N = \{v, w, x\}$. Find each set.

39. $M \times N$
40. $N \times M$
41. $M \times M$
42. $N \times N$

Section 2-3

For Exercises 43–48, use the Venn diagram below. Describe the region or regions provided in each problem, using set operations on A and B. There may be more than one right answer.

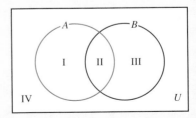

43. Region I
44. Region II
45. Region III
46. Region IV
47. Regions I and III
48. Regions I and IV

For Exercises 49–52, draw a Venn diagram and shade the appropriate area for each.

49. $A' \cap B$
50. $(A \cup B)'$
51. $(A' \cap B') \cup C$
52. $A \cap (B \cup C)'$
53. If $n(A) = 15$, $n(B) = 9$, and $n(A \cap B) = 4$, find $n(A \cup B)$.
54. If $n(A) = 24$, $n(B) = 20$, and $n(A \cap B) = 14$, find $n(A \cup B)$.

The table and Venn diagram below are to be used for Exercises 55–58. The table shows the top five states in terms of number of violent crimes per 100,000 citizens in each year from 2004 to 2006. For each exercise, write the region of the Venn diagram that would include the state listed.

Year	2004	2005	2006
State	1. South Carolina	1. South Carolina	1. South Carolina
	2. Florida	2. Tennessee	2. Tennessee
	3. Maryland	3. Florida	3. Nevada
	4. Tennessee	4. Maryland	4. Florida
	5. New Mexico	5. New Mexico	5. Louisiana

Source: swivel.com

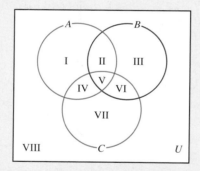

Note: Set A represents 2004, set B represents 2005, and set C represents 2006.

55. Florida
56. Louisiana
57. New Mexico
58. Nevada

Section 2-4

59. In a recent survey of 25 students, 10 had used a chat room that day, 5 posted a new blog that day, and 2 students used a chat room and posted a new blog that day.

    (a) How many did not use a chat room or post a blog that day?
    (b) How many only posted a new blog that day?

60. In a group of 24 students asked what they did last Saturday night, 9 tailgated after the big game, 18 went to a rave, and 3 tailgated and went to a rave.

    (a) How many only went to a rave?
    (b) How many did not go to a rave?

61. Fifty-three callers to the campus radio station were asked what they usually listened to while driving to school. Of those asked, 22 listened to a local radio station, 18 listened to satellite radio, 33 listened to MP3 players, 8 listened to a local radio station and satellite radio, 13 listened to satellite radio and MP3 players, 11 listened to a local radio station and an MP3 player, and 6 listened to all three.

    (a) How many listened to only satellite radio?
    (b) How many listened to local radio stations and MP3 players but not satellite radio?
    (c) How many listened to none of these?

62. Of the last 41 customers at the student bookstore, 15 paid in cash, 16 used a debit card, 20 used a financial aid voucher, 4 used cash and a debit card, 8 used a debit card and a financial aid voucher, 8 used cash and a financial aid voucher, and 1 used all three.

    (a) How many used none of these payment types?
    (b) How many only used a debit card?
    (c) How many used cash and a financial aid voucher but not a debit card?

Section 2-5

63. Find a general term for the set $\{-5, -7, -9, -11, -13, \ldots\}$
64. Show that the set $\{12, 24, 36, 48, 60, \ldots\}$ is an infinite set.

Chapter Test

For Exercises 1–8, write each set in roster notation.

1. The set P is the set of even natural numbers between 90 and 100.
2. The set J is the set of odd natural numbers between 40 and 50.
3. The set K is the set of letters in the word *envelope*.
4. The set W is the set of letters in the word *Washington*.
5. $X = \{x \mid x \in N \text{ and } x < 80\}$
6. $Y = \{x \mid x \in N \text{ and } 16 < x < 25\}$
7. The set J is the set of months of the year that begin with the letter J.
8. The set L is the set of days of the week that end in the letter a.

For Exercises 9–12, write each set using set-builder notation.

9. {12, 14, 16, 18}
10. {30, 35, 40, 45}
11. {201, 203, 205, 207,...}
12. {4, 8, 16,...128}

For Exercises 13–17, state whether the set is finite or infinite.

13. {15, 16, 17, 18,...}
14. $\{x \mid x \in N$ and x is a multiple of 6\}
15. {a, b, c}
16. {4, 7, 8, 10}
17. The set V is the set of people with three eyes.
18. Find all subsets of {d, e, f}.
19. Find all subsets of {p, q, r}.
20. How many subsets and proper subsets does the set {a, b, c, d, e} have?

For Exercises 21–30, let U = {a, b, c, d, e, f, g, h, i, j, k}, A = {a, b, d, e, f}, B = {a, g, i, j, k}, and C = {e, h, j}. Find each.

21. $A \cap B$
22. $B \cup C$
23. B'
24. $(A \cup B)'$
25. $(A \cap B)' \cup C'$
26. $A - B$
27. $B - C$
28. $(A - B) - C$
29. $A - C$
30. Draw and shade a Venn diagram for the area representing $A - B$.

For Exercises 31–34, let A = {@, !, α} and B = {π, #}. Find each set.

31. $A \times B$
32. $B \times A$
33. $B \times B$
34. $A \times A$

For Exercises 35–37, draw a Venn diagram for each set.

35. $A' \cap B$
36. $(A \cap B)'$
37. $(A' \cup B') \cap C'$
38. If $n(A) = 1,500$, $n(B) = 1,150$, and $n(A \cap B) = 350$, find $n(A \cup B)$.
39. At a special graduation ceremony of 24 honors students, 8 used a digital camera, 9 used a camera in their cell phones, and 4 used both digital cameras and cell phone cameras.

   (a) How many did not use either of these?
   (b) How many used a digital camera only?

40. Find a general term for the set {15, 30, 45, 60, 75,...}.
41. Show that the set {1, −1, 2, −2, 3, −3,...} is an infinite set.

For Exercises 42–53, state whether each is true or false.

42. {a, b, c} is equal to {x, y, z}.
43. {1, 2, 3, 4} is equivalent to {p, q, r, s}.
44. {4, 8, 12, 16,...} ⊆ {2, 4, 6, 8,...}
45. {15} ⊂ {3, 6, 9, 12,...}
46. 4 ∈ {even natural numbers}
47. 9 ∉ {2, 4, 5, 6, 10}
48. {a, e, i, o, u, y} ⊆ {a, e, i, o, u}
49. {12} ∈ {12, 24, 36,...}
50. For any set, $\varnothing' = U$
51. 0 ∈ ∅
52. For any set, $A \cap \varnothing = U$.
53. For any set, $A \cup B = B \cup A$.

Projects

1. Have the students in your class fill out this questionnaire:

   A. Gender: Male _____ Female _____
   B. Age: Under 21 _____ 21 or older _____
   C. Work: Yes _____ No _____

   Draw a Venn diagram, and from the information answer these questions:

   (a) How many students are female?
   (b) How many students are under 21?
   (c) How many students work?
   (d) How many students are under 21 and work?
   (e) How many students are males and do not work?
   (f) How many students are 21 or older and work?
   (g) How many students are female, work, and are under 21?

2. Select five of these set properties. Explain why they are true for all sets. Then illustrate, using Venn diagrams.

   (a) $(A')' = A$
   (b) $\varnothing' = U$ and $U' = \varnothing$
   (c) $A \cup \varnothing = A$ and $A \cap \varnothing = \varnothing$
   (d) $A \cup U = U$ and $A \cap U = A$
   (e) $A \cup A' = U$ and $A \cap A' = \varnothing$
   (f) $A \cup A = A$ and $A \cap A = A$
   (g) $A \cup B = B \cup A$ and $A \cap B = B \cap A$
   (h) $(A \cup B) \cup C = A \cup (B \cup C)$ and $(A \cap B) \cap C = A \cap (B \cap C)$
   (i) $A \cup (B \cap C) = (A \cup B) \cap (A \cup C)$ and $A \cap (B \cup C) = (A \cap B) \cup (A \cap C)$
   (j) $(A \cup B)' = A' \cap B'$ and $(A \cap B)' = A' \cup B'$

Logic

Outline

MATH IN ▶ The Art of Persuasion

Everywhere you turn in modern society, somebody is trying to convince you of something. "Vote for me!" "Buy my product!" "Lease a car from our dealership!" "Bailing out the auto industry is a bad idea!" "You should go out with me this weekend!" "Join our fraternity!" Logic is sometimes defined as correct thinking or correct reasoning. Some people refer to logic by a more casual name: *common sense*. Regardless of what you call it, the ability to think logically is crucial for all of us because our lives are inundated daily with advertisements, contracts, product and service warranties, political debates, and news commentaries, to name just a few. People often have problems processing these things because of misinterpretation, misunderstanding, and faulty logic.

You can look up the truth or falseness of a fact on the Internet, but that won't help you in analyzing whether a certain claim is logically valid. The term *common sense* is misleading, because evaluating logical arguments can be a challenging and involved process. This chapter introduces the basic concepts of formal symbolic logic and shows how to determine whether arguments are valid or invalid by using truth tables. One of our biggest goals will be to examine the form of an argument and determine if its conclusion follows logically from the statements in the argument.

To that end, we've written some claims below. Your job is to determine which of the arguments is valid, meaning that a conclusion can be logically drawn from a set of statements. The skills you learn in this chapter will help you to do so.

- Where there's smoke, there's fire.
- Having a lot of money makes people happy. My neighbor is a really happy guy, so he must have a lot of money.
- Every team in the SEC is good enough to play in a bowl game. Florida State is not in the SEC, so they're not good enough to play in a bowl game.
- Scripture is the word of God. I know this because it says so in the Bible.
- If Iraq has weapons of mass destruction, we should go to war. It turns out that they don't have them, so we should not go to war.
- It will be a snowy day in Hawaii before Tampa Bay makes it to the World Series. Tampa Bay played in the 2008 World Series, so it must have snowed in Hawaii.

For answers, see Math in the Art of Persuasion Revisited on Page 141

Section 3-1 Statements and Quantifiers

LEARNING OBJECTIVES

- ❑ 1. Define and identify statements.
- ❑ 2. Define the logical connectives.
- ❑ 3. Write the negation of a statement.
- ❑ 4. Write statements symbolically.

As the world gets more complex and we are bombarded with more and more information, it becomes more important than ever to be able to make sensible, objective evaluations of that information. One of the most effective tricks that advertisers, politicians, and con artists use is to encourage emotions to enter into these evaluations. They use carefully selected words and images that are designed to keep you from making decisions objectively. The field of **symbolic logic** was designed exactly for this reason. Symbolic logic uses letters to represent statements and special symbols to represent words like *and, or,* and *not.* Use of this symbolic notation in place of the statements themselves allows us to analytically evaluate the validity of the logic behind an argument without letting bias and emotion cloud our judgment. And these unbiased evaluations are the main goal of this chapter.

Statements

In the English language there are many types of sentences, including factual statements, commands, opinions, questions, and exclamations. In the objective study of logic, we will use only factual statements.

> A **statement** is a declarative sentence that can be objectively determined to be true or false, but not both.

For example, sentences like

It is raining.
The United States has sent a space probe to Mars.
$2 + 2 = 4$
$10 - 5 = 4$

are statements because they are either true or false and you don't use an opinion to determine this.

Whether a sentence is true or false doesn't matter in determining if it is a statement. Notice in the above example the last statement "$10 - 5 = 4$" is false, but it's still a statement.

The following sentences, however, are not statements:

Give me onion rings with my order.
What operating system are you running?
Sweet!
The guy sitting next to me is kind of goofy.

The first is not a statement because it is a command. The second is not a statement because it is a question. The third is not a statement because it is an exclamation, and the fourth is not a statement because the word *goofy* is subjective; that is, it requires an opinion.

EXAMPLE 1 **Recognizing Statements**

Decide which of the following are statements and which are not.

(a) Most scientists agree that global warming is a threat to the environment.
(b) Is that your laptop?
(c) Man, that hurts!
(d) $8 - 2 = 6$
(e) This book is about database management.
(f) Everybody should watch reality shows.

SOLUTION

Parts (a), (d), and (e) are statements because they can be judged as true or false in a nonsubjective manner.
Part (b) is not a statement because it is a question.
Part (c) is not a statement because it is an exclamation.
Part (f) is not a statement because it requires an opinion.

☑ 1. Define and identify statements.

▼ Try This One 1

Decide which of the following are statements and which are not.

(a) Cool!
(b) $12 - 8 = 5$
(c) Ryan Seacrest is the host of *American Idol*.
(d) Cat can send text messages with her cell phone.
(e) When does the party start?
(f) History is interesting.

Simple and Compound Statements

Statements can be classified as *simple* or *compound*. A **simple statement** contains only one idea. Each of these statements is an example of a simple statement.

These cargo pants are khaki.

My dorm room has three beds in it.

Daytona Beach is in Florida.

A statement such as "I will take chemistry this semester, and I will get an A" is called a **compound statement** since it consists of two simple statements.

Compound statements are formed by joining two simple statements with what is called a *connective*.

The basic **connectives** are *and, or, if . . . then,* and *if and only if*.

Math Note

In standard usage, the word *then* is often omitted from a conditional statement; instead of "If it snows, then I will go skiing," you'd probably just say, "If it snows, I'll go skiing."

Each of the connectives has a formal name: *and* is called a **conjunction,** *or* is called a **disjunction,** *if . . . then* is called a **conditional,** and *if and only if* is called a **biconditional.** Here are some examples of compound statements using connectives.

John studied for 5 hours, and he got an A.   (conjunction)

Luisa will run in a mini triathlon or she will play in the campus tennis tournament.   (disjunction)

If I get 80% of the questions on the LSAT right, then I will get into law school. (conditional)

We will win the game if and only if we score more points than the other team. (biconditional)

EXAMPLE 2   **Classifying Statements as Simple or Compound**

Math Note

Technically, we've given the names *conjunction, disjunction, conditional,* and *biconditional* to the connectives, but from now on, we'll refer to whole statements using these connectives by those names. For example, we would call the compound statement in Example 2d a disjunction.

☑ 2. Define the logical connectives.

Classify each statement as simple or compound. If it is compound, state the name of the connective used.

(a) Our school colors are red and white.
(b) If you register for WiFi service, you will get 3 days of free access.
(c) Tomorrow is the last day to register for classes.
(d) I will buy a hybrid or I will buy a motorcycle.

SOLUTION

(a) Don't let use of the word *and* fool you! This is a simple statement.
(b) This if…then statement is compound and uses a conditional connective.
(c) This is a simple statement.
(d) This is a compound statement, using a disjunction.

▼ **Try This One 2**

Classify each statement as simple or compound. If it is compound, state the name of the connective used.

(a) The jacket is trendy and it is practical.
(b) This is an informative website on STDs.
(c) If it does not rain, then I will go windsurfing.
(d) I will buy a flash drive or I will buy a zip drive.
(e) Yesterday was the deadline to withdraw from a class.

Sidelight A BRIEF HISTORY OF LOGIC

The basic concepts of logic can be attributed to Aristotle, who lived in the fourth century BCE. He used words, sentences, and deduction to prove arguments using techniques we will study in this chapter. In addition, in 300 BCE. Euclid formalized geometry using deductive proofs. Both subjects were considered to be the "inevitable truths" of the universe revealed to rational people.

In the 19th century, people began to reject the idea of inevitable truths and realized that a deductive system like Euclidean geometry is only true based on the original assumptions. When the original assumptions are changed, a new deductive system can be created. This is why there are different types of geometry. (See the Sidelight entitled "Non-Euclidean Geometry" in Chapter 10.)

Eventually, several people developed the use of symbols rather than words and sentences in logic. One such person was George Boole (1815–1864). Boole created the symbols used in this chapter and developed the theory of symbolic logic. He also used symbolic logic in mathematics. His manuscript, entitled "An Investigation into the Laws of Thought, on Which Are Founded the Mathematical Theories of Logic and Probabilities," was published when he was 39 in 1854.

Boole was a friend of Augustus De Morgan, who formulated De Morgan's laws, which we studied in Chapter 2. Much earlier, Leonhard Euler (1707–1783) used circles to represent logical statements and proofs. The idea was refined into Venn diagrams by John Venn (1834–1923).

Math Note

We'll worry later about determining whether statements involving quantifiers and connectives are true or false. For now, focus on learning and understanding the terms.

Quantified Statements

Quantified statements involve terms such as *all, each, every, no, none, some, there exists,* and *at least one*. The first five (*all, each, every, no, none*) are called *universal quantifiers* because they either include or exclude every element of the universal set. The latter three (*some, there exists, at least one*) are called *existential quantifiers* because they show the existence of something, but do not include the entire universal set. Here are some examples of quantified statements:

> Every student taking Math for Liberal Arts this semester will pass.
>
> Some people who are Miami Hurricane fans are also Miami Dolphin fans.
>
> There is at least one professor in this school who does not have brown eyes.
>
> No Marlin fan is also a Yankee fan.

The first and the fourth statements use universal quantifiers, and the second and third use existential quantifiers. Note that the statements using existential quantifiers are not "all inclusive" (or all exclusive) as the other two are.

Negation

The *negation* of a statement is a corresponding statement with the opposite truth value. For example, for the statement "My dorm room is blue," the negation is "My dorm room is not blue." It's important to note that the truth values of these two are completely opposite: one is true, and the other is false—period. You can't negate "My dorm room is blue" by saying "My dorm room is yellow," because it's completely possible that *both* statements are false. To make sure that you have a correct negation, check that if one of the statements is true, the other must be false, and vice versa. The typical way to negate a simple statement is by adding the word *not,* as in these examples:

Statement	Negation
Auburn will win Saturday.	Auburn will not win Saturday.
I took a shower today.	I did not take a shower today.
My car is clean.	My car is not clean.

Math Note

The words *each, every,* and *all* mean the same thing, so what we say about *all* in this section applies to the others as well. Likewise, *some, there exists,* and *at least one* are considered to be the same and are treated that way as well.

You have to be especially careful when negating quantified statements. Consider the example statement "All dogs are fuzzy." It's not quite right to say that the negation is "All dogs are not fuzzy," because if some dogs are fuzzy and others aren't, then both statements are false. All we need for the statement "All dogs are fuzzy" to be false is to find at least one dog that is not fuzzy, so the negation of the statement "All dogs are fuzzy" is "Some dogs are not fuzzy." (In this setting, we define the word *some* to mean *at least one*.)

We can summarize the negation of quantified statements as follows:

Statement Contains...	Negation
All do	Some do not, or not all do
Some do	None do, or all do not
Some do not	All do
None do	Some do

EXAMPLE 3 **Writing Negations**

Write the negation of each of the following quantified statements.

(a) Every student taking Math for Liberal Arts this semester will pass.
(b) Some people who are Miami Hurricane fans are also Miami Dolphin fans.
(c) There is at least one professor in this school who does not have brown eyes.
(d) No Marlin fan is also a Yankee fan.

SOLUTION

(a) Some student taking Math for Liberal Arts this semester will not pass (or, not every student taking Math for Liberal Arts this semester will pass).
(b) No people who are Miami Hurricane fans are also Miami Dolphin fans.
(c) All professors in this school have brown eyes.
(d) Some Marlin fan is also a Yankee fan.

CAUTION

Be especially careful when negating statements. Remember that the negation of "Every student will pass" is *not* "Every student will fail".

☑ 3. Write the negation of a statement.

▼ Try This One 3

Write the negation of each of the following quantified statements.

(a) All cell phones have cameras.
(b) No woman can win the lottery.
(c) Some professors have PhDs.
(d) Some students in this class will not pass.

Math Note

For three of the four connectives in Table 3-1, the order of the simple statements doesn't matter: for example, $p \wedge q$ and $q \wedge p$ represent the same compound statement. The same is true for the connectives $\vee$ (disjunction) and $\leftrightarrow$ (biconditional). The one exception is the conditional ($\rightarrow$), where order is crucial.

Symbolic Notation

Recall that one of our goals in this section is to write statements in symbolic form to help us evaluate logical arguments objectively. Now we'll introduce the symbols and methods that will be used. The symbols for the connectives *and, or, if…then,* and *if and only if* are shown in Table 3-1.

Simple statements in logic are usually denoted with lowercase letters like p, q, and r. For example, we could use p to represent the statement "I get paid Friday" and q to represent the statement "I will go out this weekend." Then the conditional statement "If I get paid Friday, then I will go out this weekend" can be written in symbols as $p \rightarrow q$.

The symbol $\sim$ (tilde) represents a negation. If p still represents "I get paid Friday," then $\sim p$ represents "I do not get paid Friday."

We often use parentheses in logical statements when more than one connective is involved in order to specify an order. (We'll deal with this in greater detail in the next section.) For example, there is a difference between the compound statements $\sim p \wedge q$ and $\sim(p \wedge q)$. The statement $\sim p \wedge q$ means to negate the statement p first, then use the negation of p in conjunction with the statement q. For example, if p is the statement "Fido is a dog" and q is the statement "Pumpkin is a cat," then $\sim p \wedge q$ reads, "Fido is not a dog and Pumpkin is a cat." The statement $\sim p \wedge q$ could also be written as $(\sim p) \wedge q$.

TABLE 3-1   Symbols for the Connectives

Connective	Symbol	Name
and	$\wedge$	Conjunction
or	$\vee$	Disjunction
if…then	$\rightarrow$	Conditional
if and only if	$\leftrightarrow$	Biconditional

The statement $\sim(p \wedge q)$ means to negate the conjunction of the statement p and the statement q. Using the same statements for p and q as before, the statement $\sim(p \wedge q)$ is written, "It is not the case that Fido is a dog and Pumpkin is a cat."

The same reasoning applies when the negation is used with other connectives. For example, $\sim p \rightarrow q$ means $(\sim p) \rightarrow q$.

Example 4 illustrates in greater detail how to write statements symbolically.

EXAMPLE 4 **Writing Statements Symbolically**

Let p represent the statement "It is cloudy" and q represent the statement "I will go to the beach." Write each statement in symbols.

(a) I will not go to the beach.
(b) It is cloudy, and I will go to the beach.
(c) If it is cloudy, then I will not go to the beach.
(d) I will go to the beach if and only if it is not cloudy.

SOLUTION

(a) This is the negation of statement q, which we write as $\sim q$.
(b) This is the conjunction of p and q, written as $p \wedge q$.
(c) This is the conditional of p and the negation of q: $p \rightarrow \sim q$.
(d) This is the biconditional of p and not q: $p \leftrightarrow \sim q$.

▼ **Try This One 4**

Let p represent the statement "I will buy a Coke" and q represent the statement "I will buy some popcorn." Write each statement in symbols.

(a) I will buy a Coke, and I will buy some popcorn.
(b) I will not buy a Coke.
(c) If I buy some popcorn, then I will buy a Coke.
(d) I will not buy a Coke, and I will buy some popcorn.

You probably noticed that some of the compound statements we've written sound a little awkward. It isn't always necessary to repeat the subject and verb in a compound statement using *and* or *or*. For example, the statement "It is cold, and it is snowing" can be written "It is cold and snowing." The statement "I will go to a movie, or I will go to a play" can be written "I will go to a movie or a play." Also the words *but* and *although* can be used in place of *and*. For example, the statement "I will not buy a television set, and I will buy a CD player" can also be written as "I will not buy a television set, but I will buy a CD player."

Statements written in symbols can also be written in words, as shown in Example 5.

EXAMPLE 5 **Translating Statements from Symbols to Words**

Write each statement in words. Let $p =$ "My dog is a golden retriever" and $q =$ "My dog is fuzzy."

(a) $\sim p$ (b) $p \vee q$ (c) $\sim p \rightarrow q$ (d) $q \leftrightarrow p$ (e) $q \wedge p$

If this is your dog (which it's not, because it's mine), statement (e) describes it pretty well.

☑ 4. Write statements symbolically.

SOLUTION

(a) My dog is not a golden retriever.
(b) My dog is a golden retriever or my dog is fuzzy.
(c) If my dog is not a golden retriever, then my dog is fuzzy.
(d) My dog is fuzzy if and only if my dog is a golden retriever.
(e) My dog is fuzzy, and my dog is a golden retriever.

▼ **Try This One 5**

Write each statement in words. Let p = "My friend is a football player" and q = "My friend is smart."

(a) $\sim p$ (b) $p \vee q$ (c) $\sim p \to q$ (d) $p \leftrightarrow q$ (e) $p \wedge q$

In this section, we defined the basic terms of symbolic logic and practiced writing statements using symbols. These skills will be crucial in our objective study of logical arguments, so we're off to a good start.

Answers to Try This One

1 (b), (c), and (d) are statements.

2 (a) (conjunction), (c) (conditional), and (d) (disjunction) are compound; (b) and (e) are simple.

3 (a) Some cell phones don't have cameras.
(b) Some women can win the lottery.
(c) No professors have Ph.Ds.
(d) All students in this class will pass.

4 (a) $p \wedge q$ (b) $\sim p$ (c) $q \to p$ (d) $\sim p \wedge q$

5 (a) My friend is not a football player.
(b) My friend is a football player or my friend is smart.
(c) If my friend is not a football player, then my friend is smart.
(d) My friend is smart if and only if my friend is a football player.
(e) My friend is smart and my friend is a football player.

EXERCISE SET 3-1

Writing Exercises

1. Define the term *statement* in your own words.
2. Explain the difference between a simple and a compound statement.
3. Describe the terms and symbols used for the four connectives.
4. Explain why the negation of "All spring breaks are fun" is not "All spring breaks are not fun."

Real-World Applications

For Exercises 5–14, state whether the sentence is a statement or not.

5. Please do not use your cell phone in class.
6. $5 + 9 = 14$
7. $9 - 3 = 2$
8. Nicki is a student in vet school.
9. Who will win the student government presidency?
10. Neither Sam nor Mary arrives to the exam on time.
11. You can carry a cell phone with you.
12. Bill Gates is the creator of Microsoft.
13. Go with the flow.
14. Math is not hard.

For Exercises 15–24, decide if each statement is simple or compound.

15. He goes to parties and hangs out at the coffee shop.
16. Sara got her hair highlighted.
17. Raj will buy an iMac or a Dell computer.
18. Euchre is fun if and only if you win.
19. February is when Valentine's Day occurs.
20. Diane is a chemistry major.
21. If you win the Megabucks multistate lottery, then you will be rich.
22. He listened to his iPod and he typed a paper.
23. $8 + 9 = 12$
24. Malcolm and Alisha will both miss the spring break trip.

For Exercises 25–32, identify each statement as a conjunction, disjunction, conditional, or biconditional.

25. Bob and Tom like stand-up comedians.
26. Either he passes the test, or he fails the course.
27. A number is even if and only if it is divisible by 2.
28. Her nails are long, and they have rhinestones on them.
29. I will go to the big game, or I will go to the library.
30. If a number is divisible by 3, then it is an odd number.
31. A triangle is equiangular if and only if three angles are congruent.
32. If your battery is dead, then you need to charge your phone overnight.

For Exercises 33–38, write the negation of the statement.

33. The sky is blue.
34. It is not true that your computer has a virus.
35. The dorm room is not large.
36. The class is not full.
37. It is not true that you will fail this class.
38. He has large biceps.

For Exercises 39–50, identify the quantifier in the statement as either universal or existential.

39. All fish swim in water.
40. Everyone who passes algebra has studied.
41. Some people who live in glass houses throw stones.
42. There is at least one person in this class who won't pass.
43. Every happy dog wags its tail.
44. No men can join a sorority.
45. There exists a four-leaf clover.
46. Each person who participated in the study will get $100.
47. No one with green eyes wears glasses.
48. Everyone in the class was bored by the professor's lecture.
49. At least one of my friends has an iPhone.
50. No one here gets out alive.

For Exercises 51–62, write the negation of the statements in Exercises 39–50.

For Exercises 63–72, write each statement in symbols. Let p = "Sara is a political science major" and let q = "Jane is a quantum physics major."

63. Sara is a political science major, and Jane is a quantum physics major.
64. Sara is not a political science major.
65. If Jane is not a quantum physics major, then Sara is a political science major.
66. It is not true that Jane is a quantum physics major or Sara is a political science major.
67. It is false that Jane is a quantum physics major.
68. It is not true that Sara is a political science major.
69. Jane is a quantum physics major, or Sara is not a political science major.
70. Jane is not a quantum physics major, or Sara is a political science major.
71. Jane is a quantum physics major if and only if Sara is a political science major.
72. If Sara is a political science major, then Jane is a quantum physics major.

For Exercises 73–82, write each statement in symbols. Let p = "My dad is cool" and q = "My mom is cool." Let nerdy *mean* not cool.

73. My mom is not cool.
74. Both my dad and my mom are nerdy.
75. If my mom is cool, then my dad is cool.
76. It is not true that my dad is cool.
77. Either my mom is nerdy, or my dad is cool.
78. It is not true that my mom is nerdy and my dad is cool.
79. My mom is cool if and only if my dad is cool.
80. Neither my mom nor my dad is cool.
81. If my mom is nerdy, then my dad is cool.
82. My dad is nerdy if and only if my mom is not cool.

For Exercises 83–92, write each statement in words. Let p = "The plane is on time." Let q = "The sky is clear."

83. $p \wedge q$
84. $\sim p \vee q$
85. $q \rightarrow p$
86. $q \rightarrow \sim p$
87. $\sim p \wedge \sim q$

88. $q \leftrightarrow p$
89. $p \vee \sim q$
90. $\sim p \leftrightarrow \sim q$
91. $q \rightarrow (p \vee \sim p)$
92. $(p \rightarrow q) \vee \sim p$

For Exercises 93–102, write each statement in words. Let p = "Mark lives on campus." Let q = "Trudy lives off campus."

93. $\sim q$
94. $p \rightarrow q$
95. $p \vee \sim q$
96. $q \leftrightarrow p$
97. $\sim p \rightarrow \sim q$

98. $\sim p$
99. $p \vee q$
100. $(\sim p \vee q) \vee \sim q$
101. $q \vee p$
102. $(p \vee q) \rightarrow \sim(\sim q)$

Critical Thinking

103. Explain why the sentence "All rules have exceptions" is not a statement.

104. Explain why the sentence "This statement is false" is not a statement.

Section 3-2 Truth Tables

LEARNING OBJECTIVES

☐ 1. Construct truth tables for negation, disjunction, and conjunction.

☐ 2. Construct truth tables for the conditional and biconditional.

☐ 3. Construct truth tables for compound statements.

☐ 4. Identify the hierarchy of logical connectives.

☐ 5. Construct truth tables by using an alternative method.

"You can't believe everything you hear." Chances are you were taught this when you were younger, and it's pretty good advice. In an ideal world, everyone would tell the truth all the time, but in the real world, it is extremely important to be able to separate fact from fiction. When someone is trying to convince you of some point of view, the ability to logically evaluate the validity of an argument can be the difference between being informed and being deceived—and maybe between you keeping and you being separated from your hard-earned money!

This section is all about deciding when a compound statement is or is not true, based not on the situation itself, but simply on the structure of the statement and the truth of the underlying components. We learned about logical connectives in Section 3-1. In this section, we'll analyze these connectives using *truth tables*. A **truth table** is a diagram in table form that is used to show when a compound statement is true or false based on the truth values of the simple statements that make up the compound statement. This will allow us to analyze arguments objectively.

Negation

According to our definition of *statement,* a statement is either true or false, but never both. Consider the simple statement p = "Today is Tuesday." If it is in fact Tuesday, then p is true, and its negation ($\sim p$) "Today is not Tuesday" is false. If it's not Tuesday, then p is false and $\sim p$ is true. The truth table for the negation of p looks like this.

p	$\sim p$
T	F
F	T

There are two possible conditions for the statement p—true or false—and the table tells us that in each case, the negation $\sim p$ has the opposite truth value.

Conjunction

If we have a compound statement with two component statements p and q, there are four possible combinations of truth values for these two statements:

Possibilities		Symbolic value of each

	p	q
1. p and q are both true.	T	T
2. p is true and q is false.	T	F
3. p is false and q is true.	F	T
4. p and q are both false.	F	F

So when setting up a truth table for a compound statement with two component statements, we'll need a row for each of the four possibilities.

Now we're ready to analyze conjunctions. Recall that a conjunction is a compound statement involving the word *and*. Suppose a friend who's prone to exaggeration tells you, "I bought a new computer and a new iPod." This compound statement can be symbolically represented by $p \wedge q$, where $p =$ "I bought a new computer" and $q =$ "I bought a new iPod." When would this conjunctive statement be true? If your friend actually had made both purchases, then of course the statement "I bought a new computer and a new iPod" would be true. In terms of a truth table, that tells us that if p and q are both true, then the conjunction $p \wedge q$ is true as well, as shown below.

p	q	$p \wedge q$
T	T	T

On the other hand, suppose your friend bought only a new computer or only a new iPod, or maybe neither of those things. Then the statement "I bought a new computer and a new iPod" would be false. In other words, if either or both of p and q are false, then the compound statement $p \wedge q$ is false as well. With this information, we complete the truth table for a basic conjunction:

	p	q	$p \wedge q$
Bought computer and iPod	T	T	T
Bought computer, not iPod	T	F	F
Bought iPod, not computer	F	T	F
Bought neither	F	F	F

Truth Values for a Conjunction

The conjunction $p \wedge q$ is true only when both p and q are true.

Disjunction

Next, we'll look at truth tables for *or* statements. Suppose your friend from the previous example made the statement, "I bought a new computer *or* a new iPod" (as opposed to *and*). If your friend actually did buy one or the other, then this statement would be true. And if he or she bought neither, then the statement would be false. So a partial truth table looks like this:

	p	q	$p \vee q$
Bought computer and iPod	T	T	T
Bought computer, not iPod	T	F	T
Bought iPod, not computer	F	T	T
Bought neither	F	F	F

Sidelight   **Logical Gates and Computer Design**

Logic is used in electrical engineering in designing circuits, which are the heart of computers. The truth tables for *and, or,* and *not* are used for computer gates. These gates determine whether electricity flows through a circuit. When a switch is closed, the current has an uninterrupted path and will flow through the circuit. This is designated by a 1. When a switch is open, the path at the current is broken, and it will not flow. This is designated by a 0. The logical gates are illustrated here—notice that they correspond exactly with our truth tables.

This simple little structure is responsible for the operation of almost every computer in the world—at least until quantum computers become a reality. If you're interested, do a Google search for *quantum computer* to read about the future of computing.

AND Gate   OR Gate   NOT Gate

But what if the person actually bought both items? You might lean toward the statement "I bought a new computer or a new iPod" being false. Believe it or not, it depends on what we mean by the word *or*. There are two interpretations of that word, known as the *inclusive or* and the *exclusive or*. The inclusive or has the possibility of both statements being true; but the exclusive or does not allow for this, that is, exactly one of the two simple statements must be true. In English when we use the word *or,* we typically think of the exclusive or. If I were to say, "I will go to work or I will go to the beach," you would assume I am doing one or the other, but not both. In logic we generally use the inclusive or. When the inclusive or is used, the statement "I will go to work or I will go to the beach" would be true if I went to both work and the beach. For the remainder of this chapter we will assume the symbol $\vee$ represents the inclusive or and will drop *inclusive* and just say *or*.

The completed truth table for the disjunction is

	p	q	$p \vee q$
Bought computer and iPod	T	T	T
Bought computer, not iPod	T	F	T
Bought iPod, not computer	F	T	T
Bought neither	F	F	F

Truth Values for a Disjunction

1. Construct truth tables for negation, disjunction, and conjunction.

The disjunction $p \vee q$ is true when either p or q or both are true. It is false only when both p and q are false.

Conditional Statement

A conditional statement, which is sometimes called an *implication,* consists of two simple statements using the connective if...then. For example, the statement "If I bought a ticket, then I can go to the concert" is a conditional statement. The first component, in this case "I bought a ticket," is called the *antecedent.* The second component, in this case "I can go to the concert," is called the *consequent.*

Conditional statements are used commonly in every area of math, including logic. You might remember statements from high school algebra like "If two lines are parallel, then they have the same slope." Remember that we represent the conditional statement "If p, then q" by using the symbol $p \rightarrow q$.

To illustrate the truth table for the conditional statement, think about the following simple example: "If it is raining, then I will take an umbrella." We'll use p to represent "It is raining" and q to represent "I will take an umbrella," then the conditional statement is $p \rightarrow q$. We'll break the truth table down into four cases.

Case 1: It is raining and I do take an umbrella (p and q are both true). Since I am doing what I said I would do in case of rain, the conditional statement is true. So the first line in the truth table is

Raining, take umbrella

p	q	$p \rightarrow q$
T	T	T

Case 2: It is raining and I do not take an umbrella (p is true and q is false). Since I am not doing what I said I would do in case of rain, I'm a liar and the conditional statement is false. So the second line in the truth table is

Raining, do not take umbrella

p	q	$p \rightarrow q$
T	T	T
T	F	F

Case 3: It is not raining and I do take an umbrella (p is false and q is true). This requires some thought. I never said in the original statement what I would do if it were not raining, so there's no reason to regard my original statement as false. Based on the information given, we consider the original statement to be true, and the third line of the truth table is

Not raining, take umbrella

p	q	$p \rightarrow q$
T	T	T
T	F	F
F	T	T

Case 4: It is not raining, and I do not take my umbrella (p and q are both false). This is essentially the same as case 3—I never said what I would do if it did not rain, so there's no reason to regard my statement as false based on what we know. So we consider the original statement to be true, and the last line of the truth table is

Not raining, do not take umbrella

p	q	$p \rightarrow q$
T	T	T
T	F	F
F	T	T
F	F	T

For cases 3 and 4, it might help to think of it this way: unless we have definite proof that a statement is false, we will consider it to be true.

Truth Values for a Conditional Statement

The conditional statement $p \rightarrow q$ is false only when the antecedent p is true and the consequent q is false.

Biconditional Statement

A biconditional statement is really two statements in a way; it's the conjunction of two conditional statements. For example, the statement "I will stay in and study Friday if and only if I don't have any money" is the same as "If I don't have any money, then I will stay in and study Friday *and* if I stay in and study Friday, then I don't have any money." In symbols, we can write either $p \leftrightarrow q$ or $(p \to q) \wedge (q \to p)$. Since the biconditional is a conjunction, for it to be true, both of the statements $p \to q$ and $q \to p$ must be true. We will once again look at cases to build the truth table.

Case 1: Both p and q are true. Then both $p \to q$ and $q \to p$ are true, and the conjunction $(p \to q) \wedge (q \to p)$, which is also $p \leftrightarrow q$, is true as well.

p	q	$p \leftrightarrow q$
T	T	T

Case 2: p is true and q is false. In this case, the implication $p \to q$ is false, so it doesn't even matter whether $q \to p$ is true or false—the conjunction has to be false.

p	q	$p \leftrightarrow q$
T	T	T
T	F	F

Case 3: p is false and q is true. This is case 2 in reverse. The implication $q \to p$ is false, so the conjunction must be as well.

p	q	$p \leftrightarrow q$
T	T	T
T	F	F
F	T	F

A technician who designs an automated irrigation system needs to decide whether the system should turn on *if* the water in the soil falls below a certain level or *if and only if* the water in the soil falls below a certain level. In the first instance, other inputs could also turn on the system.

Case 4: p is false and q is false. According to the truth table for a conditional statement, both $p \to q$ and $q \to p$ are true in this case, so the conjunction is as well. This completes the truth table.

p	q	$p \leftrightarrow q$
T	T	T
T	F	F
F	T	F
F	F	T

2. Construct truth tables for the conditional and biconditional.

Truth Values for a Biconditional Statement

The biconditional statement $p \leftrightarrow q$ is true when p and q have the same truth value and is false when they have opposite truth values.

Table 3-2 on the next page provides a summary of the truth tables for the basic compound statements and the negation. The last thing you should do is to try and memorize these tables! If you understand how we built them, you can rebuild them on your own when you need them.

Truth Tables for Compound Statements

Once we know truth values for the basic connectives, we can use truth tables to find the truth values for any logical statement. The key to the procedure is to take it step

TABLE 3-2   **Truth Tables for the Connectives and Negation**

Conjunction "and"

p	q	$p \wedge q$
T	T	T
T	F	F
F	T	F
F	F	F

Disjunction "or"

p	q	$p \vee q$
T	T	T
T	F	T
F	T	T
F	F	F

Conditional "if...then"

p	q	$p \rightarrow q$
T	T	T
T	F	F
F	T	T
F	F	T

Biconditional "if and only if"

p	q	$p \leftrightarrow q$
T	T	T
T	F	F
F	T	F
F	F	T

Negation "not"

p	$\sim p$
T	F
F	T

by step, so that in every case, you're deciding on truth values based on one of the truth tables in Table 3-2.

EXAMPLE 1   **Constructing a Truth Table**

Construct a truth table for the statement $\sim p \vee q$.

SOLUTION

Step 1   Set up a table as shown.

p	q
T	T
T	F
F	T
F	F

The order in which you list the Ts and Fs doesn't matter as long as you cover all the possible combinations. For consistency in this book, we'll always use the order TTFF for p and TFTF for q when these are the only two letters in the logical statement.

Step 2   Find the truth values for $\sim p$ by negating the values for p, and put them into a new column, column 3, marked $\sim p$.

p	q	$\sim p$
T	T	F
T	F	F
F	T	T
F	F	T

②   ③   *Truth values for $\sim p$ are opposite those for p.*

"My leg isn't better, or I'm taking a break" is an example of a statement that can be written as $\sim p \vee q$.

Step 3 Find the truth values for the disjunction $\sim p \vee q$. Use the T and F values for $\sim p$ and q in columns 2 and 3, and use the disjunction truth table from earlier in the section.

p	q	$\sim p$	$\sim p \vee q$
T	T	F	T
T	F	F	F
F	T	T	T
F	F	T	T
			④

The disjunction is true unless $\sim p$ and q are both false.

The truth values for the statement $\sim p \vee q$ are found in column 4. The statement is true unless p is true and q is false.

▼ Try This One 1

Construct a truth table for the statement $p \vee \sim q$.

When a statement contains parentheses, we find the truth values for the statements in parentheses first, as shown in Example 2. This is similar to the order of operations used in arithmetic and algebra.

EXAMPLE 2   Constructing a Truth Table

"It is not true that if it rains, then we can't go out" is an example of a statement that can be written as $\sim(p \rightarrow \sim q)$.

Construct a truth table for the statement $\sim(p \rightarrow \sim q)$.

SOLUTION

Step 1 Set up the table as shown.

p	q
T	T
T	F
F	T
F	F

Step 2 Find the truth values for $\sim q$ by negating the values for q, and put them into a new column.

p	q	$\sim q$
T	T	F
T	F	T
F	T	F
F	F	T
①		③

Truth values for $\sim q$ are opposite those for q.

Step 3 Find the truth values for the implication $p \rightarrow \sim q$, using the values in columns 1 and 3 and the implication truth table from earlier in the section.

p	q	$\sim q$	$p \rightarrow \sim q$
T	T	F	F
T	F	T	T
F	T	F	T
F	F	T	T
			④

The conditional is true unless p is true and $\sim q$ is false.

Step 4 Find the truth values for the negation $\sim(p \rightarrow \sim q)$ by negating the values for $p \rightarrow \sim q$ in column 4.

p	q	$\sim q$	$p \rightarrow \sim q$	$\sim(p \rightarrow \sim q)$
T	T	F	F	T
T	F	T	T	F
F	T	F	T	F
F	F	T	T	F
			④	⑤

The negation has opposite values from column 4.

The truth values for $\sim(p \rightarrow \sim q)$ are in column 5. The statement is true only when p and q are both true.

▼ Try This One 2

Construct a truth table for the statement $p \leftrightarrow (\sim p \wedge q)$.

We can also construct truth tables for compound statements that involve three or more components. For a compound statement with three simple statements p, q, and r, there are eight possible combinations of Ts and Fs to consider. The truth table is set up as shown in step 1 of Example 3.

EXAMPLE 3 Constructing a Truth Table with Three Components

Construct a truth table for the statement $p \vee (q \rightarrow r)$.

SOLUTION

Step 1 Set up the table as shown.

p	q	r
T	T	T
T	T	F
T	F	T
T	F	F
F	T	T
F	T	F
F	F	T
F	F	F
	②	③

"I'll do my math assignment, or if I think of a good topic, then I'll start my English essay" is an example of a statement that can be written as $p \vee (q \rightarrow r)$.

Again, the order of the Ts and Fs doesn't matter as long as all the possible combinations are listed. Whenever there are three letters in the statement, we'll use the order shown above for consistency.

Step 2 Find the truth value for the statement in parentheses, $q \to r$. Use the values in columns 2 and 3 and the conditional truth table from earlier in the section. Put those values in a new column.

p	q	r	$q \to r$
T	T	T	T
T	T	F	F
T	F	T	T
T	F	F	T
F	T	T	T
F	T	F	F
F	F	T	T
F	F	F	T
①			④

The conditional is true unless q is true and r is false.

Step 3 Find the truth values for the disjunction $p \vee (q \to r)$, using the values for p from column 1 and those for $q \to r$ from column 4. Use the truth table for disjunction from earlier in the section, and put the results in a new column.

p	q	r	$q \to r$	$p \vee (q \to r)$
T	T	T	T	T
T	T	F	F	T
T	F	T	T	T
T	F	F	T	T
F	T	T	T	T
F	T	F	F	F
F	F	T	T	T
F	F	F	T	T
				⑤

The disjunction is true unless both p and q → r are false.

The truth values for the statement $p \vee (q \to r)$ are found in column 5. The statement is true unless p and r are false while q is true.

☑ 3. Construct truth tables for compound statements.

▼ Try This One 3

Construct a truth table for the statement $(p \wedge q) \vee \sim r$.

In the method we've demonstrated for constructing truth tables, we begin by setting up a table with all possible combinations of Ts and Fs for the component letters from the statement. Then we build new columns, one at a time, by writing truth values for parts of the compound statement, using the basic truth tables we built earlier in the section.

We have seen that when we construct truth tables, we find truth values for statements inside parentheses first. To avoid having to always use parentheses, a hierarchy of connectives has been agreed upon by those who study logic.

1. Biconditional $\leftrightarrow$
2. Conditional $\rightarrow$
3. Conjunction $\wedge$, disjunction $\vee$
4. Negation $\sim$

When we find the truth value for a compound statement without parentheses, we find *the truth value of a lower-order connective first*. For example, $p \vee q \rightarrow r$ is a conditional statement since the conditional ($\rightarrow$) is of a higher order than the disjunction ($\vee$). If you were constructing a truth table for the statement, you would find the truth value for $\vee$ first. The statement $p \leftrightarrow q \wedge r$ is a biconditional statement since the biconditional ($\leftrightarrow$) is of a higher order than the order of the conjunction ($\wedge$). When constructing a truth table for the statement, the truth value for the conjunction ($\wedge$) would be found first. The conjunction and disjunction are of the same order; the statement $p \wedge q \vee r$ cannot be identified unless parentheses are used. In this case, $(p \wedge q) \vee r$ is a disjunction and $p \wedge (q \vee r)$ is a conjunction.

Math Note

When parentheses are used to emphasize order, the statement $p \vee q \rightarrow r$ is written as $(p \vee q) \rightarrow r$. The statement $p \leftrightarrow q \wedge r$ is written as $p \leftrightarrow (q \vee r)$.

EXAMPLE 4 | **Using the Hierarchy of Connectives**

For each, identify the type of statement using the hierarchy of connectives, and rewrite by using parentheses to indicate order.

(a) $\sim p \vee \sim q$ (b) $p \rightarrow \sim q \wedge r$ (c) $p \vee q \leftrightarrow q \vee r$ (d) $p \rightarrow q \leftrightarrow r$

SOLUTION

(a) The $\vee$ is higher than the $\sim$; the statement is a disjunction and looks like $(\sim p) \vee (\sim q)$ with parentheses.
(b) The $\rightarrow$ is higher than the $\wedge$ or $\sim$; the statement is a conditional and looks like $p \rightarrow (\sim q \wedge r)$ with parentheses.
(c) The $\leftrightarrow$ is higher than $\vee$; the statement is a biconditional and looks like $(p \vee q) \leftrightarrow (q \vee r)$ with parentheses.
(d) The $\leftrightarrow$ is higher than the $\rightarrow$; the statement is a biconditional and looks like $(p \rightarrow q) \leftrightarrow r$ with parentheses.

▼ **Try This One 4**

☑ 4. Identify the hierarchy of logical connectives.

For each, identify the type of statement using the hierarchy of connectives, and rewrite by using parentheses to indicate order.

(a) $\sim p \vee q$ (c) $p \vee q \leftrightarrow \sim p \vee \sim q$ (e) $p \leftrightarrow q \rightarrow r$
(b) $p \vee \sim q \rightarrow r$ (d) $p \wedge \sim q$

EXAMPLE 5 | **An Application of Truth Tables**

Use the truth value of each simple statement to determine the truth value of the compound statement.

p: O. J. Simpson was convicted in California in 1995.
q: O. J. Simpson was convicted in Nevada in 2008.
r: O. J. Simpson gets sent to prison.

Statement: $(p \vee q) \rightarrow r$

SOLUTION

In probably the most publicized trial of recent times, Simpson was acquitted of murder in California in 1995, so statement p is false. In 2008, however, Simpson was convicted of robbery and kidnapping in Nevada, so statement q is true. Statement r is also true, as Simpson was sentenced in December 2008.

Now we'll analyze the compound statement. First, the disjunction $p \vee q$ is true when either p or q is true, so in this case, $p \vee q$ is true. Finally, the implication $(p \vee q) \to r$ is true when both r and $p \vee q$ are true, which is the case here. So the compound statement $(p \vee q) \to r$ is true.

▼ **Try This One 5**

Using the simple statements in Example 5, find the truth value of the compound statement $(\sim p \wedge \sim q) \to r$.

An Alternative Method for Constructing Truth Tables

In the next two examples, we will illustrate a second method for constructing truth tables so that you can make a comparison. The problems are the same as Examples 2 and 3.

EXAMPLE 6   Constructing a Truth Table by Using an Alternative Method

Construct a truth table for $\sim(p \to \sim q)$.

SOLUTION

Step 1 Set up the table as shown.

p	q	$\sim(p \to \sim q)$
T	T	
T	F	
F	T	
F	F	

Step 2 Write the truth values for p and q underneath the respective letters in the statement as shown, and label the columns as 1 and 2.

p	q	$\sim(p \to \sim q)$	
T	T	T	T
T	F	T	F
F	T	F	T
F	F	F	F
		①	②

Step 3 Find the negation of q since it is inside the parentheses, and place the truth values in column 3. Draw a line through the truth values in column 2 since they will not be used again.

p	q	$\sim(p \to \sim q)$		
T	T	T	F	T
T	F	T	T	F
F	T	F	F	T
F	F	F	T	F
		①	③	②

"It is not true that if it rains, then we can't go out," is an example of a statement that can be written as $\sim(p \rightarrow \sim q)$.

Math Note

It isn't necessary to label the columns with numbers or to draw a line through the truth values in the columns when they are no longer needed; however, these two strategies can help reduce errors.

Step 4 Find the truth values for the conditional ($\rightarrow$) by using the T and F values in columns 1 and 3 and the conditional truth table from earlier in the section.

Place these values in column 4 and draw a line through the T and F values in columns 1 and 3, as shown.

p	q	$\sim(p$	$\rightarrow$	$\sim$	$q)$
T	T	T	F	F	T
T	F	T	T	T	F
F	T	F	T	F	T
F	F	F	T	T	F
		①	④	③	②

The conditional is true unless p is true and ~q is false.

Step 5 Find the negations of the truth values in column 4 (since the negation sign is outside the parentheses).

p	q	$\sim$	$(p$	$\rightarrow$	$\sim$	$q)$
T	T	T	T	F	F	T
T	F	F	T	T	T	F
F	T	F	F	T	F	T
F	F	F	F	T	T	F
		⑤	①	④	③	②

The negation has values opposite those in column 4.

The truth value of $\sim(p \rightarrow \sim q)$ is found in column 5. Fortunately, these are the same values we found in Example 2.

▼ Try This One 6

Construct a truth table for the statement $p \leftrightarrow (\sim p \wedge q)$, using the alternative method.

EXAMPLE 7 Constructing a Truth Table by Using an Alternative Method

Construct a truth table for the statement $p \vee (q \rightarrow r)$.

SOLUTION

Step 1 Set up the table as shown.

p	q	r	$p \vee (q \rightarrow r)$
T	T	T	
T	T	F	
T	F	T	
T	F	F	
F	T	T	
F	T	F	
F	F	T	
F	F	F	

Step 2 Recopy the values of p, q, and r under their respective letters in the statement as shown.

p	q	r	p	$\vee$	$(p$	$\rightarrow$	$r)$
T	T	T	T		T		T
T	T	F	T		T		F
T	F	T	T		F		T
T	F	F	T		F		F
F	T	T	F		T		T
F	T	F	F		T		F
F	F	T	F		F		T
F	F	F	F		F		F

① ② ③

Step 3 Using the truth values in columns 2 and 3 and the truth table for the conditional ($\rightarrow$), find the values inside the parentheses for the conditional and place them in column 4.

p	q	r	p	$\vee$	$(q$	$\rightarrow$	$r)$
T	T	T	T		T	T	T
T	T	F	T		T	F	F
T	F	T	T		F	T	T
T	F	F	T		F	T	F
F	T	T	F		T	T	T
F	T	F	F		T	F	F
F	F	T	F		F	T	T
F	F	F	F		F	T	F

① ② ④ ③

The conditional is true unless q is true and r is false.

Step 4 Complete the truth table, using the truth values in columns 1 and 4 and the table for the disjunction ($\vee$), as shown.

p	q	r	p	$\vee$	$(q$	$\rightarrow$	$r)$
T	T	T	T	T	T	T	T
T	T	F	T	T	T	F	F
T	F	T	T	T	F	T	T
T	F	F	T	T	F	T	F
F	T	T	F	T	T	T	T
F	T	F	F	F	T	F	F
F	F	T	F	T	F	T	T
F	F	F	F	T	F	T	F

① ⑤ ② ④ ③

The disjunction is true unless p and $q \rightarrow r$ are both false.

The truth value for $p \vee (q \rightarrow r)$ is found in column 5. These are the same values we found in Example 3.

▼ Try This One 7

5. Construct truth tables by using an alternative method.

Construct a truth table for the statement $(p \wedge q) \vee \sim r$ using the alternative method.

The best approach to learning truth tables is to try each of the two methods and see which one is more comfortable for you. In any case, we have seen that truth tables are an effective way to organize truth values for statements, allowing us to determine the truth values of some very complicated statements in a systematic way.

Answers to Try This One

1

p	q	$\sim q$	$p \vee \sim q$
T	T	F	T
T	F	T	T
F	T	F	F
F	F	T	T

2

p	q	$\sim p$	$\sim p \wedge q$	$p \leftrightarrow (\sim p \wedge q)$
T	T	F	F	F
T	F	F	F	F
F	T	T	T	F
F	F	T	F	T

3

p	q	r	$p \wedge q$	$\sim r$	$(p \wedge q) \vee \sim r$
T	T	T	T	F	T
T	T	F	T	T	T
T	F	T	F	F	F
T	F	F	F	T	T
F	T	T	F	F	F
F	T	F	F	T	T
F	F	T	F	F	F
F	F	F	F	T	T

4
(a) Disjunction; $(\sim p) \vee q$
(b) Conditional; $(p \vee \sim q) \to r$
(c) Biconditional; $(p \vee q) \leftrightarrow (\sim p \vee \sim q)$
(d) Conjunction; $p \wedge (\sim q)$
(e) Biconditional; $p \leftrightarrow (q \to r)$

5 True

6

p	q	p	$\leftrightarrow$	$(\sim$	p	$\wedge$	$q)$
T	T	T	F	F	T	F	T
T	F	T	F	F	T	F	F
F	T	F	F	T	F	T	T
F	F	F	T	T	F	F	F
		①	⑤	③	①	④	②

7

p	q	r	$(p$	$\wedge$	$q)$	$\vee$	$\sim$	r
T	T	T	T	T	T	T	F	T
T	T	F	T	T	T	T	T	F
T	F	T	T	F	F	F	F	T
T	F	F	T	F	F	T	T	F
F	T	T	F	F	T	F	F	T
F	T	F	F	F	T	T	T	F
F	F	T	F	F	F	F	F	T
F	F	F	F	F	F	T	T	F
			①	④	②	⑥	⑤	③

EXERCISE SET 3-2

Writing Exercises

1. Explain the purpose of a truth table.
2. Explain the difference between the inclusive and exclusive disjunctions.
3. Explain the difference between the conditional and biconditional statements.
4. Describe the hierarchy for the basic connectives.

Computational Exercises

For Exercises 5–34, construct a truth table for each.

5. $\sim(p \vee q)$
6. $q \rightarrow p$
7. $\sim p \wedge q$
8. $\sim q \rightarrow \sim p$
9. $\sim p \leftrightarrow q$
10. $(p \vee q) \rightarrow \sim p$
11. $\sim(p \wedge q) \rightarrow p$

12. $(p \vee q) \wedge (q \wedge p)$
13. $(\sim q \wedge p) \rightarrow \sim p$
14. $q \wedge \sim p$
15. $(p \wedge q) \leftrightarrow (q \vee \sim p)$
16. $p \rightarrow (q \vee \sim p)$
17. $(p \wedge q) \vee p$
18. $(q \rightarrow p) \vee \sim r$

19. $(r \wedge q) \vee (p \wedge q)$
20. $(r \rightarrow q) \vee (p \rightarrow r)$
21. $\sim(p \vee q) \rightarrow \sim(p \wedge r)$
22. $(\sim p \vee \sim q) \rightarrow \sim r$
23. $(\sim p \vee q) \wedge r$
24. $p \wedge (q \vee \sim r)$
25. $(p \wedge q) \leftrightarrow (\sim r \vee q)$
26. $\sim(p \wedge r) \rightarrow (q \wedge r)$

27. $r \rightarrow \sim(p \vee q)$
28. $(p \vee q) \vee (\sim p \vee \sim r)$
29. $p \rightarrow (\sim q \wedge \sim r)$
30. $(q \vee \sim r) \leftrightarrow (p \wedge \sim q)$
31. $\sim(q \rightarrow p) \wedge r$
32. $q \rightarrow (p \wedge r)$
33. $(r \vee q) \wedge (r \wedge p)$
34. $(p \wedge q) \leftrightarrow \sim r$

Real-World Applications

For Exercises 35–40, use the truth value of each simple statement to determine the truth value of the compound statement. Use the Internet if you need help determining the truth value of a simple statement.

35. p: Japan bombs Pearl Harbor.
    q: The United States stays out of World War II.
    Statement: $p \rightarrow q$

36. p: Barack Obama wins the Democratic nomination in 2008.
    q: Mitt Romney wins the Republican nomination in 2008.
    Statement: $p \wedge q$

37. p: NASA sends a manned spacecraft to the Moon.
    q: NASA sends a manned spacecraft to Mars.
    Statement: $p \vee q$

38. p: Michael Phelps wins eight gold medals.
    q: Michael Phelps gets a large endorsement deal.
    Statement: $p \rightarrow q$

39. p: Apple builds a portable MP3 player.
    q: Apple stops making computers.
    r: Microsoft releases the Vista operating system.
    Statement: $(p \vee q) \wedge r$

40. p: Hurricane Katrina hits New Orleans.
    q: New Orleans Superdome is damaged.
    r: New Orleans Saints play home games in 2006 in Baton Rouge.
    Statement: $(p \wedge q) \rightarrow r$

Exercises 41–46 are based on the compound statement below.

A new weight loss supplement claims that if you take the product daily and cut your calorie intake by 10%, you will lose at least 10 pounds in the next 4 months.

41. This compound statement is made up of three simple statements. Identify them and assign a letter to each.

42. Write the compound statement in symbolic form, using conjunctions and the conditional.

43. Construct a truth table for the compound statement you wrote in Exercise 42.

44. If you take this product daily and don't cut your calorie intake by 10%, and then don't lose 10 pounds, is the claim made by the advertiser true or false?

45. If you take the product daily, don't cut your calorie intake by 10%, and do lose 10 pounds, is the claim true or false?

46. If you don't take the product daily, cut your calorie intake by 10%, and do lose 10 pounds, is the claim true or false?

Exercises 47–52 are based on the compound statement below.

The owner of a professional baseball team publishes an open letter to fans after another losing season. He claims that if attendance for the following season is over 2 million, then he will add $20 million to the payroll and the team will make the playoffs the following year.

47. This compound statement is made up of three simple statements. Identify them and assign a letter to each.

48. Write the compound statement in symbolic form, using conjunction and the conditional.

49. Construct a truth table for the compound statement you wrote in Exercise 48.

50. If attendance goes over 2 million the next year and the owner raises payroll by $20 million, but the team fails to make the playoffs, is the owner's claim true or false?

51. If attendance is less than 2 million but the owner still raises the payroll by $20 million and the team makes the playoffs, is the owner's claim true or false?

52. If attendance is over 2 million, the owner doesn't raise the payroll, but the team still makes the playoffs, is the owner's claim true or false?

Critical Thinking

53. Using the hierarchy for connectives, write the statement $p \rightarrow q \vee r$ by using parentheses to indicate the proper order. Then construct truth tables for $(p \rightarrow q) \vee r$ and $p \rightarrow (q \vee r)$. Are the resulting truth values the same? Are you surprised? Why or why not?

54. The hierarchy of connectives doesn't distinguish between conjunctions and disjunctions. Does that matter? Construct truth tables for $(p \vee q) \wedge r$ and $p \vee (q \wedge r)$ to help you decide.

55. In 2003, New York City Council was considering banning indoor smoking in bars and restaurants. Opponents of the ban claimed that it would have a negligible effect on indoor pollution, but a huge negative effect on the economic success of these businesses. Eventually, the ban was enacted, and a 2004 study by the city department of health found that there was a sixfold decrease in indoor air pollution in bars and restaurants, but jobs, liquor licenses, and tax revenues all increased. Assign truth values to all the premises of the opponents' claim; then write the claim as a compound statement and determine its validity.

Section 3-3 Types of Statements

LEARNING OBJECTIVES

☐ 1. Classify a statement as a tautology, a self-contradiction, or neither.

☐ 2. Identify logically equivalent statements.

☐ 3. Write negations of compound statements.

☐ 4. Write the converse, inverse, and contrapositive of a statement.

It's no secret that weight loss has become big business in the United States. It seems like almost every week, a new company pops into existence with the latest miracle pill to turn you into a supermodel.

A typical advertisement will say something like "Use of our product may result in significant weight loss." That sounds great, but think about what that statement really means. If use of the product "may" result in signifi-

cant weight loss, then it also may not result in weight loss at all! The statement could be translated as "You will lose weight or you will not lose weight." Of course, this statement is always true. In this section, we will study statements of this type.

Tautologies and Self-Contradictions

In our study of truth tables in Section 3-2, we saw that most compound statements are true in some cases and false in others. What we have not done is think about whether that's true for *every* compound statement. Some simple examples should be enough to convince you that this is most definitely not the case.

Consider the simple statement "I'm going to Cancun for spring break this year." Its negation is "I'm not going to Cancun for spring break this year." Now think about these two compound statements:

"I'm going to Cancun for spring break this year, or I'm not going to Cancun for spring break this year."

"I'm going to Cancun for spring break this year, and I'm not going to Cancun for spring break this year."

Hopefully, it's pretty clear to you that the first statement is always true, while the second statement is always false (whether you go to Cancun or not). The first is an example of a *tautology*, while the second is an example of a *self-contradiction*.

When a compound statement is always true, it is called a **tautology.**
When a compound statement is always false, it is called a **self-contradiction.**

CAUTION

Don't make the mistake of thinking that every statement is either a tautology or a self-contradiction. We've seen many examples of statements that are sometimes true and other times false.

The sample statements above are simple enough that it's easy to tell that they are always true or always false based on common sense. But for more complicated statements, we'll need to construct a truth table to decide if a statement is a tautology, a self-contradiction, or neither.

EXAMPLE 1   Using a Truth Table to Classify a Statement

Let p = "I am going to a concert" and q = "I will wear black." Translate each statement in Example 1 into a word statement using this choice of p and q. Can you predict which statements are tautologies, self-contradictions, or neither?

Determine if each statement is a tautology, a self-contradiction, or neither.

(a) $(p \wedge q) \to p$ (b) $(p \wedge q) \wedge (\sim p \wedge \sim q)$ (c) $(p \vee q) \to q$

SOLUTION

(a) The truth table for statement (a) is

p	q	$p \wedge q$	$(p \wedge q) \to p$
T	T	T	T
T	F	F	T
F	T	F	T
F	F	F	T

Since the truth table value consists of all Ts, the statement is always true, that is, a tautology.

(b) The truth table for statement (b) is

p	q	$\sim p$	$\sim q$	$p \wedge q$	$\sim p \wedge \sim q$	$(p \wedge q) \wedge (\sim p \wedge \sim q)$
T	T	F	F	T	F	F
T	F	F	T	F	F	F
F	T	T	F	F	F	F
F	F	T	T	F	T	F

Since the truth value consists of all Fs, the statement is always false, that is, a self-contradiction.

(c) The truth table for statement (c) is

p	q	$p \vee q$	$(p \vee q) \to q$
T	T	T	T
T	F	T	F
F	T	T	T
F	F	F	T

Since the statement can be true in some cases and false in others, it is neither a tautology nor a self-contradiction.

▼ Try This One 1

Determine if each statement is a tautology, a self-contradiction, or neither.

(a) $(p \vee q) \wedge (\sim p \to q)$ (b) $(p \wedge \sim q) \wedge \sim p$ (c) $(p \to q) \vee \sim q$

☑ 1. Classify a statement as a tautology, a self-contradiction, or neither.

The statements "If the red dial is set to A, then use only speaker A" and "The red dial is not set to speaker A, or only speaker A is used" can be modeled with the logic statements $p \to q$ and $\sim p \vee q$.

Logically Equivalent Statements

Next, consider the two logical statements $p \to q$ and $\sim p \vee q$. The truth table for the two statements is

p	q	$\sim p$	$p \to q$	$\sim p \vee q$
T	T	F	T	T
T	F	F	F	F
F	T	T	T	T
F	F	T	T	T

Notice that the truth values for both statements are *identical,* that is, TFTT. When this occurs, the statements are said to be *logically equivalent;* that is, both compositions of the same simple statements have the same meaning. For example, the statement "If it snows, I will go skiing" is logically equivalent to saying "It is not snowing or I will go skiing." Formally defined,

Two compound statements are **logically equivalent** if and only if they have the same truth table values. The symbol for logically equivalent statements is $\equiv$.

EXAMPLE 2   Identifying Logically Equivalent Statements

Determine if the two statements $p \to q$ and $\sim q \to \sim p$ are logically equivalent.

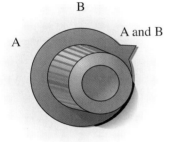

In the red dial example, $\sim q \to \sim p$ would be "If speaker A is not the only one used, then the red dial is not set to A."

☑ 2. Identify logically equivalent statements.

SOLUTION

The truth table for the statements is

p	q	$\sim p$	$\sim q$	$p \to q$	$\sim q \to \sim p$
T	T	F	F	T	T
T	F	F	T	F	F
F	T	T	F	T	T
F	F	T	T	T	T

Since both statements have the same truth values, they are logically equivalent.

▼ Try This One 2

Determine which two statements are logically equivalent.

(a) $\sim(p \wedge \sim q)$ (b) $\sim p \wedge q$ (c) $\sim p \vee q$

De Morgan's laws for logic give us an example of equivalent statements.

De Morgan's Laws for Logic

For any statements p and q,

$\sim(p \vee q) \equiv \sim p \wedge \sim q$ and $\sim(p \wedge q) \equiv \sim p \vee \sim q$

Notice the similarities between De Morgan's laws for sets and De Morgan's laws for logic. De Morgan's laws can be proved by constructing truth tables; the proofs will be left to you in the exercises.

De Morgan's laws are most often used to write the negation of conjunctions and disjunctions. For example, the negation of the statement "I will go to work or I will go to the beach" is "I will not go to work and I will not go to the beach." Notice that when you negate a conjunction, it becomes a disjunction; and when you negate a disjunction, it becomes a conjunction—that is, the *and* becomes an *or,* and the *or* becomes an *and.*

EXAMPLE 3   Using De Morgan's Laws to Write Negations

Write the negations of the following statements, using De Morgan's laws.

(a) Studying is necessary and I am a hard worker.
(b) It is not easy or I am lazy.
(c) I will pass this test or I will drop this class.
(d) She is angry or she's my friend, and she is cool.

SOLUTION

(a) Studying is not necessary or I am not a hard worker.
(b) It is easy and I am not lazy.
(c) I will not pass this test and I will not drop this class.
(d) She is not angry and she is not my friend, or she is not cool.

▼ Try This One 3

Write the negations of the following statements, using De Morgan's laws.

(a) I will study for this class or I will fail.
(b) I will go to the dance club and the restaurant.
(c) It is not silly or I have no sense of humor.
(d) The movie is a comedy or a thriller, and it is awesome.

Earlier in this section, we saw that the two statements $p \rightarrow q$ and $\sim p \vee q$ are logically equivalent. Now that we know De Morgan's laws, we can use this fact to find the negation of the conditional statement $p \rightarrow q$.

$$\begin{aligned} \sim(p \rightarrow q) &\equiv \sim(\sim p \vee q) \\ &\equiv \sim(\sim p) \wedge \sim q \qquad \text{Note: } \sim(\sim p) \equiv p \\ &\equiv p \wedge \sim q \end{aligned}$$

This can be checked by using a truth table as shown.

p	q	$\sim q$	$p \rightarrow q$	$\sim(p \rightarrow q)$	$p \wedge \sim q$
T	T	F	T	F	F
T	F	T	F	T	T
F	T	F	T	F	F
F	F	T	T	F	F

So the negation of $p \rightarrow q$ is $p \wedge \sim q$.

For example, if you say, "It is false that if it is sunny, then I will go swimming," this is equivalent to the statement "It's sunny and I will not go swimming."

EXAMPLE 4   Writing the Negation of a Conditional Statement

Write the negation of the statement "If I have a computer, then I will use the Internet."

SOLUTION

Let p = "I have a computer" and q = "I will use the Internet." The statement $p \rightarrow q$ can be negated as $p \wedge \sim q$. This translates to "I have a computer and I will not use the Internet."

▼ Try This One 4

☑ 3. Write negations of compound statements.

Write the negation of the statement "If the video is popular, then it can be found on YouTube."

Table 3-3 summarizes the negations of the basic compound statements.

TABLE 3-3   Negation of Compound Statements

Statement	Negation	Equivalent Negation
$p \wedge q$	$\sim(p \wedge q)$	$\sim p \vee \sim q$
$p \vee q$	$\sim(p \vee q)$	$\sim p \wedge \sim q$
$p \rightarrow q$	$\sim(p \rightarrow q)$	$p \wedge \sim q$

Variations of the Conditional Statement

From the conditional statement $p \rightarrow q$, three other related statements can be formed: the **converse,** the **inverse,** and the **contrapositive.** They are shown here symbolically.

Statement	$p \rightarrow q$
Converse	$q \rightarrow p$
Inverse	$\sim p \rightarrow \sim q$
Contrapositive	$\sim q \rightarrow \sim p$

Using the statement "If Tessa is a chocolate Lab, then Tessa is brown" as our original conditional statement, we find the related statements are as follows:

Converse: If Tessa is brown, then Tessa is a chocolate Lab.

Inverse: If Tessa is not a chocolate Lab, then Tessa is not brown.

Contrapositive: If Tessa is not brown, then Tessa is not a chocolate Lab.

Notice that the original statement is true, but of the three related statements, only the contrapositive is also true. This is an important observation—one that we'll elaborate on shortly.

EXAMPLE 5   **Writing the Converse, Inverse, and Contrapositive**

Write the converse, the inverse, and the contrapositive for the statement "If you earned a bachelor's degree, then you got a high-paying job."

SOLUTION

It's helpful to write the original implication in symbols: $p \rightarrow q$, where p = "You earned a bachelor's degree" and q = "You got a high-paying job."

Converse: $q \rightarrow p$. "If you got a high-paying job, then you earned a bachelor's degree."

Inverse: $\sim p \rightarrow \sim q$. "If you did not earn a bachelor's degree, then you did not get a high-paying job."

Contrapositive: $\sim q \rightarrow \sim p$. "If you did not get a high-paying job, then you did not earn a bachelor's degree."

▼ Try This One 5

Write the converse, the inverse, and the contrapositive for the statement "If you do well in math classes, then you are intelligent."

Math Note

Many people using logic in real life assume that if a statement is true, the converse is automatically true. Consider the following statement: "If a person earns more than $200,000 per year, that person can buy a Corvette." The converse is stated as "If a person can buy a Corvette, then that person earns more than $200,000 per year." This may be far from the truth since a person may have to make very large payments, live in a tent, or work three jobs in order to afford the expensive car.

The relationships between the variations of the conditional statements can be determined by looking at the truth tables for each of the statements.

p	q	$p \rightarrow q$	$q \rightarrow p$	$\sim p \rightarrow \sim q$	$\sim q \rightarrow \sim p$
T	T	T	T	T	T
T	F	F	T	T	F
F	T	T	F	F	T
F	F	T	T	T	T

Since the original statement ($p \rightarrow q$) and the contrapositive statement ($\sim q \rightarrow \sim p$) have the same truth values, they are equivalent. Also note that the converse ($q \rightarrow p$) and the inverse ($\sim p \rightarrow \sim q$) have the same truth values, so they are equivalent as well. Finally, notice that the original statement is not equivalent to the converse or the inverse since the truth values of the converse and inverse differ from those of the original statement.

Since the conditional statement $p \rightarrow q$ is used so often in logic as well as mathematics, a more detailed analysis is helpful. Recall that the conditional statement $p \rightarrow q$ is also called an *implication* and consists of two simple statements; the first is the *antecedent p* and the second is the *consequent q*. For example, the statement "If I jump into the pool, then I will get wet" consists of the antecedent p, "I jump into the pool," and the consequent q, "I will get wet," connected by the if . . . then connective.

The conditional can also be stated in these other ways:

p implies q

q if p

p only if q

p is sufficient for q

q is necessary for p

All p are q

In four of these six forms, the antecedent comes first, but for "q if p" and "q is necessary for p," the consequent comes first. So identifying the antecedent and consequent is important.

For example, think about the statement "If you drink and drive, you get arrested." Writing it in the different possible forms, we get:

Drinking and driving implies you get arrested.

You get arrested if you drink and drive.

You drink and drive only if you get arrested.

Drinking and driving is sufficient for getting arrested.

Getting arrested is necessary for drinking and driving.

All those who drink and drive get arrested.

Of course, these all say the same thing. To illustrate the importance of getting the antecedent and consequent in the correct order, consider the "q if p" form, in this case "You get arrested if you drink and drive." If we don't start with the consequent, we get "You drink and drive if you get arrested." This is completely false—there are any number of things you could get arrested for other than drinking and driving.

EXAMPLE 6 **Writing Variations of a Conditional Statement**

Write each statement in symbols. Let $p =$ "A person is over 6′ 6′′" and $q =$ "A person is tall."

(a) If a person is over 6′6′′, then the person is tall.
(b) Being tall is necessary for being over 6′6′′.
(c) A person is over 6′6′′ only if the person is tall.
(d) Being 6′6′′ is sufficient for being tall.
(e) A person is tall if the person is over 6′6′′.

SOLUTION

(a) If p, then q; $p \rightarrow q$
(b) q is necessary for p; $p \rightarrow q$
(c) p only if q; $p \rightarrow q$
(d) p is sufficient for q; $p \rightarrow q$
(e) q if p; $p \rightarrow q$

Actually, these statements all say the same thing!

▼ **Try This One 6**

☑ 4. Write the converse, inverse, and contrapositive of a statement.

Write each statement in symbols. Let $p =$ "A student comes to class every day" and $q =$ "A student gets a good grade."

(a) A student gets a good grade if a student comes to class every day.
(b) Coming to class every day is necessary for getting a good grade.
(c) A student gets a good grade only if a student comes to class every day.
(d) Coming to class every day is sufficient for getting a good grade.

In this section, we saw that some statements are always true (tautologies) and others are always false (self-contradictions). We also defined what it means for two statements to be logically equivalent—they have the same truth values. Now we're ready to analyze logical arguments to determine if they're legitimate or not.

Answers to Try This One

1 (a) Neither   (b) Self-contradiction
   (c) Tautology

2 (a) and (c)

3 (a) I will not study for this class and I will not fail.
   (b) I will not go to the dance club or the restaurant.
   (c) It is silly and I have a sense of humor.
   (d) The movie is not a comedy and it is not a thriller, or it is not awesome.

4 The video is popular and it cannot be found on YouTube.

5 Converse: If you are intelligent, then you do well in math classes.
   Inverse: If you do not do well in math classes, then you are not intelligent.
   Contrapositive: If you are not intelligent, then you do not do well in math classes.

6 (a) $p \rightarrow q$ (b) $q \rightarrow p$ (c) $q \rightarrow p$ (d) $p \rightarrow q$

EXERCISE SET 3-3

Writing Exercises

1. Explain the difference between a tautology and a self-contradiction.
2. Is every statement either a tautology or a self-contradiction? Why or why not?
3. Describe how to find the converse, inverse, and contrapositive of a conditional statement.
4. How can you decide if two statements are logically equivalent?
5. How can you decide if one statement is the negation of another?
6. Is a statement always logically equivalent to its converse? Explain.

Computational Exercises

For Exercises 7–16, determine which statements are tautologies, self-contradictions, or neither.

7. $(p \vee q) \vee (\sim p \wedge \sim q)$
8. $(p \rightarrow q) \wedge (p \vee q)$
9. $(p \wedge q) \wedge (\sim p \vee \sim q)$
10. $\sim p \vee (p \rightarrow q)$
11. $(p \leftrightarrow q) \vee \sim (q \leftrightarrow p)$
12. $(p \wedge q) \leftrightarrow (p \rightarrow \sim q)$
13. $(p \vee q) \wedge (\sim p \vee \sim q)$
14. $(p \wedge q) \vee (p \vee q)$
15. $(p \leftrightarrow q) \wedge (\sim p \leftrightarrow \sim q)$
16. $(p \rightarrow q) \wedge (\sim p \vee q)$

For Exercises 17–26, determine if the two statements are logically equivalent statements, negations, or neither.

17. $\sim q \rightarrow p$; $\sim p \rightarrow q$
18. $p \wedge q$; $\sim q \vee \sim p$
19. $\sim (p \vee q)$; $p \rightarrow \sim q$
20. $\sim (p \rightarrow q)$; $\sim p \wedge q$
21. $q \rightarrow p$; $\sim (p \rightarrow q)$
22. $p \vee (\sim q \wedge r)$; $(p \wedge \sim q) \vee (p \wedge r)$
23. $\sim (p \vee q)$; $\sim (\sim p \wedge \sim q)$
24. $(p \vee q) \rightarrow r$; $\sim r \rightarrow \sim (p \vee q)$
25. $(p \wedge q) \vee r$; $p \wedge (q \vee r)$
26. $p \leftrightarrow \sim q$; $(p \wedge \sim q) \vee (\sim p \wedge q)$

For Exercises 27–32, write the converse, inverse, and contrapositive of each.

27. $p \rightarrow q$
28. $\sim p \rightarrow \sim q$
29. $\sim q \rightarrow p$
30. $\sim p \rightarrow q$
31. $p \rightarrow \sim q$
32. $q \rightarrow p$

Real-World Applications

In Exercises 33–42, use De Morgan's laws to write the negation of the statement.

33. The concert is long or it is fun.
34. The soda is sweet or it is not carbonated.
35. It is not cold and I am soaked.
36. I will walk in the Race for the Cure walkathon and I will be tired.
37. I will go to the beach and I will not get sunburned.
38. The coffee is a latte or an espresso.
39. The student is a girl or the professor is not a man.
40. I will go to college and I will get a degree.
41. It is right or it is wrong.
42. Our school colors are not blue or they are not green.

For Exercises 43–49, let p = "I need to talk to my friend" and q = "I will send her a text message." Write each of the following in symbols (see Example 6).

43. If I need to talk to my friend, I will send her a text message.
44. If I will not send her a text message, I do not need to talk to my friend.
45. Sending a text message is necessary for needing to talk to my friend.
46. I will send her a text message if I need to talk to my friend.
47. Needing to talk to my friend is sufficient for sending her a text message.

48. I need to talk to my friend only if I will send her a text message.
49. I do not need to talk to my friend only if I will not send her a text message.
50. Are any of the statements in Exercises 43–49 logically equivalent?

For Exercises 51–56, write the converse, inverse, and contrapositive of the conditional statement.

51. If he graduated with a bachelor's degree in management information systems, then he will get a good job.

52. If she does not earn $5,000 this summer as a barista at the coffeehouse, then she cannot buy the green Ford Focus.
53. If the *American Idol* finale is today, then I will host a party in my dorm room.
54. If my cell phone will not charge, then I will replace the battery.
55. I will go to Nassau for spring break if I lose 10 pounds by March 1.
56. The politician will go to jail if he gets caught taking kickbacks.

Critical Thinking

57. In this section, we wrote the negation of $p \rightarrow q$ by using a disjunction. See if you can write the negation of $p \rightarrow q$ by using a conjunction.
58. Try to write the negation of the biconditional $p \leftrightarrow q$ by using only conjunctions, disjunctions, and negations.
59. Can you think of a true conditional statement about someone you know so that the converse is true as well? How about so that the converse is false?
60. Can you think of a true conditional statement about someone you know so that the inverse is true as well? How about so that the inverse is false?

61. Prove the first of De Morgan's laws by using truth tables:

$$\sim(p \vee q) \equiv \sim p \wedge \sim q$$

62. Prove the second of De Morgan's laws by using truth tables:

$$\sim(p \wedge q) \equiv \sim p \vee \sim q$$

Section 3-4 Logical Arguments

LEARNING OBJECTIVES

☐ 1. Define *valid argument* and *fallacy*.

☐ 2. Use truth tables to determine the validity of an argument.

☐ 3. Identify common argument forms.

☐ 4. Determine the validity of arguments by using common argument forms.

Common sense is a funny thing in our society: we all think we have it, and we also think that most other people don't. This thing that we call common sense is really the ability to think logically, to evaluate an argument or situation and decide what is and is not reasonable. It doesn't take a lot of imagination to picture how valuable it is to be able to think logically. We're pretty well protected by parents for our first few years of life, but after that the main tool we have to guide us through the perils of life is our brain. The more effectively that brain can analyze and evaluate information, the more successful we're likely to be. The work we've done in building the basics of symbolic logic in the first three sections of this chapter has prepared us for the real point: analyzing logical arguments objectively. That's the topic of this important section.

Valid Arguments and Fallacies

A logical argument is made up of two parts: a premise or premises and a conclusion based on those premises. We will call an argument **valid** if assuming the premises are true guarantees that the conclusion is true as well. An argument that is not valid is called **invalid** or a **fallacy.**

Let's look at an example.

Premise 1:   All students in this class will pass.
Premise 2:   Rachel is a student in this class.
Conclusion: Rachel will pass this class.

We can easily tell that if the two premises are true, then the conclusion is true, so this is an example of a valid argument.

Sidelight LOGIC AND THE ART OF FORENSICS

Many students find it troubling that an argument can be considered valid even if the conclusion is clearly false. But arguing in favor of something that you don't necessarily believe to be true isn't a new idea by any means—lawyers do it all the time, and it's commonly practiced in the area of formal debate, a style of intellectual competition that has its roots in ancient times.

In formal debate (also known as forensics), speakers are given a topic and asked to argue one side of a related issue. Judges determine which speakers make the most effective arguments and declare the winners accordingly. One of the most interesting aspects is that in many cases, the contestants don't know which side of the issue they will be arguing until right before the competition begins. While that aspect is intended to test the debater's flexibility and preparation, a major consequence is that opinion, and sometimes truth, is taken out of the mix, and contestants and judges must focus on the validity of arguments.

A variety of organizations sponsor national competitions in formal debate for colleges. The largest is an annual

championship organized by the National Forensics Association. Students from well over 100 schools participate in a wide variety of categories. The 2008 team champions were Tennessee State University, Kansas State University, California State Long Beach, and Western Kentucky University.

It's very important at this point to understand the difference between a true statement and a conclusion to a valid argument. A statement that is known to be false can still be a valid conclusion if it follows logically from the given premises. For example, consider this argument:

Los Angeles is in California or Mexico.

Los Angeles is not in California.

Therefore, Los Angeles is in Mexico.

☑ 1. Define *valid argument* and *fallacy*.

This is a valid argument: if the two premises are true, then the conclusion, "Los Angeles is in Mexico," must be true as well. We know, however, that Los Angeles isn't actually in Mexico. That's the tricky part. In determining whether an argument is valid, *we will always assume that the premises are true*. In this case, we're assuming that the premise "Los Angeles is not in California" is true, even though in fact it is not. We will discuss this aspect of logical arguments in greater depth later in this section.

Truth Table Method

One method for determining the validity of an argument is by using truth tables. We will use the following procedure.

Procedure for Determining the Validity of Arguments

Step 1 Write the argument in symbols.

Step 2 Write the argument as a conditional statement; use a conjunction between the premises and the implication ($\Rightarrow$) for the conclusion. (*Note:* The $\Rightarrow$ is the same as $\rightarrow$ but will be used to designate an argument.)

Step 3 Set up and construct a truth table as follows:

Symbols | Premise $\wedge$ Premise $\Rightarrow$ Conclusion

Step 4 If all truth values under $\Rightarrow$ are Ts (i.e., a tautology), then the argument is valid; otherwise, it is invalid.

EXAMPLE 1 Determining the Validity of an Argument

Determine if the following argument is valid or invalid.

If a figure has three sides, then it is a triangle.

This figure is not a triangle.

Therefore, this figure does not have three sides.

SOLUTION

Step 1 *Write the argument in symbols.* Let $p =$ "The figure has three sides," and let $q =$ "The figure is a triangle."

Translated into symbols:

$$p \rightarrow q \quad \text{(Premise)}$$
$$\underline{\sim q \qquad \text{(Premise)}}$$
$$\therefore \sim p \quad \text{(Conclusion)}$$

A line is used to separate the premises from the conclusion and the three triangular dots $\therefore$ mean "therefore."

Step 2 *Write the argument as an implication* by connecting the premises with a conjunction and implying the conclusion as shown.

Premise 1		Premise 2		Conclusion
$(p \rightarrow q)$	$\wedge$	$\sim q$	$\Rightarrow$	$\sim p$

Step 3 *Construct a truth table* as shown.

p	q	$\sim p$	$\sim q$	$p \rightarrow q$	$(p \rightarrow q) \wedge \sim q$	$[(p \rightarrow q) \wedge \sim q] \Rightarrow \sim p$
T	T	F	F	T	F	T
T	F	F	T	F	F	T
F	T	T	F	T	F	T
F	F	T	T	T	T	T

Step 4 *Determine the validity of the argument.* Since all the values under the $\Rightarrow$ are true, the argument is valid.

▼ Try This One 1

Determine if the argument is valid or invalid.

I will run for student government or I will join the athletic boosters.

I did not join the athletic boosters.

Therefore, I will run for student government.

EXAMPLE 2   Determining the Validity of an Argument

Determine the validity of the following argument. "If a professor is rich, then he will buy an expensive automobile. The professor bought an expensive automobile. Therefore, the professor is rich."

SOLUTION

Step 1 *Write the argument in symbols.* Let p = "The professor is rich," and let q = "The professor buys an expensive automobile."

$$p \to q$$
$$\underline{q}$$
$$\therefore p$$

Step 2 *Write the argument as an implication.*

$$(p \to q) \wedge q \Rightarrow p$$

Step 3 *Construct a truth table* for the argument.

p	q	$p \to q$	$(p \to q) \wedge q$	$[(p \to q) \wedge q] \Rightarrow p$
T	T	T	T	T
T	F	F	F	T
F	T	T	T	F
F	F	T	F	T

Step 4 *Determine the validity of the argument.* This argument is invalid since it is not a tautology. (Remember, when the values are not all Ts, the argument is invalid.) In this case, it cannot be concluded that the professor is rich.

▼ Try This One 2

Determine the validity of the following argument. "If John blows off work to go to the playoff game, he will lose his job. John lost his job. Therefore, John blew off work and went to the playoff game."

CAUTION

Remember that in symbolic logic, whether or not the conclusion is true is not important. The main concern is whether the conclusion follows from the premises.

Consider the following two arguments.

1. Either $2 + 2 \neq 4$ or $2 + 2 = 5$
   $$\underline{2 + 2 = 4}$$
   $$\therefore 2 + 2 = 5$$

2. If $2 + 2 \neq 5$, then I passed the math quiz.
   $$\underline{\text{I did not pass the quiz.}}$$
   $$\therefore 2 + 2 \neq 5$$

The truth tables on the next page show that the first argument is valid even though the conclusion is false, and the second argument is invalid even though the conclusion is true!

Let p be the statement "$2 + 2 = 4$" and q be the statement "$2 + 2 = 5$." Then the first argument is written as

$$(\sim p \lor q)$$
$$\underline{p }$$
$$\therefore q$$

Truth table for argument 1

p	q	$\sim p$	$\sim p \lor q$	$(\sim p \lor q) \land p$	$[(\sim p \lor q) \land p]$ $\Rightarrow q$
T	T	F	T	T	T
T	F	F	F	F	T
F	T	T	T	F	T
F	F	T	T	F	T

Let p be the statement "$2 + 2 \neq 5$" and q be the statement "I passed the math quiz." The second argument is written as

$$p \to q$$
$$\underline{\sim q }$$
$$\therefore p$$

Truth table for argument 2

p	q	$\sim q$	$p \to q$	$(p \to q) \land \sim q$	$[(p \to q) \land \sim q]$ $\Rightarrow p$
T	T	F	T	F	T
T	F	T	F	F	T
F	T	F	T	F	T
F	F	T	T	T	F

The validity of arguments that have three variables can also be determined by truth tables, as shown in Example 3.

EXAMPLE 3 **Determining the Validity of an Argument**

Determine the validity of the following argument.

$$p \to r$$
$$p \land r$$
$$\underline{p }$$
$$\therefore \sim q \to p$$

SOLUTION

Step 1 *Write the argument in symbols.* This has been done already.

Step 2 *Write the argument as an implication.* Make a conjunction of all three premises and imply the conclusion:

$$(p \to r) \land (q \land r) \land p \Rightarrow (\sim q \to p)$$

Step 3 *Construct a truth table.* When there are three premises, we will begin by finding the truth values for each premise and then work the conjunction from left to right as shown.

p	q	r	$\sim q$	$p \to r$	$q \land r$	$\sim q \to p$	$(p \to r) \land (q \land r) \land p$	$[(p \to r) \land (q \land r) \land p]$ $\Rightarrow (\sim q \to p)$
T	T	T	F	T	T	T	T	T
T	T	F	F	F	F	T	F	T
T	F	T	T	T	F	T	F	T
T	F	F	T	F	F	T	F	T
F	T	T	F	T	T	T	F	T
F	T	F	F	T	F	T	F	T
F	F	T	T	T	F	F	F	T
F	F	F	T	T	F	F	F	T

Since the truth value for $\Rightarrow$ is all Ts, the argument is valid.

☑ 2. Use truth tables to determine the validity of an argument.

▼ Try This One 3

Determine whether the following argument is valid or invalid.

$$p \vee q$$
$$\underline{p \vee \sim r}$$
$$\therefore q$$

Common Valid Argument Forms

We have seen that truth tables can be used to test an argument for validity. But some argument forms are common enough that they are recognized by special names. When an argument fits one of these forms, we can decide if it is valid or not just by knowing the general form, rather than constructing a truth table.

We'll start with a description of some commonly used valid arguments.

1. *Law of detachment* (also known by Latin name *modus ponens*):

$$p \rightarrow q$$
$$\underline{p }$$
$$\therefore q$$

Example:

If our team wins Saturday, then they go to a bowl game.

Our team won Saturday.

Therefore, our team goes to a bowl game.

2. *Law of contraposition* (Latin name *modus tollens*):

$$p \rightarrow q$$
$$\underline{\sim q}$$
$$\therefore \sim p$$

Example:

If I try hard, I'll get an A.

I didn't get an A.

Therefore, I didn't try hard.

3. *Law of syllogism,* also known as *law of transitivity:*

$$p \rightarrow q$$
$$\underline{q \rightarrow r}$$
$$\therefore p \rightarrow r$$

Example:

If I make an illegal U-turn, I'll get a ticket.

If I get a ticket, I'll get points on my driving record.

Therefore, if I make an illegal U-turn, I'll get points on my driving record.

4. *Law of disjunctive syllogism:*

$$p \vee q$$
$$\underline{\sim p}$$
$$\therefore q$$

Example:

You're either brilliant or insane.

You're not brilliant.

Therefore, you're insane.

Common Fallacies

Next, we will list some commonly used arguments that are invalid.

1. *Fallacy of the converse:*

$p \rightarrow q$

q

$\therefore p$

Example:

If it's Friday, then I will go to happy hour.

I am at happy hour.

Therefore, it is Friday.

This is not valid! You can go to happy hour other days, too.

2. *Fallacy of the inverse:*

$p \rightarrow q$

$\sim p$

$\therefore \sim q$

Example:

If I exercise every day, then I will lose weight.

I don't exercise every day.

Therefore, I won't lose weight.

This is also not valid. You could still lose weight without exercising *every* day.

3. *Fallacy of the inclusive or:*

$p \vee q$

p

$\therefore \sim q$

Example:

I'm going to take chemistry or physics.

I'm taking chemistry.

Therefore, I'm not taking physics.

Remember, we've agreed that by *or* we mean *one or the other, or both.* So you could be taking both classes.

You will be asked to prove that some of these are invalid by using truth tables in the exercises.

Math Note

It's more common to mistakenly think that an invalid argument is valid rather than the other way around, so you should pay special attention to the common fallacies listed.

Sidelight CIRCULAR REASONING

Circular reasoning (sometimes called "begging the question") is a sneaky type of fallacy in which the premises of an argument contain a claim that the conclusion is true, so naturally if the premises are true, so is the conclusion. But this doesn't constitute evidence that a conclusion is true. Consider the following example: A suspect in a criminal investigation tells the police detective that his statements can be trusted because his friend Sue can vouch for him. The detective asks the suspect how he knows that Sue can be trusted, and he says, "I can assure you of her honesty." Ultimately, the suspect becomes even more suspect because of circular reasoning: his argument boils down to "I am honest because I am honest."

While this example might seem blatantly silly, you'd be surprised how often people try to get away with this fallacy. A Google search for the string *circular reasoning* brings up hundreds of arguments that are thought to be circular.

EXAMPLE 4   Recognizing Common Argument Forms

Determine whether the following arguments are valid, using the given forms of valid arguments and fallacies.

(a) $p \rightarrow q$ (b) $\sim p \rightarrow q$ (c) $\sim p \rightarrow \sim q$ (d) $\sim r \rightarrow s$

$\underline{\quad p \quad}$ $\underline{\quad \sim q \quad}$ $\underline{\quad \sim q \quad}$ $\underline{\quad s \rightarrow t \quad}$

$\therefore q$ $\therefore p$ $\therefore \sim p$ $\therefore \sim r \rightarrow t$

SOLUTION

(a) This is the law of detachment, therefore a *valid* argument.
(b) This fits the law of contraposition with the statement $\sim p$ substituted in place of p, so it is valid.
(c) This fits the fallacy of the converse, using statement $\sim p$ and $\sim q$ rather than p and q, so it is an invalid argument.
(d) This is the law of syllogism, with statements $\sim r$, s, and t, so the argument is valid.

▼ Try This One 4

☑ 3. Identify common argument forms.

Determine whether the arguments are valid, using the commonly used valid arguments and fallacies.

(a) $\sim p \vee q$ (b) $r \vee s$ (c) $\sim p \rightarrow q$ (d) $(p \wedge q) \rightarrow \sim r$

$\underline{\quad p \quad}$ $\underline{\quad s \quad}$ $\underline{\quad q \quad}$ $\underline{\quad r \quad}$

$\therefore q$ $\therefore \sim r$ $\therefore \sim p$ $\therefore \sim(p \wedge q)$

EXAMPLE 5   Determining the Validity of an Argument by Using Common Argument Forms

Determine whether the following arguments are valid, using the given forms of valid arguments and fallacies.

(a) If you like dogs, you will live to be 120.

   You like dogs.

   Therefore, you will live to be 120.

(b) If the modem is connected, then you can access the Web.

   The modem is not connected.

   Therefore, you cannot access the Web.

(c) If you watch *Big Brother,* you watch reality shows.

If you watch reality shows, you have time to kill.

Therefore, if you have time to kill, you watch *Big Brother.*

(d) The movie *Scream* is a thriller or a comedy.

The movie *Scream* is a thriller.

Therefore, the movie *Scream* is not a comedy.

(e) My iPod is in my backpack or it is at my friend's house.

My iPod is not in my backpack.

Therefore, my iPod is at my friend's house.

SOLUTION

(a) In symbolic form this argument is $(p \rightarrow q) \wedge p \Rightarrow q$. We can see that this is the law of detachment, so the argument is *valid.*

(b) In symbolic form this argument is $(p \rightarrow q) \wedge \sim p \Rightarrow \sim q$. This is the fallacy of the inverse, so the argument is *invalid.*

(c) In symbolic form this argument is $(p \rightarrow q) \wedge (q \rightarrow r) \Rightarrow (r \rightarrow p)$. We know by the law of transitivity that if $(p \rightarrow q) \wedge (q \rightarrow r)$, then $p \rightarrow r$. The given conclusion, $r \rightarrow p$, is the converse of $p \rightarrow r$, so is not equivalent to $p \rightarrow r$ (the valid conclusion). So the argument is *invalid.*

(d) In symbolic form the argument is $(p \vee q) \wedge p \Rightarrow \sim q$. This is the fallacy of the inclusive or, so the argument is *invalid.*

(e) In symbolic form the argument is $(p \vee q) \wedge \sim p \Rightarrow q$. This is the law of disjunctive syllogism, so the argument is *valid.*

▼ Try This One 5

☑ 4. Determine the validity of arguments by using common argument forms.

Determine whether the following arguments are valid using the given forms of valid arguments and fallacies.

(a) If Elliot is a freshman, he takes English.

Elliot is a freshman.

Therefore, Elliot takes English.

(b) If you work hard, you will be a success.

You are not a success.

Therefore, you do not work hard.

(c) Jon is cheap or financially broke.

He is not financially broke.

Therefore, he is cheap.

(d) If Jose asks me out, I will not study Friday.

I didn't study Friday.

Therefore, Jose asked me out.

There are two big lessons to be learned in this section. First, sometimes an argument can appear to be legitimate superficially, but if you study it carefully, you may find out that it's not. Second, the validity of an argument is not about whether the conclusion is true or false—it's about whether the conclusion follows logically from the premises.

Answers to Try This One

1 Valid

2 Invalid

3 Invalid

4 (a) Valid   (b) Invalid   (c) Invalid   (d) Valid

5 (a) Valid   (b) Valid   (c) Valid   (d) Invalid

EXERCISE SET 3-4

Writing Exercises

1. Describe the structure of an argument.
2. Is it possible for an argument to be valid, yet have a false conclusion? Explain your answer.
3. Is it possible for an argument to be invalid, yet have a true conclusion? Explain your answer.
4. When you are setting up a truth table to determine the validity of an argument, what connective is used between the premises of an argument? What connective is used between the premises and the conclusion?
5. Describe what the law of syllogism says, in your own words.
6. Describe why the fallacy of the inclusive or is a fallacy.

Computational Exercises

For Exercises 7–16, using truth tables, determine whether each argument is valid.

7. $p \rightarrow q$
   $\underline{p \wedge q}$
   $\therefore p$

8. $p \vee q$
   $\underline{\sim q}$
   $\therefore p$

9. $\sim p \vee q$
   $\underline{p}$
   $\therefore p \wedge \sim q$

10. $p \leftrightarrow \sim q$
    $\underline{p \wedge \sim q}$
    $\therefore p \vee q$

11. $\sim q \vee p$
    $\underline{q}$
    $\therefore \sim p$

12. $p \vee q$
    $\underline{\sim p \wedge \sim q}$
    $\therefore p$

13. $p \leftrightarrow q$
    $\underline{\sim q}$
    $\therefore \sim p$

14. $p \vee \sim q$
    $\underline{\sim q \rightarrow p}$
    $\therefore p$

15. $p \wedge \sim q$
    $\underline{\sim r \rightarrow q}$
    $\therefore q$

16. $p \leftrightarrow q$
    $\underline{q \leftrightarrow r}$
    $\therefore p \wedge q$

17. Write the law of detachment in symbols; then prove that it is a valid argument by using a truth table.
18. Write the law of contraposition in symbols; then prove that it is a valid argument by using a truth table.
19. Write the law of syllogism in symbols; then prove that it is a valid argument by using a truth table.
20. Write the law of disjunctive syllogism in symbols; then prove that it is a valid argument by using a truth table.

21. Write the fallacy of the converse in symbols; then prove that it is not a valid argument by using a truth table.
22. Write the fallacy of the inclusive or in symbols; then prove that it is not a valid argument by using a truth table.

For Exercises 23–32, determine whether the following arguments are valid, using the given forms of valid arguments and fallacies.

23. $p \rightarrow q$
    $\underline{\sim q}$
    $\therefore \sim p$

24. $p \vee q$
    $\underline{q}$
    $\therefore \sim p$

25. $\sim p \rightarrow q$
    $\underline{\sim q}$
    $\therefore \sim p$

26. $p \vee \sim q$
    $\underline{q}$
    $\therefore p$

27. $p \rightarrow q$
    $\underline{r \rightarrow \sim q}$
    $\therefore p \rightarrow \sim r$

28. $p \rightarrow \sim q$
    $\underline{\sim q}$
    $\therefore p$

29. $\sim p \vee q$
    $\underline{\sim q}$
    $\therefore \sim p$

30. $\sim p \rightarrow q$
    $\underline{\sim q}$
    $\therefore p$

31. $p \vee \sim q$
    $\underline{q}$
    $\therefore \sim p$

32. $p \rightarrow \sim q$
    $\underline{\sim r \rightarrow q}$
    $\therefore p \rightarrow r$

Real-World Applications

For Exercises 33–42, identify p, q, and r if necessary. Then translate each argument to symbols and use a truth table to determine whether the argument is valid or invalid.

33. If it rains, then I will watch the Real World marathon.
    It did not rain.

    ∴ I did not watch the Real World marathon.

34. Ted will get a Big Mac or a Whopper with cheese.
    Ted did not get a Whopper with cheese.

    ∴ Ted got a Big Mac.

35. If Julia uses monster.com to send out her resume, she will get an interview.
    Julia got an interview.

    ∴ Julia used monster.com to send out her resume.

36. If it snows, I can go snowboarding.
    It did not snow.

    ∴ I cannot go snowboarding.

37. I will go to the party if and only if my ex-boyfriend is not going.
    My ex-boyfriend is not going to the party.

    ∴ I will go to the party.

38. If you are superstitious, then do not walk under a ladder.
    If you do not walk under a ladder, then you are superstitious.

    ∴ You are superstitious and you do not walk under a ladder.

39. Either I did not study or I passed the exam.
    I did not study.

    ∴ I failed the exam.

40. I will run the marathon if and only if I can run 30 miles by Christmas.
    I can run 30 miles by Christmas or I will not run the marathon.

    ∴ If I ran the marathon, then I was able to run 30 miles by Christmas.

41. If you eat seven pieces of pizza, then you will get sick.
    If you get sick, then you will not be able to go to the game.

    ∴ If you eat seven pieces of pizza, then you will not be able to go to the game.

42. If you back up your hard drive, then you are protected.
    Either you are protected or you are daring.

    ∴ If you are daring, you won't back up your hard drive.

For Exercises 43–50, write the argument in symbols; then decide whether the argument is valid by using the common forms of valid arguments and fallacies.

43. If the cheese doesn't melt, the nachos are ruined.
    The nachos are ruined.

    ∴ The cheese didn't melt.

44. I studied or I failed the class.
    I did not fail the class.

    ∴ I studied.

45. If I go to the student symposium on environmental issues, I will fall asleep.
    If the speaker is interesting, I will not fall asleep.

    ∴ If I go to the student symposium on environmental issues, the speaker will not be interesting.

46. If it is sunny, I will wear SPF 50 sun block.
    It is not sunny.

    ∴ I will not wear SPF 50 sun block.

47. If I get an A in this class, I will do a dance.
    I did a dance.

    ∴ I got an A in this class.

48. I will not wear a Speedo at the beach or I will be embarrassed.
    I am not embarrassed.

    ∴ I did not wear a Speedo at the beach.

49. If I see the movie at an IMAX theater, I will get dizzy.
    I see the movie at an IMAX theater.

    ∴ I get dizzy.

50. I will backpack through Europe if I get at least a 3.5 grade point average.
    I do not get at least a 3.5 grade point average.

    ∴ I will not backpack through Europe.

Critical Thinking

51. Oscar Wilde once said, "Few parents nowadays pay any regard to what their children say to them. The old-fashioned respect for the young is fast dying out." This statement can be translated to an argument, as shown next.

    If parents respected their children, then parents would listen to them.
    Parents do not listen to their children.

    ∴ Parents do not respect their children.

Using a truth table, determine whether the argument is valid or invalid.

52. Winston Churchill once said, "If you have an important point to make, don't try to be subtle or clever. Use a pile driver. Hit the point once. Then come back and hit it again. Then a third time—a tremendous wack!" This statement can be translated to an argument as shown.

If you have an important point to make, then you should not be subtle or clever.

You are not being subtle or clever.
∴ You will make your point.

Using a truth table, determine whether the argument is valid or invalid.

53. Write an argument matching the law of syllogism that involves something about your school. Then explain why the conclusion of your argument is valid.

54. Write an example of the fallacy of the inverse that involves something about your school. Then explain why the conclusion of your argument is invalid.

55. Look up the literal translation of the Latin term *modus ponens* on the Internet, and explain how that applies to the law of detachment.

56. Look up the literal translation of the Latin term *modus tollens* on the Internet, and explain how that applies to the law of contraposition.

Section 3-5 Euler Circles

LEARNING OBJECTIVES

☐ 1. Define *syllogism*.

☐ 2. Use Euler circles to determine the validity of an argument.

Abraham Lincoln once said, "You can fool some of the people all of the time, and all of the people some of the time, but you cannot fool all of the people all of the time." Lincoln was a really smart guy—he understood the power of logical arguments and the fact that cleverly crafted phrases could be an effective tool in the art of persuasion. What's interesting about this quote from our perspective is the liberal use of the quantifiers *some* and *all*. In this section, we will study a particular type of argument that uses these quantifiers, along with *no* or *none*. A technique developed by Leonhard Euler way back in the 1700s is a useful method for analyzing these arguments and testing their validity.

Euler circles are diagrams similar to Venn diagrams. We will use them to study arguments using four types of statements. The statement types are listed in Table 3-4, and the Euler circle that illustrates each is shown in Figure 3-1 on the next page.

Each statement can be represented by a specific diagram. The universal affirmative "All A is B" means that every member of set A is also a member of set B. For example,

TABLE 3-4	**Types of Statements Illustrated by Euler Circles**

Type	General Form	Example
Universal affirmative	All A is B	All chickens have wings.
Universal negative	No A is B	No horses have wings.
Particular affirmative	Some A is B	Some horses are black.
Particular negative	Some A is not B	Some horses are not black.

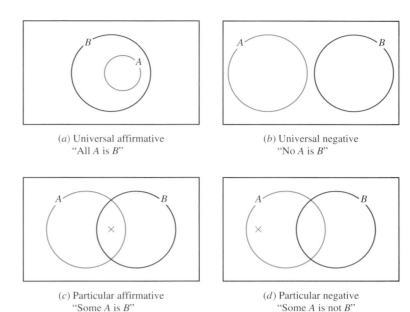

(a) Universal affirmative
"All A is B"

(b) Universal negative
"No A is B"

(c) Particular affirmative
"Some A is B"

(d) Particular negative
"Some A is not B"

Figure 3-1

Math Note

If I say that "Some horses are black," you cannot assume that "Some horses are not black." If I say, "Some horses are not black," you cannot assume that "Some horses are black."

☑ 1. Define *syllogism*.

the statement "All chickens have wings" means that the set of all chickens is a subset of the set of animals that have wings.

The universal negative "No A is B" means that no member of set A is a member of set B. In other words, set A and set B are *disjoint sets*. For example, "No horses have wings" means that the set of all horses and the set of all animals with wings are disjoint (nonintersecting).

The particular affirmative "Some A is B" means that there is at least one member of set A that is also a member of set B. For example, the statement "Some horses are black" means that there is at least one horse that is a member of the set of black animals. The $\times$ in Figure 3-1(*c*) means that there is at least one black horse.

The particular negative "Some A is not B" means that there is at least one member of set A that is not a member of set B. For example, the statement "Some horses are not black" means that there is at least one horse that does not belong to the set of black animals. The diagram for the particular negative is shown in Figure 3-1(*d*). The $\times$ is placed in circle A but not in circle B. The $\times$ in this example means that there exists at least one horse that is some color other than black.

Many of the arguments we studied in Section 3-4 consisted of two premises and a conclusion. This type of argument is called a **syllogism.** We will use Euler circles to test the validity of syllogisms involving the statement types in Table 3-4. Here's a simple example:

Premise	All cats have four legs.
Premise	Some cats are black.
Conclusion	Therefore, some four-legged animals are black.

Remember that we are not concerned with whether the conclusion is true or false, but only whether the conclusion logically follows from the premises. If yes, the argument is valid. If no, the argument is invalid.

Euler Circle Method for Testing the Validity of an Argument

To determine whether an argument is valid, diagram both premises in the same figure. If the conclusion is shown in the figure, the argument is valid.

Many times the premises can be diagrammed in several ways. If there is even one way in which the diagram contradicts the conclusion, the argument is *invalid* since the conclusion does not necessarily follow from the premises.

Examples 1, 2, and 3 show how to determine the validity of an argument by using Euler circles.

EXAMPLE 1   Using Euler Circles to Determine the Validity of an Argument

Use Euler circles to determine whether the argument is valid.

All cats have four legs.

Some cats are black.
_____

Therefore, some four-legged animals are black.

SOLUTION

The first premise, "All cats have four legs," is the universal affirmative; the set of cats diagrammed as a subset of four-legged animals is shown.

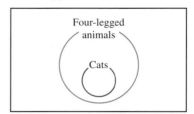

The second premise, "Some cats are black," is the particular affirmative and is shown by placing an $\times$ in the intersection of the cats' circle and the black animals' circle. The diagram for this premise is drawn on the diagram of the first premise and can be done in two ways, as shown.

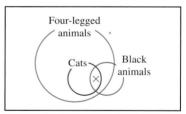

The conclusion is that some four-legged animals are black, so the diagram for the conclusion must have an $\times$ in the four-legged animals' circle and in the black animals' circle. Notice that both of the diagrams corresponding to the premises do have an $\times$ in both circles, so the conclusion matches the premises and the argument is valid. Since there is no other way to diagram the premises, the conclusion is shown to be true without a doubt.

▼ **Try This One   1**

Use Euler circles to determine whether the argument is valid.

All college students buy textbooks.

Some book dealers buy textbooks.
_____

Therefore, some college students are book dealers.

It isn't necessary to use actual subjects such as cats, four-legged animals, etc. in syllogisms. Arguments can use letters to represent the various sets, as shown in Example 2.

EXAMPLE 2 **Using Euler Circles to Determine the Validity of an Argument**

Use Euler circles to determine whether the argument is valid or invalid.

Some A is not B.
All C is B.
$\therefore$ Some A is C.

SOLUTION

The first premise, "Some A is not B," is diagrammed as shown.

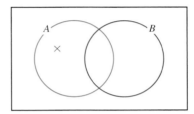

The second premise, "All C is B," is diagrammed by placing circle C inside circle B. This can be done in several ways, as shown.

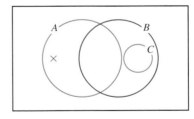

The third diagram shows that the argument is invalid. It matches both premises, but there are no members of A that are also in C, so it contradicts the conclusion "Some A is C."

▼ **Try This One 2**

Use Euler circles to determine whether the argument is valid.

Some A is B.
Some A is not C.
$\therefore$ Some B is not C.

Let's try one more specific example.

EXAMPLE 3   Using Euler Circles to Determine the Validity of an Argument

Use Euler circles to determine whether the argument is valid.

No criminal is admirable.

Some athletes are not criminals.

∴ Some admirable people are athletes.

SOLUTION

Diagram the first premise, "No criminal is admirable."

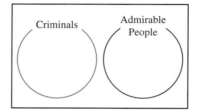

We can add the second premise, "Some athletes are not criminals," in at least two different ways:

 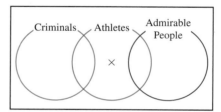

In the first diagram, the conclusion appears to be valid: some athletes are admirable. But the second diagram doesn't support that conclusion, so the argument is invalid.

☑ 2. Use Euler circles to determine the validity of an argument.

▼ Try This One 3

Use Euler circles to determine whether the argument is valid.

All dogs bark.

No animals that bark are cats.

∴ No dogs are cats.

We have now seen that for syllogisms that involve the quantifiers *all*, *some*, or *none*, Euler circles are an efficient way to determine the validity of the argument. We diagram both premises on the same figure, and if all possible diagrams display the conclusion, then the conclusion must be valid.

Answers to Try This One

1   Invalid

2   Invalid

3   Valid

EXERCISE SET 3-5

Writing Exercises

1. Name and give an example of each of the four types of statements that can be diagrammed with Euler circles.
2. Explain how to decide whether an argument is valid or invalid after drawing Euler circles.
3. What is a syllogism?
4. How do Euler circles differ from Venn diagrams?

Computational Exercises

For Exercises 5–14, draw an Euler circle diagram for each statement.

5. All computers are calculators.
6. No unicorns are real.
7. Some people do not go to college.
8. Some CD burners are DVD burners.
9. No math courses are easy.
10. Some fad diets do not result in weight loss.
11. Some laws in the United States are laws in Mexico.
12. All members of Mensa are smart.
13. No cheeseburgers are low in fat.
14. Some politicians are crooks.

For Exercises 15–24, determine whether each argument is valid or invalid.

15. All X is Y.
    Some Y is Z.
    $\therefore$ Some X is Z.

16. Some A is not B.
    No B is C.
    $\therefore$ Some A is not C.

17. Some P is Q.
    No Q is R.
    $\therefore$ Some P is not R.

18. All S is T.
    No S is R.
    $\therefore$ Some T is R.

19. No M is N.
    No N is O.
    $\therefore$ Some M is not O.

20. Some U is V.
    Some U is not W.
    $\therefore$ No W is U.

21. Some A is not B.
    No A is C.
    $\therefore$ Some A is not C.

22. All P is Q.
    All Q is R.
    $\therefore$ All P is R.

23. No S is T.
    No T is R.
    $\therefore$ No S is R.

24. Some M is N.
    Some N is O.
    $\therefore$ Some M is O.

Real-World Applications

For Exercises 25–38, use Euler circles to determine if the argument is valid.

25. All phones are communication devices.
    Some communication devices are inexpensive.
    $\therefore$ Some phones are inexpensive.

26. Some students are overachievers.
    No overachiever is lazy.
    $\therefore$ Some students are not lazy.

27. Some animated movies are violent.
    No kids' movies are violent.
    $\therefore$ No kids' movies are animated.

28. Some protesters are angry.
    Some protesters are not civil.
    $\therefore$ Some civil people are not angry.

29. Some math tutors are patient.
    No patient people are demeaning.
    $\therefore$ Some math tutors are not demeaning.

30. Some students are hard-working.
    Some hard-working people are not successful.
    $\therefore$ Some students are not successful.

31. Some movie stars are fake.
    No movie star is talented.
    $\therefore$ No fake people are talented.

32. Some CEOs are women.
    Some women are tech-savvy.
    ∴ Some CEOs are not tech-savvy.

33. Some juices have antioxidants.
    Some fruits have antioxidants.
    ∴ No juices are fruits.

34. Some funny people are sad.
    No serious people are sad.
    ∴ No funny people are serious.

35. Some women have highlighted hair.
    All women watch soap operas.
    All people who watch soap operas are emotional.
    ∴ Some emotional people watch soap operas.

36. All students text message during class.
    Some students in class take notes.
    All students who take notes in class pass the test.
    ∴ Some students pass the test.

37. Some birds can talk.
    Some animals that can talk can also moo.
    All cows can moo.
    ∴ Some cows can talk.

38. All cars use gasoline.
    All things that use gasoline emit carbon dioxide.
    Some cars have four doors.
    ∴ Some things with four doors emit carbon dioxide.

Critical Thinking

For Exercises 39–42, write a conclusion so that the argument is valid. Use Euler circles.

39. All A is B.
    All B is C.
    ∴

40. No M is P.
    All S is M.
    ∴

41. All calculators can add.
    No adding machines can make breakfast.
    ∴

42. Some people are prejudiced.
    All people have brains.
    ∴

CHAPTER **3** Summary

Section	Important Terms	Important Ideas
3-1	Statement Simple statement Compound statement Connective Conjunction Disjunction Conditional Biconditional Negation	**Formal** symbolic logic uses statements. A statement is a sentence that can be determined to be true or false but not both. A simple statement contains only one idea. A compound statement is formed by joining two or more simple statements with connectives. The four basic connectives are the conjunction (which uses the word *and* and the symbol $\wedge$), the disjunction (which uses the word *or* and the symbol $\vee$), the conditional (which uses the words *if...then* and the symbol $\rightarrow$), and the biconditional (which uses the words *if and only if* and the symbol $\leftrightarrow$). The symbol for negation is $\sim$. Statements are usually written using logical symbols and letters of the alphabet to represent simple statements.
3-2	Truth table	**A truth** table can be used to determine when a compound statement is true or false. A truth table can be constructed for any logical statement.
3-3	Tautology Self-contradiction Logically equivalent statements Converse Inverse Contrapositive De Morgan's laws	**A statement** that is always true is called a tautology. A statement that is always false is called a self-contradiction. Two statements that have the same truth values are said to be logically equivalent. De Morgan's laws are used to find the negation of a conjunction or disjunction. From the conditional statement, three other statements can be made: the converse, the inverse, and the contrapositive.
3-4	Argument Premise Conclusion	**Truth** tables can be used to determine the validity of an argument. An argument consists of two or more statements called premises and a statement called the conclusion. An argument is valid if when the premises are true, the conclusion is true. Otherwise, the argument is invalid.
3-5	Syllogism Euler circles Universal affirmative Universal negative Particular affirmative Particular negative	**A mathematician** named Leonhard Euler developed a method using circles to determine the validity of an argument that is particularly effective for syllogisms involving quantifiers. This method uses four types of statements: (1) the universal affirmative, (2) the universal negative, (3) the particular affirmative, and (4) the particular negative. Euler circles are similar to Venn diagrams.

MATH IN ▶ **The Art of Persuasion REVISITED**

All the arguments on the list are logically invalid except the last one. Even though the claim made by the last argument is false—it did not snow in Hawaii in 2008—this is so because the first premise is false. Remember, the validity of an argument is based on whether it follows from the premises, not on its actual truth.

The first is invalid because there are sources of smoke other than fire. The second is invalid because it's possible to be happy for some reason other than having lots of money. The third is invalid because the initial statement says nothing about teams not in the SEC. The fourth is invalid because it is circular reasoning (see Sidelight in Section 3-4). The fifth is invalid because the first statement doesn't say that weapons of mass destruction are the *only* reason to go to war.

Review Exercises

Section 3-1

For Exercises 1–5, decide whether the sentence is a statement.

1. Let's go with the flow.
2. My duvet cover is indigo.
3. The girls at this school are smart.
4. Ignorance is always a choice.
5. Are we there yet?

For Exercises 6–10, decide whether each statement is simple or compound.

6. Andre is interesting and caring.
7. The monitor is blinking.
8. If it is not raining, I will go kiteboarding.
9. The book is stimulating or informative.
10. There is a silver lining behind every cloud.

For Exercises 11–20, write the negation of the statement.

11. It is scary.
12. The cell phone is out of juice.
13. The Popsicle is green.
14. No people who live in glass houses throw stones.
15. Some failing students can learn new study methods.
16. Everyone will pass the test on logic.
17. There is a printer that has no ink.
18. None of these links are broken.
19. At least one of the contestants will be voted off the island.
20. All SUVs are gas guzzlers.

For Exercises 21–25, classify the statement as a conjunction, disjunction, conditional, or biconditional.

21. In the department store the air is scented and stuffy.
22. If you dream it, you can achieve it.
23. I will go to the 7-Eleven or to the IHOP.
24. It is dangerous if and only if there is ice on the sidewalk.
25. I will slip if I walk on the icy sidewalk.

For Exercises 26–35, let p = "It is ambitious" and let q = "It is worthwhile." Write each statement in symbols.

26. It is ambitious and worthwhile.
27. If it is worthwhile, then it is ambitious.
28. It is worthwhile if and only if it is ambitious.
29. It is worthwhile and not ambitious.
30. If it is not ambitious, then it is not worthwhile.
31. It is not true that it is worthwhile and ambitious.
32. It is not true that if it is ambitious, then it is worthwhile.
33. It is not worthwhile if and only if it is not ambitious.
34. It is not true that it is not worthwhile.
35. It is neither ambitious nor worthwhile.

For Exercises 36–40, let p = "It is cool." Let q = "It is cloudy." Write each statement in words.

36. $p \vee \sim q$
37. $q \rightarrow p$
38. $p \leftrightarrow q$
39. $(p \vee q) \rightarrow p$
40. $\sim(\sim p \vee q)$

Section 3-2

For Exercises 41–48, construct a truth table for each statement.

41. $p \leftrightarrow \sim q$
42. $\sim p \rightarrow (\sim q \vee p)$
43. $(p \rightarrow q) \wedge \sim q$
44. $\sim p \vee (\sim q \rightarrow p)$
45. $\sim q \leftrightarrow (p \rightarrow q)$
46. $(p \rightarrow \sim q) \vee r$
47. $(p \vee \sim q) \wedge r$
48. $r \rightarrow (\sim p \vee q)$

For Exercises 49–52, use the truth value of each simple statement to determine the truth value of the compound statement.

49. p: January is the first month of the year.
    q: It snows in January in every state.
    Statement: $p \rightarrow q$

50. p: Gas prices reached record highs in 2008.
    q: Automobile makers started making more fuel-efficient cars.
    Statement: $p \wedge q$

51. p: Barack Obama was a Presidential candidate in 2008.
    q: Lindsay Lohan was a Presidential candidate in 2008.
    r: Obama won the Democratic nomination in 2008.
    Statement: $(p \vee q) \rightarrow r$

52. p: Attending college costs thousands of dollars.
    q: Lack of education does not lead to lower salaries.
    r: The average college graduate will make back more than they paid for school.
    Statement: $(p \wedge \sim q) \leftrightarrow r$

Section 3-3

For Exercises 53–57, determine if the statement is a tautology, self-contradiction, or neither.

53. $p \rightarrow (p \vee q)$
54. $(p \rightarrow q) \rightarrow (p \vee q)$
55. $(p \wedge \sim q) \leftrightarrow (q \wedge \sim p)$
56. $q \rightarrow (p \vee \sim p)$
57. $(\sim q \vee p) \wedge q$

For Exercises 58–60, determine whether the two statements are logically equivalent.

58. $\sim(p \rightarrow q)$; $\sim p \wedge \sim q$
59. $\sim p \vee \sim q$; $\sim(p \leftrightarrow q)$
60. $(\sim p \wedge q) \vee r$; $(\sim p \vee r) \wedge (q \vee r)$

For Exercises 61–64, use De Morgan's laws to write the negation of each statement.

61. The Internet connection is either dial-up or DSL.
62. We will increase sales or our profit margin will go down.
63. The signature is not authentic and the check is not valid.
64. It is not strenuous and I am tired.

For Exercises 65 and 66, assign a letter to each simple statement and write the compound statement in symbols.

65. I will be happy only if I get rich.
66. Having a good career is sufficient for a fulfilling life.

For Exercises 67–69, write the converse, inverse, and contrapositive of the statement.

67. If gas prices go any higher, I will start riding my bike to work.
68. If I don't pass this class, my parents will kill me.
69. The festival will move inside the student center only if it rains.

Section 3-4

For Exercises 70–73, use truth tables to determine whether each argument is valid or invalid.

70. $p \rightarrow \sim q$
    $\underline{\sim q \leftrightarrow \sim p}$
    $\therefore p$

71. $\sim q \vee p$
    $\underline{p \wedge q}$
    $\therefore \sim q \leftrightarrow p$

72. $\sim p \vee q$
    $\underline{q \vee \sim r}$
    $\therefore q \rightarrow (\sim p \wedge \sim r)$

73. $\sim r \rightarrow \sim p$
    $\underline{\sim q \vee \sim r}$
    $\therefore p \leftrightarrow q$

For Exercises 74–77, write the argument in symbols; then use a truth table to determine if the argument is valid.

74. If I go to Barnes & Noble, then I will buy the latest Stephen King novel.
    I did not buy the latest Stephen King novel.
    $\therefore$ I did not go to Barnes and Noble.

75. I'm going to Wal-Mart and McDonald's.
    If I go to McDonald's, I will get the sweet tea.
    $\therefore$ I did not get sweet tea and go to Wal-Mart.

76. If we don't hire two more workers, the union will strike.
    If the union strikes, our profit will not increase.
    We hired two more workers.
    $\therefore$ Our profit will not increase.

77. If I don't study, I won't make honor roll.
    I made the honor roll.
    $\therefore$ I didn't study or I cheated.

For Exercises 78–81, use the commonly used forms of arguments from Section 3-4 to determine if the argument is valid.

78. I will drink a mineral water or a Gatorade.
    I drank a Gatorade.
    $\therefore$ I did not drink mineral water.

79. If it is early, I will get tickets to the comedy club.
    It is not early.
    $\therefore$ I will not get tickets to the comedy club.

80. If I am cold, I will wear a sweater.
    If I wear a sweater, I am warm.
    $\therefore$ If I am cold, I am warm.

81. If pigs fly, then I'm a monkey's uncle.
    Pigs fly or birds don't sing.
    Birds do sing.
    $\therefore$ I'm a monkey's uncle.

Section 3-5

For Exercises 82–86, use Euler circles to determine whether the argument is valid or invalid.

82. No A is B.
    Some B is C.
    $\therefore$ No A is C.

83. Some A is not C.
    Some B is not C.
    $\therefore$ Some A is not B.

84. All money is green.
    All grass is green.
    $\therefore$ Grass is money.

85. No humans have three eyes.
    Some Martians have three eyes.
    $\therefore$ No Martians are humans.

86. Some movies are rated "R."
    All R-rated movies are inappropriate for children.
    $\therefore$ Some movies are inappropriate for children.

Chapter Test

For Exercises 1–4, decide whether the sentence is a statement.

1. I'm going to the karaoke club.
2. $4 + 7 = 10$
3. That woman is really smart.
4. Don't let it get to you.

For Exercises 5–8, write the negation of the statement.

5. The image is uploading to my online bio.
6. All men have goatees.
7. Some students ride a bike to school.
8. No short people can dunk a basketball.

For Exercises 9–14, let p = "It is warm." Let q = "It is sunny." Write each statement in symbols.

9. It is warm and sunny.
10. If it is sunny, then it is warm.
11. It is warm if and only if it is sunny.
12. It is warm or sunny.
13. It is false that it is not warm and sunny.
14. It is not sunny, and it is not warm.

For Exercises 15–19, let p = "It is sunny." Let q = "It is warm." Write each in words.

15. $p \vee \sim q$
16. $q \rightarrow p$
17. $p \leftrightarrow q$
18. $(p \vee q) \rightarrow p$
19. $\sim(\sim p \vee q)$

For Exercises 20–24, construct a truth table for each statement.

20. $p \rightarrow \sim q$
21. $(p \rightarrow \sim q) \wedge r$
22. $(p \wedge \sim q) \vee \sim r$
23. $(\sim q \vee p) \wedge p$
24. $p \rightarrow (\sim q \vee r)$

For Exercises 25–29, determine whether each statement is a tautology, self-contradiction, or neither.

25. $(p \wedge q) \wedge \sim p$
26. $(p \vee q) \rightarrow (p \rightarrow q)$
27. $(p \vee \sim q) \leftrightarrow (p \rightarrow \sim q)$
28. $q \wedge (p \vee \sim p)$
29. $\sim(p \wedge q) \vee p$

For Exercises 30–31, determine if the two statements are logically equivalent.

30. $p; \sim(\sim p)$
31. $(p \vee q) \wedge r; (p \wedge r) \vee (q \wedge r)$
32. Write the converse, inverse, and contrapositive for the statement "If I exercise regularly, then I will be healthy."

For Exercises 33–34 use De Morgan's laws to write the negation of the compound statement.

33. It is not cold and it is snowing.
34. I am hungry or thirsty.

For Exercises 35–38, use truth tables to determine the validity of each argument.

35. $p \leftrightarrow \sim q$
    $\dfrac{\sim q \rightarrow \sim p}{\therefore p}$

36. $p \rightarrow q$
    $\dfrac{\sim q \vee \sim r}{\therefore q \leftrightarrow (\sim p \wedge \sim r)}$

37. $\sim q \vee p$
    $\dfrac{p \vee q}{\therefore \sim q \rightarrow p}$

38. $\sim p \rightarrow \sim r$
    $\dfrac{\sim r \vee \sim q}{\therefore q \leftrightarrow p}$

For Exercises 39–41, determine if the argument is valid or invalid by using the given forms of valid arguments and fallacies.

39. If I finish my paper early, I will have my professor proofread it.
    I have my professor proofread my paper.
    ∴ I finish my paper early.

40. The scratch-off ticket is a winner or a loser.
    The scratch-off ticket is a winner.
    ∴ The scratch-off ticket is not a loser.

41. If Starbuck's is not too busy, I will study there.
    If Starbuck's is too busy, I will study at the library.
    ∴ If I do not study at Starbuck's, I will study at the library.

For Exercises 42–45, use Euler circles to determine whether the argument is valid or invalid.

42. No B is A.
    Some A is C.
    ∴ No B is C.

43. Some C is not A.
    Some B is not A.
    ∴ Some C is not B.

44. No good relationship has bad moments.
    Fred and Suzie have a good relationship.
    ∴ Fred and Suzie never have bad moments.

45. Some computer mice are wireless.
    All computer devices that are wireless are expensive.
    ∴ Some computer mice are expensive.

Projects

1. Truth tables are related to Euler circles. Arguments in the form of Euler circles can be translated into statements by using the basic connectives and the negation as follows:

   Let p be "The object belongs to set A." Let q be "The object belongs to set B."

   All A is B is equivalent to $p \rightarrow q$.
   No A is B is equivalent to $p \rightarrow \sim q$.
   Some A is B is equivalent to $p \wedge q$.
   Some A is not B is equivalent to $p \wedge \sim q$.

   Determine the validity of the next arguments by using Euler circles; translate the statements into logical statements using the basic connectives; and using truth tables, determine the validity of the arguments. Compare your answers.

   (a) No A is B.
       Some C is A.
       ∴ Some C is not B.

   (b) All B is A.
       All C is A.
       ∴ All C is B.

2. Politicians argue in favor of positions all the time. An informed voter doesn't vote for a candidate because of the candidate's party, gender, race, or how good they look on TV—an informed voter listens to the candidates' positions and evaluates them.

   Do a Google search for the text of a speech by each of the main candidates in the 2008 Presidential election. Then find at least three logical arguments within the text, write the arguments in symbols, and use truth tables or commonly used argument forms to analyze the arguments, and see if they are valid.

3. Electric circuits are designed using truth tables. A circuit consists of switches. Two switches wired in *series* can be represented as $p \wedge q$. Two switches wired in *parallel* can be represented as $p \vee q$.

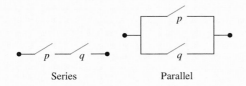

Series   Parallel

In a series, circuit electricity will flow only when both switches p and q are closed. In a parallel circuit, electricity will flow when one or the other or both switches are closed. In a truth table, T represents a closed switch and F represents an open switch. So the truth table for $p \wedge q$ shows electricity flowing only when both switches are closed.

Truth table

p	q	$p \wedge q$
T	T	T
T	F	F
F	T	F
F	F	F

Circuit

p	q	$p \wedge q$
closed	closed	current
closed	open	no current
open	closed	no current
open	open	no current

Also, when switch p is closed, switch $\sim p$ will be open and vice versa, and p and $\sim p$ are different switches. Using this knowledge, design a circuit for a hall light that has switches at both ends of the hall so that the light can be turned on or off from either switch.

CHAPTER 9

Measurement

Outline

9-1 Measures of Length: Converting Units and the Metric System

9-2 Measures of Area, Volume, and Capacity

9-3 Measures of Weight and Temperature Summary

MATH IN ▸ Travel

To measure something means to assign a number that represents its size. In fact, measurement might be the most common use of numbers in everyday life. Numbers are used to measure heights, weights, distances, grades, weather, sizes of homes, capacities of bottles and cans, and much more. Even in our monetary system, we are using numbers to measure sizes: little ones, like the cost of a candy bar, and big ones, like an annual salary.

The one thing that every measurement has in common is that it's good for absolutely nothing unless there are units attached to the number. If a friend asks you how far you live from campus and you answer "three," at best they'll look at you funny and cautiously back away. An answer like that is meaningless because without units, there's no context to describe what the number represents. And that's entirely because there are many different units that can be used to describe similar measurements. That number 3 could mean 3 miles, kilometers, blocks, houses, even parsecs if you come from a galaxy far, far away.

In this chapter, we will study the different ways that things are measured in our world, with a special focus on the different units that are used. You probably have at least a passing familiarity with the metric system, since measurements in units like liters and kilometers are becoming more common. When you gather information of interest to you, you don't always get to choose the units that the information is provided in, so the ability to convert measurements from one unit to another is a particularly useful skill in the information age.

One obvious application of this skill comes into play when traveling outside the United States. Most countries use the metric system almost exclusively, meaning that to understand various bits of information, you need to be able to interpret measurements in an unfamiliar system. Suppose that you and your sweetie are planning a dream week in Aruba: the following questions might be of interest. By the time you complete this chapter, you'll be able to answer the questions, making you a more well-informed traveler.

1. A check of a tourist web site informs you that the temperature is expected to range from 24° to 32° Celsius. How should you pack?

2. The airline that will fly you to Aruba allows a maximum of 30 kilograms for each piece of luggage. If your empty suitcase weighs 4 pounds, how many pounds can you pack into it?

3. The resort you will be staying at is 4.2 kilometers from the airport and 0.6 kilometers from downtown. Can you walk downtown? And how long will it take to drive your rental car from the airport at 35 miles per hour?

4. At the gas station closest to the airport, gas costs $0.43 per liter. If you use ¾ of the car's 16-gallon tank, how much will it cost to refill?

For answers, see Math in Travel Revisited on page 506

481

Section 9-1 Measures of Length: Converting Units and the Metric System

LEARNING OBJECTIVES

☐ 1. Convert measurements of length in the English system.

☐ 2. Convert measurements in the metric system.

☐ 3. Convert between English and metric units of length.

Units of length are among the oldest and most common units used to measure objects. They are used to measure everything from your waistline to the distance between the earth and far away planets. In this section, we will study two systems for measuring length, and become expert at converting from one unit to another. This skill will serve you well in any topic where different units of measure are used.

The units of length that are commonly used in the United States are the inch, foot, yard, and mile. These are all part of the **English system of measurement,** which is very old indeed. (See Sidelight on page 483 for some historical perspective.) The basic conversion factors between units in the English system are shown in Table 9-1.

There are several ways to convert from one unit of measure to another. Many people use the "common sense" method. For example, to convert 6 yards to feet, multiply 6×3 feet $= 18$ feet, since there are 3 feet in 1 yard. To convert 564 inches to feet, divide 564 inches by $12 = 47$ feet, since there are 12 inches in 1 foot.

A more systematic, and reliable, method for converting units is known as **dimensional analysis.** It is based on one simple idea: if measurements in two different units represent the same length, like 1 yard and 3 feet, then a fraction formed with the two measurements is equal to 1. For example,

$$\frac{1 \text{ yd}}{3 \text{ ft}} = 1 \quad \text{and} \quad \frac{3 \text{ ft}}{1 \text{ yd}} = 1$$

We call a fraction of this type a **unit fraction.** Our procedure for converting units will be to multiply by one or more unit fractions in such a way that the units we don't want can be divided out, leaving behind the units that we do want. Since all we're really doing is multiplying by 1, we won't be changing the actual value of the measurement—just the units it's measured in. The procedure is illustrated in Examples 1 to 4 below.

TABLE 9-1	Units of Length in the English System

12 inches (in.) = 1 foot (ft)
3 feet = 1 yard (yd)
36 inches = 1 yard
5,280 feet = 1 mile (mi)
1,760 yards = 1 mile

EXAMPLE 1	Converting Yards to Feet

Convert 6 yards to feet.

Math Note

You might find it helpful to write the original measurement as a fraction with denominator 1 as in Example 1, but it isn't necessary.

SOLUTION

The goal is to eliminate the units of yards, and leave behind feet. So we would like to use a unit fraction that has yards in the denominator (to divide out yards) and feet in the numerator. That would be the second one shown above $\left(\frac{3 \text{ ft}}{1 \text{ yd}}\right)$:

$$\frac{6 \text{ y\!\!\!/d}}{1} \cdot \frac{3 \text{ ft}}{1 \text{ y\!\!\!/d}} = 18 \text{ ft}$$

The yards divided out, leaving behind feet in the numerator.

▼ **Try This One** 1

Convert 81 feet to yards.

EXAMPLE 2 **Converting Feet to Miles**

The height of Mount Everest is 29,035 feet. How many miles is that?

SOLUTION

This time, we want a unit fraction with feet in the denominator and miles in the numerator: that is, $\frac{1\text{ mi}}{5,280\text{ ft}}$.

$$\frac{29,035\text{ ft}}{1} \cdot \frac{1\text{ mi}}{5,280\text{ ft}} = \frac{29,035\text{ mi}}{5,280} \approx 5.5\text{ mi}$$

▼ **Try This One** 2

The maximum cruising height of a Boeing 737 is about 7.77 miles. How many feet is that?

Sometimes we will need to multiply by more than one unit fraction to make a conversion.

Sidelight **A BRIEF HISTORY OF MEASURING LENGTHS**

Nobody knows how and when human beings started measuring physical objects, but historians seem to be in general agreement that the earliest recorded measurements were lengths. In particular, they were based on parts of the human body. If you search the Internet for early units of measurement, the most common one you will find is the **cubit,** first used by the Egyptians around 5,000 years ago. The cubit was equal to the distance from a person's elbow to the outstretched middle finger. (If you try to measure something that way, make sure to stretch out your other fingers as well.) Other early units were the **palm** (the distance across the base of a person's four fingers) and the **digit** (the thickness of a person's middle finger).

This leads us to believe that one of two things was true: either everyone was exactly the same size in ancient Egypt, or their units of measurement were pretty imprecise. Things got a little more specific sometime around the year 1100 CE, when King Henry I of England declared that the distance from the tip of his nose to the end of his thumb would be known as a **yard.** (At least this distance was based on one specific person's physical size.) The oldest known yardstick still in existence, believed to have been made in 1445, is accurate to a modern yard within about $\frac{1}{300}$th of an inch.

A couple hundred years later, King Edward I declared that one third of a yard should be called a **foot.** In 1595, Queen Elizabeth changed the length of a mile from the Roman tradition of 5,000 feet to the current 5,280 feet so that it was exactly 8 furlongs. (Perhaps she was a big fan of horse racing, which still uses furlongs.) Eventually, the English system of measurement became standard throughout the world. Of course, these units are still used in the United States today. The real irony? England has been officially using the metric system since 1965. In fact, only three countries in the world have not officially adopted the metric system, which we'll study later in this section: the United States, Liberia, and Myanmar.

EXAMPLE 3   Converting Measurements Using Two Unit Fractions

The distance by air from JFK airport to LaGuardia airport in New York is about 11 miles. How many inches is that?

SOLUTION

Looking at Table 9-1, there is no conversion factor for miles to inches. But we can go from miles to feet $\left(\text{using } \frac{5,280 \text{ ft}}{1 \text{ mi}}\right)$ then from feet to inches $\left(\text{using } \frac{12 \text{ in.}}{1 \text{ ft}}\right)$:

$$\frac{11 \text{ mi}}{1} \cdot \frac{5,280 \text{ ft}}{\text{mi}} \cdot \frac{12 \text{ in.}}{1 \text{ ft}} = 11 \times 5,280 \times 12 \text{ in.} = 696,960 \text{ in.}$$

> **Math Note**
>
> Notice that we put the units we wanted to eliminate in the denominator, and the units we wanted to keep in the numerator.

▼ Try This One 3

A football field is 100 yards long. How many inches is that?

Dimensional analysis can also be used to convert more complicated units, like those for speed, as shown in Example 4.

EXAMPLE 4   Converting Units for Speed

A decent major league pitcher can throw a baseball 90 miles per hour. How fast is that in feet per second?

SOLUTION

Notice that we can write 90 miles per hour as a fraction: $\frac{90 \text{ mi}}{1 \text{ hr}}$. Now we can multiply by unit fractions that convert miles to feet $\left(\frac{5,280 \text{ ft}}{1 \text{ mi}}\right)$, hours to minutes $\left(\frac{1 \text{ h}}{60 \text{ min}}\right)$, and minutes to seconds $\left(\frac{1 \text{ min}}{60 \text{ s}}\right)$.

$$\frac{90 \text{ mi}}{1 \text{ h}} \cdot \frac{5,280 \text{ ft}}{1 \text{ mi}} \cdot \frac{1 \text{ h}}{60 \text{ min}} \cdot \frac{1 \text{ min}}{60 \text{ s}} = \frac{90 \times 5,280 \text{ ft}}{60 \times 60 \text{ s}} = 132 \frac{\text{ft}}{\text{s}}$$

CAUTION

In this case, we wanted seconds in the denominator, so we had to be extra careful to put the units we wanted to eliminate in the numerator, and the ones we wanted to keep in the denominator.

▼ Try This One 4

The speed of sound at sea level and room temperature is about 1,126 feet per second. How fast is that in miles per hour?

☑ 1. Convert measurements of length in the English system.

The Metric System

If you grew up in the United States, you're probably perfectly happy with the English system of measurement. You've been using it your whole life, after all. But the truth

Sidelight **THE LUNAR WEIGHT-LOSS PLAN**

Since weight is a measure of gravitational pull, your weight is less in locations where gravity is not as strong. The effect is negligible pretty much anywhere on earth, although you would weigh about 0.3% less at the top of Mt. Everest than you would at sea level. But once you leave earth, weight can vary widely. The force of gravity on the moon, for example, is about one-sixth of what it is on earth. So by heading to the moon, you would instantly shed five-sixths of your weight!

Of course, you would still be the same size (i.e., your mass won't change), but the scale would seem like a much friendlier place to most of us.

Math Note

Technically speaking, the gram is a unit of mass, not weight, and the two are slightly different. The weight of an object is the measure of the gravitational pull on it, so your weight can vary depending on where you are. (See Sidelight above.) Mass is a constant measure of the physical size of an object regardless of location. Since we all live on the earth, we'll consider mass and weight to be synonymous.

is that it's not that great of a system because there's no rhyme or reason to it. Why is 12 inches a foot? Why is 5,280 feet a mile? They just are. Somebody decided, and that was that. The metric system, on the other hand, makes a bit more sense because the different units of measure are all related by powers of 10. We'll see exactly what that means after introducing the base units. The metric system uses three basic units of measure: the *meter,* the *liter,* and the *gram.*

Length in the metric system is measured using **meters.** One meter is a bit more than a yard, about 39.4 inches. The symbol for meter is "m."

The basic unit for capacity in the metric system is the **liter,** which is a little bit more than a quart. (You're probably familiar with 2-liter bottles of soda—that's close to a half gallon.) The symbol for liter is "L."

The basic unit for measuring weight in the metric system is the **gram.** This is a very small unit—a nickel weighs about 5 grams. The symbol for gram is "g."

Now back to other units in the metric system. All units other than the three basic units are based on multiples of the basic units, with those multiples all being powers of 10. For example, a standard unit of weight for people in the metric system is the kilogram: this is equal to 1,000 grams. A commonly used unit of length for smaller measurements is the centimeter, which is $\frac{1}{100}$ meter. It's the prefix in front of the basic unit that determines the size. The most common metric prefixes are listed in Table 9-2.

TABLE 9-2   **Metric Prefixes**

Prefix	Symbol	Meaning
kilo	k	1,000 units
hecto	h	100 units
deka	da	10 units
	m, L, g	1 unit
deci	d	$\frac{1}{10}$ of a unit
centi	c	$\frac{1}{100}$ of a unit
milli	m	$\frac{1}{1,000}$ of a unit

The relationship between units in the metric system is a lot like the units used in our monetary system. Table 9-3 demonstrates this comparison for the base unit of meter.

TABLE 9-3   **Relationship between Metric Units and U.S. Currency**

Metric Unit	Meaning	Monetary Comparison
kilometer	1,000 meters	$1,000
hectometer	100 meters	100
dekameter	10 meters	10
meter (base unit)	1 meter	dollar (base unit)
decimeter	0.1 meter	0.10 (10 cents)
centimeter	0.01 meter	0.01 (1 cent)
millimeter	0.001 meter	0.001 (1/10 cent)

There are several ways to do conversions in the metric system. The easiest way is to multiply or divide by powers of 10. The basic rules are given next.

Conversion When You Use the Metric System

To change a larger unit to a smaller unit in the metric system, multiply by 10^n, where n is the number of steps that you move down in Table 9-4.

To change a smaller unit to a larger unit in the metric system, divide by 10^n, where n is the number of steps that you move up in Table 9-4.

TABLE 9-4   **Metric Unit Conversions**

$$\text{divide} \left\{ \begin{array}{l} \text{kilo} \\ \text{hecto} \\ \text{deka} \\ \text{base unit} \\ \text{deci} \\ \text{centi} \\ \text{milli} \end{array} \right\} \text{multiply}$$

Units get smaller as you read down the chart.

EXAMPLE 5   **Converting Metric Units**

Many rulers and tape measures are marked with both inches and centimeters.

Convert 42.5 kilometers to centimeters.

SOLUTION

The prefix "kilo" is higher in Table 9-4 than "centi," so we're converting to smaller units, which means we need to multiply. There are 5 steps from "kilo" to "centi" in the table, so the power of 10 we multiply by is 10^5. This can be quickly accomplished by moving the decimal point 5 places to the right:

$$42.5 \text{ km} \times 10^5 = 42.50000 = 4{,}250{,}000 \text{ cm}$$

▼ Try This One 5

Convert 170 dekagrams to milligrams.

EXAMPLE 6 **Converting Metric Units**

Convert 1,253.7 milligrams to grams.

SOLUTION

The gram is the base unit of weight, and the prefix "milli" is below the base unit in the table, so we are converting to a larger unit and must divide. There are 3 steps from "milli" to the base unit in the table, so we divide by 10^3. This can be quickly done by moving the decimal point 3 places to the left:

$$1{,}253.7 \text{ mg} \div 10^3 = 1253.7 = 1.2537 \text{ grams}$$

▼ Try This One 6

Convert 173.6 deciliters to dekaliters.

Conversion in the metric system can also be done using dimensional analysis. We will use Table 9-2 to convert first to the base unit, then the unit we want.

EXAMPLE 7 **Converting in the Metric System with Dimensional Analysis**

Convert 42.5 kilometers to centimeters using dimensional analysis.

SOLUTION

According to Table 9-2, 1 kilometer is 1,000 meters, and 1 meter is 100 centimeters.

$$\frac{42.5 \text{ km}}{1} \cdot \frac{1{,}000 \text{ m}}{1 \text{ km}} \cdot \frac{100 \text{ cm}}{1 \text{ m}} = 42.5 \times 100{,}000 = 4{,}250{,}000 \text{ cm}$$

This agrees with our answer to Example 5.

Math Note

You will be able to do metric conversion a lot more efficiently if you take a few minutes to learn which prefixes indicate units larger than the base unit, and which indicate units smaller than the base unit.

☑ 2. Convert measurements in the metric system.

Many road signs now list mileages in both miles and kilometers.

▼ Try This One 7

Convert 170 dekagrams to milligrams using dimensional analysis.

Because most of the world uses the metric system while the United States uses the English system, it is often necessary to convert between the two systems. We will use dimensional analysis, along with the table below, which provides conversion factors for units of length.

English and Metric Equivalents for Length

1 in. = 2.54 cm	1 mm ≈ 0.03937 in.
1 ft = 30.48 cm = 0.3048 m	1 cm ≈ 0.3937 in.
1 yd = 91.44 cm = 0.9144 m	1 m ≈ 1.0936 yd = 3.2808 ft
1 mi ≈ 1.61 km	1 km ≈ 0.6214 mi

EXAMPLE 8   **Converting Between English and Metric Lengths**

Convert each.

(a) 135 feet to centimeters   (b) 87 centimeters to inches
(c) 213.36 millimeters to feet

SOLUTION

(a) To convert feet to centimeters use the unit fraction $\frac{30.48 \text{ cm}}{1 \text{ ft}}$.

$$135 \text{ ft} \cdot \frac{30.48 \text{ cm}}{1 \text{ ft}} = 135 \cdot 30.48 \text{ cm} = 4{,}114.8 \text{ cm}$$

(b) To convert centimeters to inches use the unit fraction $\frac{1 \text{ in.}}{2.54 \text{ cm}}$.

$$87 \text{ cm} \cdot \frac{1 \text{ in.}}{2.54 \text{ cm}} = \frac{87 \text{ in.}}{2.54} = 34.25 \text{ in. (rounded)}$$

(c) To convert from millimeters to feet, we first convert millimeters to centimeters using the unit fraction $\frac{1 \text{ cm}}{10 \text{ mm}}$, then convert centimeters to feet using the unit fraction $\frac{1 \text{ ft}}{30.48 \text{ cm}}$.

$$213.36 \text{ mm} \cdot \frac{1 \text{ cm}}{10 \text{ mm}} \cdot \frac{1 \text{ ft}}{30.48 \text{ cm}} = \frac{213.36 \text{ ft}}{(10 \cdot 30.48)} = 0.7 \text{ ft}$$

Alternatively, we could convert millimeters to inches, then inches to feet:

$$213.36 \text{ mm} \cdot \frac{0.03937 \text{ in.}}{1 \text{ mm}} \cdot \frac{1 \text{ ft}}{12 \text{ in.}} \approx \frac{213.36 \cdot 0.0397}{12} \text{ ft} \approx 0.7 \text{ ft}$$

The results are close, but not exactly the same. The first worked out to be exactly 0.7, while the second came out to 0.6999986.

Math Note

Because some of the English-metric conversions are approximations due to rounding, the converted measurements are often approximations as well. This accounts for the fact that the two methods shown for part (c) lead to slightly different results.

☑ 3. Convert between English and metric units of length.

▼ **Try This One 8**

Convert each of the following. Round to two decimal places.
(a) 237 feet to meters   (b) 128 cm to inches   (c) 23,342 mm to feet

Answers to Try This One

1 27 yd   **3** 3,600 in.   **5** 1,700,000 mg   **7** 1,700,000 mg

2 41,025.6 ft   **4** About 767.7 mi/h **6** 1.736 daL   **8** (a) 72.24 m (b) 50.39 in. (c) 76.58 ft

EXERCISE SET 9-1

Writing Exercises

1. What are the basic units of length in the English measurement system, and how are they related?
2. What are the basic units of length, capacity, and weight in the metric system?

3. What importance do prefixes play in different units of measure in the metric system?
4. Describe how to use dimensional analysis to convert units of measure.

Computational Exercises

For Exercises 5–16, convert each using dimensional analysis. round to 2 decimal places if necessary.
5. 12 feet to yards   6. 36 inches to feet

7. 17 feet to yards
8. 10,345 feet to miles
9. 6 yards to feet

10. 5 miles to yards
11. 21 inches to feet
12. 10 yards to feet

13. 18 inches to yards
14. 5,237,834 inches to miles
15. 876 inches to yards
16. 182 feet to yards

For Exercises 17–56, convert each measurement to the specified unit.

17. 8 m = _____ cm
18. 0.25 m = _____ dm
19. 12 dam = _____ m
20. 24 hm = _____ dam
21. 0.6 km = _____ hm
22. 30 cm = _____ dm
23. 90 m = _____ dm
24. 18,426 mm = _____ m
25. 375.6 cm = _____ m
26. 63 m = _____ km
27. 405.3 m = _____ km
28. 0.6 dam = _____ hm
29. 12 km = _____ cm
30. 50,000 cm = _____ km
31. 1.85 km = _____ mm
32. 650,000 mm = _____ km
33. 12.62 km = _____ dm
34. 39 m = _____ cm

35. 8 hm = _____ km
36. 540 dm = _____ cm
37. 5 meters = _____ inches
38. 14 yards = _____ meters
39. 16 inches = _____ millimeters
40. 50 meters = _____ yards
41. 235 feet = _____ dekameter
42. 563 decimeters = _____ inches
43. 1,350 meters = _____ feet
44. 4,375 dekameters = _____ feet
45. 0.6 inch = _____ millimeters
46. 256 kilometers = _____ miles
47. 0.06 hectometers = _____ feet
48. 54 inches = _____ centimeters
49. 1,345 feet = _____ decimeters
50. 44,000 millimeters = _____ yards
51. 2.35 kilometers = _____ miles
52. 837 miles = _____ kilometers
53. 42 decimeters = _____ yards
54. 75 centimeters = _____ inches
55. 333 inches = _____ meters
56. 1,256 kilometers = _____ inches

Real-World Applications

57. Steve sprinted the last 5 yards of a race. How many feet did he sprint?
58. A professional basketball court is 94 feet long. How many inches is that?
59. On a baseball diamond, the bases are 90 feet apart. How many yards does a batter run in reaching second base?
60. A football player completed a 45-yard pass. How many inches did he throw the ball?
61. A traffic reporter announced a backup on I-95 of 1,500 yards. How far is that in miles?
62. Sarah wanted to buy a new queen-sized mattress. She only has an area that measures 5 ft × 6 ft to put the mattress. The mattress size is 60 in. × 80 in. Will the mattress fit? Convert the measurements to feet to determine this.
63. Celia used a tape measure to section off areas for her vegetable garden. She measured the section for tomatoes to be 126 inches long. How many yards long is the section for Celia's tomatoes?
64. What are the dimensions of a 6 dm by 5 dm piece of poster board in centimeters? In millimeters?
65. To make a batch of an energy drink, Gina used 2.3 grams of citric acid. How many milligrams of citric acid did she use?
66. If a millipede has 1,000 legs, how many legs would a decipede have?
67. Sanford's gym coach made him run 20 laps on a 700-m track. How many kilometers did he run?
68. How many miles will a runner cover in a 10-km race?

69. Frank drives 65 miles per hour on a freeway in Detroit. When he crosses into Windsor, Ontario, he resumes the same speed. How fast does Frank drive in kilometers per hour?
70. Mary brings a 20-inch by 24-inch picture to the frame shop, but the frame she wants only lists measurements in terms of centimeters. What are the measurements of her picture in centimeters?
71. A bowling lane from the foul line to the pins is 62 feet $10\frac{3}{16}$ inches long. How many meters is a bowling lane?
72. A 5-carat round-cut diamond measures half an inch in diameter. How many millimeters is the diameter of the diamond?
73. The new Mars Pathfinder postage stamp measures 1.5 × 3 inches. What are the stamp's measurements in millimeters?
74. Light travels at 186,283 miles every second. How many feet per hour does light travel?
75. The earth is on average 92,900,000 miles from the sun. In July, the distance is 94,400,000 miles, the farthest of any month. What is the distance in feet of the difference of the distance in July from the average?
76. To build a loft in his dorm room, Jay got 8-foot planks from the lumber yard. To get the right size, he had to cut off a quarter of each plank. How many inches did he cut off each?
77. A college is building a new basketball court that is 94 feet long and 50 feet wide, but the wood for the

court comes only in 10-meter planks that are 8 centimeters wide. How many planks are needed to surface the court? (*Hint:* Round each measurement up to estimate the number of planks needed.)

78. If three servings of ice cream have 20 grams of fat, how many milligrams of fat does one serving have?

79. A popular pain-relieving drug has 200 mg of its active ingredient in one capsule. If a bottle has 100 capsules, how many grams of the active ingredient are in the bottle?

80. The campus fitness center is installing an Olympic-sized swimming pool that measures 164 ft × 82 ft. The builders want to put 6-inch tiles around the border. How many tiles will they need?

81. If one U.S. dollar was worth 1.22 Canadian dollars when Sal went to a debate tournament in Toronto, and he had $400 in U.S. currency as spending money, how much was his money worth in Canadian dollars?

82. While in Chile, where $1 in U.S. currency was worth 610.045 in Chilean pesos, you won 10,000,000 Chilean pesos. Did you plan to eat a nice dinner out, buy a new car, or buy a new house? Explain your answer.

83. On her summer abroad in France, Jane bought a pair of shoes for 54.23 euros. The store owner only had francs to give her as change. She gave him 60 euros. How much did he give her back in francs? At the time, 1 euro was worth 6.55957 francs.

84. In August of 2008, one dollar could buy 9.86 Mexican pesos. In early February of 2009, that same dollar could buy 14.49 Mexican pesos. If you paid 750 pesos per night at a hotel in Cancun in August 2008, and your friend paid the same rate the following February, how much less per night in dollars did he spend?

Critical Thinking

85. Suppose that four world-class sprinters compare times after running different distances. The first ran the 100-yard dash in 9.12 seconds; the second ran the 100-meter dash in 9.72 seconds; the third ran the 220-yard dash in 19.75 seconds; the fourth ran the 200-meter dash in 19.71 seconds. Which is the most impressive feat? Explain your reasoning.

86. What units would 7,000 cm have to be converted to so that the result has no zeros?

87. What units would 0.006 m have to be converted to so that the result has no zeros?

Section 9-2 Measures of Area, Volume, and Capacity

The units of length we studied in Section 9-1 are useful for measuring many things, but they have a major limitation: length is a one-dimensional measurement, and we live in a three-dimensional world. It's equally important to be able to measure in two dimensions, like the size of a lot for a new home, and in three dimensions, like the capacity of a swimming pool. So in this section, we will study area (two dimensions) and volume and capacity (both three dimensions).

LEARNING OBJECTIVES

☐ 1. Convert units of area.

☐ 2. Convert units of volume.

Conversions of Area

Units of length are also called **linear units,** because they are used to measure along a line. The units used to measure the size of an object in two dimensions are called **square units.** They are based on a very simple idea: one square unit is defined to be the area of a square that is one unit long on each side. For example, a square inch is the area of a square that is 1 inch on each side, as shown in Figure 9-1.

The area of other figures is then defined to be the number of square units that will fit inside the figure. For example, the rectangle in Figure 9-2 is 3 inches by 5 inches, and we can see that 15 one-inch by one-inch squares will fit inside. So its area is 15 square inches, which we abbreviate as 15 in.^{2}.

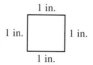

Figure 9-1   One square inch

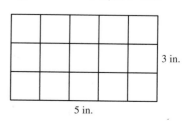

Figure 9-2   15 in.^{2}

Finding the area of various geometric shapes will be covered in Chapter 10. In this section we will focus on conversions between different units of area.

Because the units used in measuring area are square units, the conversions will be the squares of the conversions in linear measure. For example, we know that 1 ft = 12 in., so $(1 \text{ ft})^2 = (12 \text{ in.})^2$, or $1 \text{ ft}^2 = 144 \text{ in.}^2$. The conversions for area are summarized in Table 9-5.

TABLE 9-5 English and Metric Equivalents for Area

English Conversions for Area	English/Metric Conversions for Area
$1 \text{ ft}^2 = 144 \text{ in.}^2$	$1 \text{ in.}^2 \approx 6.45 \text{ cm}^2$
$1 \text{ yd}^2 = 9 \text{ ft}^2 = 1{,}296 \text{ in.}^2$	$1 \text{ ft}^2 \approx 0.093 \text{ m}^2$
$1 \text{ mi}^2 = 27{,}878{,}400 \text{ ft}^2 = 3{,}097{,}600 \text{ yd}^2$	$1 \text{ yd}^2 \approx 0.836 \text{ m}^2$
$1 \text{ acre} = 43{,}560 \text{ ft}^2$	$1 \text{ mi}^2 \approx 2.59 \text{ km}^2$
$1 \text{ mi}^2 = 640 \text{ acres}$	$1 \text{ acre} \approx 4{,}047 \text{ m}^2$

Math Note

The acre is a very old measure of area, traditionally thought to be the area that could be plowed by one man behind one ox in one day.

The next examples will show how to use dimensional analysis to convert measures of area.

EXAMPLE 1 Converting Square Inches to Square Feet

A 52-in. wide-screen TV has a screen area of $1{,}064 \text{ in.}^2$. How many square feet is that?

SOLUTION

We want to replace in.^{2} with ft^2, so we multiply by the unit fraction $\frac{1 \text{ ft}^2}{144 \text{ in.}^2}$.

$$\frac{1{,}064 \text{ in.}^2}{1} \cdot \frac{1 \text{ ft}^2}{144 \text{ in.}^2} \approx 7.39 \text{ ft}^2$$

▼ Try This One 1

A 32-in. wide-screen TV has screen area 3.05 ft^2. How many square inches is that?

EXAMPLE 2 Converting Acres to Square Miles

Yellowstone National Park has an area of 2,219,789 acres. How large is it in square miles?

SOLUTION

From Table 9-5, the unit fraction we need is $\frac{1 \text{ mi}^2}{640 \text{ acres}}$.

$$\frac{2{,}219{,}789 \text{ acres}}{1} \cdot \frac{1 \text{ mi}^2}{640 \text{ acres}} \approx 3{,}468.42 \text{ mi}^2$$

▼ Try This One 2

The state of Delaware has an area of 2,490 square miles. How many acres is that?

EXAMPLE 3 **Converting Square Yards to Acres**

An average of 2,191,781 square yards of carpet is discarded into landfills every day in the United States. How many acres would that carpet cover?

SOLUTION

There is no direct conversion between square yards and acres in Table 9-5, so we will convert to square feet (using $\frac{9 \text{ ft}^2}{1 \text{ yd}^2}$) and then to acres (using $\frac{1 \text{ acre}}{43,560 \text{ ft}^2}$).

$$\frac{2,191,781 \text{ yd}^2}{1} \cdot \frac{9 \text{ ft}^2}{1 \text{ yd}^2} \cdot \frac{1 \text{ acre}}{43,560 \text{ ft}^2} \approx 452.85 \text{ acres}$$

Math Note

We could also have used Table 9-5 to convert square yards to square miles, then square miles to acres.

▼ **Try This One 3**

An American football field is about 1.32 acres, counting the end zones. Promoters are planning to unfurl a giant flag covering the entire field at a playoff game. How many square yards of fabric will be needed?

Because both the metric and English systems are widely used today, it's useful to be able to convert between English and metric units of area.

EXAMPLE 4 **Converting Area from English to Metric Units**

The plans for building a deck call for 28 square meters of deck boards. John has already bought 300 square feet. Does he have enough?

SOLUTION

John needs to convert 28 square meters to square feet to see how much wood is required. This is done using the unit fraction $\frac{1 \text{ ft}^2}{0.093 \text{ m}^2}$.

$$28 \text{ m}^2 \cdot \frac{1 \text{ ft}^2}{0.093 \text{ m}^2} \approx 301.1 \text{ ft}^2$$

The 300 ft² that John bought is not quite enough.

▼ **Try This One 4**

Fussy University prohibits any displays on bulletin boards that have an area greater than 300 square inches. Does a poster with an area of 1,700 square centimeters meet this restriction?

EXAMPLE 5 **Converting Area from Metric to English Units**

Prince Edward County in Ontario, Canada, has an area of 1,050.1 square kilometers. Is it larger or smaller than Butler County, Ohio, which is 470 square miles?

SOLUTION

To find how many square miles in 1,050.1 square kilometers, multiply by the unit fraction $\frac{1\ mi^2}{2.59\ km^2}$.

$$1{,}050.1\ km^2 \cdot \frac{1\ mi^2}{2.59\ km^2} \approx 405.4\ mi^2$$

Butler County is about 64.6 square miles larger.

▼ **Try This One 5**

The campus of the University of Guelph in Ontario has an area of $4.1\ km^2$. How many square miles is that?

The next example shows a very common and very useful application of area conversions for homeowners.

EXAMPLE 6 **Finding the Cost of Carpeting a Room**

Jane plans to have new carpet installed in her living room. She measures and finds that the room is $300\ ft^2$. The carpet she wants sells for \$14 per square yard installed. How much will it cost to have the room carpeted?

SOLUTION

We first convert square feet to square yards, then use the unit fraction $\frac{\$14}{1\ yd^2}$ to find the cost.

$$300\ ft^2 \cdot \frac{1\ yd^2}{9\ ft^2} \cdot \frac{\$14}{1\ yd^2} = \$466.67$$

▼ **Try This One 6**

Find the cost of carpeting Jane's basement, which is 520 square feet, with cheaper carpet costing \$9.50 per square yard.

☑ 1. Convert units of area.

Conversions of Volume and Capacity

Just as the measurements of area are based on the two-dimensional square, measurements of volume are based on the three-dimensional analog, the cube. So volume is measured in cubic units.

In the English system, this is typically cubic inches (in.^{3}), cubic feet (ft^3), and cubic yards (yd^3). For example, 1 cubic foot consists of a cube whose measure is 12 inches on each side. Recall that to find the volume of a cube, we multiply the length times the width times the height. Since all these measures are the same for a cube, 1 cubic foot = 12 inches × 12 inches × 12 inches or 1,728 cubic inches. Also, 1 cubic yard = 3 feet × 3 feet × 3 feet or 27 cubic feet. See Figure 9-3.

1 cubic foot = 1,728 cubic inches   1 cubic yard = 27 cubic feet

Figure 9-3

Measures of volume also include measures of capacity. The capacity of a container is equal to the amount of fluid the container can hold. In the English system, capacity is measured in fluid ounces, pints, quarts, and gallons. The conversion factors for capacity are shown in Table 9-6.

TABLE 9-6　**Units of Capacity in the English System**

1 pint (pt) = 16 fluid ounces (oz)
1 quart (qt) = 2 pints (pt)
1 gallon (gal) = 4 quarts (qt)

Since volume and capacity are both measures of size in three dimensions, we can compare the units.

A cubic foot (ft^3) of water is about 7.48 gallons, and a cubic yard of water is about 202 gallons. If a gallon of water is poured into a container, it would take up about 231 cubic inches. Finally, a cubic foot of freshwater weighs about 62.5 pounds and a cubic foot of seawater weighs about 64 pounds. These measures are summarized in Table 9-7.

TABLE 9-7　**Conversion Factors for Capacity in the English System**

1 cubic foot $\approx$ 7.48 gal
1 cubic yard $\approx$ 202 gal
1 gal. $\approx$ 231 in.^{3}
1 ft^3 freshwater $\approx$ 62.5 lb
1 ft^3 seawater $\approx$ 64 lb

EXAMPLE 7　**Converting Cubic Feet to Gallons**

If a water tank at an aquarium has a volume of 3,000 cubic feet, how many gallons of water will the tank hold?

SOLUTION

From Table 9-6, 1 cubic foot = 7.48 gallons.
Use dimensional analysis as shown.

$$3{,}000 \; ft^3 \cdot \frac{7.48 \text{ gal}}{1 \; ft^3} = 22{,}440 \text{ gallons}$$

▼ **Try This One 7**

How many cubic feet of water are in a 100-gallon freshwater fish tank?

EXAMPLE 8　**Finding Weight of a Liquid**

If the tank in the previous example contains freshwater, find its weight.

SOLUTION

1 cubic foot of freshwater weighs 62.5 pounds, so $\frac{62.5\ lb}{1\ ft^3}$ is a unit fraction.

$$3{,}000 \text{ cubic feet} = \frac{3{,}000\ \cancel{ft^3}}{1} \cdot \frac{62.5 \text{ pounds}}{1\ \cancel{ft^3}} = 187{,}500 \text{ pounds}$$

▼ Try This One 8

What is the weight of the water in the freshwater fish tank in Try This One 7?

EXAMPLE 9 **Computing the Weight of Water in Bottles**

The team managers for a college football team carry quart bottles of water for the players to drink during breaks at practice. The bottles are stored in carrying racks that weigh 6 pounds and hold 16 bottles. How heavy (in pounds) is a rack when full? (Ignore the weight of the empty bottles).

SOLUTION

First we will need to know how much a quart of freshwater weighs.

$$1\ \cancel{qt} \cdot \frac{1\ \cancel{gal}}{4\ \cancel{qt}} \cdot \frac{1\ \cancel{ft^3}}{7.48\ \cancel{gal}} \cdot \frac{62.5\ lb}{1\ \cancel{ft^3}} = 2.1 \text{ lb}$$

So 16 bottles weigh $16 \times 2.1 = 33.6$ lb; adding the 6 pounds for the rack, a full load weighs 39.6 pounds.

▼ Try This One 9

A pallet of 1-pint water bottles delivered to a grocery store contains 288 bottles. How much does that much water weigh in pounds?

In the metric system, a cubic centimeter consists of a cube whose measure is 1 centimeter on each side. Since there are 100 centimeters in 1 meter, 1 cubic meter is equal to 100 cm $\times$ 100 cm $\times$ 100 cm or 1,000,000 cubic centimeters. See Figure 9-4.

The base unit for volume in the metric system is the liter. One liter is defined to be 1,000 cubic centimeters (see Figure 9-5). Cubic centimeters are abbreviated cm^3 or cc.

1 cubic centimeter   1 cubic meter = 1,000,000 cubic centimeters   1 liter = 1,000 cubic centimeters

Figure 9-4   **Figure 9-5**

This provides a simple and interesting connection between two of the base units in the metric system, meters and liters: 1 cubic centimeter is the same as 1 milliliter. Comparisons of other volume units are shown in Table 9-8.

TABLE 9-8 **Conversion Factors for Capacity in the Metric System**

$1 \text{ cm}^3 = 1 \text{ mL}$
$1 \text{ dm}^3 = 1{,}000 \text{ cm}^3 = 1 \text{ L}$
$1 \text{ m}^3 = 1{,}000 \text{ dm}^3 = 1 \text{ kL}$
$1 \text{ L} \approx 1.06 \text{ quarts}$

EXAMPLE 10 **Converting Metric Units of Volume**

A typical backyard in-ground pool has a volume of about 82.5 cubic meters. How many milliliters of water are needed to fill such a pool?

SOLUTION

There's a conversion in Table 9-8 from mL to cm^3, so we first convert to cm^3, then to mL. Since $100 \text{ cm} = 1 \text{ m}$, $(100 \text{ cm})^3 = (1 \text{ m})^3$; that is, $1 \text{ m}^3 = 1{,}000{,}000 \text{ cm}^3$.

$$82.5 \, \cancel{m^3} \cdot \frac{1{,}000{,}000 \, \cancel{cm^3}}{1 \, \cancel{m^3}} \cdot \frac{1 \text{ mL}}{1 \, \cancel{cm^3}} = 82{,}500{,}000 \text{ mL}$$

▼ **Try This One 10**

On average, 2,476,000 cubic centimeters of Coke are consumed worldwide every second. How many kiloliters is that?

The last equation in Table 9-8 provides a conversion between English and metric units of volume.

EXAMPLE 11 **Converting Liters to Gallons**

How many gallons of Mountain Dew are in one 2-liter bottle?

SOLUTION

We know that 1 liter is about 1.06 quarts, and that 1 gallon is 4 quarts:

$$2 \, \cancel{L} \cdot \frac{1.06 \, \cancel{qt}}{1 \, \cancel{L}} \cdot \frac{1 \text{ gal}}{4 \, \cancel{qt}} \approx 0.53 \text{ gal}$$

▼ **Try This One 11**

☑ 2. Convert units of volume.

How many liters of gas does an SUV with a 21-gallon tank hold?

Answers to Try This One

1 439.2 in.^{2}

2 1,593,600 acres

3 6,388.8 yd^2

4 Yes, it is about 263.6 in.^{2}.

5 1.58 mi^2

6 $548.89

7 13.37 ft^3

8 835.625 lb

9 300.8 lb

10 2.476 kL

11 79.25 L

EXERCISE SET 9-2

Writing Exercises

1. Explain what "square units" mean. Use examples like "square inches" and "square miles."
2. If 1 yd = 3 ft, how come 1 yd^2 ≠ 3 ft^2?
3. What is the connection between the base units of length and capacity in the metric system?
4. Describe three things in your house, dorm, or apartment that could be measured using linear units, and explain why those units would be appropriate.
5. Repeat Question 4 for square units.
6. Repeat Question 4 for cubic units.

Computational Exercises

For Exercises 7–76, convert each measurement to the specified equivalent unit.

7. 3,456 in.^{2} = _____ ft^2
8. 245,678 ft^2 = _____ acres
9. 4,653 acres = _____ mi^2
10. 45,678,231 yd^2 = _____ mi^2
11. 12 yd^2 = _____ ft^2
12. 7 mi^2 = _____ acres
13. 345 yd^2 = _____ acres
14. 77,234,587 in.^{2} = _____ acres
15. 654,543 in.^{2} = _____ yd^2
16. 10 yd^2 = _____ in.^{2}
17. 18 in.^{2} = _____ cm^2
18. 52 ft^2 = _____ m^2
19. 40 m^2 = _____ yd^2
20. 72 mi^2 = _____ km^2
21. 32 acres = _____ km^2
22. 43 in.^{2} = _____ cm^2
23. 18 ft^2 = _____ dm^2
24. 93 cm^2 = _____ in.^{2}
25. 3 yd^2 = _____ dm^2
26. 15.6 m^2 = _____ ft^2
27. 103 km^2 = _____ acres
28. 80,000 cm^2 = _____ in.^{2}
29. 42 dm^2 = _____ in.^{2}
30. 19.4 cm^2 = _____ ft^2
31. 1,875 in.^{2} = _____ dm^2
32. 35 yd^2 = _____ m^2
33. 5,326 mm^2 = _____ in.^{2}

34. 152 acres = _____ km^2
35. 777 dm^2 = _____ ft^2
36. 1,000,000 m^2 = _____ yd^2
37. 3 cubic feet = _____ fluid ounces
38. 6 cubic yards = _____ gallons
39. 400 gallons = _____ cubic feet
40. 3,724 gallons = _____ cubic yards
41. 12,561 fluid ounces = _____ gallons
42. 12,000 cubic inches = _____ cubic feet
43. 22,000 cubic feet = _____ gallons
44. 32 pints = _____ cubic inches
45. 8 cubic yards = _____ gallons
46. 4,532 cubic inches = _____ gallons
47. 4.5 liters = _____ cubic centimeters
48. 97 milliliters = _____ cubic meters
49. 28.5 cubic centimeters = _____ milliliters
50. 140 cubic decimeters = _____ deciliters
51. 433 milliliters = _____ cubic centimeters
52. 87,250 cubic centimeters = _____ liters
53. 32 liters = _____ cubic centimeters
54. 437 centiliters = _____ cubic meters
55. 32 centiliters = _____ cubic meters
56. 1.6 liters = _____ cubic centimeters
57. 500 mL = _____ L
58. 80 hl = _____ L
59. 92 L = _____ dL
60. 48 daL = _____ hL
61. 8 dL = _____ cL
62. 42 L = _____ mL

63. 6.7 hL = _____ daL
64. 92 L = _____ hL
65. 12 gallons = _____ L
66. 1.9 L = _____ gallons
67. 19 L = _____ gallons
68. 155 gallons = _____ L
69. 19 quarts = _____ mL
70. 1,500 mL = _____ quarts
71. 21,050 mL = _____ quarts
72. 27 quarts = _____ mL

73. 175 kL = _____ gallons
74. 940 pints = _____ kL
75. 11,460 ounces = _____ kL
76. 84.1 kL = _____ gallons
77. Find the weight of 500 cubic feet of freshwater.
78. Find the weight of 23 cubic feet of saltwater.
79. Find the volume in cubic feet of 200 pounds of freshwater.
80. Find the volume in cubic feet of 755 pounds of saltwater.

Real-World Applications

81. Becky wants to paint the walls in her bedroom. A gallon of paint will cover 400 ft². She measures the surface to be painted and it is 69,120 in.². How many gallons of paint should she buy?

82. Jose has a 15-m² garden and plans to buy some mulch to cover his garden. On the bag of mulch it says that one bag covers 20 ft². If each bag costs $2, how much will it cost to mulch his garden?

83. Dan wants to pour a concrete patio in his backyard. He measures the length, width, and thickness of the patio and finds that the amount of concrete he needs is 200 ft³. When he called the concrete company they asked how many cubic yards of concrete he wanted. Help Dan answer the question.

84. Chloe drank two 20-oz bottles of Diet Pepsi while she was studying. She poured the soda into the only clean glass she could find, which was a 1-pint beer glass. How many glasses did she fill?

85. A new campus was built on a 1,000-acre plot of land. How many square miles does it cover?

86. A new extension center is being built on 5 acres of campus north of the engineering building. How many square yards is the extension center being built on?

87. A pump added 5 gallons of water to the pool to level it after a diver displaced too much water during a cannonball jump. How many cubic feet of water were added?

88. A bottle containing a quarter of a cubic meter of a potent drug is half empty. Nurses give doses of 100 cc at a time. How many doses are left?

89. Sally wants to tile the backsplash in her kitchen. She measures and finds that the area she plans to cover is 32 square feet. She orders custom tiles that measure 8 square inches. How many tiles should she order?

90. A store has twenty 1-quart containers of milk, but the manager wants to pour the milk into gallon containers to sell at a higher price. How many gallon containers can the manager fill?

91. Five cubic feet of seawater have flooded into a boat through a leak in the side. If the boat itself weighs 200 lb, how much does it weigh with the seawater?

92. Gianna determines she needs 10,000 square inches of material to make a slipcover for her sofa. At the fabric store, the material is sold by the square yard. How much of the fabric she chose should she tell the clerk to cut?

93. Shelly buys eight 20-oz containers of Gatorade for a race, but the bikers' water bottles are quart-sized. If she fills each biker's bottle completely, how many bikers will have Gatorade for the race?

94. A dump truck with 1,500 gallons of soil arrives on campus to fill in the new planters on the quad. Each planter needs 2 cubic yards of soil. How many planters can be filled?

95. A search party covered 6 square miles of territory looking for a prized statue that fell from a cargo plane. How many square kilometers did they search?

96. A Jacuzzi was filled with 200 gallons of water. The Jacuzzi itself weighed 50 lb. If a person who weighs 120 lb and a person who weighs 180 lb get into the Jacuzzi, how much is the total weight including the two people, the tub, and the water?

Critical Thinking

97. The capacity of a dump truck is listed by the manufacturer as 10 yd³. A construction site requires the removal of 200 m³ of dirt, and the contractor has three identical trucks. How many trips will each need to make?

98. After the excavation at the construction site in Exercise 97, a period of bad weather delays the construction. When the weather clears up, the crew chief finds that the excavated dirt has been replaced with water that now needs to be pumped out of the hole dug for the foundation. The contractor has two industrial pumps that can each pump water out at the rate of 750 gallons per minute. How long will the pumps need to empty the site?

99. Traditionally, carpet and tile have been priced by the square yard, but in recent years, more and more stores are listing prices by the square foot. Why do you suppose they made this change?

Section 9-3 Measures of Weight and Temperature

LEARNING OBJECTIVES

☐ 1. Converting weights in the English system.

☐ 2. Converting weights in the metric system.

☐ 3. Converting weights between English and metric units.

☐ 4. Converting temperatures between the Fahrenheit and Celsius scales.

According to the Nintendo Corporation, the weight limit for the fitness board that can be used with its Wii game system is 150 kg. If you're like the average American, you have no idea exactly how heavy you can be and still safely use the board. This, of course, is because you are so accustomed to weights being measured in pounds. But like any other form of measurement, there are a variety of units that can be used for weight. We will study them in this section, then conclude with a quick look at measuring temperatures.

Conversions for Weight

In Section 9-1, we learned that weight and mass are not quite the same thing. But in this section, we'll assume that all the objects we're weighing are earthbound, so that mass and weight are equivalent.

In the English system, weight is most often measured in ounces, pounds, and tons. In the metric system, the base unit for weight is the gram, but this is a very small unit—a dollar bill weighs about a gram, for example. So a more common unit is the kilogram, which is 1,000 grams. There is also a metric equivalent of the ton: a metric ton, sometimes written "tonne," is 1,000 kg. The basic conversions for weight, along with the symbols used to represent units, are shown in Table 9-9.

TABLE 9-9   Units of Weight

English Units	Metric Units	English/Metric Conversions
16 ounces (oz) = 1 pound (lb)	1 kilogram (kg) = 1,000 grams (g)	1 kg ≈ 2.2 lb
2,000 lb = 1 ton (T)	1,000 kg = 1 metric ton (t)	1 oz ≈ 28 g

Conversions within the metric system follow the same procedures we learned for converting lengths in Section 9-1. In the English system, our old friend dimensional analysis will do the work for us.

EXAMPLE 1   Converting Weights in the English System

According to the Guinness Book of World Records, the largest healthy baby ever delivered weighed 360 ounces. How much did he weigh in pounds?

SOLUTION

The unit fraction we need is $\frac{1 \text{ lb}}{16 \text{ oz}}$:

$$360 \, \cancel{oz} \cdot \frac{1 \text{ lb}}{16 \, \cancel{oz}} = 22.5 \text{ lb}$$

This is almost exactly 3 times as large as an average newborn boy!

▼ **Try This One 1**

How many ounces is a 12-pound bowling ball?

EXAMPLE 2 Converting Weights in the English System

An empty Boeing 747 weighs about 175 tons. How much does it weigh in ounces?

SOLUTION

We will need to first convert tons to pounds, then pounds to ounces.

$$175 \, T \cdot \frac{2,000 \, lb}{1 \, T} \cdot \frac{16 \, oz}{1 \, lb} = 5,600,000 \, oz$$

☑ 1. Converting weights in the English system.

▼ Try This One 2

An average male African elephant weighs about 176,000 ounces. How many tons does he weigh?

EXAMPLE 3 Converting Metric Units of Weight

Convert each of the following:

(a) 150 grams of protein powder to milligrams
(b) 23 grams of salt to kilograms
(c) 3 kilograms of chicken to milligrams

SOLUTION

For reference, here is the order of the metric prefixes from Table 9-4 from largest to smallest: kilo, hecto, deka, base unit, deci, centi, milli.

(a) The prefix milli is three steps below the base unit, so multiply by 1,000 (or move the decimal three places right).

$$150 \, g = 150.000 \, g = 150,000 \, mg$$

(b) The prefix kilo is three units above the base unit, so divide by 1,000 (or move the decimal three places left).

$$23 \, g = 0023 \, g = 0.023 \, kg$$

(c) The prefix milli is six steps below the prefix kilo, so multiply by 1,000,000 (which is easy in this case, without moving the decimal).

$$3 \, kg \times 1,000,000 = 3,000,000 \, mg$$

Math Note

Recall that when converting metric units, we multiply or divide by powers of 10. When moving three steps in Table 9-4, we multiply or divide by 10^3, or 1,000. When moving six steps, we multiply or divide by 10^6, or 1,000,000.

☑ 2. Converting weights in the metric system.

▼ Try This One 3

Convert each of the following:

(a) A 10-kilogram dumbbell to grams
(b) A 250-milligram aspirin to grams
(c) 400 milligrams of a steroid to kilograms

One of the most common uses of weight conversion is converting between English and metric units, as in Example 4.

EXAMPLE 4 Converting between English and Metric Units of Weight

(a) The heaviest amount ever successfully lifted in Olympic competition was in the clean and jerk competition in Athens in 2004: 263.5 kg. How many pounds is that?
(b) An average adult hummingbird weighs one-eighth of an ounce. How many grams does it weigh?

SOLUTION

(a) We can use the unit fraction $\frac{2.2\ \text{lb}}{1\ \text{kg}}$:

$$263.5\ \cancel{\text{kg}} \cdot \frac{2.2\ \text{lb}}{1\ \cancel{\text{kg}}} \approx 579.7\ \text{lb}$$

(b) This time, the unit fraction $\frac{28\ \text{g}}{1\ \text{oz}}$ is helpful:

$$\frac{1}{8}\ \cancel{\text{oz}} \cdot \frac{28\ \text{g}}{1\ \cancel{\text{oz}}} \approx = \frac{28}{8}\ \text{g} \approx 3.5\ \text{g}$$

Math Note

Since 1 kg ≈ 2.2 lb, for a very quick (and very imprecise) idea of the equivalent in pounds for a weight in kilograms, double the weight and add a bit more.

▼ Try This One 4

(a) One of the weight classes in Olympic boxing is 81 kg. How heavy is that in pounds?
(b) An average golden retriever puppy weighs $12\frac{1}{2}$ ounces at birth. How many grams does it weigh?

EXAMPLE 5 Assessing Weight Loss

Megan decides that she absolutely will not go to Florida for spring break unless she loses 15 pounds in the next 3 months. She finds an advertisement online for a British weight loss system that guarantees loss of 3 kg per month. If that claim is true, will she reach her goal?

SOLUTION

We can do this in one calculation by multiplying by the unit fraction $\frac{2.2\ \text{lb}}{1\ \text{kg}}$ to eliminate kg, then multiplying by 3 months:

$$\frac{3\ \cancel{\text{kg}}}{1\ \cancel{\text{month}}} \cdot \frac{2.2\ \text{lb}}{1\ \cancel{\text{kg}}} \cdot 3\ \cancel{\text{months}} \approx 19.8\ \text{lb}$$

If the claim is accurate (a *very* big if), Megan should start saving money for her trip.

▼ Try This One 5

 3. Converting weights between English and metric units.

Bart's football coach tells him that he'll start next year if he gains 10 pounds in the 14 weeks between spring practice and summer drills. He hires a personal trainer who promises him a gain of 1 kg every 3 weeks. Will he make his goal?

Sidelight IT'S ABSOLUTELY FREEZING!

You're probably perfectly satisfied with the Fahrenheit scale, and when you mix in Celsius, that seems more than sufficient for measuring temperatures. Physicists and chemists would tend to disagree with you, however. In their view, temperature is a measure of how much heat is contained in some medium, so negative temperatures just don't seem right. In 1948, a third temperature scale was developed to address this issue. It is known as the **Kelvin** scale, in honor of the British physicist who introduced it. Zero degrees Celsius might be a bit warm for our friend the polar bear, and zero degrees Fahrenheit is more to his liking. But zero Kelvins (the terminology used, rather than "zero degrees Kelvin") would be far too cold even for him.

On the Kelvin scale, one degree corresponds to the same amount of temperature difference as the Celsius scale. The difference is the temperature that corresponds to zero degrees. On the Kelvin scale, this temperature is known as **absolute**

zero, which is the coldest possible temperature. Heat comes from an interaction of molecules, and at absolute zero, there is no heat because molecules stop moving. This temperature corresponds to

$-459.67°F$ and $-237.15°C$, and because one Kelvin is the same amount of heat as one degree Celsius, you can convert temperatures between those two scales by simply adding or subtracting $237.15°$.

It is theoretically impossible to cool anything to absolute zero, but in 2000, Finnish scientists reported reaching a low of 1 ten-billionth of a Kelvin in the lab.

Conversions for Temperature

Temperature is measured in the English system using degrees **Fahrenheit.** On this scale, water freezes at $32°$ and boils at $212°$. The average temperature of the human body is $98.6°$. In the metric system, temperatures are measured in degrees **Celsius** (also known as **centigrade**). Like all metric measurements, the Celsius scale is based on powers of 10 in some form: water freezes at $0°$ and boils at $100°$. The average temperature of the human body is $37°$.

One degree Celsius corresponds to $\frac{9}{5}$ degrees Fahrenheit, and there are relatively simple formulas for converting between the two.

Fahrenheit–Celsius Conversions

To convert Celsius to Fahrenheit:

$$F = \frac{9}{5}C + 32$$

To convert Fahrenheit to Celsius:

$$C = \frac{5}{9}(F - 32)$$

EXAMPLE 6   Converting Celsius to Fahrenheit

In preparing for vacation, Randy and Catalina check the Internet and find that the average temperature over the next week at their destination is predicted to be $28°$ Celsius. Should they pack coats or bathing suits?

SOLUTION

Substitute 28 for C in the first formula above:

$$F = \frac{9}{5}C + 32$$

$$= \frac{9}{5} \cdot 28 + 32 = 82.4°$$

Swimsuits and sunblock it is!

▼ Try This One 6

The average high temperature for March in Moose Jaw, Saskatchewan, is –1° Celsius. Find the temperature on the Fahrenheit scale.

EXAMPLE 7 **Converting Fahrenheit to Celsius**

A frozen pizza needs a 450° Fahrenheit oven to cook. Suppose you bought a cheap oven on eBay, and found that it had been scavenged from Romania, so the temperatures on the dial are Celsius. At what temperature should you set the oven?

SOLUTION

Substitute $F = 450$ into the second conversion formula:

$$C = \frac{5}{9}(F - 32)$$

$$C = \frac{5}{9}(450 - 32) \approx 232.2°$$

You should set it close to 230°.

▼ Try This One 7

☑ 4. Converting temperatures between the Fahrenheit and Celsius scales.

The pizza box recommends 225° Fahrenheit for rewarming. Where should the dial be set for rewarming?

Answers to Try This One

1 192 oz

2 $5\frac{1}{2}$ T

5 Yes, by about 0.3 lb

3 (a) 10,000 g (b) 0.250 g (c) 0.000400 kg

6 30.2°F

4 (a) ≈178.2 lb (b) ≈350 g

7 About 110°C (225°F ≈ 107.2°C)

EXERCISE SET 9-3

Writing Exercises

1. Even though mass and weight are technically different, we usually treat them as equivalent. Why is that reasonable?

2. Metric measurements are based on powers of 10. How does the Celsius scale fit that pattern?

Computational Exercises

For Exercises 3–12, convert to the indicated unit.

3. 33 oz to pounds
4. 48 oz to pounds

5. 2.3 lb to ounces
6. 3.1 lb to ounces

7. 4.2 T to pounds
8. 3.8 T to pounds
9. 3,500 lb to tons

10. 2,350 lb to tons
11. 34,567 oz to tons
12. 2.1 T to ounces

For Exercises 13–32, convert each metric weight to the indicated unit.

13. 9 dg = _____ cg
14. 6 mg = _____ cg
15. 44 kg = _____ hg
16. 16.34 hg = _____ g
17. 18 dg = _____ cg
18. 27 cg = _____ g
19. 71 cg = _____ dg
20. 215 g = _____ dag
21. 5 g = _____ dg
22. 32 kg = _____ hg

23. 0.325 g = _____ mg
24. 3,217 cg = _____ g
25. 4,325 kg = _____ g
26. 5 dag = _____ kg
27. 86 mg = _____ g
28. 24 hg = _____ g
29. 400 g = _____ kg
30. 6.6 kg = _____ g
31. 5,632 g = _____ hg
32. 150 mg = _____ cg

For Exercises 35–52, convert each unit to the specified equivalent unit.

33. 120 grams = _____ ounces
34. $15\frac{3}{4}$ ounces = _____ grams
35. 4,823 centigrams = _____ pounds
36. 27 metric tons = _____ pounds
37. 3 tons = _____ hectograms
38. 14 decigrams = _____ ounces
39. 357,201 pounds = _____ metric tons
40. 13 pounds = _____ decigrams
41. 5.75 tons = _____ metric tons
42. 16.3 metric tons = _____ tons

43. 213 ounces = _____ decigrams
44. 64 pounds = _____ dekagrams
45. 815 dekagrams = _____ ounces
46. 37 tons = _____ metric tons
47. 183 ounces = _____ decigrams
48. 550 hectograms = _____ ounces
49. 27 pounds = _____ decigrams
50. 14,625 milligrams = _____ pounds
51. 41 pounds = _____ grams
52. 42 grams = _____ ounces

For Exercises 53–62, convert each Celsius temperature to an equivalent Fahrenheit temperature.

53. 14°C
54. 27°C
55. 55°C
56. 100°C
57. 150°C

58. –5°C
59. –18°C
60. –20°C
61. –33°C
62. –50°C

For Exercises 63–72, convert each Fahrenheit temperature to an equivalent Celsius temperature.

63. 5°F
64. 27°F
65. 32°F
66. 158°F
67. 100°F

68. –3°F
69. –10°F
70. –22°F
71. –14°F
72. 212°F

Real-World Applications

73. Cindy and Juan are the proud parents of a 100-oz baby. Juan's parents think this sounds like a rather large baby! Convert the baby's weight to pounds and decide if Juan's parents are correct.

74. Billy's pickup truck is capable of carrying $\frac{3}{4}$ ton. Billy is picking up a load of rock that weighs 1,700 pounds. Will his pickup truck be able to handle the load?

75. The maximum weight a certain elevator can withstand is 4,400 kilograms. Ten large men, weighing about 210 pounds each, step into the elevator. Will the elevator hold them?

76. On the scale at the doctor's office Susan weighed 68 kilograms. The healthy weight for a person her height is 130 lb. Does Susan need to go on a diet?

77. Olivia Sanchez is going to visit Europe on vacation; she checked the local weather of the country she's visiting and found that the average temperature this time of year is about 35°C. This temperature sounds pretty cold to the American-born Olivia, but she decides before packing she should convert this to °F. After converting, will Olivia pack a coat?

78. For a chicken Marsala recipe, Janine needed 24 oz of boneless, skinless chicken breasts. At the supermarket, the chicken was measured in pounds. How many pounds did she need to buy?

79. Five cars weighing 2,540 lb each are put onto a ferry. The ferry has a maximum weight capacity of 6 tons. Will the ferry be able to hold all the cars without sinking into the bay?

80. A chemistry teacher has 750 grams of a substance and he wants to separate the substance into 3-oz jars. How many 3-oz jars can he fill?

81. A thermometer in the window of your car reads 20 degrees Celsius, but the other side where the Fahrenheit scale is located has faded in the sun. What is the Fahrenheit temperature?

82. On a summer trip to France, you catch a virus and feel like you have a fever. The only thermometer they sell at the store shows you have a 38.8 degrees Celsius temperature. What is your Fahrenheit temperature?

83. The border patrol seizes 5 lb of an illegal substance at a check point. How many grams of the substance did they seize?

84. While building a new playground at the city recreation center, a truck pours 3,000 kg of sand into the foundation. The specs require 2.5 metric tons of sand. Did the truck pour the right amount into the foundation?

85. Shirl lost 3.6 lb of fat on her diet. How many ounces of fat did she lose?

86. During a dinner at Outback Steakhouse, a family of six eats four 12-oz filet mignons and two 20-oz porterhouse steaks. How many pounds of steak did the family consume during the dinner?

87. An elevator says the maximum capacity is 1,000 kg. Twelve people are already on the elevator, their weight totaling 2,000 lb. Another man who weighs 260 lb wants to get on. Should they let him onto the elevator?

88. To mold silver into a ring, Tawny has to heat it up to its boiling point, which is 3,924 degrees Fahrenheit. Her heating element can only heat to 2,000 degrees Celsius before it will cool down for safety reasons. Can she make the ring?

89. The cement Yuan bought at the hardware store weighs 52 lb per cubic foot. To pour his driveway, the specifications require at least a weight of 25 kg per cubic foot. Did Yuan buy the right type of cement?

90. A 1.7-ton truck crosses the border into Canada. The scale measures in kilograms. How much does the scale say the car weighs?

91. The sugar fructose melts at between 103 and 105 degrees Celsius. Julia heats up the fructose on a burner to 222.8 degrees Fahrenheit. Is the sugar melted yet?

92. A lab tech had a fifth of a kilogram left of a substance and wanted to divide it into 50 bags for the next day's experiment. Each bag needed 4,500 mg of the substance. Would the lab tech have enough?

93. On a see-saw, three Americans weighing a total of 450 lb are sitting on one side. Two Europeans weighing a total of 137 kg sit on the other side. What would a person have to weigh in kilograms to balance out the see-saw?

CHAPTER 9 Summary

Section	Important Terms	Important Ideas
9-1	English system of measurement Dimensional analysis Unit fractions The metric system Base unit	**Unit** fractions such as $\frac{1\text{ ft}}{12\text{ in.}}$ are used to convert between different units of measure. Conversions within the metric system can be done by moving the decimal the appropriate number of places, based on the prefix of the units. Conversions between metric and English units of measure can be done with dimensional analysis.
9-2	Linear units Square units Cubic units	**Area** is measured in square units. Volume is measured in cubic units. Squaring/cubing the conversions for linear measure will give the conversions necessary for measure of area/volume.
9-3	Pounds Ounces Tons Grams Fahrenheit Celsius	**Pounds,** ounces, and tons are units commonly used to measure weight in the English system. The base unit for weight in the metric system is the gram. Dimensional analysis is used to convert between units of weight. Degrees Fahrenheit are the units for temperature in the English system, and degrees Celsius are the units in the metric system. There are simple formulas to convert from one to the other.

MATH IN ▶ Travel REVISITED

1. The Fahrenheit equivalents are 75.2° and 89.6°, so beach wear is the way to go.
2. Thirty kilograms is about 66 pounds, so you can pack 62 pounds of clothes and personal items.
3. Walking to downtown shouldn't be a problem—0.6 kilometers is about 0.37 miles. The distance from the airport is about 2.6 miles, which will take just about 4½ minutes at 35 miles per hour.
4. You used 12 gallons, which is about 45.3 liters. At 43 cents per liter, the refill costs $19.48.

Review Exercises

Section 9-1

For Exercises 1–16, convert each of the following using dimensional analysis.

1. 4 yards to feet
2. 23,564 feet to miles
3. 21 inches to feet
4. 356 inches to yards
5. 8,245,264 inches to miles
6. 10 m to cm
7. 0.36 m to dm
8. 13.54 km to dm
9. 34,500 mm to m
10. 0.56 dam to hm
11. 7 m to inches
12. 35 m to yards
13. 85 cm to inches
14. 23 yd to dm
15. 345 feet to dm
16. 1,235,543 in. to km
17. How many meters are run in a 100-yard dash?
18. Traffic is backed up for 10 km on a major highway. How many miles is the backup?
19. The 2009 Chevrolet Corvette has a top speed of 205 miles per hour. How fast is that in kilometers per hour? In feet per second?
20. It is about 3,600 meters from the Lincoln Memorial to the United States Capitol. How long would it take to walk that distance at a speed of 3 miles per hour?
21. The Eiffel Tower stands 1,986 feet tall. The Chrysler Building in New York City is 319 meters. Which is taller?

Section 9-2

For Exercises 22–41, convert each of the following to the indicated units.

22. 5,698 in.^{2} to square feet
23. 543 yd^2 to acres
24. 2 mi^2 to square feet
25. 456,321 in.^{2} to square yards
26. 5,643 acres to square miles
27. 23 in.^{2} to square centimeters
28. 23 ft^2 to square decimeters
29. 123 acres to square kilometers
30. 32.5 cm^2 to square feet
31. 324 km^2 to square feet
32. 7 ft^3 to fluid ounces
33. 42,000 ft^3 to cubic inches
34. 6 yd^3 to gallons
35. 3.5 L to cubic centimeters
36. 45 pints to cubic inches
37. 300 L to mL
38. 673 hL to liters
39. 54,457 mL to kL
40. 231 cL to L
41. 45,672 dL to kL
42. A nurse is instructed to give a patient 500 cc's (cubic centimeters) of a drug. The only thing she has to measure with is marked off in milliliters, so she measures out 500,000 mL and gives it to the patient (her reasoning, be it right or not, is that milli is 10 times centi). Is the patient in danger?
43. The instructions on a dechlorinator for a fish tank says to put in five drops per gallon. Geoff has a fish tank that holds 2.27 cubic feet of water. How many drops should he use?
44. The football field and surrounding sideline area at Enormous State U. covers an area of 79,000 square feet. The athletic department decides to replace the natural grass with Field Turf, a popular synthetic alternative. The cost of installing field turf is $119 per square yard. How much will the project cost?
45. Juan is considering two properties to buy for investment purposes. One is 2 acres and will cost $41,000. The other is 9,500 square meters and will cost $46,000. Which costs less per square foot?
46. Ron's Lawnscaping Artists charge $45 for one fertilizer treatment on a 5,000-square-foot lawn. How much should they charge for a lawn that is 5,000 square meters?

Section 9-3

For Exercises 47–62, convert each of the following to the indicated units.

47. 65 oz to pounds
48. 2.4 T to pounds
49. 34,500 lb to tons
50. 1.3 T to ounces
51. 567,376 oz to tons
52. 7 dg to cg
53. 0.457 g to mg
54. 5.6 kg to g
55. 4 dag to kg
56. 34,345 g to hg
57. 130 g to ounces
58. 4,536 cg to pounds
59. 45.5 oz to grams
60. 156 oz to decigrams
61. 23,456 mg to pounds
62. 456 hg to ounces

For Exercises 63–66, convert each Celsius temperature to Fahrenheit.

63. 13°C
64. 23°C
65. –5°C
66. –12°C

For Exercises 67–70, convert each Fahrenheit temperature to Celsius.

67. 67°F
68. 92°F
69. –21°F
70. –9°F

71. How many pounds is a baby who weighs 3,200 g?
72. Heinrich's temperature is 38.5°C. A person is running a fever if his or her temperature is above 100°F. Does Heinrich have a fever?

73. If the high temperature for a day was 8° Celsius higher than the low temperature for that day, and the low temperature was 52° F, what was the high temperature in degrees Fahrenheit?
74. A contestant on the TV Show "The Biggest Loser" started out weighing 346 pounds and lost 58 kg on the show. What was the contestant's ending weight?
75. On the American side of Niagara Falls, a home improvement center sells landscaping rock for $65 per ton. On the Canadian side, a different business sells a similar stone for $58 per metric ton. Which is the better buy?

Chapter Test

Convert each of the following:

1. 132 in. to yards
2. 8,665 ft to miles
3. 0.123 m to centimeters
4. 2 hm to decimeters
5. 34 cm to inches
6. 12 ft to meters
7. 3,475 in.² to square feet
8. 3,235 acres to square miles
9. 10 cm² to square inches
10. 12 ft² to square meters
11. 100 cm³ to cubic inches
12. 15,154 in.³ to cubic meters
13. 3 yd³ to gallons
14. 34 pints to cubic inches
15. 365 oz to pounds
16. 34,675 oz to tons
17. 245,231 oz to tons
18. 5 dg to cg
19. 250 g to ounces
20. 2,854 cg to pounds
21. 13°C to °F
22. 85°F to °C
23. A marathon is 26 miles. How many kilometers is a marathon?
24. How many pounds does a 88-kg man weigh?
25. Tyron has a choice between two carpets that he likes equally well. One costs $12.50 per square yard; the other costs $1.70 per square foot. Which is the better buy?

26. How many feet is a 5-km race?
27. It is about 353 km from Toronto to Ottawa. How long would it take to make that drive averaging 65 miles per hour?
28. The Ironman Triathlon is a race in which participants swim 2.4 miles, bike 112 miles, and run 26.2 miles. Find the total distance covered in kilometers.
29. A carpet installer brags that he can install Berber and pad at the rate of 50 square feet per hour. Convert that rate to square yards per minute.
30. The famous rotunda of the Capitol building has a floor area of about 7,238 square feet. A marble restoration company charges $40 per square yard for its services. How much would it cost to restore the entire floor in the rotunda?
31. A young family is looking to buy a house and decides they need at least a ¾-acre lot so there's room for the kids and their dog Moose to play. Their agent plans to show them a house with a 30,000-sq-ft lot. Will she be wasting her time?
32. The ill-fated ship *Titanic* weighed 46,000 tons. How many kilograms did it weigh?
33. The warmest month in Aruba is September, with an average high of 32.8° Celsius. The coolest month is January, with an average low of 24.4°C. What is the difference between these temperatures in degrees Fahrenheit?

Project

While the metric system has never been officially adopted by the United States government, at various times the government and other entities have made attempts to make use of the metric system more common. Using a library or the Internet as a resource:

a. Make a list of the top 20 countries in the world in terms of population, and find when each of those countries officially adopted the metric system.

b. Research the metric system in Great Britain. (While it has been officially adopted there, many people still cling to the English system. See if you can find any information on governmental attempts to encourage more people to abandon the English system.)

c. Write about any initiatives you can find in the United States to make the metric system either official, or at least more commonly used, both today and historically.

d. Make a list of difficulties that you think our society would encounter if the government decided to switch to the metric system for all measurements overnight.

CHAPTER 10

Geometry

Outline

10-1 Points, Lines, Planes, and Angles
10-2 Triangles
10-3 Polygons and Perimeter
10-4 Areas of Polygons and Circles

10-5 Volume and Surface Area
10-6 Right Triangle Trigonometry
10-7 A Brief Survey of Non-Euclidean and Transformational Geometries
Summary

MATH IN ▷ Home Improvement

It probably won't surprise you to learn that one of the most common questions that math students ask is "How can I actually use this stuff?" Of course, how math is used in our world is the main theme of this book, and this chapter fits that framework especially well. The ideas presented in this chapter are commonly used in everyday things like working around the home, so we'll present some actual projects that geometry was used for in the home of one of the authors.

Geometry is one of those topics that most people recognize when they see it, but might have a hard time writing an actual definition for. If you look up a mathematical definition on the Web, it will refer to specific figures, like points, lines, triangles, and so forth. A more casual definition might say that geometry is the study of physical shapes and objects. Since we live in a physical world, in a very real sense, geometry is the study of the world around us.

If you really look for simple geometric figures, you can see them almost everywhere. The roads or sidewalks you took to get where you are right now are kind of like lines. The desk or table you're working at is probably rectangular, and the pen or pencil you're writing with is basically a cylinder. One way to think of the value of geometry in studying our world is that most of the things we encounter are in some way made up of basic geometric figures. This makes geometry one of the easiest areas of math to apply to the real world.

In each of the projects described below, one or more of the techniques you will learn in this chapter was used to solve a problem. By the time you finish the chapter, you should be able to solve the problems yourself.

1. The diagram shows the measurements of all countertops in our kitchen. The two styles we liked cost $42 per square foot and $60 per square foot. How much did we save by going with the less expensive style?

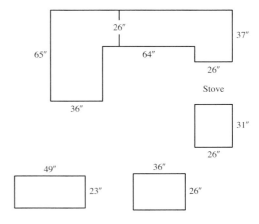

2. When finishing the basement, we needed trim along the new stairwell. From the landing at the top of the stairs in the top right photo on the facing page, the stairs extend 57 inches horizontally, and drop 42 inches. I wanted to cut the trim running along the stairs so that the bottom was parallel to the floor. At what angle did it need to be cut?

3. We built a bar out of 28 glass blocks arranged in four rows of seven each. Each block is $7\frac{3}{4}$ inches on a side, with $\frac{1}{4}$-inch mortar joints in between. We wanted to put a 3-inch trim around the outside of the blocks. How many square feet of wood did we need for the trim?

4. The boards for a cornbag toss game are 4 feet long. The bottom edge has a height of 4 inches, and the top edge has a height of 12 inches. The legs are attached so that they are perpendicular to the top. What angle did the bottom of the legs need to be cut at so that they sit flat on the ground?

For answers, see Math in Home Improvement Revisited on page 566

511

Section 10-1 Points, Lines, Planes, and Angles

LEARNING OBJECTIVES

☐ 1. Write names for angles.

☐ 2. Use complementary and supplementary angles to find angle measure.

☐ 3. Use vertical angles to find angle measure.

☐ 4. Find measures of angles formed by a transversal.

If you've ever watched really good billiards players, you probably noticed that they make bank shots look very easy. But if you try them yourself, you find they're not so easy at all. The secret to bank shots, and really to being a good pool player at all, is angles. Understanding the relationship between the angle at which two balls hit and the angles at which they move after impact is the most important part of the game.

There are many, many applications in which understanding angles is key, so our main focus in this section will be an understanding of angles. To begin, we will need to familiarize ourselves with some background information that will form the fundamentals of our entire study of geometry.

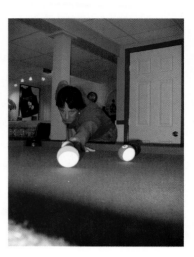

Points, Lines, and Planes

The most basic geometric figures we will study are points, lines, and planes. A **point** is easiest thought of as a location, like a particular spot on this page. We represent points with dots, but in actuality a point has no length, width, or thickness. (We call it *dimensionless*.) A **line** is a set of connected points that has an infinite length, but no width. We draw representations of lines, but again, in actuality a line cannot be seen because it has no thickness. We will assume that lines are straight, meaning that they follow the shortest path between any two points on the line. This means that only two points are needed to describe an entire line. A **plane** is a two-dimensional flat surface that is infinite in length and width, but has no thickness. You might find it helpful to think of a plane as an infinitely thin piece of paper that extends infinitely far in each direction. Examples of the way we represent these basic figures are shown in Figure 10-1.

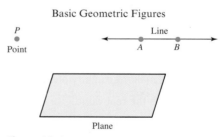

Basic Geometric Figures

P • Point   Line, A • B •

Plane

Figure 10-1

We typically use capital letters to represent points, and symbolize them as dots. To name lines, we usually identify two points on the line, like A and B in Figure 10-1, and write $\overleftrightarrow{AB}$. We will sometimes assign a lowercase letter to represent a line, like l.

Points and lines can be used to make other geometric figures. A **line segment** is a finite portion of a line consisting of two distinct points, called **endpoints,** and all of the points on a line between them. The line segment connecting two points A and B is written as $\overline{AB}$.

Any point on a line separates the line into two halves, which we call **half lines.** A half-line beginning at point A and continuing through point B is written as $\overset{\circ}{\overrightarrow{AB}}$. The open circle over A indicates that the point A is not included. When the endpoint of a half line is included, we call the resulting figure a **ray.** A ray with endpoint A that continues through point B is written as $\overrightarrow{AB}$. The figures described in the last few paragraphs are summarized in Table 10-1.

Rays can be represented by rays of light starting at a source and continuing outward.

TABLE 10-1   **Lines and Portions of Lines**

Name	Figure	Symbol
Line	A B	$\overleftrightarrow{AB}$
Line segment	A B	$\overline{AB}$
Half line	A B	$\overset{\circ\longrightarrow}{AB}$
Ray	A B	$\overrightarrow{AB}$

Rays are used to define angles, which are the most important figures in this section.

An **angle** is a figure formed by two rays with a common endpoint. The rays are called the **sides** of the angle, and the endpoint is called the **vertex.**

Math Note

In using three letters to name an angle, the vertex is always the letter in the middle.

Some angles are represented in Figure 10-2. The symbol for angle is $\angle$, and there are a number of ways to name angles. The angle in Figure 10-2a could be called $\angle ABC$, $\angle CBA$, $\angle B$, or $\angle 1$.

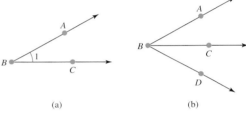

(a)   (b)

Figure 10-2

CAUTION

You should only use a single letter to denote an angle if there's no question as to the angle represented. In Figure 10-2b, $\angle B$ is ambiguous, because there are three different angles with vertex at point B.

EXAMPLE 1   **Naming Angles**

Name the angle shown here in four different ways.

SOLUTION

$\angle RST$, $\angle TSR$, $\angle S$, and $\angle 3$.

▼ **Try This One 1**

☑ 1. Write names for angles.

Write three different ways to represent the bottom angle in the diagram.

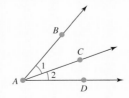

One way to measure an angle is in **degrees,** symbolized by °. One degree is defined to be $\frac{1}{360}$ of a complete rotation.

The instrument that is used to measure an angle is called a **protractor.** Figure 10-3 shows how to measure an angle using a protractor. The center of the base of the protractor is placed at the vertex of the angle, and the bottom of the protractor is placed on one side of the angle. The angle measure is marked where the other side falls on the scale. The angle shown in Figure 10-3 has a measure of 40°. The symbol for the measure of an angle is $m\angle$; so we would write $m\angle ABC = 40°$.

Angles can be classified by their measures.

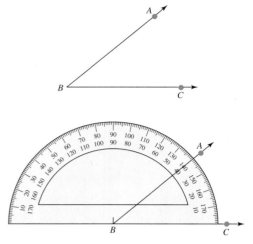

Figure 10-3

An **acute angle** has a measure between 0° and 90°.

A **right angle** has a measure of 90°.

An **obtuse angle** has a measure between 90° and 180°.

A **straight angle** has a measure of 180°.

See Figure 10-4.

(a) Adjacent angles

(b) Complementary angles
$m\angle 1 + m\angle 2 = 90°$

(c) Supplementary angles
$m\angle 1 + m\angle 2 = 180°$

Figure 10-5

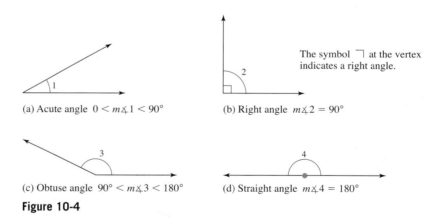

(a) Acute angle $0 < m\angle 1 < 90°$

(b) Right angle $m\angle 2 = 90°$

The symbol ⌐ at the vertex indicates a right angle.

(c) Obtuse angle $90° < m\angle 3 < 180°$

(d) Straight angle $m\angle 4 = 180°$

Figure 10-4

Pairs of Angles

Pairs of angles have various names depending on how they are related.

Two angles are called *adjacent angles* if they have a common vertex and a common side. Figure 10-5a shows a pair of adjacent angles, $\angle ABC$ and $\angle CBD$. The common vertex is B and the common side is $\overrightarrow{BC}$.

Two angles are said to be **complementary** if the sum of their measures is 90°. Figure 10-5b shows two complementary angles. The sum of the measures of $\angle GHI$ and $\angle IHJ$ is 90°.

Two angles are said to be **supplementary** if the sum of their measures is equal to 180°. Figure 10-5c shows two supplementary angles. The sum of the measures of $\angle WXY$ and $\angle YXZ$ is 180°.

Math Note

Two angles are complementary when together they form a right angle. Two angles are supplementary when together they form a straight angle.

EXAMPLE 2 | **Using Complementary Angles**

If $\measuredangle FEG$ and $\measuredangle GED$ are complementary and $m\measuredangle FEG$ is 28°, find $m\measuredangle GED$.

SOLUTION

Since the two angles are complementary, the sum of their measures is 90°, so $m\measuredangle GED + m\measuredangle FEG = 90°$, and solving we get:

$$m\measuredangle GED = 90° - m\measuredangle FEG$$
$$= 90° - 28°$$
$$= 62°$$

We say that the **complement** of an angle with measure 28° has measure 62°.

Math Note

It's not always *necessary* to draw a diagram for a geometry problem, but it is always *helpful*.

▼ **Try This One 2**

Find the measure of the complement of an angle with measure 41°.

EXAMPLE 3 | **Using Supplementary Angles**

If $\measuredangle RQS$ and $\measuredangle SQP$ are supplementary and $m \measuredangle RQS = 135°$, find the measure of $\measuredangle SQP$.

SOLUTION

Since $\measuredangle RQS$ and $\measuredangle SQP$ are supplementary, the sum of their measures is 180°, so $m\measuredangle SQP + m\measuredangle RQS = 180$, and solving we get

$$m\measuredangle SQP = 180° - m\measuredangle RQS$$
$$= 180° - 135°$$
$$= 45°$$

We say that the **supplement** of an angle with measure 135° has measure 45°.

▼ **Try This One 3**

Find the measure of the supplement of an angle with measure 74°.

EXAMPLE 4　Using Supplementary Angles

If two adjacent angles are supplementary and one angle is 3 times as large as the other, find the measure of each.

SOLUTION

Let x = the measure of the smaller angle. The larger is three times as big, so $3x$ = the measure of the larger. The angles are supplementary, so their measures add to 180°. This gives us an equation:

$$x + 3x = 180°$$ *Smaller angle plus larger angle is 180°.*
$$4x = 180°$$
$$\frac{4x}{4} = \frac{180°}{4}$$
$$x = 45°$$

The smaller angle has measure 45°, and the larger has measure $3 \times 45°$, or 135°.

☑ 2. Use complementary and supplementary angles to find angle measure.

▼ Try This One 4

Two angles are complementary, and the smaller has measure 17° less than the larger. Find the measure of each.

$\angle 1$ and $\angle 3$ are vertical angles; $m\angle 1 = m\angle 3$
$\angle 2$ and $\angle 4$ are vertical angles; $m\angle 2 = m\angle 4$

Figure 10-6

Just as two intersecting streets have four corners at which you can cross, when two lines intersect, four angles are formed, as we see in Figure 10-6. Angles 1 and 3 are called **vertical angles,** as are angles 2 and 4. It's easy to believe from the diagram that *two vertical angles have the same measure.*

If the measure of one of the four angles is known, then the measure of the other three angles can be found. This is shown in Example 5.

Sidelight　THE FATHER OF GEOMETRY

The geometry that we are studying in most of this chapter is known as Euclidean geometry, in honor of Euclid, who was a professor of mathematics at the University of Alexandria sometime around 300 BCE. That particular university was formed to serve as the center of all of the knowledge that had been accumulated to that point. By all indications, it wasn't terribly different from a modern university—it had lecture rooms, laboratories, gardens, museums, and a library with over 600,000 papyrus scrolls. There is no record of off-campus bars, but it probably had those, too.

The bible is the only book ever written that has been more widely translated, edited, and read than Euclid's famous *Elements*, which consists of 13 books on geometry, number theory, and algebra. The book remained for the most part unchanged for over 2,000 years, but in the 1800s some logical flaws were corrected by mathematicians of the time. All of the geometry we study in the first six sections of this chapter has its roots in the works of Euclid. In Section 10-7, however, we will take just a quick look at some other geometries that don't adhere to Euclid's framework.

EXAMPLE 5 | Using Vertical Angles

Find $m\angle 2$, $m\angle 3$, and $m\angle 4$ when $m\angle 1 = 40°$.

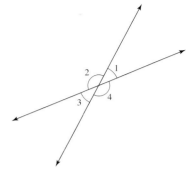

SOLUTION

Since $\angle 1$ and $\angle 3$ are vertical angles and $m\angle 1 = 40°$, $m\angle 3 = 40°$. Since $\angle 1$ and $\angle 2$ form a straight angle (180°), $m\angle 1 + m\angle 2 = 180°$, and

$$m\angle 2 = 180° - m\angle 1$$
$$= 180° - 40°$$
$$= 140°$$

Finally, since $\angle 2$ and $\angle 4$ are vertical angles, $m\angle 4 = 140°$.

Math Note

When two angles are supplementary, you can always find the measure of one by subtracting the measure of the other from 180°.

☑ 3. Use vertical angles to find angle measure.

▼ Try This One 5

Find $m\angle 2$, $m\angle 3$, and $m\angle 4$ when $m\angle 1 = 75°$.

Two lines in the same plane are called **parallel** if they never intersect. You might find it helpful to think of them as lines that go in the exact same direction. If two lines l_1 and l_2 are parallel, we write $l_1 \parallel l_2$. When two parallel lines are intersected by a third line, we call the third line a **transversal.** As you can see in Figure 10-7 on the next page, eight angles are formed. The angles between the parallel lines (angles 3–6) are called **interior angles,** and the ones outside the parallel lines (angles 1, 2, 7, and 8) are called **exterior angles.** The box below Figure 10-7 defines special relationships among these angles that allow us to find the measure of all of the angles if we know just one.

You can find parallel roads and transversals on almost any city map.

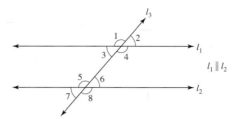

Pairs of alternate interior angles
$\angle 3$ and $\angle 6$ $m\angle 3 = m\angle 6$
$\angle 4$ and $\angle 5$ $m\angle 4 = m\angle 5$

Pairs of alternate exterior angles
$\angle 1$ and $\angle 8$ $m\angle 1 = m\angle 8$
$\angle 2$ and $\angle 7$ $m\angle 2 = m\angle 7$

Pairs of corresponding angles
$\angle 1$ and $\angle 5$ $m\angle 1 = m\angle 5$
$\angle 2$ and $\angle 6$ $m\angle 2 = m\angle 6$
$\angle 3$ and $\angle 7$ $m\angle 3 = m\angle 7$
$\angle 4$ and $\angle 8$ $m\angle 4 = m\angle 8$

Figure 10-7

Alternate interior angles are the angles formed between two parallel lines on the opposite sides of the transversal that intersects the two lines. Alternate interior angles have equal measures.

Alternate exterior angles are the opposite exterior angles formed by the transversal that intersects two parallel lines. Alternate exterior angles have equal measures.

Corresponding angles consist of one exterior and one interior angle with no common vertex on the same side of the transversal that intersects two parallel lines. Corresponding angles have equal measures.

EXAMPLE 6   Finding Angles Formed by a Transversal

Find the measures of all the angles shown when the measure of $\angle 2$ is 50°.

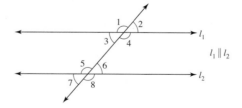

SOLUTION

First, let's identify the angles that have the same measure as $\angle 2$. They are $\angle 3$ (vertical angles), $\angle 6$ (corresponding angles), and $\angle 7$ (alternate exterior angles). Mark all of these as 50° on the diagram (Figure 10-8).

Since $\angle 1$ and $\angle 2$ are supplementary, $m\angle 1 = 180° - 50° = 130°$. This allows us to find the remaining angles: $\angle 4$ is a vertical angle with $\angle 1$, so it has measure 130° as well. Now $\angle 8$ is a corresponding angle with $\angle 4$, and $\angle 5$ is an alternate interior angle with $\angle 4$, which means they both have measure 130° as well.

Figure 10-8

▼ Try This One 6

☑ 4. Find measures of angles formed by a transversal.

Find the measures of all the angles shown when the measure of $\angle 1$ is $165°$.

$l_1 \parallel l_2$

Answers to Try This One

1 $\angle 2, \angle CAD, \angle DAC$

2 $49°$

3 $106°$

4 $36\frac{1}{2}°$ and $53\frac{1}{2}°$

5 $m\angle 2 = 105°, m\angle 3 = 75°, m\angle 4 = 105°$

6 $m\angle 2, \angle 3, \angle 6, \angle 7 = 15°; m\angle 4, \angle 5, \angle 8 = 165°$

EXERCISE SET 10-1

Writing Exercises

1. Explain why you can't actually draw a point or a line, just figures that represent them.
2. What is the difference between a half line and a ray?
3. Describe the four different ways that we name angles.
4. Explain why the two lines below are not parallel even though they don't meet in the diagram.

5. Describe how to find the complement and supplement of an angle.
6. When parallel lines are intersected by a transversal, there are four types of pairs of angles with equal measures formed. Describe each, using a diagram to illustrate.

Computational Exercises

For Exercises 7–12, identify and name each figure.

7. $\overset{\bullet\quad\bullet}{\underset{A\quad\;\; B}{\longrightarrow}}$

8. $\overset{\bullet\quad\bullet}{\underset{R\quad\; S}{\longleftrightarrow}}$

9. $\overset{}{\underset{}{\longleftrightarrow}}\, l$

10. $\bullet\, P$

11. $\underset{T}{\bullet}\qquad\underset{U}{\bullet}$

12. $\underset{E}{\circ}\qquad\underset{F}{\bullet}\longrightarrow$

For Exercises 13–14, name each angle in four different ways.

13.

14.

For Exercises 15–18, classify each angle as acute, right, obtuse, or straight.

15. $\longleftarrow\!\!\bullet\!\!\longrightarrow$

16.

17.

18.

For Exercises 19–26, identify each pair of angles as alternate interior, alternate exterior, corresponding, or vertical.

$l_1 \parallel l_2$

19. $\angle 1$ and $\angle 4$ 23. $\angle 1$ and $\angle 5$
20. $\angle 3$ and $\angle 6$ 24. $\angle 2$ and $\angle 7$
21. $\angle 2$ and $\angle 6$ 25. $\angle 1$ and $\angle 8$
22. $\angle 5$ and $\angle 8$ 26. $\angle 4$ and $\angle 8$

For Exercises 27–32, find the measure of the complement of each angle.

27. $8°$ 30. $56°$
28. $24°$ 31. $78°$
29. $32°$ 32. $84°$

For Exercises 33–38, find the measure of the supplement for each angle.

33. $156°$ 36. $143°$
34. $90°$ 37. $120°$
35. $62°$ 38. $38°$

For Exercises 39–42, find the measures of $\angle 1$, $\angle 2$, and $\angle 3$.

39.   40.

41.   42.

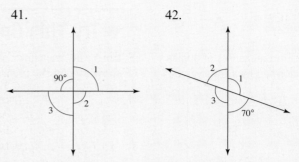

For Exercises 43 and 44, find the measure of $\angle 1$ through $\angle 7$.

43.

44.

Real-World Applications

For Exercises 45–48, identify the measure of the angle made by the hands of a clock at these times:

45. 3 o'clock   47. 2 o'clock
46. 6 o'clock   48. 4 o'clock

Exercises 49–56 use the following description: Euclid Avenue and Prospect Avenue are parallel, both running west to east, with Euclid north of Prospect. East Ninth Street is a transversal running northwest to southeast. The angle made with Euclid on the northwest corner is 76°. Find what angle a motorist turns at when making the following turns.

49. Driving west on Euclid and turning northwest on E. Ninth

50. Driving east on Prospect and turning northwest on E. Ninth
51. Driving southeast on E. Ninth and turning east on Euclid
52. Driving northwest on E. Ninth and turning east on Euclid
53. Driving east on Euclid and turning southeast on E. Ninth
54. Driving west on Prospect and turning northwest on E. Ninth
55. Driving northwest on E. Ninth and turning west on Prospect
56. Driving southeast on E. Ninth and turning west on Prospect

Critical Thinking

57. Find the measure of $\angle 3$ and $\angle 4$ if $m\angle 1 = m\angle 2$ and line l_1 is parallel to line l_2.

58. Find $m\angle 1$ if line l_1 is parallel to line l_2.

Section 10-2 Triangles

LEARNING OBJECTIVES

☐ 1. Identify types of triangles.

☐ 2. Find one missing angle in a triangle.

☐ 3. Use the Pythagorean theorem to find side lengths.

☐ 4. Use similar triangles to find side lengths.

If you look for them, you can find familiar geometric shapes in a surprising number of places. Architects in particular are fascinated by creating complex designs out of basic shapes. The pyramid structure at the famous Louvre in Paris is one of the most well-known examples, blending an assortment of simple shapes into an architectural masterpiece.

As we continue our study of geometry in our world, we use points, lines, rays, and angles to form more complex figures, beginning with the triangle. Although they are very simple figures, triangles have a surprising number of applications to real-world situations.

A geometric figure is said to be **closed** when you can start at one point, trace the entire figure, and finish at the point you started without lifting your pen or pencil off the paper. One such figure is the triangle:

A **triangle** is a closed geometric figure that has three sides and three angles. The three sides of the triangle are line segments, and the points where the sides intersect are called the **vertices** (plural of "vertex").

One way we can name a triangle is according to its vertices, using the symbol $\triangle$. For example, we could call the triangle in Figure 10-9 $\triangle ABC$. (In this case, the order of the vertices doesn't matter.)

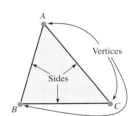

Figure 10-9

Types of Triangles

Special names are given to certain types of triangles based on either the lengths of their sides or the measures of their angles. For sides:

An **isosceles triangle** has two sides with the same length.

An **equilateral triangle** has three sides with the same length.

A **scalene triangle** has sides that are three different lengths.

Examples are shown in Figure 10-10a.

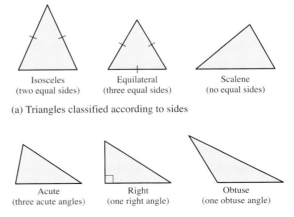

Isosceles (two equal sides) Equilateral (three equal sides) Scalene (no equal sides)

(a) Triangles classified according to sides

Acute (three acute angles) Right (one right angle) Obtuse (one obtuse angle)

(b) Triangles classified according to angles

Figure 10-10

Math Note

Because an isosceles triangle has two equal sides, it also has two equal angles. The equilateral triangle has three equal angles. The dash marks on the sides of the triangles indicate the sides have the same length.

For angles:

An **acute triangle** has three acute angles (less than 90°).

A **right triangle** has one right angle (90°).

An **obtuse triangle** has one obtuse angle (greater than 90° and less than 180°).

Examples are shown in Figure 10-10b.

EXAMPLE 1   Identifying Types of Triangles

Identify the type of triangle.

(a)   (b)   (c)

SOLUTION

(a) Obtuse triangle since one angle is greater than 90°.
(b) Equilateral triangle since all sides are equal, or acute triangle since all angles are acute.
(c) Right triangle since one angle is 90°.

☑ 1. Identify types of triangles.

▼ Try This One 1

Identify the type of triangle.

(a)   (b)   (c)

It is very useful to know the following fact:

The Sum of Angle Measures in a Triangle

In any triangle, the measures of the three angles add to 180°.

Figure 10-11

We will outline a proof of this fact in Exercises 47–51, but you can see that it's true with a simple demonstration. Draw any triangle on a piece of paper, then tear it into three pieces, one containing each angle. Now arrange the three angles next to each other, as shown in Figure 10-11: you will find that when the vertices of the three angles are placed together, they always form a straight line (or a 180° angle).

EXAMPLE 2 **Finding an Angle in a Triangle**

Find the measure of angle C in the triangle.

SOLUTION

Since the sum of the measures of the angles of a triangle is $180°$,

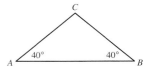

$$m\angle A + m\angle B + m\angle C = 180°$$
$$40° + 40° + m\angle C = 180°$$
$$80° + m\angle C = 180°$$
$$m\angle C = 180° - 80°$$
$$= 100°$$

$m\angle A$ and $m\angle B = 40°$.
Add on left side.
Subtract $80°$ from both sides.

The measure of angle C is $100°$.

☑ 2. Find one missing angle in a triangle.

▼ **Try This One 2**

Find the measure of angle B.

The Pythagorean Theorem

Right triangles are very special because there is a simple relationship among their sides. This is the famous Pythagorean theorem, which is attributed to the Greek mathematician Pythagoras around 500 BCE, although it was actually known much earlier in some form (see Sidelight on the next page). In any case, a **theorem** is a fact that has been proven true using deductive reasoning. This particular theorem allows us to find the third side of a right triangle if we know two sides. The side across from the right angle is called the **hypotenuse,** and the other two sides are called the **legs.**

The Pythagorean Theorem

The sum of the squares of the lengths of the two legs in a right triangle always equals the square of the length of the hypotenuse. If we use a and b to represent the lengths of the legs and c to represent the length of the hypotenuse, as in the figure, then

$$a^2 + b^2 = c^2$$

In addition, if the sides of any triangle satisfy this equation, the triangle is a right triangle.

CAUTION   Remember, the Pythagorean theorem only holds true if the triangle is a right triangle!

Sidelight PYTHAGORAS AND THE PYRAMIDS

The great pyramids in Egypt were completed about 2,000 years before Pythagoras was born, but the theorem that now bears his name played an important role in their construction. Three whole numbers that satisfy the equation in the Pythagorean theorem are called a **Pythagorean triple.** For example, $3^2 + 4^2 = 5^2$, so 3, 4, and 5 form a Pythagorean triple. So if a triangle has legs of length 3 units and 4 units, and a hypotenuse of length 5 units, it must be a right triangle.

This brings us back to the pyramid builders. Right angles are tremendously important in building structures, especially massive structures like the Pyramids. If all of the angles are off by just a little bit, the result is a crooked pyramid. To

was supposed to be a right angle, then the angle was off.

ensure that angles were right angles, the Egyptians used a rope divided into even sections of 3, 4, and 5 units long with knots. If the rope wouldn't stretch into a taut triangle with sides of length 3 and 4 against an edge that was supposed to be a right angle, then they would know that

---

EXAMPLE 3   Using the Pythagorean Theorem

Calculator Guide

To find the hypotenuse in Example 3:

Standard Scientific Calculator:

10 $\boxed{x^2}$ $\boxed{+}$ 24 $\boxed{x^2}$ $\boxed{=}$ $\boxed{\sqrt{}}$

Standard Graphing Calculator:

$\boxed{2nd}$ $\boxed{x^2}$ 10 $\boxed{x^2}$ $+$ 24 $\boxed{x^2}$ $\boxed{)}$

$\boxed{Enter}$

Note: $\boxed{2nd}$ $\boxed{x^2}$ is the square root operator: if your calculator does not automatically put in a (, you will need to do so manually.

For the right triangle shown, find the length of the hypotenuse (i.e., side c).

SOLUTION

$c^2 = a^2 + b^2$ *The two legs are 10 in. and 24 in.*

$\quad = 10^2 + 24^2$

$\quad = 100 + 576$

$\quad = 676$ *Apply square root to both sides.*

$c = \sqrt{676}$ *c is a length, so ignore the negative solution.*

$\quad = 26$

The hypotenuse is 26 inches long.

▼ Try This One 3

If the hypotenuse of a right triangle is 13 feet long and one leg is 5 feet long, find the length of the other leg.

EXAMPLE 4   Applying the Pythagorean Theorem

To build the frame for the roof of a shed, the carpenter must cut a 2×4 to fit on the diagonal. If the length of the horizontal beam is 12 feet and the height is 3 feet, find the length of the diagonal beam.

Triangles play a very important role in roof construction.

☑ 3. Use the Pythagorean theorem to find side lengths.

Math Note

Actually, since the sum of all three angle measures in a triangle is 180°, if two triangles have two corresponding angles equal, the third angle must be equal as well, and they are similar triangles.

SOLUTION

The frame forms two right triangles with legs of 3 feet and 6 feet. The length of the diagonal beam can be found using the Pythagorean theorem.

$$c^2 = a^2 + b^2 \quad \text{Use } a = 3, b = 6.$$
$$= 3^2 + 6^2 \quad \text{Square each.}$$
$$= 9 + 36 \quad \text{Add.}$$
$$= 45 \quad \text{Apply square root to both sides.}$$
$$c = \sqrt{45}$$
$$\approx 6.7 \text{ feet}$$

The length of the beam should be about 6.7 feet.

▼ Try This One 4

The rectangular frame for a large sign is 10 feet long and 8 feet high. Find the length of a diagonal beam that will be used for bracing. (*Hint:* Draw a diagram.)

Similar Triangles

When two triangles have the same shape but not necessarily the same size, they are called **similar triangles.** Consider the triangles in Figure 10-12. Since the measure of angle A and the measure of angle A' are equal, they are called *corresponding angles.* Likewise, angle B and angle B' are corresponding angles since they have the same measure. Finally, angle C and angle C' are corresponding angles. When two triangles are similar, then their corresponding angles will have the same measure. Also, if all of the corresponding angles have equal measure, we know that two triangles are similar.

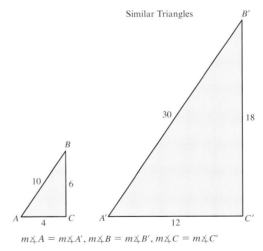

$m\angle A = m\angle A', m\angle B = m\angle B', m\angle C = m\angle C'$

$$\frac{\text{Length of side } AB}{\text{Length of side } A'B'} = \frac{\text{Length of side } BC}{\text{Length of side } B'C'} = \frac{\text{Length of side } AC}{\text{Length of side } A'C'}$$

Figure 10-12

The sides that are opposite the corresponding angles are called *corresponding sides.* When two triangles are similar, the ratios of the corresponding sides are equal. For the two triangles shown in Figure 10-12,

$$\frac{\text{Length of side } AB}{\text{Length of side } A'B'} = \frac{10}{30} = \frac{1}{3}$$
$$\frac{\text{Length of side } AC}{\text{Length of side } A'C'} = \frac{4}{12} = \frac{1}{3}$$
$$\frac{\text{Length of side } BC}{\text{Length of side } B'C'} = \frac{6}{18} = \frac{1}{3}$$

Since these three ratios are all equal, we can describe the situation by saying that the lengths of the corresponding sides are in proportion. In summary:

Similar Triangle Relationships

If triangle ABC is similar to triangle $A'B'C'$ then

$$\frac{\text{Length of side } AB}{\text{Length of side } A'B'} = \frac{\text{Length of side } AC}{\text{Length of side } A'C'} = \frac{\text{Length of side } BC}{\text{Length of side } B'C'}$$

EXAMPLE 5   Using Similar Triangles

If the two triangles below are similar, find the length of side $B'C'$.

SOLUTION

To begin, we will use the variable x to represent the length we're asked to find. Now we want to write ratios of corresponding sides. Sides AB and $A'B'$ are corresponding, and sides BC and $B'C'$ are as well. So the ratios formed from these corresponding sides will be equal:

$$\frac{\text{Length of side } AB}{\text{Length of side } A'B'} = \frac{\text{Length of side } BC}{\text{Length of side } B'C'}$$

Now we substitute in the lengths and solve for x.

$$\frac{8}{6} = \frac{12}{x} \quad \textit{Cross multiply.}$$

$$8x = 72 \quad \textit{Divide both sides by 8.}$$

$$x = 9$$

The length of side $B'C'$ is 9 inches.

Math Note

In the proportion $\frac{8}{6} = \frac{12}{x}$, both numerators are sides from one triangle, and both denominators are sides from the other. Both lengths on the left side are left sides of the triangles, and both lengths on the right side are bottom sides. This can help assure you've set up the proportion correctly.

▼ Try This One 5

The two triangles shown are similar. Find the length of side AC.

One clever use of similar triangles is to measure the height of objects that are difficult to measure directly. Example 6 shows how to use this form of indirect measurement.

EXAMPLE 6 Using Similar Triangles in Measurement

If a tree casts a shadow 12 feet long and at the same time a person who is 5 feet 10 inches tall casts a shadow of 5 feet, find the height of the tree.

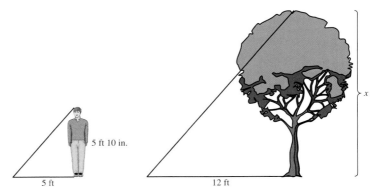

SOLUTION

Both triangles in the diagram are right triangles, and since the sun makes the same angle with the ground in both diagrams, the triangles have two corresponding angles equal, and must be similar. That means we can set up and solve a proportion:

$$\frac{\text{Height of person}}{\text{Length of person's shadow}} = \frac{\text{Height of tree}}{\text{Length of tree's shadow}}$$

$$\frac{5\frac{10}{12}}{5} = \frac{x}{12} \qquad \textit{Cross multiply.}$$

$$5x = 70 \qquad \textit{Divide both sides by 5.}$$

$$x = 14 \text{ feet}$$

The height of the tree is 14 feet.

▼ Try This One 6

☑ 4. Use similar triangles to find side lengths.

Find the length of a pole if it casts a 20-foot shadow at the same time that a man 6 feet tall casts a 15-foot shadow.

Answers to Try This One

1 (a) Scalene and acute
(b) Isosceles and acute
(c) Right

2 60°

3 12 feet

4 12.8 feet

5 7.5 km

6 8 feet

EXERCISE SET 10-2

Writing Exercises

1. Describe the three ways that triangles can be classified based on lengths of sides.
2. Describe the three ways that triangles can be classified based on measures of angles.
3. Explain why the following statement is incorrect: the sum of the squares of the lengths of two sides in a triangle is equal to the square of the length of the third side.
4. What does it mean for two triangles to be similar?
5. Explain how to find the measure of the third angle in a triangle if you know the measures of the other two.

6. Explain how to find the length of the third side of a right triangle when you know the lengths of the other two sides.
7. What does it mean for a geometric figure to be closed? Is a plane a closed figure?
8. Explain why two triangles have to be similar if they have two pairs of corresponding angles that are equal.

Computational Exercises

For Exercises 9-14, classify each triangle.

9.

3 ft, 3 ft, 2 ft

12.

7 ft, 7 ft, 7 ft

10.

13.

80°, 40°, 60°

11.

120°

14.

60°, 60°, 60°

For Exercises 15–20, find the measure of angle C.

15.

C, 60° (A), 50° (B)

16.

B, 40°, A, C

17.
25°, 140° (B, A, C)

18.

10°, 20° (B, A, C)

19.

A, $2x°$, $x°$ (C), $x+20°$ (B)

20.

C, $x°$, $3x°$, $2x°$ (A, B)

For Exercises 21–26, use the Pythagorean theorem to find the measure of side x.

21.
16 ft, x, 30 ft

24.

178 mi, 160 mi, x

22.
272 in., x, 510 in.

25.

504 yd, 954 yd, x

23.
330 cm, x, 650 cm

26.
306 km, 144 km, x

For Exercises 27–30, the two triangles drawn are similar. Find the length of side x.

27.

18 ft, x; 12 ft, 8 ft

28.

29.

30.
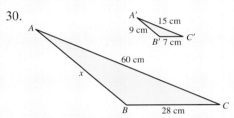

For Exercises 31–36, explain why the two triangles are similar, then find the length x.

31. $m \angle A = 35°$; $m \angle B = 35°$

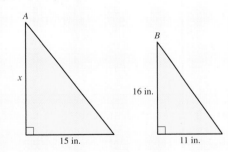

32. $m \angle C = 49°$; $m \angle D = 41°$

33.

34.

$m \angle A = m \angle E$

35.

36.

Real-World Applications

37. A baseball diamond is really a square with the bases at the corners. While playing intramural softball, Jane ran 60 feet from home plate to first base. The next batter hit the ball from home plate directly to second base. What distance did he hit the ball?

38. Television screens are sized according to the length of a diagonal across the screen, from one corner to another. The screen of a 52 in. widescreen TV is 24.5 in. high. How wide is it?

39. For the Campus Triathlon, the athletes start at point A, swim directly across Siegel Lake to point B, then cycle to point C, a distance of 7 miles. They then discard their bikes and run 2 miles to point D, then turn to run 4 miles to point E, then go under the tunnel another 2 miles back to point C. They then finish the race back on their bicycles for 7 miles to the finish line at point A. What is the distance they swam across Siegel Lake if the measure of angle A is the same as the measure of angle E?

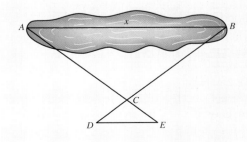

40. At the local mall, Suzette and her friends ate lunch at the food court, located at point A. Afterward, they walked 60 yd to Best Buy at point C to check out the latest CDs. From there, they went 25 yd to Macy's at point B to sample some perfume. After, they continued walking 150 yd to point D, where they saw the latest Batman movie. After the show, they found Suzette's car at point E. How far away from the movie theater was Suzette's car?

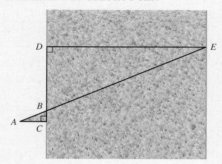

41. Find the height of the tree.

$$m\angle 1 = m\angle 2$$

42. Find the height of the tower.

43. To build a loft in their dorm room, Kevin and Neil had to figure out how long to cut a beam so that the beam would run diagonally from a point on the floor 6 feet away from the wall to the top of the 8-foot-high wall. How long should they cut the beam?

44. How high up on a wall is the top of a 20-foot ladder if its bottom is 6 feet from the base of the wall?

45. A plane flies 175 miles north then 120 miles due east. How far diagonally is the plane from its starting point?

46. Two cell phone towers are 20 feet tall and 38 feet tall and they sit 30 feet apart. How far is it from the top of one tower to the other?

Critical Thinking

In Exercises 47–51, we will prove that the measures of the angles in a triangle sum to 180°, using the diagram below.

Lines l_1 and l_2 are parallel.

47. What is $m\angle 1 + m\angle 2 + m\angle 3$? Why?
48. What is the relationship between the measures of angles 3 and 5? Why?
49. What is the relationship between the measures of angles 1 and 4? Why?
50. Using Exercises 47–49, what can you conclude about $m\angle 2 + m\angle 4 + m\angle 5$?
51. Discuss whether this proves the result for every triangle, or if there is anything special about this diagram that makes it apply only to certain triangles.

52. Explain how the Pythagorean theorem guarantees that the hypotenuse is the longest side in any right triangle.

53. The length of a side in a triangle depends on the measure of the angle across from it—larger angles means longer sides. This observation, combined with Exercise 52, shows that in a right triangle, the right angle is the largest angle. How else can you show this is true?

54. In the right triangle below, it can be shown that the lengths of the segments have these properties:

$$\frac{\text{Length of side } AD}{\text{Length of side } CD} = \frac{\text{Length of side } CD}{\text{Length of side } DB}$$

Show the proportion is true by using similar triangles.

Section 10-3 Polygons and Perimeter

LEARNING OBJECTIVES

☐ 1. Find the sum of angle measures of a polygon.

☐ 2. Find the angle measures of a regular polygon.

☐ 3. Find the perimeter of a polygon.

High-rise buildings capture our imagination and get most of the attention, but did you know that as recently as 2008, the largest building in the United States had only five floors? The Pentagon in suburban Washington, D.C., has a floor area of over $6\frac{1}{2}$ million square feet, and is one of the world's finest examples of the importance of geometry in architecture.

Triangles, as we've seen, are very useful in many settings. But of course they are limited to three sides. In this section, we will study closed figures with more than three sides, including the five-sided figure known as the pentagon.

Polygons

Closed geometric figures whose sides are line segments are classified according to the number of sides. These figures are called *polygons*. Table 10-2 shows the number of sides and some of the shapes of these polygons: triangle, **quadrilateral, pentagon, hexagon, heptagon, octagon, nonagon, decagon, dodecagon,** and **icosagon.**

In Section 10-2, we saw that the sum of the measures of the angles of a triangle is equal to 180°. The sum of the measures of the angles of any polygon can be found by using the next formula.

The sum of the measures of the angles of a polygon with n sides is $(n - 2)180°$.

TABLE 10-2 Basic Polygons

Math Note

The word "polygon" comes from the Greek word "polygonos," meaning "many-angled."

Name	Number of sides	
Triangle	3	
Quadrilateral	4	
Pentagon	5	
Hexagon	6	
Heptagon	7	
Octagon	8	
Nonagon	9	
Decagon	10	
Dodecagon	12	
Icosagon	20	

Many shapes found in nature are polygons.

EXAMPLE 1   **Finding the Sum of Angle Measures of a Polygon**

Find the sum of the measures of the angles of a heptagon.

SOLUTION

According to Table 10-2, a heptagon has seven sides, so the sum of the measures of the angles of the heptagon is

$$(n - 2)180° = (7 - 2)180° \quad \text{Use } n = 7.$$
$$= 5 \cdot 180°$$
$$= 900°$$

The sum of the measures of the angles of a heptagon is 900°.

  1. Find the sum of angle measures of a polygon.

▼ **Try This One 1**

Find the sum of the measures of the angles of an icosagon.

Types of Quadrilaterals

(a) Trapezoid

(b) Parallelogram

(c) Rectangle

(d) Rhombus

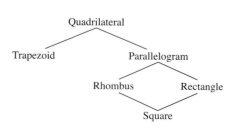

(e) Square

Figure 10-13

Quadrilaterals

Just as there are special names for certain types of triangles, there are names for certain types of quadrilaterals as well. (Recall that a quadrilateral is a polygon with four sides.)

A **trapezoid** is a quadrilateral that has exactly two parallel sides. See Figure 10-13a.

A **parallelogram** is a quadrilateral in which opposite sides are parallel and equal in measure. See Figure 10-13b.

A **rectangle** is a parallelogram with four right angles. See Figure 10-13c.

A **rhombus** is a parallelogram in which all sides are equal in length. See Figure 10-13d.

A **square** is a rhombus with four right angles. See Figure 10-13e.

The next diagram explains the relationships of the quadrilaterals.

Looking at the relationships, you can see that a square is also a rectangle and a rhombus. A rhombus and a rectangle are also parallelograms.

Most of the polygons drawn in Table 10-2 are actually special polygons: all of the sides have the same length, and all of the angles are equal in measure. We call such a figure a **regular polygon.** The most common examples of regular polygons are squares and equilateral triangles.

EXAMPLE 2   Finding Angle Measure for a Regular Polygon

☑ 2. Find the angle measures of a regular polygon.

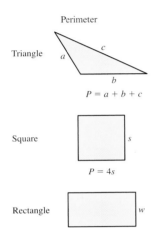

Perimeter

Triangle

$P = a + b + c$

Square

$P = 4s$

Rectangle

$P = 2l + 2w$

Figure 10-14

Find the measure of each angle of a regular hexagon.

SOLUTION

First, find the sum of the measures of the angles for a hexagon. The formula is $(n - 2) \cdot 180°$, where n is the number of sides. Since a hexagon has six sides, the sum of the measures of the angles is $(6 - 2) \cdot 180° = 720°$. Next, divide the sum by 6 since a hexagon has six angles: $720 \div 6 = 120°$.

Each angle of a regular hexagon has a measure of $120°$.

▼ Try This One 2

Find the measure of each angle of a regular pentagon.

Perimeter

The **perimeter** of a polygon is the sum of the lengths of its sides. The perimeter of a triangle with sides of length a, b, and c is simply $P = a + b + c$. For a square with side length s, the perimeter is $P = s + s + s + s$, or $P = 4s$. For a rectangle with length l and width w, there are two sides that are l units long, and two that are w units long, so the perimeter is $P = l + l + w + w$, or $P = 2l + 2w$. See Figure 10-14.

EXAMPLE 3   Finding the Perimeter of a Rectangle

The Houser family finds their dream home perfect in every way except one: the backyard is not fenced in, and their dog Bunch needs room to roam. The rectangular portion they plan to enclose is 95 feet wide and 70 feet long. How much fence will they need to enclose the yard on all four sides?

SOLUTION

The amount of fence needed is the perimeter of the rectangle.

$$
\begin{aligned}
P &= 2l + 2w \\
&= 2(70) + 2(95) \\
&= 140 + 190 = 330
\end{aligned}
$$

The Housers need 330 feet of fence.

▼ Try This One 3

The intramural field at Fiesta University is a large square measuring 600 yards on a side. Find the perimeter.

Sidelight **A TRIUMPH OF GEOMETRY**

Completed in 1943, the Pentagon is a marvel of architectural design, packing an incredible amount of floor space into a five-story building. Although it covers an area of just 29 acres, the total floor space is more than 152 acres. Over 25,000 people work there on an average day; this would make it the fourth-largest city in Alaska. There are 17.5 *miles* of corridors in the building; at an average walking pace, it would take almost 6 hours to walk all of them. And yet because of the geometric design, it takes at most 7 minutes to walk from any point in the building to any other.

EXAMPLE 4   **Finding the Perimeter of a Polygon**

The length of each outside wall of the Pentagon is 921 feet. Suppose that a sentry must walk the outside wall six times during his 4-hour shift. How many miles does he walk in one shift?

SOLUTION

A pentagon has five sides, and each has length 921 feet, so the sum of the lengths of the sides is $5 \times 921 = 4{,}605$ feet. In walking the perimeter six times, the sentry covers $6 \times 4{,}605 = 27{,}630$ feet. Now we convert to miles:

$$\frac{27{,}630 \text{ feet}}{1} \times \frac{1 \text{ mi}}{5{,}280 \text{ feet}} \approx 5.23 \text{ miles}$$

▼ **Try This One 4**

☑ 3. Find the perimeter of a polygon.

The running path at a state park is a right triangle with legs 0.7 mile and 1.3 miles. What's the total length around the path?

Answers to Try This One

1 3,240°

2 108°

3 2,400 yards

4 About 3.5 miles

EXERCISE SET 10-3

Writing Exercises

1. Is a circle a polygon? Why or why not?
2. How can you find the sum of the angle measures for a polygon?
3. What makes a polygon regular?
4. How can you find the measure of the angles for a regular polygon?

5. What is the perimeter of a polygon?

6. Is the perimeter of a pentagon five times the length of one side? Why or why not?

Computational Exercises

For Exercises 7–12, identify each polygon and find the sum of the measures of the angles.

7.

8.

9.

10.

11.

12.

For Exercises 13–16, identify each quadrilateral.

13.

14.

15.

16.

For Exercises 17–20, find the perimeter.

17.
22 yd, 16 yd

18.
15 in., 7 in.

19.
3 ft, 7 ft, 8 ft, 10 ft

20.
9 cm

21.
6 in., 6 in., 10 in., 10 in., 6 in., 6 in.

22.
8 yd, 10 yd, 5 yd, 20 yd

23.
5 ft, 3 ft, 4 ft, 7 ft, 10 ft

24. 3 in., 4.3 in., 2 in., 3.4 in., 1.6 in.

25.
7 mi

26.
14 km

Real-World Applications

27. At least how far does a major league player run when he hits a home run? The baseball diamond is a square with sides 90 feet.

28. How many feet of fence are needed to fence in a rectangular plot 24 feet by 18 feet if an opening of 3 feet is left for a gate?

29. How many feet of hedges will be needed to enclose a triangular display at an amusement park if the sides measure 62 feet, 85 feet, and 94 feet?

30. Jim and Joe have built a rectangular stage for their band that measures 40 feet by 56 feet. They want to put fiber optic lighting around the border that comes in 8-foot sections for $24.00 each. Find the cost of the lighting for their stage.

31. How much molding in length will be needed to frame an 11×14-inch picture if there is to be a 2-inch mat around the picture?

32. A carpenter needs to put baseboard around the room shown. How many feet are needed? Each door is 30 inches wide.

10 ft, 18 ft, 12 ft, 24 ft

33. How many times must a person walk around a football field in order to walk a mile? The dimensions of a football field are 360 feet by 160 feet. One mile is 5,280 feet.

34. How many times must a person walk around a soccer field in order to walk a mile? The dimensions of a soccer field are 345 feet by 223 feet.

35. Ultimate Fighting matches take place in a steel cage that is a regular octagon with sides 12 feet 3 inches. Jed and Bubba decide to build an Ultimate Fighting cage in Jed's backyard, using fence they can buy at Home Depot for $4 per foot. How much will it cost to build the cage?

36. For a LiveStrong walkathon, Cat is walking her dogs Macleod and Tessa around the perimeter of a rectangular park that is 0.4 miles by 0.7 miles. Her sponsors have pledged a total of $22.50 per mile. If Cat and the girls do four laps around the park, how much money will they raise?

37. Refer to Example 4. If the sentry was told he needed to complete two circuits around the perimeter of the Pentagon in an hour, how fast would he have to go in miles per hour?

38. Refer to Exercise 36. If Cat completed her four laps in 2 hours, what was her average speed in miles per hour?

Critical Thinking

39. For the triangle shown, $\angle BCD$ is called an exterior angle. If you know the measures of $\angle A$ and $\angle B$, explain how the measure of $\angle BCD$ can be found.

40. What is the measure of each exterior angle of a regular pentagon?

41. Make a table with the number of sides in a regular polygon in one column and the measure of each angle in the other (see Example 2). Start with 8 sides and increment by 2 until you reach 20 sides. Do you see any pattern? Where do you think that pattern is headed as the number of sides gets larger and larger?

Section 10-4 Areas of Polygons and Circles

LEARNING OBJECTIVES

☐ 1. Find areas of rectangles and parallelograms.

☐ 2. Find areas of triangles and trapezoids.

☐ 3. Find circumferences and areas of circles.

Area = 10 ft × 8 ft = 80 square ft or 80 ft²

Figure 10-15

In the 21st century, more and more people are taking on home improvement projects that would have been done only by professionals 20 years ago. Stores like Lowe's and Home Depot have become regular stops for homeowners looking to personalize their little corner of the world.

Suppose that you plan to install ceramic tile in your kitchen to cover up that ridiculous yellow linoleum—what were the previous owners thinking? Tiles come in many different sizes, and while planning the job, you want to make sure you buy enough tile. But you also don't want to buy TOO much. A calculation of area is just the ticket to make sure the job is well planned and ultimately successful. In this section we will learn how to find the area of various geometric figures.

Areas of Polygons

We already know that the area of a geometric figure is a measure of the region bounded by its sides. We also know that area is measured in square units, like square feet or square meters. Let's say that your kitchen is a rectangle measuring 8 feet by 10 feet, and that the tiles you've picked out are 12 inches on a side. Then each tile covers exactly one square foot of space. Figure 10-15 is a diagram of the kitchen.

Notice that the floor is divided into a grid by marking off 1-foot units along each side. This shows that it would take 80 tiles to cover the entire floor, so the area is 80 square feet. It is no coincidence that this number is the product of the length and width—this gives us our first area formula:

Area Formulas for Rectangles and Squares

The area of a rectangle is the product of the length and width. If l is the length and w is the width, then

$$A = lw$$

In a square, the length and width are equal, so if s is the length of the sides,

$$A = s^2$$

EXAMPLE 1 Finding the Cost of Installing Carpet

A couple plans to carpet an L-shaped living room, as shown to the left. Find the total cost of the carpet if it is priced at $25.00 per square yard.

SOLUTION

With a little bit of ingenuity, we can divide the room into two figures we know the area of: a rectangle and a square.

$$A = lw \qquad\qquad A = s^2$$
$$= 15 \cdot 10 \qquad\qquad = 5^2$$
$$= 150 \text{ square feet} \qquad = 25 \text{ square feet}$$

The total area is 150 square feet $+$ 25 square feet $=$ 175 square feet.

Now we can use dimensional analysis to finish the calculation:

$$175 \text{ ft}^2 \times \frac{1 \text{ yd}^2}{9 \text{ ft}^2} \times \frac{\$25}{1 \text{ yd}^2} = \$486.11$$

It will cost $486.11 to carpet the room.

▼ Try This One 1

A homeowner plans to install sod around his new house, as shown.

If sod costs $3.98 per square yard, find the total cost.

Figure 10-16

Once we know the formula for the area of a rectangle, we can use it to develop formulas for other polygons. We'll start with the parallelogram, shown in Figure 10-16.

The key dimensions here are the base (length of the bottom side) and height (vertical distance from the bottom side to the top side). The trick is to "cut" the bottom left corner piece off and attach it to the right side. This turns the parallelogram into a rectangle, which we can find the area of using length times width.

Area Formula for Parallelograms

The area of a parallelogram is the product of the base and the height. If b is the length of the base and h is the height,

$$A = bh$$

CAUTION

Be careful when working with parallelograms! The base is the length of the bottom (or top) side, but the height is *not* the length of the left or right side. It is the vertical distance from the bottom side to the top side.

EXAMPLE 2   Finding the Area of a Parallelogram

Find the area of the parallelogram:

SOLUTION

The base is 12 inches and the height 7 inches, so the area is

$$A = bh$$
$$= 12 \text{ in.} \times 7 \text{ in.} = 84 \text{ in.}^2$$

▼ **Try This One 2**

Find the area of the parallelogram:

☑ 1. Find areas of rectangles and parallelograms.

Figure 10-17

Now that we can find the area of a parallelogram, we can use that formula to develop one for triangles. In Figure 10-17, we see a triangle with base b and height h combined with another identical triangle to form a parallelogram.

The area of that parallelogram is $A = bh$, and since it is built from two copies of the original triangle, the area of the triangle is half as much.

Area Formula for Triangles

The area of a triangle is half the base times the height. If b is the length of the base and h is the height, then

$$A = \frac{1}{2}bh$$

CAUTION

Again, be careful! The height of a triangle is not usually the length of one of the sides.

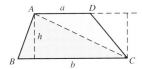

The area of $\triangle ABC = \frac{1}{2}bh$

The area of $\triangle ADC = \frac{1}{2}ah$

Figure 10-18

Math Note

When finding the area of a trapezoid, make sure that a and b are the lengths of the parallel sides.

Finally, we can use triangles to find the area of a trapezoid. In the first drawing in Figure 10-18, we see the relevant dimensions: the height h, and the lengths of the top and bottom sides, a and b. We can cut the trapezoid diagonally to form two triangles, shown in the bottom drawing of Figure 10-18. The top triangle has area $A = \frac{1}{2}ah$, while the bottom triangle has area $A = \frac{1}{2}bh$. The area of the trapezoid is the sum of these two areas:

$$A = \frac{1}{2}ah + \frac{1}{2}bh \qquad \textit{Factor out } \frac{1}{2}\textit{ h.}$$
$$= \frac{1}{2}h(a + b)$$

How would you find the area of the front of this house to estimate the amount of paint needed to paint it?

Area Formula for Trapezoids

The area of a trapezoid with parallel sides a and b and height h is

$$A = \frac{1}{2}h(a + b)$$

EXAMPLE 3   **Finding the Area of a Triangle**

Find the area of the triangle shown.

SOLUTION

The base is 15 ft and the height is 10 ft:

$$A = \frac{1}{2}bh = \frac{1}{2}(15)(10) = 75 \text{ square feet}$$

The area of the triangle is 75 square feet.

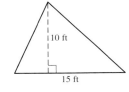

▼ **Try This One 3**

☑ 2. Find areas of triangles and trapezoids.

Find the area of the trapezoid shown.

Sidelight **CALCULUS AND AREA**

We now have a variety of formulas for finding area, but how would you find area of a figure that's curved or oddly shaped, like the front of the building shown here? This is one of the major topics of calculus. In calculus, we learn how to approximate areas, and in many cases find exact areas of figures when we don't have basic formulas for them.

It's all based on a really simple idea: we're good at computing areas of rectangles, so to approximate areas of other shapes, we'll fit little rectangles inside the shape, and

sum the areas of the rectangles. This is not terribly different than the way we started with the simple rectangle formula in this section and used it to build other area formulas.

Math Note

The center of a circle is inside the circle, but is not actually part of the circle.

Math Note

An interesting fact: manhole covers are circular because a circle is the only shape where it's completely impossible for the lid to fall in the hole.

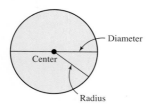

Figure 10-19

Circles

By definition, polygons have sides that are line segments. The most common geometric figure that doesn't fit that criterion is the circle—no part of a circle is straight.

A **circle** is the set of all points in a plane that are the same distance from a fixed point, which we call the **center** of the circle.

Based on the definition of circle, a line segment from any point on a circle to the center is always the same length. We call this length the **radius** of the circle. A line segment starting at a point on a circle, going through the center, and ending at a point on the opposite side is called a **diameter** of the circle, and its length is twice the radius. If we use r to represent radius and d to represent diameter,

$$d = 2r \quad \text{and} \quad r = \frac{d}{2}$$

The distance around the outside of a circle is called the **circumference** (C) of the circle. (This is analogous to the perimeter of a polygon.) The key parts of a circle are illustrated in Figure 10-19.

Thousands of years ago, people started to realize that if you divide the circumference of any circle by its diameter, the result is always the same number. Eventually, this number was given a special name, the Greek letter π (pronounced **pi**). We can't write an exact value of pi, because it is irrational, so its decimal expansion is infinitely long. But 3.14 is commonly used as an approximation. (See the Sidelight on page 237 for a discussion of pi.)

The fact that circumference divided by diameter always equals pi gives us a formula for the circumference of a circle.

Circumference Formula for Circles

The circumference of a circle is π times the diameter, or 2π times the radius:

$$C = \pi d \quad \text{or} \quad C = 2\pi r$$

EXAMPLE 4   Finding Distance Around a Track

A dirt track is set up for amateur auto racing. It consists of a rectangle with half-circles on the ends, as shown in Figure 10-20. The track is 300 yards wide, and 700 yards from end to end. What is the distance around the track?

Figure 10-20

Calculator Guide

As a substitute for using the approximation $\pi \approx 3.14$, most calculators have π built in. To find $\pi \cdot 300$ in Example 4:

Standard Scientific Calculator

$\boxed{\pi}$ $\boxed{\times}$ 300 $\boxed{=}$

Standard Graphing Calculator

$\boxed{\text{2nd}}$ $\boxed{^}$ $\boxed{\times}$ 300 $\boxed{\text{Enter}}$

SOLUTION

From the diagram, we can see that the diameter of the circular ends is 300 yards, so the circumference is $C = \pi d = \pi(300) \approx 942$ yards. (This is the total length of the curved portion, since the two half circles make one full circle.) The length of each straightaway is the total length of the track (700 yards) minus twice the radius of the circular ends, which is 150 yards (see Fig. 10-21). So each straightaway is $700 - 2(150) = 400$ yards. Now we can find the total length:

Figure 10-21

$$L = 942 + 400 + 400 = 1{,}742 \text{ yards}$$

▼ Try This One 4

The entrance to Joe's living room is an arch consisting of a rectangle that is 7 feet high and 4 feet wide with a half-circle on top. How many feet of trim would be needed to go around the outside of the arch, not including the bottom?

Through exhaustive experiments involving comparing areas of circles to other known figures, the Greeks found that the ratio of a circle's area to the square of its radius is π. This provides our next area formula:

Area Formula for Circles

The area of a circle is pi times the square of the radius: $A = \pi r^2$

EXAMPLE 5 · Finding Area Enclosed by a Track

Find the area enclosed by the track in Example 4.

SOLUTION

The area is the sum of the area of a rectangle and the area of a circle (again because the two half-circles form one full circle).

Rectangle	Circle
$A = lw$	$A = \pi r^2$
$= 400 \cdot 300$	$= \pi \cdot 150^2$
$= 120,000$	$\approx 70,650$

The combined area is about $120,000 + 70,650 = 190,650$ square yards.

▼ Try This One 5

☑ 3. Find circumferences and areas of circles.

Find the area of the doorway in Try This One 4

Sidelight MATH AND THE ORBITS OF COMETS

For most of our history, humans have been fascinated and mystified by the appearance of comets. But starting in the 16th century, astronomers were able to use math to unlock the secrets of comets and were able to predict their appearances.

The most famous such comet is Halley's Comet. It has been appearing for millions of years, but its occasional appearances remained a mystery until British astronomer Sir Edmond Halley began studying it in 1704. He noticed that earlier records showed that a comet had appeared in the same region of the sky in 1456, 1531, 1607, and 1682. He was the first person to suggest that it was the same comet appearing every 75 or 76 years, and correctly predicted that it would reappear

in 1758. (Sadly, he didn't live to see his prediction come true.)

When a circle is stretched in one direction, the resulting figure is called an ellipse. Scientists have determined that the paths comets take through the solar system are elliptical in shape. Armed with this knowledge and some data, they can use math to calculate the path, speed, and appearance dates of some comets.

Answers to Try This One

1 $5,140.39

2   4,800 square meters

3   45.5 square inches

4   20.3 feet

5   34.3 square feet

EXERCISE SET 10-4

Writing Exercises

1. How can we use the formula for the area of a rectangle to find the area of a parallelogram?
2. How can we use the formula for the area of a parallelogram to find the area of a triangle?

3. Explain the difference between perimeter and circumference.
4. What is the connection between the number π and the dimensions of a circle?

Computational Exercises

For Exercises 5–16, find the area of each figure.

5.
17 in.

6.
22 ft
12 ft

7.
15 yd
30 yd

8.
105 cm
150 cm

9.
20 m
20 m

10.
10 ft
14 ft

11.
10 miles
21 miles

12.
9 in.
9 in.

13.
20 in.
17 in.
35 in.

14.
13 km
19 km
24 km

15.
6 in.
10 in.
3 in
10 in.

16.
20 yd
6 yd

For all calculations involving π, answers may vary slightly depending on whether you use $\pi = 3.14$ or the π key on a calculator.

For Exercises 17–22, find the circumference and the area of each circle.

17.
8 in.

18.
10 ft

19.
16 m

20.
6 cm

21.
21 km

22.
9 m

Real-World Applications

23. How many square yards of carpeting are needed to cover a square dorm room that measures 10 feet on a side?

24. Find the cost of coating a rectangular driveway that measures 11 feet by 21 feet, at $2.50 per square foot.

25. Dawn printed off several 3-inch by 5-inch pictures from her digital camera onto a sheet of glossy photo paper measuring 24 by 25 inches. How many can she paste onto a 600-square-inch poster board if the images are aligned side by side so no white space is left?

26. Find the amount and the cost of artificial turf needed to cover a football field that measures 360 feet by 160 feet. The cost of the turf is $20.00 per square foot.

27. A stage floor shaped like a trapezoid with bases of 60 feet and 75 feet and a height of 40 feet is to be covered with plywood for a play. What would be the cost for the plywood if it sells for $0.60 a square foot?

28. Derek and Amir have started a lawn care service for summer money and have run into a challenge. They are to plant new sod on a lawn that is in the shape of a trapezoid, with the bases measuring 21 feet and 32 feet and a vertical height from one base to the other of 10 feet. Find the cost of the sod if each square yard sells for $7.00.

29. A triangular-shaped shelf in a student's dormitory room that is placed in a corner has a base of 5 feet and a height of 3 feet. Find the area of the shelf.

30. How many square yards of fabric are needed to make a triangular team banner whose base is 6 feet and whose height is 6 feet for a tailgating party?

31. Janelle and Sandra are planting various colors of flowers in a circular shape on the front lawn of their university to display the school's new logo. The circle has a diameter of 12 feet and the flowers cost $15.00 per square yard. Find the cost of the flowers.

32. How much more pizza do you get in a large pizza that has a diameter of 15 inches than you do in a small pizza that has a diameter of 10 inches?

33. A college radio station can broadcast over an area with a radius of 60 miles. How much area is covered?

34. Find the distance around the inside lane of a track that has the dimensions shown below.

40 yd

80 yd

35. For a Homecoming Game Gala, the cheerleading squad wants to sell ice cream to earn money for new equipment. They plan to make a sign in the shape of an ice cream cone with the dimensions given below. Find the area of the sign so they know how much plywood to buy.

4 ft

5 ft

36. Find the area of the walkway (24 inches wide) that will be installed around a circular jacuzzi with a diameter of 6 feet.

Critical Thinking

37. Under what conditions will the area of a circle be the same as its circumference?

38. In the formula for the area of a triangle, $A = \frac{1}{2}bh$, b is the length of one side of the triangle, but h typically is not. Under what circumstances is h the length of one side of the triangle?

39. Review the definition of a circle on page 540. How can you use that definition to draw a perfect circle using things you can find lying around the house? (Tracing a circular object doesn't count!)

40. The area of a triangle can be found if the measures of the three sides are known. This formula was discovered about 100 BCE by a Greek mathematician known as Heron. Heron's formula is

$$A = \sqrt{s(s-a)(s-b)(s-c)}$$

where $s = \frac{1}{2}(a + b + c)$ and a, b, and c are the measures of the lengths of the sides of the triangle. Using the formula, find the area of a triangle if the sides are 5 in., 12 in., and 13 in.

41. The triangle in Problem 40 is also a right triangle. Find the area using the formula $A = \frac{1}{2}bh$ and see if you get the same answer.

Section 10-5 Volume and Surface Area

LEARNING OBJECTIVES

☐ 1. Find the volumes of solid figures.

☐ 2. Find the surface areas of solid figures.

Figure 10-22

Owning a swimming pool sounds pretty great, especially during those hot summer weekends. But a lot of work goes into maintaining a pool, and it takes a while to learn everything you need to know. A surprising amount of math goes into it, too. Once you fill up your pool with sparkling clear water, it won't stay that way very long if you don't add chemicals. But how much should you add? The amount of chemicals you need depends on the capacity of the pool, and that's where the math comes in.

In Section 9-2, we learned that capacity is a measure of volume, which is the amount of space enclosed by a three-dimensional object. We know that volume is measured in cubic units, like cubic inches or cubic meters, and we also have conversions to write volume in terms of familiar capacity units like gallons or liters.

A **polyhedron** is a three-dimensional figure bounded on all sides by polygons. The simplest polyhedra are rectangular solids and cubes, which are bounded on all sides by rectangles or squares. A rectangular solid is shown in Figure 10-22a. It has three dimensions: length (3 in.), width (2 in.), and height (2 in.). In Figure 10-22b, we see that you could build the solid out of 12 cubes that are 1 inch on all sides. That tells us that the volume of the rectangular solid is 12 cubic inches.

This volume can be obtained by multiplying the length, width, and height, giving us our first volume formula.

Volume Formulas for Rectangular Solids and Cubes

The volume of a rectangular solid is the product of the length, width, and height. For a cube, all three dimensions are equal, so the volume is the length of a side raised to the third power (cubed).

Rectangular Solid

$$V = lwh$$

Cube

$$V = s^3$$

EXAMPLE 1   Finding the Volume of a Rectangular Solid

Figure 10-23

Find the volume of the rectangular solid pictured in Figure 10-23.

SOLUTION

The length is 4 feet, the width is 30 inches, and the height is 11 feet. First, we need to rewrite 30 inches in terms of feet:

$$30 \text{ in.} \times \frac{1 \text{ ft}}{12 \text{ in.}} = \frac{30}{12} \text{ ft} = 2.5 \text{ ft}$$

Now we use the volume formula with $l = 4$, $w = 2.5$, and $h = 11$:

$$V = lwh = 4 \times 2.5 \times 11 = 110 \text{ ft}^3$$

▼ Try This One 1

Find the volume of a rectangular solid with length 10 meters, width 12 meters, and height 50 centimeters.

EXAMPLE 2 · Finding the Volume of a Swimming Pool

In order to figure out how much chlorine to use, Judi needs to know the capacity of her pool. The pool is a rectangle 18 feet wide and 36 feet long, and has an average depth of 4 feet. How many gallons does it hold? (There are 7.48 gallons in 1 cubic foot.)

SOLUTION

With an average depth of 4 feet, we can think of the pool as a rectangular solid with $l = 36$ ft, $w = 18$ ft, and $h = 4$ ft.

$$V = lwh = 36 \times 18 \times 4 = 2{,}592 \text{ ft}^3$$

Now we use dimensional analysis to convert to gallons:

$$2{,}592 \text{ ft}^3 \times \frac{7.48 \text{ gal}}{1 \text{ ft}^3} \approx 19{,}388 \text{ gal}$$

The capacity of the pool is about 19,388 gallons.

▼ Try This One 2

A rectangular dunking tank at a carnival is 4 feet long and 5 feet wide, and is filled to a depth of 4 feet. How many gallons of water were needed to fill it?

Notice that the volume of a rectangular solid can be thought of as the area of the base (length times width) multiplied by the height. The same is true for our next solid figure, the cylinder. A **right circular cylinder** is a figure with a circular top and bottom, and with sides that make a right angle with the top and bottom. (Think of a soda can.)

Volume Formula for a Right Circular Cylinder

The volume of a right circular cylinder is given by the formula

$$V = \pi r^2 h$$

where r is the radius of the circular ends and h is the height.

Cylinder

$$V = \pi r^2 h$$

Math Note

Since the area of a circle with radius r is πr^2, the volume of a right circular cylinder is the area of the base times the height, just like a rectangular solid.

EXAMPLE 3   **Finding the Volume of a Cylinder**

How many cubic inches does a soup can hold if it is a right circular cylinder with height 4 inches and radius 1.5 inches?

SOLUTION

Using $r = 1.5$ in. and $h = 4$ in., we get

$$V = \pi r^2 h = \pi \cdot 1.5^2 \cdot 4 = 9\pi \approx 28.3 \text{ in.}^3$$

▼ **Try This One 3**

Find the volume of an oil storage tank that is a right circular cylinder with height 40 feet and radius 15 feet.

Figure 10-24

A cylinder is not a polyhedron because the edges are not polygons, but our next figure is. A **pyramid** is a polyhedron whose base is a polygon and whose sides are triangles. An example with a square base is shown in Figure 10-24.

Volume Formula for a Pyramid

The volume of a pyramid is given by the formula

$$V = \frac{1}{3}Bh$$

where B is the area of the base and h is the height.

$V = \frac{1}{3}Bh$, where B is the area of the base

EXAMPLE 4   **Finding the Volume of a Pyramid**

The Great Pyramid at Giza was built by the Egyptians roughly 4,570 years ago. It has a square base measuring 230.6 meters on a side and is 138.8 meters high. Find its volume.

SOLUTION

Since the base is a square that is 230.6 meters on a side, its area is 230.6^2, or 53,176.36 square meters. Using the volume formula with $B = 53,176.36$ and $h = 138.8$, we get

$$V = \frac{1}{3} \cdot 53,176.36 \cdot 138.8 \approx 2,460,293 \text{ m}^2$$

▼ Try This One 4

The smallest of the three great pyramids is the Pyramid of Menkaure. Its base measures 339 feet on each side, and it is 215 feet high. Find the volume.

Figure 10-25

The next figure we will discuss is the **right circular cone**. This is similar to a pyramid with a circular base, as shown in Figure 10-25.

Not surprisingly, the volume formula matches the pyramid formula: one-third times the area of the base times the height. But the base is always a circle with area πr^2, so we get the following:

Volume Formula for a Right Circular Cone

The volume of a right circular cone is given by

$$V = \frac{1}{3}\pi r^2 h$$

where r is the radius of the circular bottom and h is the height.

$$V = \frac{1}{3}\pi r^2 h$$

EXAMPLE 5 Finding the Volume of a Cone

The cups attached to a water cooler on a golf course are right circular cones with radius 1.5 inches and height 3 inches. How many ounces of water do they hold? (One ounce is about 1.8 cubic inches.)

SOLUTION

Using $r = 1.5$ and $h = 3$, we get

$$V = \frac{1}{3}\pi r^2 h = \frac{1}{3}\pi (1.5 \text{ in.})^2 (3 \text{ in.}) \approx 7.1 \text{ in.}^3$$

Now we convert to ounces:

$$7.1 \text{ in.}^3 \times \frac{1 \text{ oz}}{1.8 \text{ in.}^3} \approx 3.9 \text{ oz}$$

The cups hold about 3.9 ounces of water.

▼ Try This One 5

How many ounces of melted ice cream does an ice cream cone hold if it has a radius of 1.1 inches and a height of 5 inches?

Many of the games we play use solid objects that are circular in three dimensions—basketballs, baseballs, golf balls, pool balls, etc. The geometric name for such an object is a **sphere.** Just as a circle is the set of all points in a plane that are the same distance from a fixed point, a sphere is the set of all points in space that are the same distance away from a fixed point. And we use the same terminology: the fixed point is called the **center** of the sphere, and the distance is called the **radius.** (Twice the radius is called the **diameter.**)

Math Note

The formula for the volume of a sphere is easily developed using calculus.

Volume Formula for a Sphere

The volume of a sphere is given by the formula

$$V = \frac{4}{3}\pi r^3$$

where r is the radius of the sphere.

$V = \frac{4}{3}\pi r^3$

EXAMPLE 6   Finding the Volume of a Sphere

☑ 1. Find the volumes of solid figures.

The famous ball at Epcot center in Orlando has a diameter of 164 feet. Find its volume.

SOLUTION

To find the volume, we need the radius. The diameter is twice the radius, so the radius in this case is half of 164 feet, or 82 feet.

$$V = \frac{4}{3}\pi r^3 = \frac{4}{3}\pi(82)^3 \approx 2{,}309{,}565 \text{ ft}^3$$

The volume of the ball is about 2,309,565 cubic feet.

▼ **Try This One 6**

An official NBA basketball is a sphere with diameter 9.4 inches. What is the volume?

Math Note

In the case of the polyhedra (cube and rectangular solid) the surface area is obtained by simply adding the areas of the polygons that make up its sides.

Surface Area

The area of the outer surface of a three-dimensional figure is called the **surface area.** For example, consider a cube. A cube has six faces (think of a standard die, numbered 1 through 6). Each of them is a square with area s^2, where s is the length of a side. So the surface area is $6s^2$.

The surface areas of some of the figures we've studied are listed in Table 10-3.

TABLE 10-3   Surface Area Formulas for Solid Figures

All variables represent the same dimensions as in the volume formulas. SA represents surface area.

Cube	$SA = 6s^2$
Rectangular solid	$SA = 2lw + 2lh + 2wh$
Right circular cylinder	$SA = 2\pi r^2 + 2\pi rh$
Sphere	$SA = 4\pi r^2$

The relation between surface area and volume is important when determining how something will absorb or lose heat. Ice absorbs heat through its surface. When you break up a large piece of ice, the volume stays the same, but the surface area is greatly increased. So small ice cubes melt quickly, and large blocks of ice last much longer.

EXAMPLE 7   Finding the Surface Area of a Cylinder

How many square inches of sheet metal are needed to form the soup can in Example 3?

SOLUTION

The radius of the can is 1.5 inches, and the height is 4 inches. Using the formula from Table 10-3:

$$SA = 2\pi r^2 + 2\pi rh$$
$$= 2\pi(1.5)^2 + 2\pi(1.5)(4)$$
$$= 4.5\pi + 12\pi$$
$$= 16.5\pi \approx 51.8 \text{ in.}^2$$

▼ Try This One 7

☑ 2. Find the surface areas of solid figures.

How many square inches of leather are needed to cover an NBA basketball? (See Try This One 6 for dimensions, and ignore the seams on the ball.)

Answers to Try This One

1 60 cubic meters

2 598.4 gallons

3 About 28,274 cubic feet

4 8,236,005 cubic feet

5 About 3.5 ounces

6 About 3,479 cubic inches

7 About 1,110.4 square inches

EXERCISE SET 10-5

Writing Exercises

1. Explain why the volume of a rectangular solid is the product of length, width, and height.

2. Explain why the volume of a cube is the length of a side raised to the third power.

3. What is the difference between volume and surface area?
4. Describe the connection between the volume formulas $V = lwh$ and $V = \pi r^2 h$.

5. Explain why the surface area of a cube is $6s^2$, where s is the length of a side.
6. Is the height of a pyramid the length of one of the sides? Why or why not?

Computational Exercises

For Exercises 7–18, find the volume of each figure.

7.

5 in.

8.

2 m
3 m
6 m

9.

5 m
6 m
7 m

10.

2 cm

11.

4 m
6 m
6 m

12.

12 in.
10 in.
10 in.

13.

32 cm
28 cm

14.

7 yd   28 yd

15.

15 ft
8 ft

16. 80 km

21 km

17.

20 in.

18.
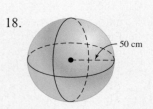
50 cm

For Exercises 19 and 20, find the volume of the solid figure not including the hole cutout.

19.

5 cm
10.5 cm
9 cm

20.
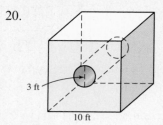
3 ft
10 ft

21. Find the surface area of the figure in Exercise 7.
22. Find the surface area of the figure in Exercise 8.
23. Find the surface area of the figure in Exercise 9.
24. Find the surface area of the figure in Exercise 10.
25. Find the surface area of the figure in Exercise 13.
26. Find the surface area of the figure in Exercise 14.
27. Find the surface area of the figure in Exercise 17.
28. Find the surface area of the figure in Exercise 18.

Real-World Applications

29. How many cubic feet of dirt must be removed to build an in-ground swimming pool whose dimensions are 18 feet in length, 12 feet in width, and 3 feet in depth?

30. At the College Tech Expo, Jamal wants to build a simple display table in the shape of a cube with each side measuring 6 feet. How many square feet of plywood will be needed?

31. A pyramid found in Central America has a square base measuring 932 feet on each side and a height of 657 feet. Find the volume of the pyramid.

32. For her class in entrepreneurship, Jenny designed a pop-up tent made for dogs that is in the shape of a pyramid with a square base measuring 6 feet on a side with a height of 4 feet. Find the volume of the tent.

33. A cylindrical-shaped gasoline tank has a 22-inch diameter and is 36 inches long. Find its volume.

34. Find the surface area of a can of Zoom Energy Drink with a diameter of 8 cm and a height of 8.5 cm.

35. Find the volume of a cone-shaped funnel whose base diameter is 7 inches and whose height is 11 inches.

36. Find the volume of a cone-shaped Christmas tree that is 6 feet tall and has a base diameter of 4 feet.

37. The diameter of Mars is 4,200 miles. How many square miles is the surface of Mars?

38. The diameter of the moon is 3,474 kilometers. If the moon were made of green cheese, how many cubic kilometers of cheese would there be?

39. How many cubic inches of packing peanuts can be held by a rectangular box that is 1 foot long, 8 inches wide, and 2 feet tall?

40. A storage shed maker charges $2.50 per cubic foot. Find the price of a custom shed measuring 4 yards long, 5 yards wide, and 8 feet tall.

41. What is the minimum number of square inches of cardboard required to make a rectangular box that is 1 foot long, 2 feet wide, and 7 inches high?

42. What is the minimum number of square centimeters of wrapping paper needed to wrap a rectangular box that is 40 cm wide, 60 cm long, and 85 mm high?

43. A cereal box is required to have length 9 inches and height 13 inches to fit in the space allotted by major grocery chains. To hold the weight of this particular cereal required, it needs to have a volume of 400 cubic inches. How wide should it be?

44. A motor oil manufacturer is designing a new cylindrical can for its economy size. They want it to be 23 cm tall so it fits store shelves, and they want it to hold 2 liters of oil. What should the radius be? (Recall that 1 cubic centimeter = 1 milliliter.)

For Exercises 45–48, suppose that a particular brand of paint claims that under normal conditions, each gallon will cover 350 square feet. The paint is sold in 5-gallon and 1-gallon cans, with the 5-gallon costing the same as 4 1-gallon cans. Find how many cans of each should be bought for each situation to keep the cost as low as possible.

45. To paint the walls and flat roof of a rectangular building that is 40 feet long, 30 feet wide, and 12 feet high.

46. To paint forty 55-gallon drums that are being reconditioned for sale, including the top and bottom. Each drum has a height of 35 inches and a diameter of 24 inches.

47. To paint the outside walls of a round above-ground swimming pool with a diameter of 25 feet and a height of 4 feet.

48. To paint a giant papier-mâché model of the moon, which is a sphere with a diameter of 26 feet.

Critical Thinking

49. Twelve rubber balls with 3-inch diameters are placed in a box with dimensions 12 inches × 9 inches × 3 inches. Find the volume of the space that is left over.

50. A rain gutter (cross section shown) is 24 feet long. How much water will it hold when it is full? One cubic foot of water is equal to 7.48 gallons.

51. Find the surface area of the pyramid in Exercise 11. (*Hint:* Find the area of each side first. You will need the Pythagorean theorem.)

52. By finding the area of the top, bottom, and sides separately, prove the formula for the surface area of a cylinder provided in Table 10-3. (*Hint:* What would the sides look like if you unrolled the cylinder?)

53. Find the surface area of a silo that is a cylinder with radius 9 feet and height 22 feet, with a dome-shaped top that is half of a sphere.

Section 10-6 Right Triangle Trigonometry

LEARNING OBJECTIVES

☐ 1. Find basic trigonometric ratios.

☐ 2. Use trigonometric ratios to find sides of a right triangle.

☐ 3. Use trigonometric ratios to find angles of a right triangle.

☐ 4. Solve problems using trigonometric ratios.

Math Note

Remember, in a right triangle, the side across from the right angle is called the hypotenuse. It's always the longest side.

Math Note

Generations of students have remembered the trigonometric ratios using this simple mnemonic device: SOHCAHTOA (which most students pronounce "sow-cah-tow-ah"). This stands for Sine is Opposite over Hypotenuse, Cosine is Adjacent over Hypotenuse, Tangent is Opposite over Adjacent.

We have seen that triangles can be used to solve many practical problems, but there are still many problems involving triangles that we can't solve using what we've learned so far. Here's a simple example. Like pretty much everything you buy today, ladders come with a variety of safety warnings designed to keep the manufacturer from getting sued. Suppose you buy a 12-foot ladder to do some work around the house, and the safety warning tells you it should not be placed at an angle steeper than $65°$ with the ground. Assuming that you don't have a protractor handy, how can you decide if it's safe to place the bottom 4 feet from the wall?

In this section we will study the basics of **trigonometry,** a very old subject whose name literally means "angle measurement." In trigonometry, we use relationships among the sides and angles of triangles to solve problems. This is in some ways like the work we did earlier with similar triangles, but is more widely applicable.

The big restriction we will work with when studying the basics of trigonometry is that all triangles have to be right triangles. In this section, we will use capital letters A, B, and C to represent the angles, and lowercase letters a, b, and c to represent the lengths of the sides. **We will always use C to represent the right angle.** In each case, the letter of an angle matches the letter of the side across from it. For example, a will represent the length of the side across from angle A. (See Figure 10-26.)

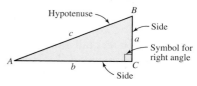

Figure 10-26

The Trigonometric Ratios

There are three basic trigonometric ratios. They are called the **sine** (abbreviated sin), the **cosine** (abbreviated cos), and the **tangent** (abbreviated tan). The trigonometric ratios are defined as follows:

The Trigonometric Ratios

$$\sin A = \frac{\text{Length of side opposite angle } A}{\text{Length of hypotenuse}} = \frac{a}{c}$$

$$\cos A = \frac{\text{Length of side adjacent to angle } A}{\text{Length of hypotenuse}} = \frac{b}{c}$$

$$\tan A = \frac{\text{Length of side opposite angle } A}{\text{Length of side adjacent to angle } A} = \frac{a}{b}$$

EXAMPLE 1   Finding Basic Trigonometric Ratios

For the triangle shown in Figure 10-27, find $\sin B$, $\cos B$, and $\tan B$.

SOLUTION

Since two of the three ratios involve the length of the hypotenuse, we need to find that first, using the Pythagorean

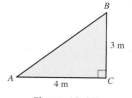

Figure 10-27

Theorem. (Since the hypotenuse is across from angle C, we label its length c.)

$$c^2 = a^2 + b^2$$
$$= 4^2 + 3^2 = 16 + 9 = 25 \quad \textit{Apply the square root to both sides.}$$
$$c = \sqrt{25} = 5 \text{ m}$$

Now we can use the trigonometric ratios from the definitions above; the hypotenuse is 5 m, the side opposite B is 4 m, and the side adjacent to B is 3 m.

$$\sin B = \frac{\text{Opposite}}{\text{Hypotenuse}} = \frac{4 \text{ m}}{5 \text{ m}} = \frac{4}{5}$$

$$\cos B = \frac{\text{Adjacent}}{\text{Hypotenuse}} = \frac{3 \text{ m}}{5 \text{ m}} = \frac{3}{5}$$

$$\tan B = \frac{\text{Opposite}}{\text{Adjacent}} = \frac{4 \text{ m}}{3 \text{ m}} = \frac{4}{3}$$

Math Note

Notice that the units divide out when you compute the trigonometric ratios, so the units of length are unimportant in defining the ratios.

☑ 1. Find basic trigonometric ratios.

▼ Try This One 1

Find $\sin A$, $\cos A$, and $\tan A$ for the triangle below.

Calculator Guide

To use a calculator in solving problems involving trigonometric ratios, you will have to make sure your calculator is set to degree mode:

Standard Scientific Calculator

Press [Mode], [Deg], or [Rad] until you see "Deg" in the display window.

Standard Graphing Calculator

Press [Mode], use arrow keys to select "DEGREE," then exit by pressing [2nd] [Mode]

The trigonometric ratios would not be very useful if they gave different values for the same measure angle in different triangles—certainly we want $\sin 30°$ to be the same regardless of the size of the triangle the $30°$ angle came from. Fortunately, this is the case, because of what we learned about similar triangles. In Figure 10-28, we see two different right triangles with a $30°$ angle. Because the triangles are similar, the ratios of corresponding sides are equal, so $\sin 30°$ is $\frac{1}{2}$ in both triangles.

One situation that trigonometry is often used for is to find the lengths of sides of a triangle. If we know one side and one of the acute angles, we can find either of the remaining sides, as in Example 2.

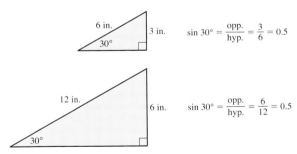

Figure 10-28

EXAMPLE 2 Finding a Side of a Triangle Using Tangent

In the right triangle ABC, find the length of side a when $m\angle A = 30°$ and $b = 200$ feet.

SOLUTION

Step 1 Draw and label the figure.

Step 2 Choose an appropriate trigonometric ratio and substitute values into it. In this case, we know the side

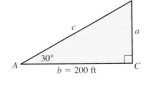

adjacent to angle A, and are asked to find the side opposite, so tangent is a good choice.

$$\tan A = \frac{\text{Opposite}}{\text{Adjacent}} = \frac{a}{b}$$

$$\tan 30° = \frac{a}{200}$$

Step 3 Solve the resulting equation for a.

$$\tan 30° = \frac{a}{200} \qquad \textit{Multiply both sides by 200.}$$

$$a = 200 \tan 30°$$

To evaluate this answer, we use a calculator in degree mode (see Calculator Guide on previous page) and press 200 $\boxed{\times}$ 30 $\boxed{\text{Tan}}$ $\boxed{=}$ (standard scientific calculator), or 200 $\boxed{\text{Tan}}$ 30 $\boxed{\text{Enter}}$ (standard graphing calculator). The result in either case, rounded to two decimal places, is 115.47, so the length of side a is 115.47 feet.

▼ Try This One 2

In the right triangle ABC, find the length of side b if $m\angle B = 58°$ and $a = 12$ inches.

EXAMPLE 3   Finding a Side of a Triangle Using Cosine

In the right triangle ABC, find the measure of side c when $m\angle B = 72°$ and the length of side a is 24 feet.

SOLUTION

Step 1 Draw and label the figure.

Step 2 We know the side adjacent to B and want to find the hypotenuse, so cosine is a good choice.

$$\cos B = \frac{a}{c}$$

$$\cos 72° = \frac{24}{c}$$

Step 3 Solve for c.

$$\cos 72° = \frac{24}{c} \qquad \textit{Multiply both sides by c.}$$

$$c \cdot \cos 72° = 24 \qquad \textit{Divide both sides by cos 72°.}$$

$$c = \frac{24}{\cos 72°} \approx 77.67 \text{ ft (to two decimal places)}$$

▼ Try This One 3

In the right triangle ABC, find the measure of side b when $m\angle A = 53°$ and the hypotenuse (side c) is 18 cm.

☑ 2. Use trigonometric ratios to find sides of a right triangle.

Trigonometric ratios can be used to find angles as well, provided that we know at least two sides of a right triangle. To accomplish this, we will need to use special routines programmed into a calculator known as **inverse trigonometric functions.** They are accessed using the 2nd key on most calculators, as illustrated in Example 4.

EXAMPLE 4   Finding an Angle Using Trigonometric Ratios

In the right triangle ABC, side c (the hypotenuse) measures 25 inches and side b measures 24 inches. Find the measure of angle B.

SOLUTION

Step 1 Draw and label the figure.

Step 2 We know the hypotenuse and the side opposite angle B, so sine is a good choice.

$$\sin B = \frac{\text{Opposite}}{\text{Hypotenuse}} = \frac{24}{25} = 0.96$$

Step 3 Solve for B. To accomplish this, we will need to access the inverse sine feature on a calculator: .96 2nd Sin (standard scientific calculator), or 2nd Sin .96 Enter (standard graphing calculator). The result, rounded to two decimal places, is 73.74, so $m\angle B \approx 73.74°$.

Math Note

The symbol $\sin^{-1}$ is used to represent the inverse of sine. Likewise, $\cos^{-1}$ and $\tan^{-1}$ represent the inverses of cosine and tangent, respectively.

☑ 3. Use trigonometric ratios to find angles of a right triangle.

▼ Try This One 4

Find the measure of angle A for the right triangle ABC if the measure of side a is 42 inches and the measure of side b is 18 inches.

In the remainder of the section, we will demonstrate just a few of the many, many real-world problems that can be solved using trigonometry. To begin, we return to the ladder question that began the section.

EXAMPLE 5   An Application of Trigonometry to Home Improvement

The safety label on a 12-foot ladder says that the ladder should not be placed at an angle steeper than 65° with the ground. What is the closest safe distance between the base of the ladder and the wall?

SOLUTION

Step 1 Draw and label the figure.

Step 2 Choose the appropriate formula and substitute the values for the variables. Since we need to find the length of side b and we are given the measures of angle A and side c, cosine is a good choice.

$$\cos A = \frac{\text{Adjacent}}{\text{Hypotenuse}} = \frac{b}{c}$$

$$\cos 65° = \frac{b}{12}$$

Step 3 Solve for b. $\cos 65° = \dfrac{b}{12}$

$$b = 12 \cos 65° \approx 5.07 \text{ feet}$$

The bottom of the ladder can't be any closer than 5.07 feet from the wall.

Calculator Guide

Keystrokes for finding b:

Standard Scientific Calculator

12 × 65 Cos =

Standard Graphing Calculator

12 × Cos 65 Enter

▼ Try This One 5

Being afraid of heights, a homeowner determines that he's unwilling to place the ladder in Example 5 any steeper than a 50° angle with the ground. How far up the wall will the ladder reach at that angle?

Trigonometry is used extensively in surveying.

Angle of Elevation and Angle of Depression

Many applications of right angle trigonometry use what is called the *angle of elevation* or the *angle of depression*.

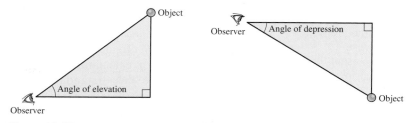

Figure 10-29

The **angle of elevation** of an object is the measure of the angle from a horizontal line at the point of an observer upward to the line of sight to the object. The angle of **depression** is the measure of an angle from a horizontal line at the point of an observer downward to the line of sight to the object. See Figure 10-29.

EXAMPLE 6 | Finding the Height of a Tall Object Using Trigonometry

In order to find the height of a building, an observer who is 6 feet tall measures the angle of elevation from his head to the top of the building to be 32° when he is standing at a point 200 feet from the building. How tall is the building?

SOLUTION

Step 1 Draw and label the figure.

Step 2 Choose the appropriate formula and substitute the values for the variables. Since we are given the measure of angle A and the measure of side b, we can use tangent.

$$\tan A = \frac{\text{Opposite}}{\text{Adjacent}} = \frac{a}{b}$$

$$\tan 32° = \frac{a}{200}$$

Step 3 Solve for a.

$$\tan 32° = \frac{a}{200} \qquad \text{Multiply both sides by 200.}$$

$$a = 200 \tan 32° \approx 125 \text{ feet (to the nearest foot)}$$

Looking back at the diagram, we see that the height of the building is side a (125 feet) plus 6 feet, so the building is 131 feet tall.

Calculator Guide

Keystrokes for finding a:

Standard Scientific Calculator

200 ⨯ 32 Tan =

Standard Graphing Calculator

200 ⨯ Tan 32 Enter

▼ **Try This One 6**

A hiker standing on top of a 150-foot cliff sights a boat at an angle of depression of 24°. How far is the boat from the base of the cliff? (The hiker's eye level is 5.6 feet above the top of the cliff.)

EXAMPLE 7 **Finding an Angle of Depression**

A local photographer gets a hot tip that a famous starlet is sunbathing on a boat cruising down a river. He sets up his camera on a bridge that is 22 feet above the water and 60 feet from a bend in the river, hoping to get a shot as the boat comes into view. At what angle of depression should he aim the camera?

SOLUTION

Step 1 Draw and label the figure (in the margin).

Step 2 We are looking for angle B, and have the opposite and adjacent sides, so we choose tangent.

$$\tan B = \frac{\text{Opposite}}{\text{Adjacent}} = \frac{60}{22}$$

Step 3 Solve for B using the inverse tangent feature on a calculator (see Calculator Guide).

$$B \approx 69.86°$$

The angle of depression should be a bit less than 70°.

Calculator Guide

Keystrokes for finding angle B:

Standard Scientific Calculator

60 ÷ 22 = 2nd Tan

Standard Graphing Calculator

2nd Tan 60 ÷ 22 Enter

☑ 4. Solve problems using trigonometric ratios.

▼ **Try This One 7**

Marie hopes to photograph the rising sun as it just peeks over the top of a 20-foot-tall house across the street, 120 feet from where she is sitting on the ground. At what angle of elevation should she aim the camera?

CAUTION When using trig ratios to solve applied problems, never forget that there must be a right triangle in the diagram, or the trig ratios do not apply.

Answers to Try This One

1 $\sin A = \frac{5}{13}$; $\cos A = \frac{12}{13}$; $\tan A = \frac{5}{12}$

2 19.20 inches

3 10.83 cm

4 66.80°

5 9.19 feet

6 349.48 feet

7 9.46°

EXERCISE SET 10-6

Writing Exercises

1. Describe each of the trigonometric ratios in terms of sides of a right triangle.
2. Given a right triangle ABC with right angle C, explain how we would label the lengths of the sides using the letters we used in this section.
3. Why can we be sure that sin 30° always has the same value regardless of the size of the right triangle containing the 30° angle?
4. Describe what is meant by an angle of elevation and an angle of depression.

Computational Exercises

For Exercises 5–10, use the given right triangle to find cos A, sin A, and tan A.

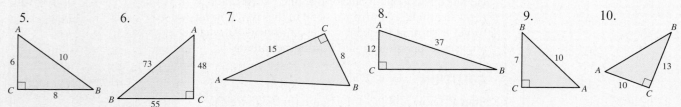

5.

6.

7.

8.

9.

10.

Exercises 11–30 refer to right triangles labeled like the one below. Use trigonometric ratios to find each measure.

11. Side a if $m\angle B = 72°$ and side $c = 300$ cm
12. Side b if $m\angle A = 41°$ and side $c = 200$ yd
13. Side c if $m\angle A = 76°$ and side $b = 18.6$ in.
14. Side a if $m\angle A = 30°$ and side $c = 40$ km
15. Side b if $m\angle B = 8°$ and side $c = 10$ mm
16. Side c if $m\angle B = 62°$ and side $a = 313$ mi

17. Side a if $m\angle A = 60°$ and side $b = 71$ in.
18. Side b if $m\angle B = 85°$ and side $a = 110$ yd
19. Side c if $m\angle A = 28°$ and side $a = 872$ ft
20. Side a if $m\angle A = 22°$ and side $b = 27$ ft
21. Side b if $m\angle B = 53°$ and side $c = 97$ mi
22. Side c if $m\angle A = 15°$ and side $b = 1,250$ ft
23. $m\angle A$ if side $b = 183$ ft and side $c = 275$ ft
24. $m\angle B$ if side $b = 104$ yd and side $c = 132$ yd
25. $m\angle A$ if side $b = 18$ mi and side $c = 36$ mi
26. $m\angle B$ if side $a = 529$ mi and side $c = 1,000$ mi
27. $m\angle A$ if side $a = 306$ in. and side $b = 560$ in.
28. $m\angle B$ if side $a = 1,428$ ft and side $c = 1,800$ ft
29. $m\angle B$ if side $a = 413$ ft and side $b = 410$ ft
30. $m\angle A$ if side $a = 532$ yd and side $c = 780$ yd

Real-World Applications

31. An airplane is flying at an altitude of 6,780 feet and sights the angle of depression to a control tower at the next airport to be 16°. Find the horizontal distance the plane is from the control tower. (Disregard the height of the tower.)
32. If the angle of elevation from ground level to the top of a building is 38° and the observer is 500 feet from the building, find the height of the building.
33. How high is a satellite radio tower if the angle of elevation from the ground is 82 degrees and the observation point is 700 meters from the base of the tower?
34. The front of a 6-foot-long treadmill is 4 inches higher than the back. At what angle is it inclined?
35. One common use of trigonometry is to measure inaccessible objects. Based on the measurements in the diagram, how wide is the lake?

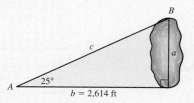

36. During a recent intramural game of Capture the Flag, Pete noticed the flag was hidden atop a light pole. Pete was standing 105 feet from the pole and he estimated that the angle of elevation from his feet to the top of the pole was 40 degrees. How far must he climb up the pole to capture the flag?

37. If a two-story building that is 20 feet tall casts a shadow 8 feet long, what is the angle of elevation of the sun at that time of day?

38. Trey locked his keys in his house again and desperately needs to get his term paper from his desk on the second floor of his house. He grabs a 25-foot ladder and leans it 63 degrees against the house to the bottom of the second floor window. How high is the window from the ground?

39. In a moment of frustration, Kelly tosses her math book out the window of her dorm room. (Legal disclaimer: don't try this at home.) The window is 138 feet from the ground, and the book was thrown at a 21 degree angle of depression. Find the horizontal distance from where the book landed to Kelly's dorm. (Assume that the book traveled a straight-line path.)

40. Archaeologists find a lost city with a map room leading them to the treasure of a long-dead civilization. When the instructions carved into a stone tablet are translated, they find that that location of the treasure room is found by following the shadow of a 10-foot staff to a location on the map at 2 P.M. on the day of the winter solstice. They check with meteorologists at a nearby university and find that the angle of elevation of the sun at that location on that day and time is 44°. How far away from the staff is the location of the treasure on the map?

41. Patty sits on a bench with her laptop 2,456 feet from the base of the WiFi antenna and the angle of elevation from her laptop, which is 2.5 feet from the ground, to the top of the antenna is 58 degrees. How tall is the antenna?

42. Sara takes an elevator 349 feet up to the science wing of the lecture hall and then walks 1,000 feet to her classroom. What is the angle of elevation from where Sara got on the elevator to the classroom?

43. On a military training exercise, a group of artillerymen are instructed to train their weapon on a target that is $\frac{3}{4}$ mile away and 80 feet high. At what angle of elevation should they set the weapon?

44. While finishing his basement, Dave finds that the stairs have a horizontal span of 12 feet while going down 8.5 feet. At what angle should the hand railing be placed to match the incline of the stairs?

45. A business jet is instructed to make a straight-line approach and landing, starting at an altitude of 4,500 feet and a distance of 7 miles from the runway. At what angle of depression should the pilot fly?

46. A sniper sets up on a roof across the street from a hostage situation. The roof is 36 feet high, and the laser distance finder on his rifle indicates that his straight-line distance from the target is 90 yards. At what angle of depression should he aim his rifle to train in on the target?

Critical Thinking

47. From the top of a building 300 feet high, the angle of elevation to a plane is 33° and the angle of depression to an automobile directly below the plane is 24°. Find the height of the plane and the distance the automobile is from the base of the building.

48. The angle of elevation to the top of a tree sighted from ground level is 18°. If the observer moves 80 feet closer, the angle of elevation from ground level to the top of the tree is 38°. Find the height of the tree.

49. Suppose that there is no trigonometric ratio known as tangent. Can you solve the problem in Example 2 without it? Describe the procedure you would use.

50. How can you solve the problem in Example 3 without using the cosine ratio?

Section 10-7 A Brief Survey of Non-Euclidean and Transformational Geometries

The Euclidean geometry that we have studied so far in this chapter helps us to solve many real-world problems, and because of this, many people would say that Euclidean geometry is the geometry that describes our physical world. But does it really? Suppose you hop in your car and drive 500 miles due south. In your perception, you have driven a straight-line path. But in fact, you were driving

along a curved path, matching the surface of the earth. This is why when you look out over the ocean, you can't see the other side—the water literally curves out of your sight at some point, which we call the horizon.

LEARNING OBJECTIVES

☐ 1. Identify the basics of elliptic geometry.

☐ 2. Identify the basics of hyperbolic geometry.

☐ 3. Create fractal figures.

☐ 4. Create tessellations.

Math Note

There are no parallel lines at all in elliptic geometry because all of the lines are great circles. To see that any two lines must meet, picture the lines of longitude on a globe. They look parallel near the equator, but meet at the poles.

☑ 1. Identify the basics of elliptic geometry.

Figure 10-32 A triangle in elliptic geometry

After thousands of years of accepting Euclid's geometry as the only one, in the 1800s mathematicians and scientists started to question whether the principles of Euclidean geometry really were universal, or if maybe there were other systems in which Euclid's principles didn't apply. And so the area of non-Euclidean geometry was born. There are entire courses taught on non-Euclidean geometries, so in this section we will simply take a quick look at some of them.

Figure 10-30

A **postulate** is a fundamental assumption underlying an area of study that cannot be proved, but rather is assumed to be true. It turns out that Euclidean geometry has at its foundation the **parallel postulate,** which says that given any line m and a point A not on that line, there is exactly one line parallel to m through A. See Figure 10-30.

Mathematicians spent about 2,000 years trying to prove the parallel postulate without success. Many of these attempts tried proof by contradiction: it was assumed that the parallel postulate didn't always hold, and an attempt was made to find something that contradicted the known theorems of geometry. Along the way, though, an interesting thing happened: new geometries were discovered that didn't follow the rules set out by Euclid. One such system is elliptic geometry.

Elliptic Geometry

Elliptic geometry was developed by the German mathematician Bernhard Riemann (1826–1866). While Euclidean geometry is based on planes, elliptic geometry is based on spheres. In elliptic geometry, the lines are finite in length, and are defined to be *great circles* of a sphere. A **great circle** is a circle on the sphere that has the same center as the sphere. See Figure 10-31.

Figure 10-31 Great circles on a sphere

One interesting aspect of elliptic geometry is that the sum of the angles of a triangle is greater than 180° (see Figure 10-32). The sum of the measures of the angles varies with the area of the triangle, and approaches 180° as the area of the triangle decreases.

If you find it hard to imagine an elliptic geometry, consider the fact that you live on one! That's why that 500-mile path you drove felt like a line to you even though it was curved—when you live on a sphere, lines follow the contour of the sphere.

Hyperbolic Geometry

Hyperbolic geometry was developed independently by the Russian mathematician Nikolay Lobachevsky (1792–1856) and the Hungarian mathematician János Bolyai (1802–1860).

Hyperbolic geometry is based on the assumption that, given a line m and a point not on the line, there are an infinite number of lines parallel to m. The shapes in hyperbolic geometry are drawn not on planes, but on a funnel-shaped surface known as a **pseudosphere.** A line on a pseudosphere is pictured in Figure 10-33.

Figure 10-33 A line in hyperbolic geometry

Figure 10-34 A triangle in hyperbolic geometry

☑ 2. Identify the basics of hyperbolic geometry.

In hyperbolic geometry, the shortest distance between two points is a curved line, the sides of a triangle are arcs, and the sum of the angles of a triangle is less than 180°. See Figure 10-34 on the previous page.

The remaining types of geometries we will study are called **transformational geometries** because they are based on transforming basic geometric shapes.

Fractal Geometry

☑ 3. Create fractal figures.

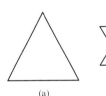

Figure 10-35

One type of transformational geometry is called **fractal geometry.** This geometry was developed by Benoit Mandelbrot (1924–). Fractal geometry makes geometric figures by using shapes that are repeated. See Figure 10-35 for an example. In this case, an equilateral triangle was used repeatedly. This figure is called the Sierpinski triangle.

The repeating process is called **iteration.** Computers can generate fractal figures very easily and quickly. Many nature forms, such as ferns, flowers, mountains, etc. can be duplicated, or at least simulated, using fractals.

Let's look at a method for creating another fractal figure.

Step 1 Start with an equilateral triangle.
Step 2 Replace each – side with ⌃.
Step 3 Repeat step 2 in the new figure.
Step 4 Continue the process as long as you wish. See Figure 10-36 for several iterations of the process. The figure is called the Koch snowflake.

(a)　　　　　(b)　　　　　(c)　　　　　(d)　　　　　(e)

Figure 10-36

Sidelight THE MOBIUS STRIP

An unusual mathematical shape can be created from a flat strip of paper. After cutting a strip, give it a half twist and tape the ends together to make a closed ring as shown.

The shape you have made is called a Mobius strip, named for the German mathematician Augustus Ferdinand Mobius (1790–1868) who created it. What is unusual about the Mobius strip is that it has only one side. You can draw a line through the center of the strip, starting anywhere and ending where you started without crossing over an edge. You can color the entire strip with one color by starting anywhere and ending where you started without crossing over an edge.

The Mobius strip has more unusual properties. Take a scissors and cut through the center of the strip following the line you drew as shown.

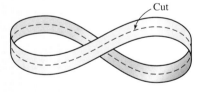

You will not get two strips as you might suspect, but you will have one long continuous two-sided strip.

Finally, make a new strip and cut it one-third of the way from the edge. You will find that you can make two complete trips around the strip using one continuous cut. The result of this cut will be two distinct strips: one will be a two-sided strip, and the other will be another one-sided Mobius strip.

The Mobius strip is a shape that belongs to a recently developed branch of mathematics called *topology*. Topology is a kind of geometry in which solid shapes are bent or stretched into different shapes. The properties of the shape that remain unchanged in the new shape are then studied.

Fractals have been used to study natural phenomenon such as seashores, mountains, trees, galaxies, and weather patterns. In addition, a radio antenna using a fractal pattern has been found more efficient than the traditional standard telescoping metal antenna.

Tessellations

☑ 4. Create tessellations.

An interesting aspect of transformational geometry is called a *tessellation*. The formal mathematical study of tessellations dates to the 1600s, but the concept itself is almost surely one of the oldest in all of math. For thousands and thousands of years, civilizations have used tessellation in art and architecture.

> A **tessellation,** also called a **tiling,** is a pattern that uses the same geometric shape to cover a plane without any gaps.

Math Note

Not every regular polygon can be used to create a tessellation. For example, it can be shown that regular pentagons alone cannot create a tessellation.

Figure 10-37 shows several tessellations. These figures are made by using regular polygons. (Recall that a regular polygon is a polygon in which all sides have the same length and all interior angles have the same measure.) The tessellation shown in Figure 10-37a is made from equilateral triangles. The one shown in Figure 10-37b is made from squares, and the one shown in Figure 10-37c is made from regular hexagons.

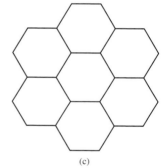

(a)　　　　　　　(b)　　　　　　　(c)

Figure 10-37

A tessellation can be made by following these steps.

Step 1　Draw a regular geometric polygon. In this case, we'll use a square.
Step 2　Cut the square from top to bottom using any design. See Figure 10-38a.

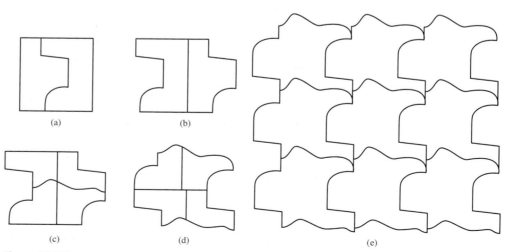

(a)　　　　　(b)　　　　　(c)　　　　　(d)　　　　　(e)

Figure 10-38

Sidelight M. C. ESCHER

A Dutch graphic artist, Maurits Cornelius Escher (1898–1972), used tessellations in his artwork and lithography. Escher had no formal training in mathematics; however, he was inspired by the beauty of Moorish artwork in the Alhambra Palace in Granada, Spain. Escher then read articles on symmetry, non-Euclidean geometry, and other areas of mathematics associated with tessellations. He is recognized for his works containing infinite repeating geometric patterns and created paintings of objects that could be drawn in two dimensions but were impossible to create in three dimensions.

Step 3 Move the left piece to the right side. Tape the pieces together. See Figure 10-38b.

Step 4 Cut the piece from left to right using any design. See Figure 10-38c.

Step 5 Move the top piece to the bottom piece and tape the pieces together. See Figure 10-38d.

Step 6 Trace the figure on another sheet of paper and then move it so that the sides line up like puzzle pieces.

Step 7 Continue the process as many times as you wish until a tessellation figure is complete. See Figure 10-38e.

Tessellations are very common in architectural design, but are most commonly used in mosaic designs of floors, walls, and windows. The most famous user of tessellations is without question the Dutch artist M. C. Escher, profiled in the sidelight.

EXERCISE SET 10-7

Writing Exercises

1. What is the surface on which shapes are drawn in Euclidean geometry?
2. What is the surface on which shapes are drawn in elliptic geometry?
3. How are lines represented in elliptic geometry?
4. Why are there no parallel lines in elliptic geometry?
5. Describe the shortest path between two points in hyperbolic geometry.
6. What is a pseudosphere?
7. Describe a fractal figure.
8. What is a tessellation? How are tesselations used?

Computational Exercises

9. Use a square and the procedure described on pages 562–563 to create a tessellation.
10. Use a regular hexagon and the procedure described on pages 562–563 to create a tessellation.
11. Using the letter H and putting an H at each corner, create a fractal-like figure.
12. Develop a fractal by replacing each _____ side in a square with ⌐⌐⌐.

Critical Thinking

13. Try to form a tessellation using only regular pentagons, then explain why it's not possible.
14. Repeat Exercise 13 using regular octagons.
15. Try to develop a rule for determining whether or not a given geometric shape can tessellate with itself.

CHAPTER 10 Summary

Section	Important Terms	Important Ideas
10-1	Point Line Plane Line segment Half line Ray Angle Vertex Degree Acute angle Right angle Obtuse angle Straight angle Complementary angles Supplementary angles Vertical angles Parallel lines Transversal Alternate interior angles Alternate exterior angles Corresponding angles	**The principals** of geometry have long been useful in helping people understand the physical world. The basic geometric figures are the point, the line, and the plane. From these figures, other figures such as segments, rays, and half lines can be made. When two rays have a common endpoint, they form an angle. Angles can be measured in degrees using a protractor. When lines intersect, several different types of angles are formed. They are vertical, corresponding, alternate interior, and alternate exterior. Two angles are called complementary angles if the sum of their measures is equal to $90°$. Two angles are called supplementary if the sum of their measures is equal to $180°$. Pairs of corresponding angles have the same measure, as do pairs of alternate interior angles, and pairs of alternate exterior angles.
10-2	Triangle Sides Vertices Isosceles triangle Equilateral triangle Scalene triangle Acute triangle Obtuse triangle Right triangle Hypotenuse Legs Pythagorean theorem Similar triangles	**A closed** geometric figure with three sides is called a triangle. A triangle can be classified according to the lengths of its sides or according to the measures of its angles. For a right triangle, the Pythagorean theorem states that $c^2 = a^2 + b^2$, where c is the length of the hypotenuse and a and b are the lengths of the legs. Two triangles with the same shape are called similar triangles. Corresponding sides of similar triangles are in proportion. This allows us to solve problems involving finding the lengths of sides.
10-3	Polygon Quadrilateral Pentagon Hexagon Heptagon Octagon Nonagon Decagon Dodecagon Icosagon Trapezoid Parallelogram	**A polygon** is classified according to the number of sides. A quadrilateral has four sides; a pentagon has five sides, etc. The sum of the measures of the angles of a polygon with n sides is $(n - 2)180°$. Special quadrilaterals such as the trapezoid, parallelogram, rhombus, and square are used in this chapter. A regular polygon is a polygon in which all sides are the same length and all angles have the same measure. The distance around the outside of a polygon is called the perimeter.

564

	Rectangle Rhombus Square Regular polygon Perimeter	
10-4	Area Circle Center Radius Diameter Circumference π (pi)	**The measure** of the portion of the plane enclosed by a geometric figure is called the area of the geometric figure. Area formulas can be developed for many familiar geometric figures. A circle is a closed geometric figure in which all the points are the same distance from a fixed point called the center. A segment connecting the center with any point on the circle is called a radius. A segment connecting two points on the circle and passing through the center of the circle is called a diameter. The circumference of a circle is the distance around the outside of the circle.
10-5	Volume Rectangular solid Cube Right circular cylinder Pyramid Cone Sphere Surface area	**Geometry** is also the study of solid figures. Some of the familiar solid figures are the cube, the rectangular solid, the pyramid, the cone, the cylinder, and the sphere. The volume of a solid geometric figure is the amount of space that is enclosed by the surfaces of the figure. The surface area of a solid figure is the area of the faces or surfaces of the figure.
10-6	Trigonometry Sine Cosine Tangent Inverse trigonometric functions Angle of elevation Angle of depression	**Trigonometry** is the study of the relationship between the angles and the sides of a triangle. The trigonometric ratios of sine, cosine, and tangent are used with a right triangle. The concepts of right triangle trigonometry can be used to solve many problems in navigation measurement, engineering, physics, and many other areas.
10-7	Elliptic geometry Hyperbolic geometry Fractals Tessellations	**Euclidean geometry** is based on the parallel postulate, which says that given any line m and a point not on it, there is exactly one line parallel to m through that point. In elliptic geometry, there are no parallel lines, and shapes are drawn on a sphere. In hyperbolic geometry, there are infinitely many lines parallel to any given line through a point, and shapes are drawn on a pseudosphere. Fractal figures are formed by starting with a basic shape and repeating the shape indefinitely in a pattern. Tessellations are formed when the same geometric shapes are used repeatedly to cover a plane without any gaps.

MATH IN ▷ **Home Improvement REVISITED**

1. The U-shaped section can be divided into three rectangles, giving a total of six rectangles we can find the area of using length times width. The combined area is 7,835 square inches, which is about 54.4 square feet. The cost of the style at $42 per square foot is $54.4 \times \$42 = \$2,284.80$. The cost of the style at $60 is $54.4 \times \$60 = \$3,264$. The difference is $979.20.

2. Draw a right triangle diagram with the given measurements:

Angle A of the triangle is found using the equation $\tan A = \frac{42}{57}$. Solving for A, we get 36.4°. The angle marked A along the bottom is also 36.4° because of alternate interior angles, and the angle marked with the arc, which the trim should be cut at, is the supplement of 36.4°, or 143.6°.

3. The width of the glass block part is $55\frac{3}{4}''$ (7 blocks at $7\frac{3}{4}''$ each, and 6 mortar joints at $\frac{1}{4}''$ each). The height is $31\frac{3}{4}''$ (4 blocks and 3 mortar joints). The diagram shows the trim:

The area of the trim can be found either by subtracting the area of the small rectangle from the area of the large rectangle, or by breaking the trim into four rectangles. In either case, the result is 561 square inches of trim needed, which is about 3.9 square feet.

4. This is another triangle diagram:

The 8″ side comes from the difference between the front edge and back edge heights. Solving the equation $\sin A = \frac{8}{48}$, we find that angle A measures 9.6°. If the legs were perpendicular to the hypotenuse and cut at a 90° angle, the bottom would make the same 9.6° angle with the ground (see below, left drawing). So to make it sit flat, it needs to be cut 9.6° short of 90°, or 80.4°.

None of these were made up—they are the actual calculations done by the author while doing the projects.

Review Exercises

Mixed Review

For Exercises 1–10, identify each figure.

1.
2.
3.
4.

5.
6.

7.
8.

9.
10.

Section 10-1

For Exercises 11–16, identify each type of angle or pairs of angles.

11.

12.

13.

∡1 and ∡2

14.

$l_1 \parallel l_2$

∡5 and ∡6

15.

$l_1 \parallel l_2$

∡3 and ∡4

16.

∡7 and ∡8

17. Find the complement of each angle.
    (a) 27°   (b) 88°
18. Find the supplement of each angle.
    (a) 172°   (b) 13°
19. Find the measures of ∡1, ∡2, and ∡3.

20. Find the measures of ∡1 through ∡7.

$l_1 \parallel l_2$

Section 10-2

21. Find the measure of the third angle of a triangle if the measures of the other two angles are 95° and 42°.
22. Find the measure of the hypotenuse of a right triangle if the lengths of the two legs are 8 inches and 15 inches.
23. Find the height of a water tower if its shadow is 24 feet when a 6-foot fence pole casts a shadow of 2 feet.

In Exercises 24–27, classify each triangle by angles (acute, obtuse, or right) and by sides (equilateral, isosceles, or scalene).

24.

26.

25.

27.

In Exercises 28–29, use the Pythagorean theorem to find the length of the missing side.

28.

29.

In Exercises 30–31, use the proportional property of similar triangles to find the missing sides (assume the two triangles in each exercise are similar).

30.

31.

32. If a 6-foot-tall man casts a 10-foot-long shadow, find the height of a building that casts a 150-foot-long shadow at the same time.
33. If a 12-foot ladder reaches 9 feet, 6 inches up a wall, how far up would a 20-foot ladder reach when placed at the same angle?

34. If the 20-foot ladder from Question 33 is placed with its base 9 feet from the wall, how high up does it reach?

35. A series of guy wires hold a radio antenna tower in place. If the tower is 140 feet high and the wires are attached to a point on the ground 90 feet from the base of the tower, how long are the wires?

36. While doing conditioning drills for spring training, a baseball player is supposed to run the length and width of a rectangular field that is 500 yards long and 800 feet wide. If he cheats and runs straight across on a diagonal, how much less distance does he run?

Section 10-3

In Exercises 37 and 38, identify the figure, then find the sum of the measures of the angles.

37.   38.

In Exercises 39–42, find the perimeter.

39. Find the perimeter of the figure shown.

40.

41.   42.

Section 10-4

For Exercises 43–46, find the area of each figure.

43.

44.

45.   46.

47. Find the circumference and area of a circle whose diameter is 16.5 yards.

48. The main gathering area of a newly constructed museum of modern art is shaped like a parallelogram. The north and south sides are 40 feet in length, and those two sides are 65 feet apart. Find how much it would cost to have the room tiled with marble that costs $12 per square foot installed.

49. Solar covers for swimming pools are made of a special plastic material, similar to bubble wrap, that helps to hold in heat. One supplier sells solar covers by the square foot, charging 22 cents per square foot. How much would a solar cover cost for a circular pool with a diameter of 17 feet?

50. The manufacturer of a new lawn tractor promises that in average use, it can cut 130 square yards of grass per minute. It currently takes the landscaper at East Central State an hour and 20 minutes to cut the football field, which is a rectangle with length 120 yards and width 53 yards. How much time would the new tractor save him?

Section 10-5

For Exercises 51–54, find the volume.

51.

52.

53.

54.

55. Find the surface area of the figure in Exercise 52.
56. Find the surface area of the figure in Exercise 54.
57. If the diameter of a bicycle wheel is 26 inches, how many revolutions will the wheel make if the rider rides 1 mile (1 mile = 5,280 feet)?
58. Find how many square inches of fabric are needed to make the kite shown.

59. Find the volume of a ball if the diameter is 4.2 cm.
60. Find the surface area for the walls of the building shown. (Include openings but do not include the area of the roof.)

Section 10-6

61. For the triangle shown, find $\sin B$, $\cos B$, and $\tan B$.

In Exercises 62–65, find the measure of the requested side or angle in triangle ABC. Note that C is the right angle.

62. Find b if $c = 27$ inches and $m\angle B = 49°$.
63. Find a if $b = 12$ yards and $m\angle A = 11°$.
64. Find $m\angle A$ if $c = 11$ meters and $b = 7.5$ meters.
65. Find $m\angle B$ if $a = 100$ miles and $b = 127$ miles.
66. If a tree 32 feet tall casts a shadow of 40 feet, find the angle of elevation of the sun.
67. A pole is leaning against a wall and is 15 feet from the base of the wall. If the angle of elevation from the ground to the base of the pole is 63°, find the length of the pole.
68. The ramp for a motorcycle jump is a straight, flat surface 130 feet long. The beginning is at ground level, and the end is 27 feet high. What angle does the ramp make with the ground?
69. A plane takes off in a straight line and flies for a half-hour at 160 miles per hour. At that point, the pilots are informed by air traffic control that they have flown 17° off course. They are instructed to change direction and fly at the same speed along a perpendicular path back to the line they should have flown on, then turn and continue to the destination. How long will it take them to get back on course?

Section 10-7

70. Starting with a square, create a tessellation using the procedure described in Section 10-7.
71. Make a fractal figure by starting with a square piece of paper 8 inches on a side, then drawing a square that is 3 inches on a side in each corner. Continue the process for at least four iterations, each time drawing squares in each corner that are $\frac{3}{8}$ the length of the square they are inside.
72. Describe lines in elliptic geometry in terms of a globe.

Chapter Test

1. Find the complement of an angle whose measure is 73°.
2. Find the supplement of an angle whose measure is 149°.
3. Find the measures of $\angle 1$, $\angle 2$, and $\angle 3$.

4. Find the measures of $\angle 1$ through $\angle 7$.

5. If two angles of a triangle have a measure of 85° and 47°, respectively, find the measure of the third angle.
6. If the hypotenuse of a right triangle is 29 inches and the length of one leg is 21 inches, find the length of the other leg.
7. Find the measure of side x. The two triangles are similar.

8. One way to measure the height of a tree is to cut it down and use a tape measure. But that's pretty drastic... another is to measure the length of its shadow, then measure the length of your shadow at the same time. Suppose the shadow of the tree is 13'11" long at a time when a person who is 5'10" tall casts a shadow 2'8" long. How tall is the tree?

9. Find the sum of the angles of an octagon.

10. Maureen is building a flowerbed in her backyard in the shape below. She wants to put three layers of landscape timbers along the border. If the timbers come in 8-foot lengths, how many will she need to buy?

For Exercises 11-15, find the area.

11.

12.

13.

14.

15.

16. Find the circumference of a circle whose radius is 13 cm.

For Exercises 17–22, find the volume of each.

17.

18.

19.

21.

20.

22.

For Exercises 23–25, find the surface area of each figure.

23. The figure in Exercise 17.

24.

25.

26. Are lines of latitude on a globe examples of lines in elliptic geometry? Explain why or why not.

27. Discuss whether or not a brick wall is a tessellation.

28. A city lot is shaped like a trapezoid with the front and back sides parallel and 157 feet apart. The front is 32 feet wide, and the back is 48 feet wide. Find the area of the lot.

29. Starting from home, you drive a certain distance south to Best Buy to get a new monitor for your

computer. You then drive 5 miles west to return that awful shirt your mother bought you for your birthday. You then drive 25 miles home. How far is it from your house to Best Buy?

30. You create a masterpiece in your art studio and it is selected for the student art exhibition. Your painting is 70 inches by 100 inches, and you choose framing that costs $4.35 per yard. Find the cost of the framing.

31. During your chemistry lab, you fill a cone-shaped beaker that has a 1-inch diameter and a 2-inch height with lead, which weighs 0.41 pounds per cubic inch. Find the weight of the lead in the beaker.

32. To install a satellite television transmitter, the technician digs a cylindrical hole that is 3 feet in diameter with a depth of 5 feet. How much dirt in pounds must be removed if 1 cubic foot of dirt weighs 98 pounds?

33. A bank sets up a security camera on top of a building across the street from their entrance. The camera is controlled by a computer, and the head of security needs to input an angle of depression for proper aim. If the camera is at a height of 46 feet and the base of the building across the street is 70 feet from the bank entrance, what angle should the manager input?

Projects

1. In a Sidelight feature back in Section 5-3, we referred to a website (http://www.angio.net/pi/piquery.html) where you can search for strings of numbers within the first 200 million digits of pi. Go to the site and search for the following:

   (a) Your birthday, in the form MMDDYYY
   (b) Your phone number, without area code
   (c) Your phone number with the area code
   (d) The first 8 natural numbers consecutively
   (e) The first 9 natural numbers consecutively
   (f) The first 6 even natural numbers consecutively
   (g) The first 7 odd natural numbers consecutively

   Based on these results, what can you say about the likelihood of finding a given string based on the number of digits in that string? Try to make some general conjectures about how likely you are to find a given string based on the number of digits, and try several numbers to test out your conjectures.

2. The numbers 3, 4, and 5 are called a Pythagorean triple, because a right triangle with sides 3, 4, and 5 units satisfies the Pythagorean theorem. That is, $3^2 + 4^2 = 5^2$. The numbers 5, 12, and 13 form another Pythagorean triple.

   (a) Do 6, 8, and 10 form a Pythagorean triple?
   (b) Do 9, 12, and 15 form a Pythagorean triple?
   (c) Do 10, 24, and 26 form a Pythagorean triple?
   (d) Based on your answers for parts a through c, can you make any definite statements about how many Pythagorean triples there are?
   (e) Based on parts a through c, write a general formula or formulas for finding Pythagorean triples.
   (f) Can you find a Pythagorean triple where the numbers are not multiples of either 3, 4, 5 or 5, 12, 13?

   (g) Search the Internet for the string "Pythagorean triple" and find how many Pythagorean triples there are where all three numbers are less than 100.
   (h) Research the question "are Pythagorean triples more common, or more rare, among three-digit numbers than among two-digit numbers?" In general, are they harder or easier to find as the lengths get larger?

3. Gather a variety of objects that you could pour a liquid into: glasses, buckets, pitchers, coolers, aquariums, sinks, or anything else that you could calculate (or estimate) the volume of, using the volume formulas we learned in Section 10-5.

   (a) Calculate the volume of each in both cubic inches and cubic centimeters by taking measurements and using volume formulas. If the containers are not exactly regular, like a bucket that is wider at the top than the bottom, make your best estimate of the volume.
   (b) Convert the measurements in cubic inches to gallons using the conversions from Chapter 9. Convert the measurements in cubic centimeters to liters also.
   (c) Calculate the volume of each container in gallons and liters by pouring measured amounts of water into it using a measuring cup, pitcher, or beaker.
   (d) Compare the measurements done with water to your calculations. How well did you do?

CHAPTER 11

Probability and Counting Techniques

Outline

11-1 The Fundamental Counting Principle and Permutations

11-2 Combinations

11-3 Basic Concepts of Probability

11-4 Tree Diagrams, Tables, and Sample Spaces

11-5 Probability Using Permutations and Combinations

11-6 Odds and Expectation

11-7 The Addition Rules for Probability

11-8 The Multiplication Rules and Conditional Probability

11-9 The Binomial Distribution
Summary

MATH IN ▶ Gambling

The fact that you're reading this sentence means that you're probably taking a math class right now. But maybe not . . . you could be an instructor evaluating the book, or maybe an editor looking for mistakes (unsuccessfully, we hope). Still, I would be willing to bet that you're taking a math class. The word "probably" indicates a certain likelihood of something happening, and that basic idea is the topic of this chapter. We call the study of the likelihood of events occurring *probability*.

Probability is one of the most useful concepts in math because being able to anticipate the likelihood of events can be useful in so many different areas. Games of chance, business and investing, sports, and weather forecasting are just a few samples from a seemingly limitless list of applications. What are the chances of your team winning the championship? Should you take an umbrella to the golf course today? Will stock in a company you're keeping an eye on go up or down? Is that new job offer a good opportunity, or a disaster waiting to happen? Every day you make decisions regarding possible events that are governed at least in part by chance. The more you know about the likelihood of events, the more informed your decisions are likely to be.

In order to compute probabilities of events occurring, we're going to need to know all of the possible outcomes for an event. For example, in deciding whether or not to bring an umbrella, there are only two outcomes: it will either rain, or it won't. But in considering whether or not to take a job,

there are a wide variety of possible outcomes, some good, some not so good. Since counting up the number of possible outcomes is important in probability, we will begin our study with a look at methods for counting. (Don't worry—that's not quite as elementary as it sounds!) Then we'll be ready to tackle the basic concepts of probability. Along the way, we'll learn about odds and the expected value of a probability experiment, and this is where gambling comes into play.

A handful of gambling scenarios is provided below. In each case, find the expected value (that is, the average amount a person would win or lose) if placing the bet 100 times. Then rank the scenarios from best to worst in terms of your likelihood of winning or losing money.

1. At a church fair, you bet $1 and roll two dice. If the sum is 2, 3, 11, or 12, you get back your dollar plus four more. On any other roll, you lose.

2. In a casino, you bet $1 on 33 at a roulette table. There are 38 possible numbers that can come up. If you win, you get your dollar back, plus 35 more.

3. You buy a $1 ticket to a multistate lottery. If you match all six numbers, including the Mega Ball, you win the $20 million jackpot. If not, you lose. There are 175,711,536 possible combinations, and only one of them will be a winner.

4. You bet $1 on flipping a coin with your roommate. Heads, you win, tails, your roommate wins.

For answers, see Math in Gambling Revisited on page 640

Section 11-1 The Fundamental Counting Principle and Permutations

LEARNING OBJECTIVES

☐ 1. Use the fundamental counting principle.

☐ 2. Calculate the value of factorial expressions.

☐ 3. Find the number of permutations of n objects.

☐ 4. Find the number of permutations of n objects taken r at a time.

☐ 5. Find the number of permutations when some objects are alike.

Many problems in probability and statistics require knowing the total number of ways a sequence of events can occur. Suppose that as part of an exciting new job, you're responsible for designing a new license plate for your state. You want it to look cool, of course. But if you want to keep your job, you better make sure that the sequence of letters and numbers you choose guarantees that there are enough different combinations so that every registered vehicle has a different plate number.

In this chapter, we'll study three basic rules for counting the number of outcomes for a sequence of events. The first is the *fundamental counting principle*.

The Fundamental Counting Principle

After getting that new job, you naturally want a new apartment, and furniture to go along with it. The hip furniture boutique around the corner has the couch you want in either leather or microsuede, and each comes in your choice of four colors. How many different couches do you have to choose from?

We'll illustrate the situation with a *tree diagram,* which displays all the possible combinations.

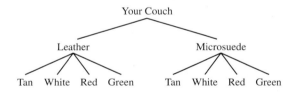

This shows us that the total number of couches possible is eight. This number can also be found by multiplying the number of materials (2) by the number of colors for each (4).

Now what if each couch can also come with or without an end recliner? Each of the eight choices in our diagram would have two more possibilities beneath it.

This would give us a total of 16 couches, which is $2 \cdot 4 \cdot 2$, or the product of the number of choices at each stage. This illustrates our first key counting principle.

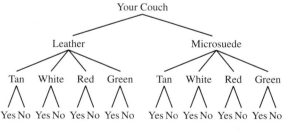

Math Note

The occurrence of the first event in no way affects the occurrence of the second event, which in turn, does not affect the occurrence of the third event, etc.

The Fundamental Counting Principle

In a sequence of n events in which the first event can occur in k_1 ways and the second event can occur in k_2 ways and the third event can occur in k_3 ways and so on, the total number of ways the sequence can occur is

$$k_1 \cdot k_2 \cdot k_3 \cdot \cdots \cdot k_n$$

EXAMPLE 1   **Using the Fundamental Counting Principle**

There are four blood types: A, B, AB, and O. Blood is also either Rh^+ or Rh^-. If a local blood bank labels donations according to type, Rh factor, and gender of the donor, how many different ways can a blood sample be labeled?

SOLUTION

There are four possibilities for blood type, two for Rh factor, and two for gender of the donor. Using the fundamental counting principle, there are

$$4 \cdot 2 \cdot 2 = 16$$

different ways that blood could be labeled.

▼ **Try This One 1**

A paint manufacturer plans to manufacture several different paints. The categories include

Color	Red, blue, white, black, green, brown, yellow
Type	Latex, oil
Texture	Flat, semigloss, high gloss
Use	Outdoor, indoor

How many different kinds of paint can be made if a person can select one color, one type, one texture, and one use?

When determining the number of different ways a sequence of events can occur, we'll need to know whether or not repetitions are permitted. The next example shows the difference between the two situations.

EXAMPLE 2   **Using the Fundamental Counting Principle with Repetition**

(a) The letters A, B, C, D, and E are to be used in a four-letter ID card. How many different cards are possible if letters are allowed to be repeated?
(b) How many cards are possible if each letter can only be used once?

SOLUTION

(a) There are four spaces to fill and five choices for each. The fundamental counting principle gives us

$$5 \cdot 5 \cdot 5 \cdot 5 = 5^4 = 625$$

(b) The first letter can still be chosen in five ways. But with no repetition allowed, there are only four choices for the second letter, three for the third, and two for the last. The number of potential cards is

$$5 \cdot 4 \cdot 3 \cdot 2 = 120$$

Hopefully, this ID card is for a pretty small organization.

How many three-digit codes are possible if repetition is not permitted?

▼ **Try This One 2**

The lock on a storage facility is controlled by a keypad containing digits 1 through 5.

(a) How many three-digit codes are possible if digits can be repeated?
(b) How many three-digit codes are possible if digits cannot be repeated?

1. Use the fundamental counting principle.

Calculator Guide

Most graphing calculators, and many scientific calculators have factorials programmed into them. To quickly compute 5!:

Standard Scientific Calculator

5 |x!|

Standard Graphing Calculator

5 |MATH|; use right arrow to choose PRB, then press |4| |ENTER|.

Factorial Notation

The next couple of counting techniques we'll learn use **factorial notation.** The symbol for a factorial is the exclamation mark (!). In general, $n!$ means to multiply the whole numbers from n down to 1. For example,

$$1! = 1 = 1$$
$$2! = 2 \cdot 1 = 2$$
$$3! = 3 \cdot 2 \cdot 1 = 6$$
$$4! = 4 \cdot 3 \cdot 2 \cdot 1 = 24$$
$$5! = 5 \cdot 4 \cdot 3 \cdot 2 \cdot 1 = 120$$

The formal definition of factorial notation is given next.

For any natural number n

$$n! = n(n-1)(n-2)(n-3) \cdots 3 \cdot 2 \cdot 1$$

$n!$ is read as "**n factorial.**"
0! is defined as 1. (This might seem strange, but will be explained later.)

Some of the formulas we'll be working with require division of factorials. This will be simple if we make two key observations:

- $\frac{n!}{n!}$ is always 1.   For example, $\frac{3!}{3!} = \frac{3 \cdot 2 \cdot 1}{3 \cdot 2 \cdot 1} = \frac{6}{6} = 1$
- You can write factorials without writing all of the factors down to 1. For example, $5! = 5 \cdot 4 \cdot 3 \cdot 2 \cdot 1$, but we can also write this as $5 \cdot 4!$, or $5 \cdot 4 \cdot 3!$, etc.

In Example 3, we'll use these ideas to simplify our calculations.

EXAMPLE 3   **Evaluating Factorial Expressions**

Evaluate each expression:

(a) 8!   (b) $\frac{12!}{10!}$

SOLUTION

(a) $8! = 8 \cdot 7 \cdot 6 \cdot 5 \cdot 4 \cdot 3 \cdot 2 \cdot 1 = 40{,}320$
(b) First, write 12! as $12 \cdot 11 \cdot 10!$, then note that $\frac{10!}{10!} = 1$.

$$\frac{12!}{10!} = \frac{12 \cdot 11 \cdot 10!}{10!} = 12 \cdot 11 = 132$$

▼ Try This One 3

☑ 2. Calculate the value of factorial expressions.

Evaluate each expression:

(a) 6!   (b) $\frac{9!}{4!}$

CAUTION

You cannot divide factorial expressions by reducing fractions. In Example 3(b), $\frac{12!}{10!}$ is *not* equal to $\frac{6!}{5!}$.

Permutations

The second rule that we can use to find the total number of outcomes for a sequence of events is the *permutation rule*.

An arrangement of n distinct objects in a specific order is called a **permutation** of the objects.

For example, suppose that a photographer wants to arrange three people, Carmen, Juan, and Christina, in a specific order for a portrait. There are six ways he could arrange them:

Carmen	Juan	Christina		Carmen	Christina	Juan
Juan	Carmen	Christina		Juan	Christina	Carmen
Christina	Juan	Carmen		Christina	Carmen	Juan

We could use the fundamental counting principle to see that there are six possible permutations as well:

$$3 \quad \cdot \quad 2 \quad \cdot \quad 1 \quad = \quad 3!$$

| Choices for | Choices for | Choices for |
| 1st position | 2nd position | 3rd position |

In general,

The number of permutations of n distinct objects using all of the objects is $n!$.

Example 4 illustrates this formula.

EXAMPLE 4 Calculating the Number of Permutations

In seven of the 10 years from 1998–2007, the five major league baseball teams in the American League East division finished in the exact same order: New York, Boston, Toronto, Baltimore, Tampa Bay. Just how unusual is this? Find the number of possible finishing orders for these five teams.

SOLUTION

This is a permutation problem since we're deciding on the number of ways to arrange five distinct objects. There are

$$5! = 120$$

possible finishing orders.

▼ Try This One 4

3. Find the number of permutations of n objects.

In how many different orders can the 11 basketball teams in the Big Ten conference finish? (Seriously, there are 11 teams in the Big Ten.)

So far, in calculating permutations, we've used all of the available objects. But what if only some of them are selected?

EXAMPLE 5   **Solving a Permutation Problem**

How many different ways can a pledge class with 20 members choose a president, vice president, and Greek Council representative? (No pledge can hold two offices.)

SOLUTION

There are 20 choices for president, 19 remaining candidates for vice president, and 18 members left to choose from for Greek Council rep. So there are $20 \cdot 19 \cdot 18 = 6,840$ different ways to assign these three offices.

▼ **Try This One 5**

How many ways can a manager and assistant manager be selected from a department consisting of 10 employees?

In Example 5, a certain number of objects (people in this case) have been chosen from a larger pool. The order of selection is important, and no repetition is allowed. (No pledge can be both president and vice president—power trip!) We call such an arrangement of objects a **permutation of n objects taken r at a time.** In the pledge problem, n is 20 and r is 3. We will use the symbol $_nP_r$ to represent this type of permutation.

We solved Example 5 using the fundamental counting principle, but the result suggests the formula below:

Permutation of n Objects Taken r at a Time

The arrangement of n objects in a specific order using r of those objects is called a **permutation of n objects taken r at a time.** It is written as $_nP_r$, and is calculated using the formula

$$_nP_r = \frac{n!}{(n-r)!}$$

EXAMPLE 6   **Solving a Permutation Problem**

How many five-digit zip codes are there with no repeated digits?

SOLUTION

This is a permutation problem because five numbers are taken from 10 possible digits, with order important and no repetition. In this case, $n = 10$ and $r = 5$.

$$_{10}P_5 = \frac{10!}{(10-5)!} = \frac{10!}{5!} = \frac{10 \cdot 9 \cdot 8 \cdot 7 \cdot 6 \cdot 5!}{5!} = 30,240$$

Calculator Guide

Most graphing calculators have the permutation formula built in. To find $_{10}P_5$ on a standard graphing calculator: 10 MATH, then use right arrow to select PRB, and press 2 to select $_nP_r$, and finally 5 ENTER.

▼ **Try This One 6**

How many six-letter passwords are there that use only lowercase letters with no letter repeated?

4. Find the number of permutations of n objects taken r at a time.

We now have two permutation formulas: there are $n!$ permutations of n objects using all of them, and $\frac{n!}{(n-r)!}$ using only r of the objects. We should probably make sure that these formulas are consistent with each other. To check, we'll use the second formula to calculate the number of permutations when n objects are taken n at a time. The result should be $n!$ (to match the first formula). Let's see.

If we arrange five people in order for a group picture, we can think of it as a permutation of the five people chosen five at a time; that is,

$$_5P_5 = \frac{5!}{(5-5)!} = \frac{5!}{0!}$$

This will agree with the first formula if we agree to define $0!$ as 1. Now we know why $0! = 1$, and we know that our two permutation formulas are consistent. This is good news, because it means we only need to remember the second permutation rule.

Problems involving permutation without duplicate objects can be solved using the fundamental counting rule; however, not all problems that can be solved with the fundamental counting rule can be solved using permutations.

When some of the objects are the same, a different permutation rule is used. Suppose that to solve a word puzzle, you need to find the number of permutations of the letters in the word *moon*. First label the letters as M, O_1, O_2, and N. This would be $4!$, or 24, permutations. But since the O's without the subscripts are the same, the permutation M, O_1, O_2, N would be the same as M, O_2, O_1, N. The duplicates are eliminated by dividing $4!$ by the number of ways to arrange the O's ($2!$) to get 12. This leads to the next rule.

Permutation Rule When Objects Are Alike

The number of permutations of n objects in which k_1 objects are alike, k_2 objects are alike, etc. is

$$\frac{n!}{k_1! k_2! \ldots k_p!}$$

where $k_1 + k_2 + \cdots + k_p = n$

EXAMPLE 7   Solving a Permutation Problem with Like Objects

How many different passwords can be made using all of the letters in the word *Mississippi*?

SOLUTION

The letters can be rearranged as M IIII SSSS PP. Then $n = 11$, $k_1 = 1$, $k_2 = 4$, $k_3 = 4$, and $k_4 = 2$.

Using our newest formula, there are

$$\frac{11!}{1! 4! 4! 2!} = 34{,}650$$

different passwords.

▼ Try This One 7

5. Find the number of permutations when some objects are alike.

Find the number of different passwords using all of the letters in the word *Massachusetts*.

In summary, the formulas for permutations are used when we're looking for the number of ways to arrange objects when the order matters, and once an object is used, it can't be used again.

Sidelight WIN A MILLION OR BE STRUCK BY LIGHTNING?

Do you think you would be more likely to win a large lottery and become a millionaire or more likely to be struck by lightning? The answer is that you would be quite a bit more likely to be struck by lightning.

An article in the Associated Press noted that researchers have found that the chance of winning $1 million or more is about 1 in 1.9 million. The chances of winning $1 million in a recent Pennsylvania lottery were 1 in 9.6 million. The chances of winning a $10 million prize in Publisher's Clearinghouse Sweepstakes were 1 in 200 million. In contrast, the chances of being struck by lightning are about 1 in 600,000. In other words, a person is at least 3 times more likely to be struck by lightning than to win $1 million.

One way to guarantee winning a lottery is to buy all possible combinations of the winning numbers. In 1992, an Australian investment group purchased 5 million of the 7 million possible combinations of the lottery numbers in

a Virginia State Lottery. Because of the time, they could not purchase the other two million tickets. However, they were able to purchase the winning number and won $27 million. Their profit was about $22 million. Not bad!

States have written laws to prevent this from happening today, and they are devising lottery games with many more possibilities so that it would be impossible to purchase all the possible tickets to win.

The consequence is that your odds of winning are now even lower! There's an old joke among statisticians: lotteries are a tax on people who are bad at math.

Answers to Try This One

1 84

2 (a) 125   (b) 60

3 (a) 720   (b) 15,120

4 39, 916, 800

5 90

6 165, 765, 600

7 64, 864, 800

EXERCISE SET 11-1

Writing Exercises

1. Explain the fundamental counting principle in your own words.
2. What do we mean by the phrase "a permutation of n distinct objects"?
3. How does a permutation of n objects differ from a permutation of n objects taken r at a time?
4. Explain what the symbols $n!$ and $_nP_r$ represent, and explain how to compute each for given values of n and r.

Computational Exercises

Evaluate each.

5. $10!$
6. $5!$
7. $9!$
8. $1!$
9. $0!$
10. $4!$
11. $(3!)(2!)$
12. $(7!)(2!)$
13. $\dfrac{8!}{5!}$
14. $\dfrac{9!}{7!}$
15. $\dfrac{7!}{2!3!}$
16. $\dfrac{10!}{2!5!}$
17. $\dfrac{150!}{148!}$
18. $\dfrac{200!}{197!}$
19. $_8P_2$
20. $_7P_5$
21. $_{12}P_{12}$
22. $_5P_3$
23. $_6P_6$
24. $_6P_0$
25. $_8P_0$
26. $_8P_8$
27. $_{11}P_3$
28. $_6P_2$

Real-World Applications

29. How many different four-letter permutations can be formed from the letters in the word *decagon*?

30. Out of a group of eight students serving on the Student Government Association, how many different ways can a president, a vice president, and a treasurer be selected?

31. How many different ID cards can be made if there are six digits on a card and no digit can be used more than once?

32. How many different ways can seven types of laser printer be displayed on a shelf in a computer store?

33. How many different ways can four Super Bowl raffle tickets be selected from 50 tickets if each ticket wins a different prize?

34. How many different ways can a psychology student select five subjects from a pool of 20 subjects and assign each one to a different experiment?

35. How many website graphics can be created by using at least three of five different bitmap images?

36. A chemistry lab group has seven experiments to choose from and five members in the group. How many different ways can the experiments be assigned if only one experiment is assigned to each group member?

37. A radio DJ has a choice of seven songs in the queue. He must select three different songs to play in a certain order after the commercial break. How many ways can he select the three different songs?

38. A professor has five different tasks to assign, one to each of her five teaching assistants. In how many different ways could she make the assignments?

39. A nursing student has six different patients assigned to her. How many different ways can she see each one exactly once in the same day?

40. A store owner has 50 items to advertise, and she can select one different item each week for the next 6 weeks to put on special. How many different ways can the selection be made?

41. Out of 17 contacts in her cell phone, how many different ways can Shana set the first four speed-dial contacts?

42. How many different ways can you visit four different stores in a shopping mall?

43. How many ways can a research company select three geographic areas from a list of six geographic areas to test market its product? One area will be selected and tested in September, a different area in October, and a third area will be used in November.

44. How many different code words can be made from the symbols *, *, *, @, @, $, #, #, #, # if each word has 10 symbols?

45. How many different permutations of the letters in the word *Alabama* are there?

46. A radio station must run commercial A three times, commercial B twice, and commercial C once. How many different ways can this be done?

47. How many desktop wallpaper designs can be created from two identical red squares, three identical white squares, and two identical blue squares?

48. How many different ways can two identical television sets, three identical DVD players, and one computer be arranged on a shelf?

49. How many ways can five DVD-ROMs, three zip discs, and two flash drives be arranged in a laptop case?

50. There are 14 teams in the Atlantic Ten Conference, and 12 qualify for the conference basketball tournament. Those 12 teams are seeded 1 through 12 for the conference tournament. In how many ways could this be done?

51. There are 16 teams in the Big East Conference. How many different ways can the top four seeds for the conference basketball tournament be selected?

52. A major league baseball team has 25 players on the active roster. How many choices does a manager have for batting order, listing the nine starters from 1 through 9?

53. A professional football team has 53 players on the active roster. How many choices of 22 starting players does a coach have without regard for their positions?

54. For the new fall season, a network president has 11 shows in development, and six openings in the prime time schedule. In how many ways can she arrange new shows to fit into the schedule?

55. For Ozzfest 2008, there were nine bands scheduled to perform on the main stage. In how many different orders could the bands have been scheduled to perform? How many are possible if Ozzy Osbourne is always scheduled to perform last?

Critical Thinking

56. A campus pizzeria offers regular crust, thin crust, or pan pizzas. You can get either white or red sauce. The owner is kind of eccentric, and only sells pizzas with one topping, chosen from pepperoni, sausage, ham, onions, and ground beef. First, use a tree diagram like the one on page 574 to diagram out all possible choices of pizza. Then show that using the fundamental counting principle yields the same answer.

Section 11-2 Combinations

LEARNING OBJECTIVES

☐ 1. Distinguish between combinations and permutations.

☐ 2. Find the number of combinations of n objects taken r at a time.

☐ 3. Use the combination rule in conjunction with the fundamental counting principle.

Suppose that after waiting in line overnight, you manage to snag the last three tickets to a big concert. Sweet! The bad news is that you can only take two of your four housemates. How many different ways can you choose the two friends that get to go?

This sounds a little bit like a permutation problem, but there's a key difference: the order in which you choose two friends doesn't make any difference. They either get to go or they don't. So choosing Ruth and Ama is exactly the same as choosing Ama and Ruth. When order matters in a selection, we call it a permutation, but when order is not important we call it a *combination*.

A selection of objects without regard to order is called a **combination.**

In Example 1, we'll examine the difference between permutations and combinations.

EXAMPLE 1   Comparing Permutations and Combinations

Given four housemates, Ruth, Elaine, Ama, and Jasmine, list the permutations and combinations when you are selecting two of them.

SOLUTION

We'll start with permutations, then eliminate those that have the same two people listed.

Permutations

Ruth Elaine	Elaine Ruth	Ruth Ama
Ama Ruth	Ruth Jasmine	Jasmine Ruth
Elaine Ama	Ama Elaine	Elaine Jasmine
Jasmine Elaine	Ama Jasmine	Jasmine Ama

Combinations

Ruth Elaine	Ruth Ama	Ruth Jasmine
Elaine Ama	Elaine Jasmine	Ama Jasmine

There are 12 permutations, but only 6 combinations.

▼ **Try This One 1**

If you are choosing two business classes from three choices, list all the permutations and combinations.

It will be very valuable in our study of counting and probability to be able to decide if a given selection is a permutation or a combination.

EXAMPLE 2 **Identifying Permutations and Combinations**

Decide if each selection is a permutation or a combination.

(a) From a class of 25 students, a group of 5 is chosen to give a presentation.
(b) A starting pitcher and catcher are picked from a 12-person intramural softball team.

SOLUTION

(a) This is a combination because there are no distinct roles for the 5 group members, so order is not important.
(b) This is a permutation because each selected person has a distinct position, so order matters.

▼ **Try This One 2**

Decide if each selection is a permutation or a combination.

(a) A 5-digit passcode is chosen from the numbers 0 through 9.
(b) A gardener picks 4 vegetable plants for his garden from 10 choices.

☑ 1. Distinguish between combinations and permutations.

Recall that the number of combinations in Example 1 was half as great as the number of permutations. This is because once two people are selected, there are two ways to arrange them. So the number of combinations of n objects chosen r at a time should be the number of permutations divided by the number of arrangements of r objects. But we know that is $r!$. This gives us a formula for combinations.

Math Note

Notice that the combination formula is the permutation formula from Section 11-1 with an extra factor of $r!$ in the denominator.

The Combination Rule

The number of combinations of n objects taken r at a time is denoted by $_nC_r$, and is given by the formula

$$_nC_r = \frac{n!}{(n-r)!r!}$$

EXAMPLE 3 **Using the Combination Rule**

How many combinations of four objects are there taken two at a time?

SOLUTION

Since this is a combination problem, the answer is

$$_4C_2 = \frac{4!}{(4-2)!2!} = \frac{4!}{2!2!} = \frac{4 \cdot 3 \cdot 2!}{2 \cdot 1 \cdot 2!} = 6$$

This matches our result from Example 1.

Calculator Guide

Most graphing calculators have the combination formula built in. To find $_4C_2$ on a standard graphing calculator:

4 |MATH|, then use right arrow to select PRB, and press |3| to select $_nC_r$, and finally 2 |Enter|.

▼ **Try This One 3**

How many combinations of eight objects are there taken five at a time?

EXAMPLE 4   An Application of Combinations

> **Math Note**
>
> Some people use the terminology "10 choose 3" to describe the combination $_{10}C_3$, and it is sometimes represented using the notation $\binom{10}{3}$.

While studying abroad one semester, Tran is required to visit 10 different cities. He plans to visit 3 of the 10 over a long weekend. How many different ways can he choose the 3 to visit? Assume that distance is not a factor.

SOLUTION

The problem doesn't say anything about the order in which they'll be visited, so this is a combination problem.

$$_{10}C_3 = \frac{10!}{(10-3)!3!} = \frac{10!}{7!3!} = 120$$

▼ Try This One 4

An instructor posts a list of eight group projects to her website. Every group is required to do four projects at some point during the semester. How many different ways can a group choose the four projects they want to do?

 2. Find the number of combinations of n objects taken r at a time.

In some cases, the combination rule is used in conjunction with the fundamental counting principle. Examples 5 and 6 illustrate some specific situations.

EXAMPLE 5   Choosing a Committee

At one school, the student government consists of seven women and five men. How many different committees can be chosen with three women and two men?

SOLUTION

First, we will choose three women from the seven candidates. This can be done in $_7C_3 = 35$ ways. Then we will choose two men from the five candidates in $_5C_2 = 10$ ways. Using the fundamental counting principle, there are $35 \cdot 10 = 350$ possible committees.

▼ Try This One 5

On an exam, a student must select 2 essay questions from 6 essay questions and 10 multiple choice questions from 20 multiple choice questions to answer. How many different ways can the student select questions to answer?

EXAMPLE 6   Designing a Calendar

To raise money for a charity event, a sorority plans to sell a calendar featuring tasteful pictures of some of the more attractive professors on campus. They will need to choose six models from a pool of finalists that includes nine women and six men. How many possible choices are there if they want to feature at least four women?

SOLUTION

Since we need to include at least four women, there are three possible compositions: four women and two men, five women and one man, or six women and no men.

Four women and two men:

$$_9C_4 \cdot {_6C_2} = \frac{9!}{(9-4)!\,4!} \cdot \frac{6!}{(6-2)!\,2!} = 126 \cdot 15 = 1,890$$

Five women and one man:

$$_9C_5 \cdot {_6C_1} = \frac{9!}{(9-5)!\,5!} \cdot \frac{6!}{(6-1)!\,1!} = 126 \cdot 6 = 756$$

Six women and no men:

$$_9C_6 \cdot {_6C_0} = \frac{9!}{(9-6)!\,6!} \cdot \frac{6!}{(6-0)!\,0!} = 84 \cdot 1 = 84$$

The total number of possibilities is $1,890 + 756 + 84 = 2,730$.

▼ **Try This One 6**

3. Use the combination rule in conjunction with the fundamental counting principle.

A four-person crew for the international space station is to be chosen from a candidate pool of 10 Americans and 12 Russians. How many different crews are possible if there must be at least two Russians?

Table 11-1 summarizes all of the counting rules from sections 11-1 and 11-2. It's important to know the formulas, but it's far more important to understand the situations that each formula is needed for.

TABLE 11-1 **Summary of Counting Rules**

Rule	Definition	Formula
Fundamental counting principle	The number of ways a sequence of n events can occur if the first event can occur in k_1 ways, the second event can occur in k_2 ways, etc. (Events are unaffected by the others.)	$k_1 \cdot k_2 \cdot k_3 \cdots k_n$
Permutation rule	The number or permutations of n objects taking r objects at a time. (Order is important.)	$\dfrac{n!}{(n-r)!}$
Permutation rule for duplicate objects	The number of permutations in which k_1 objects are alike, k_2 objects are alike, etc.	$\dfrac{n!}{k_1!\,k_2!,\cdots,k_p!}$
Combination rule	The number of combinations of r objects taken from n objects. (Order is not important.)	$\dfrac{n!}{(n-r)!\,r!}$

Answers to Try This One

1 Call the classes A, B, and C:

   Permutations
   A B B A A C
   C A B C C B

   Combinations
   A B A C B C

2 (a) Permutation

   (b) Combination

3 56

4 70

5 2,771,340

6 5,665

EXERCISE SET 11-2

Writing Exercises

1. What is meant by the term combination?
2. What is the difference between a permutation and a combination?
3. Describe a real-life situation in which it would be appropriate to use combinations to count possibilities.
4. Describe a situation related to the one in Exercise 3 in which it would be appropriate to use permutations to count possibilities.

Computational Exercises

For Exercises 5–14, evaluate each expression.

5. $_5C_2$
6. $_8C_3$
7. $_7C_4$
8. $_6C_2$
9. $_6C_4$
10. $_3C_0$
11. $_3C_3$
12. $_9C_7$
13. $_{12}C_2$
14. $_4C_3$

For Exercises 15–20, find both the number of combinations and the number of permutations for the given number of objects.

15. 8 objects taken 5 at a time
16. 5 objects taken 3 at a time
17. 6 objects taken 2 at a time
18. 10 objects taken 6 at a time
19. 9 objects taken 9 at a time
20. 12 objects taken 1 at a time

For Exercises 21–28, decide whether the selection described is a combination or a permutation.

21. Ten fans at a concert are chosen to go backstage after the show.
22. From a list of 20 dishes he knows how to cook, Maurice chooses different dishes for breakfast, lunch, and dinner on his girlfriend's birthday.
23. A state elects a governor and lieutenant governor from a pool of eight candidates.
24. A state elects two senators from a pool of 12 candidates.
25. Lupe chooses an eight-letter password from the letters of the alphabet.
26. Of the six optional community service projects in a service learning course, Haylee picks three of them.
27. When looking for a new car, you read about ten different models and choose four that you would like to test drive.
28. Mark looks over the novels on his bookshelf and lists his five favorites ranked 1 through 5.

Real-World Applications

29. How many different ways can five cards be selected from a standard deck of 52 cards?
30. How many ways are there to select three math help websites from a list that contains six different websites?
31. How many ways can a student select five questions from an exam containing nine questions? How many ways are there if he must answer the first question and the last question?
32. How many ways can four finalists for a job be selected from ten interviewees?
33. If a person can select three presents from 10 presents under a Christmas tree, how many different combinations are there?
34. How many different possible tests can be made from a test bank of 20 questions if the test consists of 5 questions? (Ignore the order of questions.)
35. The general manager of a fast-food restaurant chain must select 6 restaurants from 11 for a promotional program. How many different possible ways can this selection be done?
36. How many ways can 3 cars and 4 trucks be selected from 8 cars and 11 trucks to be tested for a safety inspection?
37. During the tryouts for the school jazz band, there were four trumpet players, twelve guitar players, and seven saxophonists. How many ways can the jazz band be chosen so there are two trumpet players, five guitarists, and three saxophonists?
38. There are seven men and five women in line at a Salsa dance club. The bouncer can only admit two more men and two more women. How many ways can he choose from those in line? How many ways

can he choose if instead he is told he can admit four people and at least two must be women?

39. Coca-Cola comes in two low-calorie varieties: Diet Coke and Coke Zero. If a promoter has 10 cans of each, how many ways can she select 3 cans of each for a taste test at the local mall?

40. At the movies, Shana wants to get snacks for her friends. How many ways can she select three types of candy and two types of soda from the eight types of candy and five types of soda available?

41. Steve wants to download new music into his iPod from iTunes. How many ways can Steve select two rock songs, three alternative songs, and three rap songs from a list of eight rock songs, six alternative songs, and ten rap songs?

42. How many ways can 2 men and 2 women be selected for a debate tournament if there are 10 male finalists and 12 female finalists?

43. The state narcotics bureau must form a 5-member investigative team. If it has 25 agents to choose

from, how many different possible teams can be formed?

44. How many different ways can a computer programmer select 3 jobs from a possible 15?

45. The Environmental Protection Agency must investigate nine nuclear reactors for complaints of radioactive pollution. How many different ways can a representative select five of these to investigate this week?

46. How many ways can a person select 8 DVDs from 10 DVDs?

47. How many ways can 20 students be chosen for the express line at registration if there are 30 students to choose from?

48. An advertising manager decides to have an ad campaign in which eight special items will be hidden at various locations in a shopping mall. If he has 17 locations to pick from, how many different possible combinations can he choose?

Section 11-3 Basic Concepts of Probability

LEARNING OBJECTIVES

☐ 1. Compute classical probabilities.

☐ 2. Compute empirical probabilities.

Walking into a casino without knowing anything about probability is kind of like going to a stick fight without a stick—you're likely to take a beating. Casinos aren't in the business of losing money, and the games are designed so that most people lose more than they win. But an understanding of what is likely to happen in a given situation can give you an advantage over other players, giving you a better chance of walking out the door with some cash in your pockets.

The study of probability originated in an effort to understand games of chance, like those that use coins, dice, and playing cards. Generally speaking, probability is simply a number that describes how likely an event is to occur. We will use games of chance to illustrate the ideas, but will eventually see that probability has many applications beyond simple games. In this section, we'll examine the basic concepts involved in studying probability.

Sample Spaces

Processes such as flipping a coin, rolling a die, or drawing a card from a deck are called *probability experiments.*

A **probability experiment** is a process that leads to well-defined results called outcomes. An **outcome** is the result of a single trial of a probability experiment.

Some examples of a trial are flipping a coin once, rolling a single die, and drawing one card from a deck. When a coin is tossed, there are two possible outcomes: heads or tails. When rolling a single die, there are six possible outcomes: 1, 2, 3, 4, 5, or 6.

In a probability experiment, we can predict what outcomes are possible, but we cannot predict with certainty which one will occur. We say that the outcomes occur at random. In any experiment, the set of all possible outcomes is called the *sample space*.

A **sample space** is the set of all possible outcomes of a probability experiment.

Some sample spaces for various probability experiments are shown here.

Experiment	Sample Space
Toss one coin	{head, tail}
Roll a die	{1, 2, 3, 4, 5, 6}
Answer a true-false question	{true, false}
Toss two coins	{head/head, tail/tail, head/tail, tail/head}

It is important to realize that when two coins are tossed, there are *four* possible outcomes. Consider tossing a quarter and a dime at the same time. Both coins could fall heads up. Both coins could fall tails up. The quarter could fall heads up and the dime could fall tails up and, finally, the quarter could fall tails up and the dime could fall heads up. The situation is the same even if the coins are indistinguishable.

In finding probabilities, it is sometimes necessary to consider several outcomes of a probability experiment. For example, when a die is rolled, we may want to consider obtaining an odd number, i.e., 1, 3, or 5. Getting an odd number when rolling a die is an example of an event.

Experiment: draw a card. Sample space: 52 cards. Event: drawing an ace.

An **event** is any subset of the sample space of a probability experiment.

Classical Probability

Now we're ready to specifically define what is meant by probability. The first type we will study is called *classical probability,* because it was the first type of probability to be studied in the 17th and 18th centuries. In classical probability, we study all of the possible outcomes in a sample space and determine the probability, or likelihood, of an event occurring without actually performing experiments.

There is one key assumption we make in classical probability: that every outcome in a sample space is equally likely. For example, when a single die is rolled, we assume that each number is equally likely to come up. When a card is chosen from a deck of 52 cards, we assume that each card has the same probability of being drawn.

Math Note

Because classical probabilities are based on theory, not experiments, they are also called theoretical probabilities.

Formula for Classical Probability

Let E be an event that is a subset of the sample space S. We will write $n(E)$ to represent the number of outcomes in E, and $n(S)$ to represent the number of outcomes in S. The probability of the event E is defined to be

$$P(E) = \frac{n(E)}{n(S)} = \frac{\text{Number of outcomes in } E}{\text{Number of outcomes in } S}$$

In Example 1, we'll compute some simple probabilities using the formula above.

EXAMPLE 1 **Computing Classical Probabilities**

A single die is rolled. Find the probability of getting

(a) A 2.
(b) A number less than 5.
(c) An odd number.

SOLUTION

In this case, since the sample space is 1, 2, 3, 4, 5, and 6, there are six outcomes: $n(S) = 6$.

(a) There is one possible outcome that gives a 2, so $P(2) = \frac{1}{6}$.
(b) There are four possible outcomes for the event of getting a number less than 5—1, 2, 3, or 4; so $n(E) = 4$, and

$$P(\text{a number less than 5}) = \frac{n(E)}{n(S)} = \frac{4}{6} = \frac{2}{3}$$

A die roll has six outcomes. If E = roll a 2, then $P(E) = \frac{1}{6}$. If E = roll an even number, then $P(E) = \frac{3}{6} = \frac{1}{2}$.

(c) There are three possible outcomes for the event of getting an odd number: 1, 3, or 5; so $n(E) = 3$, and

$$P(\text{odd number}) = \frac{n(E)}{n(S)} = \frac{3}{6} = \frac{1}{2}$$

▼ **Try This One 1**

Each number from one to twelve is written on a card and placed in a box. If a card is selected at random, find the probability that the number on the card is

(a) A 7.
(b) An odd number.
(c) A number less than four.
(d) A number greater than seven.

EXAMPLE 2 **Computing Classical Probabilities**

Two coins are tossed. Find the probability of getting

(a) Two heads.
(b) At least one head.
(c) At most one head.

Math Note

A good problem-solving strategy to use is to make a list of all possible outcomes in the sample space before computing the probabilities of events.

SOLUTION

The sample space is {HH, HT, TH, TT}; therefore, $n(S) = 4$.

(a) There is only one way to get two heads: HH. So

$$P(\text{two heads}) = \frac{n(E)}{n(S)} = \frac{1}{4}$$

(b) "At least one head" means one or more heads; i.e., one head or two heads. There are three ways to get at least one head: HT, TH, and HH. So $n(E) = 3$, and

$$P(\text{at least one head}) = \frac{n(E)}{n(S)} = \frac{3}{4}$$

(c) "At most one head" means no heads or one head: TT, TH, HT. So $n(E) = 3$, and

$$P(\text{at most one head}) = \frac{n(E)}{n(S)} = \frac{3}{4}$$

☑ 1. Compute classical probabilities.

▼ **Try This One 2**

Suppose that in a certain game, it is equally likely that you will win, lose, or tie. Find the probability of

(a) Losing twice in a row.
(b) Winning at least once in two tries.
(c) Having the same outcome twice in a row.

Math Note

The probability of getting tails when tossing a single coin could be given as any of ½, 0.5, or 50%.

At this point, we can make a series of simple but important observations about probabilities. Both $n(E)$ and $n(S)$ have to be zero or positive, so *probability is never negative*. Second, since S represents all possible outcomes, and E is a subset of S, $n(E)$ is always less than or equal to $n(S)$. This means that *probability is never greater than 1*. Probabilities are usually expressed as fractions or decimals between (and including) zero and one. But sometimes we will express probabilities in percent form when it seems appropriate for a given situation.

When an event cannot possibly occur, the probability is zero, and *when an event is certain to occur, the probability is one.* For example, the probability of getting 8 when rolling a single die is zero because none of the outcomes in the sample space result in 8. The probability of getting either heads or tails when flipping a single coin is 1 because that particular event is satisfied by every outcome in the sample space.

A 10% chance of rain is not the same as no chance of rain. You would expect it to rain on roughly 1 in 10 days when a 10% chance of rain was forecast.

The sum of the probabilities of all the outcomes in the sample space will always be one. For example, when a die is rolled, each of the six outcomes has a probability of $\frac{1}{6}$, and the sum of the probabilities of the six outcomes will be one.

When the probability of an event is close to zero, the event is very unlikely to occur. When the probability of an event is close to $\frac{1}{2}$ or 0.5, the event has approximately a 50% chance of occurring. When the probability of an event is near one, the event is almost certain to occur. See Figure 11-1.

In addition to finding the probability that an event will occur, it is sometimes useful to find the probability that the event will *not* occur. For example, if a die is rolled, the probability that a 4 will not occur, symbolized by $P(4')$, is $\frac{5}{6}$ since there are five ways that a 4 will not occur; i.e., 1, 2, 3, 5, 6. The solution can also be found by finding the

Unlikely Likely
Impossible | 50/50 | Certain
0   0.5   1

Figure 11-1

probability of getting a 4 and subtracting it from one; the sum of the probabilities of all outcomes in the sample space is one, so

$$P(4') = 1 - P(4) = 1 - \frac{1}{6} = \frac{5}{6}$$

The rule can be generalized as follows

For any event, E, $P(E') = 1 - P(E)$, where E' is the event "E does not occur."

$E \cup E' = U$
$P(E) + P(E') = 1$

Figure 11-2

Probability and Sets

The theory of probability is related to the theory of sets discussed in Chapter 2. For a given probability experiment, the sample space can be considered the universal set, and an event E can be considered as a subset of the universal set.

For example, when rolling a die, the sample space is $\{1, 2, 3, 4, 5, 6\}$; so the universal set is $U = \{1, 2, 3, 4, 5, 6\}$. Let the event E be getting an odd number; i.e., 1, 3, or 5. In sets, $E = \{1, 3, 5\}$. A Venn diagram can now be drawn illustrating this example. See Figure 11-2.

Notice that set E contains 1, 3, and 5 while the numbers 2, 4, and 6 are in the universal set but not in E. So $E' = \{2, 4, 6\}$. Now recall from set theory that $E \cup E' = U$. As stated previously, the sum of the probabilities of the outcomes in the sample space is one, so $P(U) = 1$. E' represents the elements in U but not in E, so $P(E) + P(E') = 1$. Subtracting $P(E)$ from both sides, we get $P(E') = 1 - P(E)$. Additional relationships between probability theory and set theory will be shown in other sections of this chapter.

Empirical Probability

The second type of probability we will study is computed using experimental data, rather than counting equally likely outcomes. For example, suppose 100 games into the season, your favorite baseball team has won 60 games and lost 40. You might reasonably guess that since they've won 60 of their 100 games so far, the probability of them winning any given game is about 60/100, or 0.6. This type of probability is called **empirical probability,** and is based on *observed frequencies*—that is, the number of times a particular event has occurred out of a certain number of trials. In this case, the observed frequency of wins is 60, the observed frequency of losses is 40, and the total number of trials is $60 + 40 = 100$.

Sidelight **YOU BET YOUR LIFE!**

You probably think of gambling as betting money at a casino or on a sporting event, but people gamble all the time in many ways. In fact, people bet their lives every day by engaging in unhealthy activities like smoking, using drugs, eating a high-fat diet, and even driving too fast. Maybe people don't care about the risks involved in these activities because they don't understand the concept of probability. On the other hand, people tend to fear things that are far less likely to harm them, like flying, because the occasional negative consequence is sensationalized in the press.

In his book *Probabilities in Everyday Life* (Ivy Books, 1986), author John D. McGrevey states:

When people have been asked to estimate the frequency of death from various causes, the most overestimated causes are those involving pregnancy, tornados, floods, fire, and homicide. The most underestimated categories include death from diseases such as diabetes, stroke, tuberculosis, asthma, and stomach cancer (although cancer in general is overestimated). Which do you think is safer: flying across the United States on a commercial airline, or driving cross country? According to our friend McGrevey, the probability of being killed on any given airline flight is about 1/1,000,000, while the probability of being killed on a transcontinental automobile trip is just 1/8,000. That means that driving across the country is 125 times more dangerous than flying!

Formula for Empirical Probability

$$P(E) = \frac{\text{Observed frequency of the specific event } (f)}{\text{Total number of trials } (n)} = \frac{f}{n}$$

In this coin toss, the empirical probability of heads was $\frac{6}{10}$, or $\frac{3}{5}$. With more tosses, you would expect $P(\text{heads})$ to approach $\frac{1}{2}$.

The information in the baseball problem can be written in the form of a *frequency distribution* that consists of classes and frequencies for the classes, as shown below:

Result (Class)	Observed Frequency
Win	60
Lose	40
Total	100

This technique is often helpful in working out empirical probabilities.

EXAMPLE 3   Computing an Empirical Probability

In a sample of 50 people, 21 had type O blood, 22 had type A blood, 5 had type B blood, and 2 had type AB blood. Set up a frequency distribution and find these probabilities for a person selected at random from the sample.

(a) The person has type O blood.
(b) The person has type A or type B blood.
(c) The person has neither type A nor type O blood.
(d) The person does not have type AB blood.

Source: Based on American Red Cross figures

SOLUTION

Type (class)	Observed Frequency
A	22
B	5
AB	2
O	21
Total	50

Type O negative blood is the least likely to react badly with a patient's blood. If it is not possible to test the patient's blood before a transfusion, then O negative is used.

Math Note

The solution to part c could also be done as $P(\text{neither A nor O}) = 1 - P(\text{A or O})$:

$$1 - \left(\frac{22}{50} + \frac{21}{50}\right)$$

$$= 1 - \frac{43}{50} = \frac{7}{50}.$$

☑ 2. Compute empirical probabilities.

(a) $P(\text{O}) = \frac{f}{n} = \frac{21}{50}$

(b) The frequency of A or B is $22 + 5 = 27$. $P(\text{A or B}) = \frac{27}{50}$

(c) Neither A nor O means either B or AB; the frequency of either B or AB is $5 + 2 = 7$. $P(\text{neither A nor O}) = \frac{7}{50}$

(d) The probability of not AB is found by subtracting the probability of AB from 1.

$$P(\text{not AB}) = 1 - P(\text{AB}) = 1 - \frac{2}{50} = \frac{48}{50} = \frac{24}{25}$$

▼ Try This One 3

A bag of Hershey's Assorted Miniatures contains 18 Hershey Milk Chocolate bars, 9 Mr. Goodbars, 9 Krackel bars, and 8 Hershey's Special Dark Chocolate bars. If a bar is selected at random from the bag, find the probability that it is

(a) A Mr. Goodbar.
(b) A Krackel or a Special Dark Chocolate bar.
(c) Not a Milk Chocolate bar.

It is important to understand the relationship between classical probability and empirical probability in certain situations. In classical probability, the probability of rolling a 3 when a die is thrown is found by looking at the sample space, and is $\frac{1}{6}$. To find the probability of getting a 3 when a die is thrown using empirical probability, you would actually toss a die a specific number of times and count the number of times a 3 was obtained; then divide that number by the number of times the die was rolled. For example, suppose a die was rolled 60 times, and a 3 occurred 12 times. Then the empirical probability of getting a 3 would be $\frac{12}{60} = \frac{1}{5}$. Most of the time, the probability obtained from empirical methods will differ from that obtained using classical probability. The question is, then, "How many times should I roll the die when using empirical probability?" There is no specific answer except to say that the more times the die is tossed, the closer the results obtained from empirical probability will be to those of classical probability.

In summary, then, classical probability uses sample spaces and assumes the outcomes are equally likely. Empirical probability uses observed frequencies and the total of the number of frequencies.

Sidelight PROBABILITY AND YOUR FEARS

All of us at one time or another have thought about dying. Some people have fears of dying in a plane crash or dying from a heart attack. In the sidelight on page 591, it was explained that it is safer to fly across the United States than to drive. Statisticians who work for insurance companies (called actuaries) also calculate probabilities for dying from other causes. For example, based on deaths in the United States, the risks of dying from various other causes are shown.

Motor vehicle accident	1 in 7,000
Shot by a gun	1 in 10,000
Accident while walking across the street	1 in 60,000
Lightning strike	1 in 3 million
Shark attack	1 in 100 million

The death risk for various diseases is much higher as shown.

Heart attack	1 in 400
Cancer	1 in 600
Stroke	1 in 2,000

As you can see, the chances of dying from diseases are much higher than dying from accidents.

Answers to Try This One

1　(a) 1/12　(b) 1/2　(c) 1/4　(d) 5/12　　**3**　(a) 9/44　(b) 17/44　(c) 13/22

2　(a) 1/9　(b) 5/9　(c) 1/3

EXERCISE SET　11-3

Writing Exercises

1. Define in your own words what the probability of an event means.
2. What is a sample space?
3. What is the difference between an outcome and an event?
4. What is the range of numbers that can represent probabilities? Why?
5. What is the probability of an event that can't occur? Explain why.
6. What is the probability of an event that is certain to occur? Explain why.
7. Explain the difference between classical and empirical probability.
8. Describe how to find the empirical probability of an event after conducting an experiment.

Computational Exercises

For Exercises 9–16, decide whether or not the given number could represent a probability.

9. $\frac{3}{4}$

10. 0.75

11. $-\frac{1}{2}$

12. 0

13. $\frac{41}{40}$

14. $\frac{40}{41}$

15. 72%

16. 111%

For Exercises 17–20, decide whether the probability described is classical or empirical.

17. At one school, 59% of the students having lunch in the union are women, so the probability of a randomly selected student from the campus phone directory being male is 0.41.

18. A pool table has 15 balls labeled 1 through 15. The probability of a ball made on the break having a number less than 6 is $\frac{1}{3}$.

19. The probability of a randomly selected state beginning with the letter A is $\frac{2}{25}$.

20. While at a casino, Catalina won 10 of the first 15 hands of blackjack she played, so she has a $\frac{2}{3}$ chance of winning the next hand.

Real-World Applications

21. If a die is rolled one time, find the probability of
    (a) Getting a 4.
    (b) Getting an even number.
    (c) Getting a number greater than 4.
    (d) Getting a number less than 7.
    (e) Getting a number greater than 0.
    (f) Getting a number greater than 3 or an odd number.
    (g) Getting a number greater than 3 and an odd number.

22. A couple has two children. Find the probability that
    (a) Both children are girls.
    (b) At least one child is a girl.
    (c) Both children are of the same gender.

23. On the *Price Is Right* game show, a contestant spins a wheel with numbers 1 through 7, with equally sized regions for each of these numbers. If the contestant spins once, what is the probability that the number is
    (a) A 6.
    (b) An even number.
    (c) A number greater than 4.
    (d) A number less than 8.
    (e) A number greater than 7.

24. A list contains the names of five anthropology students, two sociology students, and three psychology students. If one name is selected at random to assist in the professor's new study, find the probability that the chosen student is

    (a) An anthropology student.
    (b) A psychology student.
    (c) An anthropology student or a sociology student.
    (d) Not a psychology student.
    (e) Not an anthropology student.

25. On the shelf at the gaming store, there are five Sony Playstations and four Nintendo Wii consoles left. If one gaming system is selected at random, find the probability that the system is a Wii console.

26. If there are only 50 lottery tickets for the Big Game, one of which is a winning ticket, and you buy 7 of those tickets at random, what is the probability that you will win the super jackpot?

27. In a math class of seven women and nine men, if one person is selected at random to come to the board to show the solution to a problem, what is the probability that the student is a man?

28. A recent survey reported that 67% of Americans approve of human embryonic stem cell research. If an American is selected at random, find the probability that he or she will disagree or have no opinion on the issue.

29. The Federal Bureau of Investigation reported that in 2007, there were 7,624 incidents of hate crimes that had a bias motivation based on race, religion, sexual orientation, nationality, or disability. Of these incidents, 6,965 were committed by a "known offender," where one or more attributes is known about the offender. If one incident is selected at random, find the probability that the incident was committed by a known offender.

30. Thirty-nine of 50 states are currently under court order to alleviate overcrowding and poor conditions in one or more of their prisons. If a state is selected at random, find the probability that it is currently under such a court order.

    Source: *Harper's Index*

31. In a survey, 16% of male college students said they lied to get a woman to go out on a date with them. If a male college student is chosen at random, find the probability that he does not lie to get a date with a woman.

32. In the lost and found box at the campus security office, there were nine BlackBerry SmartPhones and seven Apple iPhones. If a phone is selected at random, find the probability that it is

    (a) A BlackBerry SmartPhone.
    (b) An Apple iPhone.

Exercises 33–35 refer to a standard deck of playing cards. If you are unfamiliar with playing cards, see the description on page 600.

33. During a game of Texas Hold'em poker, each of four players is dealt two cards, then the dealer "burns" a card (puts it face down), then deals the "flop" (three cards face up). He then burns another card, then flips over the "turn" card (one card face up). One player needs a spade on the "turn" to make a flush. No one else has a spade, and he has two in his hand and there are two on the flop. If neither of the burn cards are spades, what's the probability the turn card will be a spade?

34. During a game of Gin Rummy, Sven needs the eight of diamonds to make a straight in his hand. He and the other player have been dealt 10 cards each, the other player does not have the card he wants, and all other cards are in the deck. What is the probability that the next card picked from the deck is the eight of diamonds?

35. During a game of Blackjack, three players are dealt two cards each, and the dealer has two cards. No one has a card that is worth 10 or 11, which would be a 10, a face card, or an ace. What is the probability that the next player dealt a card would get a card worth 10 or 11?

36. A survey on campus revealed that 68% of the students felt that a new attendance policy was unfair. If a student is randomly asked to give an opinion of the new attendance policy, find the probability that the student will either think it's fair or have no opinion.

37. A survey of 25 students in line during registration revealed that 3 were math majors, 10 were history majors, 2 were psychology majors, 7 were biology majors, and the rest were undecided. If the clerk calls a name from the same line of students at random, find the probability the student would be either a history or biology major.

38. On a bookshelf, there are five Tess Gerritsen novels, three Stephen King novels, and seven John Grisham novels. If Sheri selects one while turned away to talk to her friend, find the probability she chose a Tess Gerritsen novel.

39. In a class of 35 students, 22 passed the first exam. If a student is chosen at random from the class, find the probability he failed the first exam.

40. On her way out the door to class, Li dumped five energy bars and three candy bars of the same size into her bag. During class, she got hungry, and she grabbed a bar without looking. It was an energy bar. Her friend then asked for something to eat, and she grabbed another bar without looking. Find the probability that she grabbed a candy bar.

41. On a 10-question true/false test, there are seven false questions and the rest are true. If Marcus answered the first eight questions correctly, and five of them were false, find the probability that when he answers true for the next question, his answer will be correct.

42. According to www.namestatistics.com, the five most popular male names and their percentages are as follows:

Name	Percentage
James	3.318%
John	3.271%
Robert	3.143%
Michael	2.629%
William	2.451%

(a) If Mary meets a man at a party, find the probability his name is one of the most popular five male names in the country.

(b) If Jane goes to the grocery store and the clerk is a man, find the probability his name would be John or Robert.

(c) If Bob and Sue rent a new apartment and the landlord is a man, find the probability his name would be in the top three most popular male names.

43. Many people blame Wall Street greed for causing the economic crisis that gripped the nation in late 2008. In February 2009, the Harris Poll surveyed 1,010 Americans, using the statement that people on Wall Street are "as honest and moral as other people." The number giving each response is summarized in the table below:

Agree	707
Disagree	263
Not sure	40

Based on these results, if you ask a randomly selected American this question,

(a) What is the probability that a randomly selected American thinks that people on Wall Street are less honest than other people?

(b) What is the probability that he or she either agrees or disagrees?

44. In December 2008, 500 men and 500 women were surveyed by Omnitel about their opinion on whether federal government bailout money should be used to help homeowners in default. The number giving each response is shown below.

Response	Men	Women
Yes	195	235
No	290	220
Not sure	15	45

(a) If a person who participated in the survey is selected at random, what is the probability that he or she answered no?

(b) What is the probability that the person is a man who answered either yes or no?

(c) Based on the data from the survey, if you had stopped a random woman on the street in December 2008 and asked her opinion, what is the probability that she would have said that bailout money should not be used to help homeowners in default?

45. In a survey conducted by Bank of America, college graduates were asked how much money they typically donate to their alma mater each year. The responses are summarized below:

Nothing	58%
Something, but less than $500	32%
$500 or more	10%

Based on these results:

(a) What is the probability that a randomly selected college graduate gives at least something in a typical year?

(b) What is the probability that a randomly selected college graduate gives less than $500 in a typical year?

46. Jockey International surveyed men to find out how old their oldest pair of underwear is. The results are summarized below:

Less than 1 year	17%
1–4 years	59%
5–9 years	15%
10–19 years	7%
20 or more years	2%

Based on these results:

(a) What is the probability that a randomly selected man has a pair of underwear that is older then 4 years? 9 years?

(b) What is the probability that a randomly selected man has no pair of underwear more than a year old?

(c) What is the probability that a randomly selected man has no underwear more than 9 years old?

47. A student passed a fountain every day on the way to class and tossed in his good luck penny with a wish. He then retrieved it because he couldn't bear to part with the penny. Out of 100 consecutive tosses of this same penny, he noticed the penny landed on tails 73 times. Can he conclude his good luck penny is unbalanced?

48. A professor stated that with a certain method of teaching statistics, a student has about a 50% chance of passing her class. She justified this by saying, "Either a student will pass or he won't pass." Comment on this statement.

49. The students at a university are classified by a 0 for freshman, a 1 for sophomores, a 2 for juniors, a 3 for seniors, and a 4 for graduate students. There are two extra scholarships to assign, so an administrator randomly selects from a box with only the numbers 0, 1, 2, 3, and 4 to choose the class of the first recipient. She then puts the number back into the box and randomly selects a number for the class of the second recipient. Find the sample space, and then find the probability of the following events:

(a) An odd number is chosen first and an even number is chosen second. (*Note:* 0 is considered an even number.)

(b) The sum of the two numbers selected is greater than 4.
(c) For both selections, an even number is drawn.
(d) The sum of the two numbers selected is odd.
(e) The same number is drawn twice.

50. Only six students attended a school charity event, so each of their names was placed into three boxes for the three raffles for the event. What is the probability that the same student's name will be drawn from each box?

Section 11-4 Tree Diagrams, Tables, and Sample Spaces

LEARNING OBJECTIVES

☐ 1. Use tree diagrams to find sample spaces and compute probabilities.

☐ 2. Use tables to find sample spaces and compute probabilities.

Math Note

Recall that we used tree diagrams to illustrate the fundamental counting principle back in Section 11-1.

For centuries, people have tried a wide variety of techniques, some of them pretty bizarre, to try and influence the gender of their children. The truth is, without the aid of cutting-edge science, you don't get to choose. But that doesn't stop many young couples from planning the type of family they hope to have. Suppose that one couple would like to have three children, but they definitely want to have at least one boy and one girl. What is the probability that they'll get their wish without having to go beyond three kids?

When working with classical probabilities, we know that we need to decide on the sample space for an event, and then find how many individual outcomes are in that event. When situations start to get complicated, it might not always be apparent how to do so. That's where tree diagrams and tables can help.

Tree Diagrams

A **tree diagram** consists of branches corresponding to the outcomes of two or more probability experiments that are done in sequence.

When constructing a tree diagram, use branches emanating from a single point to show the outcomes for the first experiment, and then show the outcomes for the second experiment using branches emanating from each branch that was used for the first experiment, etc.

In Example 1, we'll use a tree diagram to find the sample space for our hopeful young couple.

EXAMPLE 1 **Using a Tree Diagram to Find a Sample Space**

Use a tree diagram to find the sample space for the genders of three children in a family.

SOLUTION

There are two possibilities for the first child, boy or girl, two for the second, boy or girl, and two for the third, boy or girl. So the tree diagram can be drawn as shown in Figure 11-3.

After a tree diagram is drawn, the outcomes can be found by tracing through all of the branches. In this case, the sample space would be {BBB, BBG, BGB, BGG, GBB, GBG, GGB, GGG}.

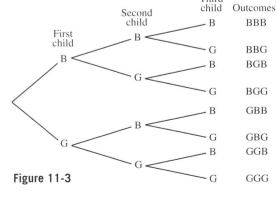

Figure 11-3

Math Note

The genders of the children are usually listed in their birth order. For example, the outcome GGB means the firstborn was a girl, the second a girl, and the third a boy.

▼ Try This One 1

A soda machine dispenses both Coke and Pepsi products, in both 12-ounce cans and 20-ounce bottles. For each brand, it has a regular cola, diet cola, and lemon-lime drink. Use a tree diagram to find the sample space for all the drinks dispensed.

Once a tree diagram is drawn and the sample space is found, you can compute the probabilities for various events.

EXAMPLE 2   Computing a Probability

If a family has three children, find the probability that all three children are the same gender; that is, all boys or all girls. (Assume that all outcomes are equally likely.)

SOLUTION

The sample space shown in Example 1 has eight outcomes, and there are two possible ways to have three children of the same gender, **BBB** or **GGG**. So, the probability of the three children being of the same gender is $\frac{2}{8}$ or $\frac{1}{4}$.

▼ Try This One 2

Suppose the soda machine from Try This One 1 goes berserk and starts dispensing drinks randomly. If you want a diet cola, what is the probability that you'll get one?

EXAMPLE 3   Using a Tree Diagram to Compute Probabilities

A coin is tossed, and then a die is rolled. Use a tree diagram to find the probability of getting heads on the coin and an even number on the die.

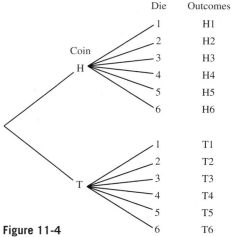

Figure 11-4

SOLUTION

First, we'll use a tree diagram to find the sample space. The coin will land on either heads or tails, and there are six outcomes for the die: 1, 2, 3, 4, 5, or 6. The tree diagram is shown in Figure 11-4.

The sample space is {H1, H2, H3, H4, H5, H6, T1, T2, T3, T4, T5, T6}.

The total number of outcomes for the experiment is 12. The number of ways to get a head on the coin and an even number on the die is 3: H2, H4, or H6. So, the probability of getting a head and an even number when a coin is tossed and a die is rolled is $\frac{3}{12}$, or $\frac{1}{4}$.

▼ Try This One 3

1. Use tree diagrams to find sample spaces and compute probabilities.

In order to collect information for a student survey, a researcher classifies students according to eye color (blue, brown, green), gender (male, female), and class rank (freshman, sophomore). A folder for each classification is then made up (e.g., freshman/female/green eyes). Find the sample space for the folders using a tree diagram. If a folder is selected at random, find the probability that

(a) It includes students with blue eyes.
(b) It includes students who are female.
(c) It includes students who are male freshmen.

In constructing tree diagrams, not all branches have to be the same length. For example, suppose two players, Alice and Diego, play chess, and the first one to win two games wins the tournament. The tree diagram would be like the one shown in Figure 11-5. For any game, A means that Alice wins, and D means that Diego wins.

Notice that if Alice wins the first two games, the tournament is over. So the first branch is shorter than the second one. But if Alice wins the first game and Diego wins the second game, they need to play a third game in order to decide who wins the tournament. Similar reasoning can be applied to the rest of the branches.

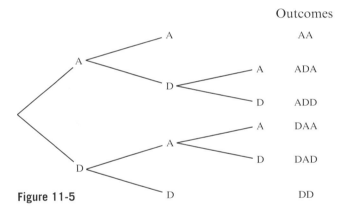

Figure 11-5

Sidelight MATH AND THE DRAFT LOTTERY

Today there are many state lotteries that offer patrons a chance to win money. At one time, there was a national lottery not to win money but to see who would be drafted for military service. During the Vietnam War, men were drafted based on their age and their birthday. The oldest men were drafted first. Men born in the last months of the year could avoid the draft since they were younger in months and days than those born earlier in the year.

In 1970, the United States decided to change the system and draft men based on a lottery. The days of the year were numbered one through 366 (leap year), placed in a barrel, and mixed up. Then numbers corresponding to birth dates were selected one at a time and men were drafted on the basis of their draft number.

It was assumed that the drawing was random. However, mathematicians found that the drawing was not random since

those born later in the year had a higher chance of being drafted than those born earlier in the year. It was concluded that the capsules containing the numbers were not thoroughly

mixed and that the numbers placed in the barrel last were on the top of the pile. They were selected first.

CAUTION

When the branches of a tree diagram are not equal in length, the outcomes are not equally likely even if the probability of every individual trial is $\frac{1}{2}$. In the tournament example above, if each player is equally likely to win any given game, the outcomes AA and DD both have probability $\frac{1}{4}$, while the outcomes ADA, ADD, DAA, and DAD all have probability $\frac{1}{8}$.

Tables

Another way of determining a sample space is by making a **table.** Consider the sample space of selecting a card from a standard deck of 52 cards. (The cards are assumed to be shuffled to make sure that the selection occurs at random.) There are four suits—hearts, diamonds, spades, and clubs, and 13 cards of each suit consisting of the denominations ace (A), 2, 3, 4, 5, 6, 7, 8, 9, 10, and 3 picture or face cards—jack (J), queen (Q), and king (K). The sample space is shown in Figure 11-6.

	A	2	3	4	5	6	7	8	9	10	J	Q	K
♥	A♥	2♥	3♥	4♥	5♥	6♥	7♥	8♥	9♥	10♥	J♥	Q♥	K♥
♦	A♦	2♦	3♦	4♦	5♦	6♦	7♦	8♦	9♦	10♦	J♦	Q♦	K♦
♠	A♠	2♠	3♠	4♠	5♠	6♠	7♠	8♠	9♠	10♠	J♠	Q♠	K♠
♣	A♣	2♣	3♣	4♣	5♣	6♣	7♣	8♣	9♣	10♣	J♣	Q♣	K♣

Figure 11-6

EXAMPLE 4   Using a Table to Compute Probabilities

A card is drawn from an ordinary deck. Use the sample space shown in Figure 11-6 to find the probabilities of getting

(a) A jack.   (b) The 6 of clubs.   (c) A 3 or a diamond.

SOLUTION

(a) There are four jacks and 52 possible outcomes, so

$$P(\text{jack}) = \frac{4}{52} = \frac{1}{13}$$

(b) Since there is only one 6 of clubs, the probability of getting a 6 of clubs is

$$P(\text{6 of clubs}) = \frac{1}{52}$$

(c) There are four 3s and 13 diamonds, but the 3 of diamonds is counted twice in this listing. So, there are 16 possibilities of drawing a 3 or a diamond, and

$$P(\text{3 or diamond}) = \frac{16}{52} = \frac{4}{13}$$

▼ Try This One 4

A single card is drawn at random from a well-shuffled deck. Using the sample space shown in Figure 11-6, find the probability that the card is

(a) An ace.   (c) A club.   (e) A 6 and a spade.
(b) A face card.   (d) A 4 or a heart.

When two dice are rolled, how many outcomes are in the sample space? Assume for the purpose of illustration that one die is red and the other is blue. The sample space for the red die is {1, 2, 3, 4, 5, 6}, and the sample space for the blue die is also {1, 2, 3, 4, 5, 6}. Now if the outcomes for each die are combined, the sample space will consist of 36 outcomes, as shown in Figure 11-7. Note that the color indicates which die the number comes from.

The outcome (3, 6) means the 3 was obtained on the red die and a 6 was obtained on the blue die. The sum of the spots on the faces then would be $3 + 6 = 9$.

Math Note

The sample space for rolling two dice is the same regardless of the color of the dice. Color helps distinguish between (2, 4) and (4, 2).

		Blue die				
Red die	**1**	**2**	**3**	**4**	**5**	**6**
1	(1, 1)	(1, 2)	(1, 3)	(1, 4)	(1, 5)	(1, 6)
2	(2, 1)	(2, 2)	(2, 3)	(2, 4)	(2, 5)	(2, 6)
3	(3, 1)	(3, 2)	(3, 3)	(3, 4)	(3, 5)	(3, 6)
4	(4, 1)	(4, 2)	(4, 3)	(4, 4)	(4, 5)	(4, 6)
5	(5, 1)	(5, 2)	(5, 3)	(5, 4)	(5, 5)	(5, 6)
6	(6, 1)	(6, 2)	(6, 3)	(6, 4)	(6, 5)	(6, 6)

Figure 11-7

EXAMPLE 5 Using a Table to Compute Probabilities

When two dice are rolled, find the probability of getting

(a) A sum of 8.
(b) Doubles.
(c) A sum less than 5.

SOLUTION

Using the sample space shown in Figure 11-7, there are 36 possible outcomes.

(a) There are five ways to get a sum of 8: (2, 6), (3, 5), (4, 4), (5, 3), and (6, 2). So $n(E) = 5, n(S) = 36$, and

$$P(\text{sum of 8}) = \frac{n(E)}{n(S)} = \frac{5}{36}$$

(b) There are six ways to get doubles: (1, 1), (2, 2), (3, 3), (4, 4), (5, 5), and (6, 6). So $n(E) = 6, n(S) = 36$, and

$$P(\text{doubles}) = \frac{n(E)}{n(S)} = \frac{1}{6}$$

(c) A sum less than 5 means a sum of 4 or 3 or 2. The number of ways this can occur is 6, as shown.

Sum of 4: (1, 3), (2, 2), (3, 1)
Sum of 3: (1, 2), (2, 1)
Sum of 2: (1, 1)
$n(E) = 6, n(S) = 36$, and so

$$P(\text{sum less than 5}) = \frac{6}{36} = \frac{1}{6}$$

▼ Try This One 5

2. Use tables to find sample spaces and compute probabilities.

Two dice are rolled. Use the sample space shown in Figure 11-7 to find the probability of

(a) Getting a sum of 9.
(b) Getting a sum that is an even number.
(c) Getting a sum greater than 6.

Answers to Try This One

1 Sample Space: {Coke, can, cola; Coke, can, diet cola; Coke, can, lemon-lime; Coke, bottle, cola; Coke, bottle, diet cola; Coke, bottle, lemon-lime; Pepsi, can, cola; Pepsi, can, diet cola; Pepsi, can, lemon-lime; Pepsi, bottle, cola; Pepsi, bottle, diet cola; Pepsi, bottle, lemon-lime}.

2 $\frac{1}{3}$

3 Sample space: {blue, male, freshman; blue, male, sophomore; blue, female, freshman; blue, female, sophomore; brown, male, freshman; brown, male, sophomore; brown, female, freshman; brown, female, sophomore; green, male, freshman; green, male, sophomore; green, female, freshman; green, female, sophomore}.

(a) $\frac{1}{3}$ (b) $\frac{1}{2}$ (c) $\frac{1}{4}$

4 (a) $\frac{1}{13}$ (c) $\frac{1}{4}$ (e) $\frac{1}{52}$

(b) $\frac{3}{13}$ (d) $\frac{4}{13}$

5 (a) $\frac{1}{9}$ (b) $\frac{1}{2}$ (c) $\frac{7}{12}$

EXERCISE SET 11-4

Writing Exercises

1. Explain how to draw a tree diagram, and how tree diagrams help to find sample spaces.

2. Think of an example, other than the one provided in the section, where a tree diagram would have branches of different lengths.

Real-World Applications

3. There are three computers on a table that are either Dells or Gateways. Using a sample space similar to the one in Example 1, find the probability that

   (a) There will be exactly two Dells.
   (b) All three will be Gateways.
   (c) There will be at least one Dell.

4. There was a die and a quarter sitting on a table, and Klutzy Kramer knocked both off the table at the same time when he passed by. Using a sample space similar to Example 3, find the probability that as each landed on the floor,

   (a) There was a head on the coin and an odd number on the die.
   (b) There was a head on the coin and a prime number on the die.
   (c) There was a tail on the coin and a number less than 5 on the die.

5. After the incident in Exercise 4, the professor got smart and dropped the die and the quarter in a box to prevent Klutzy Kramer from knocking them onto the floor again. Using a sample space similar to

Example 3, find the probability that as each landed in the box,

   (a) There was a tail on the coin and a number greater than 1 on the die.
   (b) There was a head on the coin and an even number on the die.
   (c) There was a tail on the coin and a number divisible by 3 on the die.

6. Sara came across a new website that featured a "live" fortune-teller. She typed in three questions and found (shockingly) that the fortune-teller could only answer yes or no to her questions. Draw a tree diagram for all possible answers for her three questions. Find the probability that

   (a) All answers will be yes or all answers will be no.
   (b) The answers will alternate (i.e., Yes–No–Yes or No–Yes–No).
   (c) Exactly two answers will be yes.

7. After a late night studying, Ebony decides to grab a latte before class so she can stay awake through the

lecture. She has only a one-dollar bill, a five-dollar bill, and a ten-dollar bill in her wallet. She pulls one out and looks at it, but then she puts it back. Distracted by a flyer for a new campus organization, she randomly hands a bill from her wallet to the clerk. Draw a tree diagram to determine the sample space and find the probability that

(a) Both bills have the same value.
(b) The second bill is larger than the first bill.
(c) The value of each of the two bills is even.
(d) The value of exactly one of the bills is odd.
(e) The sum of the values of both bills is less than $10.

8. When Frank threw his jeans into the washer after getting them muddy during an impromptu mud-wrestling match at the fraternity house, four coins fell out onto the floor. Find the probability that

(a) Exactly three coins land heads up.
(b) All coins land tails up.
(c) Two or more coins land heads up.
(d) No more than two coins land tails up.
(e) At least one coin lands tails up.

9. Mark and Raul play three rounds of Mortal Kombat. They are equal in ability. Draw a tree diagram to determine the sample space and find the probability that

(a) Either Mark or Raul win all three games.
(b) Either Mark or Raul win two out of three games.
(c) Mark wins only two games in a row.
(d) Raul wins the first game, loses the second game, and wins the third game.

10. Sofia is in line at the Simpsons ride at Universal Studios and notices a box containing a Bart keychain, a Homer keychain, a Marge keychain, and a Lisa keychain. She selects a keychain from the box and then puts it back. She then blindly selects another keychain from the box. Draw a tree diagram to determine the sample space and find the probability that

(a) Both key chains are the same character.
(b) The key chains are different characters.
(c) At least one is a Marge keychain.
(d) Both are Bart keychains.
(e) One keychain is Marge and the other is Homer.

11. The pool table in the student lounge is broken, and when Carrie puts her quarter into the slot, only the balls numbered 1 through 5 come down the chute. She selects one without looking and puts it on the table. She then selects another without looking. Draw a tree diagram to determine the sample space and find the probability that

(a) The sum of the numbers of the balls is odd.
(b) The number on the second ball is larger than the number on the first ball.

(c) The sum of the numbers on the balls is greater than 4.

12. Akira wants to purchase his first new car and can select one option from each category:

Model	Engine Type	Color
Ford Focus	Hybrid	Burnt copper
Honda Civic	E-85	Cobalt blue
Toyota Corolla		Metallic green

Draw a tree diagram and find the sample space for all possible choices. Find the probability that the car, if chosen at random,

(a) Has an E-85 engine.
(b) Is a burnt copper Ford Focus.
(c) Is a metallic green hybrid Honda Civic.
(d) Is cobalt blue.
(e) Is either a metallic green or cobalt blue Toyota Corolla.

13. Kimberly goes onto Dell's website to order a custom-made Tablet PC. She can select one option from each category:

Operating System	Processor	Wireless Options
Windows Vista Ultimate	Intel Core Duo	Dell Wireless Mini Card
Windows Vista Home Premium	Intel Celeron 540	Bluetooth 2.0
Windows Vista Home Basic		

Draw a tree diagram to determine the sample space and find the probability that her Tablet PC, if chosen at random, will have

(a) An Intel Celeron 540 Processor.
(b) A Windows Vista Home Premium operating system and an Intel Core 2 Duo Processor.
(c) An Intel Core 2 Duo Processor with a Bluetooth 2.0 wireless option.

14. To choose the order of bands for the finals of the campus Battle of the Bands competition, Freddy puts a penny, a nickel, a dime, a quarter, and a half-dollar into five separate envelopes and has one band choose an envelope. Another band then chooses from the envelopes remaining. Draw a tree diagram to determine the sample space and find the probability that

(a) The amount of the first coin is less than the amount of the second coin.
(b) Neither coin is a quarter.
(c) One coin is a penny and the other coin is a nickel or a dime.
(d) The sum of the amounts of both coins is even.
(e) The sum of the amounts of both coins is less than $0.40.

15. At the beginning of a magic trick, The Great Mancini shuffles an ordinary deck of 52 cards as shown in Figure 11-6, and has the nearest person in the audience draw a single card. Using the sample space for drawing a single card from this deck, find the probability that the contestant got

   (a) A 10.
   (b) A club.
   (c) The ace of hearts.
   (d) A 3 or a 5.
   (e) A 6 or a spade.
   (f) A queen or a club.
   (g) A diamond or a club.
   (h) A red king.
   (i) A black card or an 8.
   (j) A red 10.

16. After a rowdy game of 52 pickup, Lauren cleans up the mess of 52 cards from a standard deck from the floor. Use the sample space for drawing a single card from an ordinary deck as shown in Figure 11-6 to find the probability that the first card Lauren picked up was

   (a) The 6 of clubs.
   (b) A black card.
   (c) A queen.
   (d) A black 10.
   (e) A red card or a 3.
   (f) A club and a 6.

   (g) A 2 or an ace.
   (h) A club, diamond, or spade.
   (i) A diamond face card.
   (j) A red ace.

17. In between classes, Jade plays a game of online Monopoly on her laptop. Using the sample space for rolling two dice shown in Figure 11-7, find the probability that when Jade rolls the two dice, she gets a

   (a) Sum of 5.
   (b) Sum of 7 or 11.
   (c) Sum greater than 9.
   (d) Sum less than or equal to 5.
   (e) Three on one die or on both dice.
   (f) Sum that is odd.
   (g) A prime number on one or both dice.
   (h) A sum greater than 1.

18. During a charity Las Vegas Casino Night, Rosie plays craps and gets to roll the dice. Using the sample space for rolling two dice as shown in Figure 11-7, find the probability she rolled a

   (a) Sum of 8.
   (b) Sum that is prime.
   (c) Five on one or both dice.
   (d) Sum greater than or equal to 7.
   (e) Sum that is less than 3.
   (f) Sum greater than 12.
   (g) Six on one die and 3 on the other die.

Critical Thinking

19. An online math quiz made up of true-false questions starts every student out with two questions. If they get both wrong, they're done. If they get at least one right, they get a third question. Suppose that a student guesses on all questions. Draw a tree diagram and find the sample space for all possible results. Then explain why every outcome is not equally likely.

20. To get past security at a club, potential patrons must answer a series of four questions. If they get any of the first three wrong, they get no more questions and

don't get in. Draw a tree diagram and find the sample space for all possible results. Then explain why all of the outcomes are not equally likely.

21. Consider the sample space when three dice are rolled. How many different outcomes would there be?

22. When three dice are rolled, how many ways can a sum of 6 be obtained?

23. When three dice are rolled, find the probability of getting a sum of 6.

Section 11-5 Probability Using Permutations and Combinations

Sometimes a friendly game of poker can become less friendly when someone seems just a bit too lucky. Suppose one player in such a game gets dealt all four aces in one hand. Would you suspect that something fishy was going on? What is the probability of that happening?

In Section 11-4, we used tree diagrams and tables to find sample spaces and the number of outcomes in certain events. This was a pretty good strategy, but when the number of possibilities gets larger, diagrams can get out of hand. Fortunately, we know about counting techniques that are tailor-made for answering questions about

LEARNING OBJECTIVES

☐ 1. Compute probabilities using combinations.

☐ 2. Compute probabilities using permutations.

probability. If our job is to find how many ways something can happen, the combination and permutation rules from Section 11-2 will be our best friends.

Our general game plan will be to use these rules to find the number of outcomes that satisfy a certain event, as well as the total number of outcomes in the sample space. Then we can divide the first number by the second to obtain the probability of the event occurring.

EXAMPLE 1 **Using Combinations to Compute Probability**

Stacy has the option of selecting three books to read for a humanities course. The suggested book list consists of 10 biographies and five current events books. She decides to select the three books at random. Find the probability that all three books selected will be current events books.

SOLUTION

Since there are five current events books and Stacy will need to select three of them, then there are $_5C_3$ ways of doing this.

$$_5C_3 = \frac{5!}{(5-3)!3!} = \frac{5 \cdot 4 \cdot 3!}{2 \cdot 1 \cdot 3!} = 10 \quad \text{10 ways to choose 3 current events books.}$$

The total number of outcomes in the sample space is $_{15}C_3$ since she has to select three books from 15 books.

$$_{15}C_3 = \frac{15!}{(15-3)!3!} = \frac{15!}{12!3!} = \frac{15 \cdot 14 \cdot 13 \cdot 12!}{12! \cdot 3 \cdot 2 \cdot 1} = 455 \quad \text{455 total choices.}$$

The probability of selecting three current events books is

$$\frac{10}{455} = \frac{2}{91} \approx 0.022$$

▼ **Try This One 1**

There are 12 women and 8 men in a seminar course. If the professor chooses five-person groups at random, what is the probability that the first group chosen will consist of all women?

Now back to that poker game . . .

EXAMPLE 2 **Using Combinations to Compute Probability**

What is the probability of getting 4 aces when drawing 5 cards from a standard deck of 52 cards?

SOLUTION

First, we'll figure out how many five-card hands have four aces. Since there are only four aces in the deck, there's only one way to get all four of them in your hand. At that point there are 48 cards left for the other card in the hand. Using the fundamental counting principle, there are $1 \cdot 48$ ways to be dealt four aces.

Math Note

The probability in Example 2 means that you would expect to draw four aces on average once every 54,145 tries.

The total number of hands is the combinations of 5 cards chosen from 52, or $_{52}C_5$.

$$_{52}C_5 = \frac{52!}{(52-5)!5!} = \frac{52!}{47!5!} = \frac{52 \cdot 51 \cdot 50 \cdot 49 \cdot 48 \cdot \cancel{47!}}{\cancel{47!} \cdot 5 \cdot 4 \cdot 3 \cdot 2 \cdot 1} = 2{,}598{,}960$$

The probability of getting four aces is

$$\frac{48}{2{,}598{,}960} = \frac{1}{54{,}145} \approx 0.0000185$$

We hate to accuse your friend of cheating, but to say the least, it's unlikely that she would draw a hand with 4 aces.

☑ 1. Compute probabilities using combinations.

▼ Try This One 2

Suppose the deck of cards in Example 2 has all 32 cards with numbers less than 10 removed, so that only 10s, jacks, queens, kings, and aces remain. Now what is the probability of getting 4 aces when drawing 5 cards?

Example 3 uses the permutation rule.

EXAMPLE 3 | **Using Permutations to Compute Probability**

Permutations determine the number of combinations that can open a combination lock.

A combination lock has 40 numbers on it, from zero to 39. Find the probability that if the combination to unlock it consists of three numbers, it will contain the numbers 1, 2, and 3 in some order. Assume that numbers cannot be repeated in the combination. (It's interesting to note that a combination lock should really be called a permutation lock since the order of the numbers is important when you are unlocking the lock.)

SOLUTION

The number of combinations for the lock containing 1, 2, and 3 is $_3P_3$.

$$_3P_3 = \frac{3!}{(3-3)!} = \frac{3!}{0!} = \frac{3 \cdot 2 \cdot 1}{1} = 6$$

The total number of combinations is a permutation of the 40 numbers taken 3 at a time, or $_{40}P_3$.

$$_{40}P_3 = \frac{40!}{(40-3!)} = \frac{40!}{37!} = \frac{40 \cdot 39 \cdot 38 \cdot \cancel{37!}}{\cancel{37!}} = 59{,}280$$

The probability of the combination containing 1, 2, and 3 is $\frac{6}{59{,}280} \approx 0.000101$

▼ Try This One 3

☑ 2. Compute probabilities using permutations.

A different "permutation" lock has letters from A through L on it, and the combination consists of four letters with no repeats. What is the probability that the combination is I, J, K, and L in some order?

In Example 4, we will again need to use the fundamental counting principle.

EXAMPLE 4 | **Using Combinations to Compute Probability**

A store has six different fitness magazines and three different news magazines. If a customer buys three magazines at random, find the probability that the customer will pick two fitness magazines and one news magazine.

SOLUTION

There are $_6C_2$ or 15 ways to select two fitness magazines from six fitness magazines, as shown:

$$_6C_2 = \frac{6!}{(6-2)!2!} = \frac{6!}{4!2!} = \frac{6 \cdot 5 \cdot 4!}{4! \cdot 2 \cdot 1} = 15$$

There are $_3C_1$ or three ways to select one magazine from three news magazines:

$$_3C_1 = \frac{3!}{(3-1)!1!} = \frac{3!}{2! \cdot 1!} = \frac{3 \cdot 2!}{2! \cdot 1} = 3$$

Using the fundamental counting principle, there are $15 \cdot 3$ or 45 ways to select two fitness magazines *and* one news magazine.

Next, there are $_9C_3$ or 84 ways to select three magazines from nine magazines:

$$_9C_3 = \frac{9!}{(9-3)!3!} = \frac{9!}{6!3!} = \frac{9 \cdot 8 \cdot 7 \cdot 6!}{6! \cdot 3 \cdot 2 \cdot 1} = 84$$

The probability of selecting two fitness magazines and one news magazine is

$$\frac{45}{84} \approx 0.536$$

▼ **Try This One 4**

A box contains 24 imported cell phones and four of them are defective. If three phones are selected at random, find the probability that

(a) Exactly two are defective.   (c) All three are defective.
(b) None are defective.

Now we see why Chapter 11 began with a study of permutations and combinations: a large variety of probability problems can be solved using permutations and combinations in conjunction with the probability rules.

Sidelight **THE CLASSICAL BIRTHDAY PROBLEM**

What do you think the chances are that in a classroom with 23 students, two students have the same birthday (day and month)? Most people think that the probability would be very low since there are 365 days in a year. You may be surprised to find out that it is greater than 0.5, or 50%! Furthermore, as the number of people increases, the probability becomes even greater than 0.5 very rapidly. In a room of 30 students, there is a greater than 70% chance that two students have the same birthday. If you have 50 students in the room, the probability jumps to 97%!

The problem can be solved by using probability and permutation rules. It must be assumed that all birthdays are equally likely, but this assumption will have little effect on the answers. The way to solve the problem is to find the probability that no two people have the same birthday, and then subtract this probability from one. In other words, P(two students have the same birthday) $= 1 - P$(all students have different birthdays).

For example, suppose that there were only three students in a room. Then the probability that each would have a different birthday is

$$\frac{365}{365} \cdot \frac{364}{365} \cdot \frac{363}{365} = \frac{_{365}P_3}{365^3} \approx 0.992$$

So the probability that at least two of the three students have the same birthday is

$$1 - 0.992 = 0.008$$

In general, in a room with k people, the probability that at least two people have the same birthday is

$$1 - \frac{_{365}P_k}{365^k}$$

In a room with 23 students, then, the probability that at least two students will have the same birthday is

$$1 - \frac{_{365}P_{23}}{365^{23}} \approx 0.507 \text{ or } 50.7\%$$

It is interesting to note that two presidents, James K. Polk and Warren G. Harding, were both born on November 2. Also, John Adams and Thomas Jefferson both died on July 4. The unusual thing about this is that they died on the same day of the same year, July 4, 1826.

Answers to Try This One

1 $33/646 \approx 0.051$

2 $1/969 \approx 0.00103$

3 $1/495 \approx 0.002$

4 (a) $15/253 \approx 0.059$

    (b) $285/506 \approx 0.56$

    (c) $1/506 \approx 0.002$

EXERCISE SET 11-5

Writing Exercises

1. Explain how combinations and permutations are useful in computing probabilities.

2. What is the biggest advantage of combinations and permutations over tree diagrams when computing probability?

Real-World Applications

3. A student-faculty government committee of 4 people is to be formed from 20 student volunteers and 5 faculty volunteers. Find the probability that the committee will consist of the following, assuming the selection is made at random:

   (a) All faculty members.
   (b) Two students and two faculty members.
   (c) All students.
   (d) One faculty member and three students.

4. In a company there are seven executives: four women and three men. Three are selected to attend a management seminar. Find these probabilities.

   (a) All three selected will be women.
   (b) All three selected will be men.
   (c) Two men and one woman will be selected.
   (d) One man and two women will be selected.

5. A city council consists of 10 members. Four are Republicans, three are Democrats, and three are Independents. If a committee of three is to be selected, find the probability of selecting

   (a) All Republicans. (b) All Democrats.
   (c) One of each party.
   (d) Two Democrats and one Independent.
   (e) One Independent and two Republicans.

6. In a class of 18 students, there are 11 men and seven women. Four students are selected to present a demonstration on the use of graphing calculators. Find the probability that the group consists of

   (a) All men.
   (b) All women.
   (c) Three men and one woman.
   (d) One man and three women.
   (e) Two men and two women.

7. Fred needs to print his term paper. He pulls down a box of twelve ink cartridges and recalls that three of them have no more ink. If he selects four cartridges from the box, find the probability that

   (a) No cartridge has ink.
   (b) One cartridge has no ink.
   (c) Three cartridges have no ink.

8. There are 50 tickets sold for a raffle for the Student Art Auction, and there are two prizes to be awarded. If Dionte buys two tickets, find the probability that he will win both prizes.

9. An engineering company has four openings and the applicant pool consists of six database administrators and eight network engineers. If the hiring is done without regard for the specific qualifications of the applicants, find the probability that the four hired will be

   (a) All network engineers.
   (b) Two database administrators and two network engineers.
   (c) All database administrators.
   (d) Three database administrators and one network engineer.
   (e) One database administrator and three network engineers.

10. At the coffee kiosk in the mall, there are eight coffee drinks, five tea drinks, and two smoothies. Nora wants to buy three drinks for herself and her friends. Find the probability that she buys

    (a) All coffee drinks.
    (b) Two smoothie drinks.
    (c) All tea drinks.
    (d) One of each type of drink.
    (e) Two coffee drinks and one tea drink.

11. Find the probability of getting any triple-digit number where all the digits are the same in a lottery game that consists of selecting a three-digit number.
12. Binh is choosing from eight YouTube videos and nine online role-playing games to link to his MySpace page. If he randomly picks seven links total, find the probability that Binh chooses three YouTube videos and four online role-playing games.
13. Drew is on a fitness kick, so he's walking around with four protein bars and eight lowfat cereal bars in his backpack. If he reaches in and randomly grabs five bars, find the probability that he gets two protein bars and three cereal bars.
14. To win a state lottery, a person must select 5 numbers from 40 numbers. Find the probability of winning if a person buys one ticket. (*Note:* The numbers can be selected in any order.)
15. A five-digit identification card is made. Find the probability that the card will contain the digits 0, 1, 2, 3, and 4 in any order.

16. The combination lock in Example 3 has 40 numbers from zero to 39, and a combination consists of 3 numbers in a specific order with no repeats. Find the probability that the combination consists only of even numbers.

Exercises 17–22 refer to poker hands consisting of 5 cards dealt at random from a standard deck of 52 cards. Find the probability of getting each hand.

17. A full house (three of one denomination and two of another)
18. A flush (five cards of the same suit)
19. Three of a kind (three of one denomination)
20. Four of a kind (four of the same denomination)
21. A royal flush (ten, jack, queen, king, and ace of the same suit)
22. A straight flush (five cards of the same suit that are consecutive in denomination)

Critical Thinking

23. At a carnival game, the player pays a dollar, then flips a quarter, rolls two dice, and draws two cards from a standard deck. If the result is tails, 12, and a pair of aces, he wins $1,000. What is the probability of this happening?

Section 11-6 Odds and Expectation

LEARNING OBJECTIVES

☐ 1. Compute the odds in favor of and against an outcome.
☐ 2. Compute odds from probability.
☐ 3. Compute probability from odds.
☐ 4. Compute expected value.

The Pittsburgh Steelers won the Super Bowl on February 1, 2009, and by the time the ink dried on newspapers reporting the victory, oddsmakers in Las Vegas had listed the odds against the Steelers winning it again in 2010 as 9 to 1. But what exactly does that mean? The term "odds" is used all the time in describing the likelihood of something happening, but a lot of people don't understand exactly what a given set of odds means.

Odds are used by casinos, racetracks, and other gambling establishments to determine the payoffs when bets are made or lottery tickets are purchased. They're also used by insurance companies in determining the amount to charge for premiums. The formulas for computing odds are similar to the formula we've been using for classical probability, and shortly we will see a strong connection between the two concepts.

If an event E has a favorable outcomes and b unfavorable outcomes, then
1. The odds in favor of event E occurring $= \frac{a}{b}$
2. The odds against event E occurring $= \frac{b}{a}$

CAUTION Do not confuse the formula for odds in favor of an event with the formula for classical probability. The probability formula is the number of favorable outcomes over the *total* number of outcomes, while the one for odds is the number of favorable outcomes over the number of *unfavorable* outcomes.

Odds can be expressed as a fraction or a ratio. For example, the odds against Pittsburgh repeating as Super Bowl champion could be listed as $\frac{9}{1}$, 9:1, or 9 to 1. In common usage, the phrase "the odds of" really means "the odds against"; if we are told that the odds of rolling a 12 with two dice are 35 to 1, it means that the odds against rolling 12 are 35 to 1. So by setting Pittsburgh's odds at 9:1, the oddsmakers are predicting that if the season were played 10 times, Pittsburgh would win the Super Bowl 1 time, and not win it 9 times.

EXAMPLE 1   Computing Odds

Math Note

Notice that if the odds in favor of an event occurring are $a{:}b$, the odds against it occurring are $b{:}a$.

A card is drawn from a standard deck of 52 cards.

(a) Find the odds in favor of getting an ace.
(b) Find the odds against getting an ace.

SOLUTION

(a) In a deck of cards there are 52 cards and there are 4 aces, so $a = 4$ and $b = 52 - 4 = 48$. (In other words, there are 48 cards that are not aces.)

The odds in favor of an ace $= \frac{4}{48} = \frac{1}{12}$

(b) The odds against an ace $= \frac{48}{4} = \frac{12}{1}$.

The odds in favor of an ace are 1:12 and the odds against an ace are 12:1.

▼ Try This One 1

☑ 1. Compute the odds in favor of and against an outcome.

What are the odds in favor of rolling a prime number sum with a roll of two dice? What are the odds against? (Figure 11-7 on page 601 will help.)

When an event E has a favorable and b unfavorable outcomes, there are $a + b$ total outcomes, and the probability of E is

$$P(E) = \frac{a}{a + b}$$

The probability of E not occurring is

$$1 - P(E), \quad \text{or} \quad \frac{b}{a + b}$$

If we divide these two probabilities, we get

$$\frac{P(E)}{1 - P(E)} = \frac{\dfrac{a}{a + b}}{\dfrac{b}{a + b}} = \frac{a}{a + b} \cdot \frac{a + b}{b} = \frac{a}{b}$$

The result is the odds in favor of event E. This gives us a strong connection between probability and odds.

Math Note

Recall that
$P(E') = 1 - P(E)$.

Formulas for Odds in Terms of Probability

$$\text{Odds in favor} = \frac{P(E)}{1 - P(E)}$$

$$\text{Odds against} = \frac{P(E')}{1 - P(E')}$$

where $P(E)$ is the probability that event E occurs and $P(E')$ is the probability that the event E does not occur.

EXAMPLE 2 **Finding Odds from Probability**

The probability of getting exactly one pair in a five-card poker hand is 0.423. Find the odds in favor of getting exactly one pair, and the odds against.

SOLUTION

This is a direct application of the formula relating probability and odds. The odds in favor of getting exactly one pair are

$$\frac{P(\text{getting exactly one pair})}{1 - P(\text{getting exactly one pair})} = \frac{0.423}{1 - 0.423} = \frac{0.423}{0.577}$$

We can convert this into fraction form by multiplying both the numerator and denominator by 100.

$$\frac{0.423}{0.577} \cdot \frac{100}{100} = \frac{423}{577}$$

So the odds in favor of getting exactly one pair are 423:577, and the odds against are 577:423.

▼ Try This One 2

2. Compute odds from probability.

According to the American Cancer Society, the probability of an American female developing some type of cancer at some point in her life is about $\frac{1}{3}$. Find the odds in favor of and against an American woman developing cancer.

In Example 2, the odds for an event were found when the probabilities were known. As we saw on page 610, when the odds of an event are given, the probability of an event can be found.

Math Note

When the odds are 1:1, a game is said to be fair. That is, both parties have an equal chance of winning or losing.

Formula for Probability in Terms of Odds

If the odds in favor of an event E are $a:b$, then the probability that the event will occur is

$$P(E) = \frac{a}{a + b}$$

EXAMPLE 3 **Finding Probability from Odds**

According to the National Safety Council, the odds of dying due to injury at some point in your life are about 10:237. Find the probability of dying from injury.

SOLUTION

In the formula for converting to probability, the odds in favor are $a:b$. In this case, those odds are 10:237, so $a = 10$ and $b = 237$.

$$P(\text{dying from injury}) = \frac{10}{10 + 237} = \frac{10}{247} \approx 0.040$$

▼ Try This One 3

3. Compute probability from odds.

When two dice are rolled, the odds in favor of getting a sum of 9 are 1:8. Find the probability of not getting a sum of 9 when two dice are rolled.

Sidelight ODDS AND BETTING

In almost any gambling enterprise, from Vegas to a church raffle, odds are used to determine what the payouts will be. Let's use the game of roulette as an example. There are 38 partitions on a roulette wheel, with a small ball that is equally likely to land in any of them. Players make various bets on where the ball will land. If you simply bet on a particular number, the odds against you are 37:1. If you win, the casino will pay 35 times what you bet. So if you bet a dollar on each spin, on average, in 38 spins, you would lose 37 times and win once, meaning you'd be two dollars in the hole. That doesn't sound like the recipe for the casino making a lot

of money, but when you consider the large number of people in a typical casino, and the fact that they're placing multiple bets at frequent intervals, it starts to make more sense.

This is where it becomes clear that state lotteries are an awful bet. In the Ohio lottery's "Classic Lotto" game, for example, the odds in favor of matching 5 of 6 numbers are 1:54,021. So to make the game completely fair, the payout should be in the neighborhood of $54,000 on a $1 ticket. The actual payout? Just $1,500! Any gambler or statistician will tell you that lotteries offer the worst odds of just about any game of chance.

Expected Value

Another concept related to odds and probability is **expectation,** or **expected value.** Expected value is used to determine the result that would be expected over the long term in some sort of gamble. It is used not only for games of chance, but in areas like insurance, management, engineering, and others. *The key element is that the events in question must have numerical outcomes.*

For example, rolling a die has a numerical outcome (1 through 6), and expected value can be used to determine what the average long-run result is likely to be. (We'll find out in Example 4.)

To find expected value, multiply the numerical result of each outcome by the corresponding probability of the outcome, then add those products.

Expected Value

The expected value for the outcomes of a probability experiment is

$$E = X_1 \cdot P(X_1) + X_2 \cdot P(X_2) + \cdots + X_n \cdot P(X_n)$$

where the X's correspond to the numerical outcomes and the $P(X)$'s are the corresponding probabilities of the outcomes.

EXAMPLE 4   Computing Expected Value

Math Note

In Example 4, a die cannot show 3.5 spots: It can only show 1, 2, 3, 4, 5, or 6 spots. However, in this case, the expected value would be the long run average—that is, if you add up the total number of spots, then divide by the number of times the die is rolled, the average would be close to 3.5.

When a single die is rolled, find the expected value of the outcome.

SOLUTION

Since each numerical outcome, 1 through 6, has a probability of $\frac{1}{6}$, the expected value is

$$E = 1 \cdot \frac{1}{6} + 2 \cdot \frac{1}{6} + 3 \cdot \frac{1}{6} + 4 \cdot \frac{1}{6} + 5 \cdot \frac{1}{6} + 6 \cdot \frac{1}{6} = \frac{21}{6} = 3.5$$

▼ Try This One 4

If seven cards are numbered with integers from -2 to 4, then placed into a box and picked out at random, find the expected value.

In gambling games, the expected value is found by multiplying the amount won, or net gain, and the amount lost by the corresponding probabilities and then finding the sum.

EXAMPLE 5 Computing Expected Value

One thousand tickets are sold at $1 each for a color television valued at $350. What is the expected value if a person purchases one ticket?

SOLUTION

We begin with two notes. First, for a win, the net gain is $349, since the person does not get the cost of the ticket ($1) back. Second, for a loss, the gain is represented by a negative number, in this case, $-\$1$.

The problem can then be set up as follows:

	Win	Lose
Gain, X	$349	$-\$1$
Probability, $P(X)$	$\dfrac{1}{1,000}$	$\dfrac{999}{1,000}$

The solution, then, is

$$E(X) = \$349 \cdot \frac{1}{1,000} + (-\$1) \cdot \frac{999}{1,000} = -\$0.65$$

▼ Try This One 5

With his house in foreclosure, a homeowner comes up with a plan to salvage the situation: he sells 10,000 raffle tickets at $50 each for the home, which is valued at $200,000. Find the expected value from buying one ticket.

Note that the expectation in Example 5 is $-\$0.65$. This does not mean that a person would ever actually lose 65 cents, since the person can only win a television set valued at $350 or lose $1 on the ticket. What this expectation means is that the average of the losses is $0.65 for each of the 1,000 ticket holders. Here is another way of looking at this situation: If a person purchased one ticket each week over a long period of time, the average loss would be $0.65 per ticket, since theoretically, on average, that person would win the television set once for each 1,000 tickets purchased.

Sidelight MATH AND SLOT MACHINES

Today most slot machines are run electronically, much the same as video games are. However, early slot machines were mechanical in nature. The first slot machines were invented by the Fey Manufacturing Company of San Francisco in 1895. They consisted of three large wheels, which were spun when the handle on the side of the machine was pulled. In order to control the number of wins and the payoffs, each wheel contains 20 symbols. However, the number of the same symbols is not the same on each wheel. For example, there may be two oranges on wheel 1, six oranges on wheel 2, and no oranges on wheel 3. When a person gets two orange symbols, he may think that he almost won; i.e., 2 out of 3. However, since there is no orange symbol on the third wheel, the probability of getting three oranges is zero! The higher the probability of getting three oranges, the lower the payoff. Using probability theory, the owner of the machines can determine his long-run profit.

EXAMPLE 6 Computing Expected Value

A stock you bought two years ago with high hopes is now selling for less than you paid, and things look grim for the company. Do you sell, or hold on and hope it will come back to the original price before you sell?

A model economists use for such situations is a game no one wants to play: Suppose you have a choice: lose $100, or take a $\frac{50}{50}$ chance between losing nothing, and losing $300. Which do you choose? Find the expected value for each strategy over 10 trials. (See Exercise 24.)

☑ 4. Compute expected value.

One thousand tickets are sold at $1 each for four prizes of $100, $50, $25, and $10. What is the expected value if a person purchases two tickets?

SOLUTION

Find the expected value if the person purchases one ticket.

Gain, x	$99	$49	$24	$9	−$1
Probability, $P(x)$	$\frac{1}{1,000}$	$\frac{1}{1,000}$	$\frac{1}{1,000}$	$\frac{1}{1,000}$	$\frac{996}{1,000}$

$$E(x) = \$99 \cdot \frac{1}{1,000} + \$49 \cdot \frac{1}{1,000} + \$24 \cdot \frac{1}{1,000} + \$9 \cdot \frac{1}{1,000} - \$1 \cdot \frac{996}{1,000} = -\$0.815$$

Now multiply by 2 since two tickets were purchased.

$$-\$0.815(2) = -\$1.63$$

▼ Try This One 6

A small ski resort loses $70,000 per season when it does not snow very much and makes $250,000 profit when it does snow a lot. The probability of it snowing at least 75 inches (i.e., a good season) is 40%. Find the expectation for the profit.

Math Note

In American roulette, there are 22 different types of bet you can place, but it is interesting to note that all but one of them have the exact same expected value: −$0.053 on a $1 bet. (Betting on 0, 00, 1, 2, and 3, called a five-number bet, is worse, at −$0.079.)

In gambling games, if the expected value of the gain is 0, the game is said to be fair. If the expected value of the gain of a game is positive, then the game is in favor of the player. That is, the player has a better-than-even chance of winning. If the expected value of the gain is negative, then the game is said to be in favor of the house. That is, in the long run, the players will lose money. Can you guess what the sign of the expected value is for every game in a casino?

Answers to Try This One

1	In favor: 5:7; against: 7:5	**3**	$\frac{8}{9}$	**5**	−$30
2	In favor: 1:2; against: 2:1	**4**	1	**6**	$58,000

EXERCISE SET 11-6

Writing Exercises

1. Explain the difference between the odds in favor of an event and the odds against an event.

2. Explain the numerical relationship between the odds in favor of an event and the odds against an event.

3. Explain the meaning of odds in a gambling game.
4. Explain how to find the probability of an event occurring when given the odds in favor of an event.
5. Explain what is meant by the expected value of an event.
6. Why does every game in a casino have a negative expected value for the player?

Real-World Applications

7. In planning a gambling booth for a charity festival, Antoine needs to know the odds of various combinations in order to decide on payouts that will be high enough that people want to play, but low enough that the charity will make money. If the player rolls two dice, find the odds
   (a) In favor of getting a sum of 10.
   (b) In favor of getting a sum of 12.
   (c) Against getting a sum of 7.
   (d) Against getting a sum of 3.
   (e) In favor of getting doubles.

8. If the game in Exercise 7 has players who roll only one die, find the odds
   (a) In favor of getting a 3.
   (b) In favor of getting a 6.
   (c) Against getting an odd number.
   (d) Against getting an even number.
   (e) In favor of getting a prime number.

9. Steve shuffled a deck of 52 cards and asked Sally to draw one card to start a magic trick. Find the odds
   (a) In favor of getting a queen.
   (b) In favor of getting a face card.
   (c) Against getting a club.
   (d) In favor of getting an ace.
   (e) In favor of getting a black card.

10. While cleaning her dorm room, Monica mistakenly pushed three coins off the desk. When they land on the chair below, find the odds
    (a) In favor of getting exactly three heads.
    (b) In favor of getting exactly three tails.
    (c) Against getting exactly two heads.
    (d) Against getting exactly one tail.
    (e) In favor of getting at least one tail.

11. Your friends have taken bets on whether you will pass this class. (Sounds like maybe you need new friends.) Find the probability that you will pass given these odds:
    (a) 7:4 in favor of you passing
    (b) 2:5 against you passing
    (c) 3:1 in favor of you passing
    (d) 1:4 against you passing

12. Find the probability that you will win a Wii bowling tournament given these odds:
    (a) 3:4 in favor of you winning
    (b) 1:7 against you winning
    (c) 5:4 in favor of you winning
    (d) 6:5 in favor of you winning

13. If the odds against a horse winning a race are 9:5, find the probability that the horse will win the race.

14. A person rolls two dice and wins if he or she throws doubles. What are the odds in favor of the event? What are the odds against the event?

15. A cash prize of $5,000 is to be awarded at a fundraiser. If 2,500 tickets are sold at $5 each, find the expected value.

16. You start your shift as a cashier with your drawer containing ten $1 bills, five $2 bills, three $5 bills, one $10 bill, and one $100 bill. Find the expectation if one bill is selected.

17. In a scratch-off game, if you scratch the two dice on the ticket and get doubles, you win $5. For the game to be fair, how much should you pay to play the game?

18. At this year's State Fair, there was a dice rolling game. If you rolled two dice and got a sum of 2 or 12, you won $20. If you rolled a 7, you won $5. Any other roll was a loss. It cost $3 to play one game with one roll of the dice. What is the expectation of the game?

19. Melinda buys one raffle ticket at the Spring Fling since there is one $1,000 prize, one $500 prize, and five $100 prizes. There were a total of 1,000 tickets sold at $3 each. What is Melinda's expectation?

20. If Melinda buys two tickets to the raffle in Exercise 19, what is her expectation?

21. For a daily lottery, a person selects any three-digit number from 000 to 999. If a person plays for $1, the person can win $500. Find the expectation. In the same daily lottery, if a person boxes a number, the person can win $80. Find the expectation if the number 123 is played for $1 and boxed. (When a number is "boxed," it can win when the digits occur in any order.)

22. If a 60-year-old buys a $1,000 life insurance policy at a cost of $60 and has a probability of 0.972 of living to age 61, find the expectation of the policy until the person reaches 61.

Critical Thinking

23. Consider the following problem: You stop on the street between errands to engage in a shell game with a street vendor. The vendor shows you a two-headed penny under one shell, a two-tailed penny under the second shell and a fair penny (one head and one tail) under the third shell. He shuffles the shells around and then

you choose a shell. He shows you that under the shell is a penny with the head side up. He is willing to bet you $5 that it is the two-headed penny. He says it cannot be the two-tailed penny because a head is showing. Therefore, he says there is a 50-50 chance of it being the two-headed coin. Should you take the bet?

24. Stuck in a bad situation, you're given a choice: lose $100, or take a 50-50 chance between losing nothing and losing $300. Choose the option that sounds better to you, then find the expected value of each option over 10 trials.

25. Since expected value only applies to numerical outcomes, it takes some ingenuity to use it for flipping a coin.

  (a) Choose any two numbers at random, assigning one to heads and another to tails. Then find the expected value of flipping the coin.

  (b) Repeat part (a) for two different numbers. What can you conclude?

26. Chevalier de Mere, a famous gambler, won money when he bet unsuspecting patrons that in four rolls of a die, he could get at least one 6, but he lost money when he bet that in 24 rolls of two dice, he could get a double 6. Using the probability rules, find the probability of each event and explain why he won the majority of the time on the first game but lost the majority of the time when playing the second game.

27. A roulette wheel has 38 numbers: 1 through 36, 0, and 00. A ball is rolled, and it falls into one of the 38 slots, giving a winning number. If a player bets $1 on a number and wins, the player gets $35 plus his $1 back. Otherwise, he loses the $1 he bet. Show that the expected value of the game matches that shown in the Math Note on page 614.

Section 11-7 The Addition Rules for Probability

LEARNING OBJECTIVES

☐ 1. Decide if two events are mutually exclusive.

☐ 2. Use the addition rule for mutually exclusive events.

☐ 3. Use the addition rule for events that are not mutually exclusive.

Many interesting problems in probability involve finding the probability of more than one event. Usually, some careful thought is required. For example, when the U.S. House of Representatives is in session, suppose that a political commentator feels like a certain bill is most likely to be supported by women and Democrats. She would likely be interested in the probability that a member of the House

is either a woman or a Democrat. She could find the number of women representatives, and the number of Democratic representatives easily, but then what? Should she add those numbers and divide by the total number of representatives? What about those who are both women *and* Democrats? They would get counted twice.

The situation would be simpler if the commentator were interested in the probability of a representative being either a Republican or an Independent. The key difference is that any individual has to be one or the other. These two events are called *mutually exclusive*, which indicates that either one or the other must occur, but not both.

> Two events are **mutually exclusive** if they cannot both occur at the same time. That is, the events have no outcomes in common.

EXAMPLE 1   **Deciding if Two Events Are Mutually Exclusive**

In drawing cards from a standard deck, determine whether the two events are mutually exclusive or not.

(a) Drawing a 4, drawing a 6.   (b) Drawing a 4, drawing a heart.

SOLUTION

(a) Every card has just one denomination, so a card can't be both a 4 and a 6. The events are mutually exclusive.
(b) You could draw the 4 of hearts, which is one outcome satisfying both events. The events are not mutually exclusive.

▼ **Try This One 1**

☑ 1. Decide if two events are mutually exclusive.

If you select one of these T-shirts at random in the morning, the probability that it is blue or red is $\frac{1}{5} + \frac{1}{5}$.

If student government picks students at random to win free books for a semester, determine whether the two events are mutually exclusive or not.

(a) The winner is a sophomore or a business major.
(b) The winner is a junior or a senior.

The probability of two or more events occurring can be determined by using the **addition rules.** The first addition rule is used when the events are mutually exclusive.

Addition Rule 1

When two events A and B are mutually exclusive, the probability that A or B will occur is

$$P(A \text{ or } B) = P(A) + P(B)$$

In Exercise 2, you will examine why this formula makes sense.

EXAMPLE 2 **Using Addition Rule 1**

A restaurant has three pieces of apple pie, five pieces of cherry pie, and four pieces of pumpkin pie in its dessert case. If a customer selects at random one kind of pie for dessert, find the probability that it will be either cherry or pumpkin.

SOLUTION

The events are mutually exclusive. Since there is a total of 12 pieces of pie, five of which are cherry and four of which are pumpkin,

$$P(\text{cherry or pumpkin}) = P(\text{cherry}) + P(\text{pumpkin})$$
$$= \frac{5}{12} + \frac{4}{12} = \frac{9}{12} = \frac{3}{4}$$

Math Note

Sometimes it's a bad idea to reduce fractions in the individual probabilities when using the addition rule: you'll need a common denominator to add them. Your final answer should always be reduced if possible, though.

▼ **Try This One 2**

A liberal arts math class contains 7 freshmen, 11 sophomores, 5 juniors, and 2 seniors. If the professor randomly chooses one to present a homework problem at the board, find the probability that it's either a junior or senior.

EXAMPLE 3   Using Addition Rule 1

A card is drawn from a standard deck. Find the probability of getting an ace or a queen.

SOLUTION

The events are mutually exclusive. There are four aces and four queens; therefore,

$$P(\text{ace or queen}) = P(\text{ace}) + P(\text{queen})$$
$$= \frac{4}{52} + \frac{4}{52} = \frac{8}{52} = \frac{2}{13}$$

▼ Try This One 3

At a political rally, there are 20 Republicans, 13 Democrats, and 6 Independents. If a person is selected at random, find the probability that he or she is either a Democrat or an Independent.

The addition rule for mutually exclusive events can be extended to three or more events as shown in Example 4.

EXAMPLE 4   Using the Addition Rule with Three Events

A card is drawn from a deck. Find the probability that it is either a club, a diamond, or a heart.

SOLUTION

In the deck of 52 cards there are 13 clubs, 13 diamonds, and 13 hearts, and any card can be only one of those suits. So

$$P(\text{club, diamond, or heart}) = P(\text{club}) + P(\text{diamond}) + P(\text{heart})$$
$$= \frac{13}{52} + \frac{13}{52} + \frac{13}{52} = \frac{39}{52} = \frac{3}{4}$$

▼ Try This One 4

In rolling two dice, find the probability that the sum is 2, 3, or 4.

☑ 2. Use the addition rule for mutually exclusive events.

In Example 4, we used an extended version of addition rule 1:

$$P(A \text{ or } B \text{ or } C) = P(A) + P(B) + P(C)$$

When two events are not mutually exclusive, any outcomes that are common to two events are counted twice. We account for this by subtracting the probability of both events occurring, which results in addition rule 2.

Math Note

Addition rule 2 can actually be used when events are mutually exclusive, too—in that case, $P(A \text{ and } B)$ will always be zero, and you'll get addition rule 1 back. But it's still important to distinguish between the two situations.

Addition Rule 2

When two events A and B are not mutually exclusive, the probability that A or B will occur is

$$P(A \text{ or } B) = P(A) + P(B) - P(A \text{ and } B)$$

EXAMPLE 5   Using Addition Rule 2

A single card is drawn from a standard deck of cards. Find the probability that it is a king or a club.

SOLUTION

In this case, there are 4 kings and 13 clubs. However, the king of clubs has been counted twice since the two events are not mutually exclusive. When finding the probability of getting a king or a club, the probability of getting the king of clubs (i.e., a king and a club) must be subtracted, as shown.

$$P(\text{king or club}) = P(\text{king}) + P(\text{club}) - P(\text{king and club})$$
$$= \frac{4}{52} + \frac{13}{52} - \frac{1}{52} = \frac{16}{52} = \frac{4}{13}$$

▼ Try This One 5

A card is drawn from an ordinary deck. Find the probability that it is a heart or a face card.

EXAMPLE 6   Using Addition Rule 2

Two dice are rolled. Find the probability of getting doubles or a sum of 6.

SOLUTION

Using the sample space shown in Section 11-2, there are six ways to get doubles: (1, 1), (2, 2), (3, 3), (4, 4), (5, 5), (6, 6). So $P(\text{doubles}) = \frac{6}{36}$. There are five ways to get a sum of 6: (1, 5), (2, 4), (3, 3), (4, 2), (5, 1). So $P(\text{sum of 6}) = \frac{5}{36}$. Notice that there is one way of getting doubles and a sum of 6, so $P(\text{doubles and a sum of 6}) = \frac{1}{36}$. Finally,

$$P(\text{doubles or a sum of 6}) = P(\text{doubles}) + P(\text{sum of 6}) - (\text{doubles and sum of 6})$$
$$= \frac{6}{36} + \frac{5}{36} - \frac{1}{36} = \frac{10}{36} = \frac{5}{18}$$

▼ Try This One 6

 3. Use the addition rule for events that are not mutually exclusive.

When two dice are rolled, find the probability that both numbers are more than three, or that they differ by exactly two.

In many cases, the information in probability problems can be arranged in table form in order to make it easier to compute the probabilities for various events. Example 7 uses this technique.

EXAMPLE 7   Using a Table and Addition Rule 2

In a hospital there are eight nurses and five physicians. Seven nurses and three physicians are females. If a staff person is selected, find the probability that the subject is a nurse or a male.

SOLUTION

The sample space can be written in table form.

Staff	Females	Males	Total
Nurses	7	1	8
Physicians	3	2	5
Total	10	3	13

Looking at the table, we can see that there are 8 nurses and 3 males, and there is one person who is both a male and a nurse. The probability is

$$P(\text{nurse or male}) = P(\text{nurse}) + P(\text{male}) - P(\text{male and a nurse})$$

$$= \frac{8}{13} + \frac{3}{13} - \frac{1}{13} = \frac{10}{13}$$

▼ **Try This One 7**

In a class of students, there are 15 freshmen and 10 sophomores. Six of the freshmen are males and four of the sophomores are males. If a student is selected at random, find the probability that the student is a sophomore or a male.

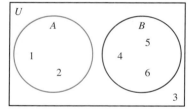

(a) Mutually exclusive events
$A \cap B = \varnothing$
$P(A \cup B) = P(A) + P(B)$

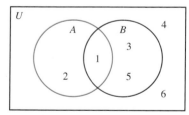

(b) Events not mutually exclusive
$A \cap B \neq \varnothing$
$P(A \cup B) = P(A) + P(B) - P(A \cap B)$

Figure 11-8

Probability and Sets

The addition rules for probability can be represented by Venn diagrams. First, consider two mutually exclusive events. For example, we will use the probability experiment of rolling a die. Let A be the event of getting a number less than 3 and B be the event of getting a number greater than 3. In set notation, $U = \{1, 2, 3, 4, 5, 6\}$, $A = \{1, 2\}$, and $B = \{4, 5, 6\}$. The Venn diagram for mutually exclusive events is shown in Figure 11-8(a). Notice that $A \cup B = \{1, 2\} \cup \{4, 5, 6\} = \{1, 2, 4, 5, 6\}$; now $P(A \cup B) = P(A) + P(B)$ or in probability language, $P(A \text{ or } B) = P(A) + P(B)$. Since $P(A) = \frac{2}{6}$, and $P(B) = \frac{3}{6}$, then $P(A \text{ or } B) = \frac{5}{6}$.

Next, consider two events that are not mutually exclusive. Let A be the event of getting a number less than 3 and B be the event of getting an odd number. The sample space for A is $\{1, 2\}$. The sample space for B is $\{1, 3, 5\}$. The Venn diagram for this example is shown in Figure 11-8(b). We can see that 4 of the 6 outcomes are in $A \cup B$, so $P(A \cup B) = \frac{4}{6}$. Also, there are 2 outcomes in A, 3 in B, and 1 in $A \cap B$, so $P(A) = \frac{2}{6}$, $P(B) = \frac{3}{6}$, and $P(A \cap B) = \frac{1}{6}$. Then

$$P(A \cup B) = P(A) + P(B) - P(A \cap B)$$

$$= \frac{2}{6} + \frac{3}{6} - \frac{1}{6} = \frac{4}{6} = \frac{2}{3}$$

In probability notation, this is equivalent to $P(A \text{ or } B) = P(A) + P(B) - P(A \text{ and } B)$.

Answers to Try This One

1 (a) Not mutually exclusive
    (b) Mutually exclusive

2 $\frac{7}{25}$

3 $\frac{19}{39}$

4 $\frac{1}{6}$

5 $\frac{11}{26}$

6 $\frac{5}{12}$

7 $\frac{16}{25}$

EXERCISE SET 11-7

Writing Exercises

1. Explain how to tell if two events are mutually exclusive or not.

For Exercises 2–8, determine whether or not the events are mutually exclusive, and explain your answer.

2. Roll a die: Get an even number, or get a number less than 3.
3. Roll a die: Get a prime number (2, 3, 5), or get an odd number.
4. Roll a die: Get a number greater than 3, or get a number less than 3.
5. Select a student in your class: the student has blond hair, or the student has blue eyes.
6. Select a student in your college: the student is a sophomore, or the student is a business major.
7. Select any course: It is a calculus course, or it is an English course.
8. Select a registered voter: The voter is a Republican, or the voter is a Democrat.

Real-World Applications

9. A young couple who plan to marry decide to select a month for their wedding. Find the probability that it will be April or May. Assume that all months have an equal opportunity of being selected.
10. At the animal shelter where Miguel volunteers on the weekends, there were two Siamese cats, four tabby cats, sixteen mixed-breed dogs, and four iguanas in their cages. If a customer picks any of these animals at random, find the probability that the animal is either a mixed-breed dog or a Siamese cat.
11. When Milo went to register for classes at the last minute, the only classes left to take were seven math courses, five computer science courses, three statistics courses, and four science courses. He shut his eyes and picked one at random. Find the probability that Milo selected either a science course or a math course. (The probability that Milo will ever graduate using this strategy is an interesting question, too.)
12. When Shana looked at the favorites list on her boyfriend's MP3 player, there were 10 songs she liked, 7 songs she'd heard but did not like, and 5 songs she hadn't heard. She let the MP3 player select a song at random. What is the probability that the selected song was one she liked or one she'd heard but did not like?
13. The bookstore has eight red school jerseys, nine blue school jerseys, and three black school jerseys to choose from. If a student selects one at random, find the probability that it is
    (a) A red or a blue jersey.
    (b) A red or a black jersey.
    (c) A blue or a black jersey.
14. In my Tae Kwon Do class, there are two black belts, three red belts, five blue belts, three green belts, and six yellow belts. If the sensei selects a student at random to lead the warm-up, find the probability that the person is
    (a) Either a green belt or a yellow belt.
    (b) Either a black belt or a blue belt.
    (c) Either a black belt, a green belt, or a yellow belt.
15. On a small college campus, there are five English professors, four mathematics professors, two science professors, three psychology professors, and three history professors. If a professor is selected at random, find the probability that the professor is
    (a) An English or psychology professor.
    (b) A mathematics or science professor.
    (c) A history, science, or mathematics professor.
    (d) An English, mathematics, or history professor.
16. A deck of cards is randomly dealt by the computer during a game of Spider Solitaire. Find the probability the first card dealt is
    (a) A 4 or a diamond.
    (b) A club or a diamond.
    (c) A jack or a black card.
17. In a statistics class there are 18 juniors and 10 seniors; 6 of the seniors are females, and 12 of the juniors are males. If a student is selected at random, find the probability of selecting
    (a) A junior or a female.
    (b) A senior or a female.
    (c) A junior or a senior.
18. A cell phone company gets a good deal on 400 new Motorola RAZR phones. Of them, 250 have digital cameras and 150 have touch screens. Of the RAZR phones that have digital cameras, 140 are lime green and the rest are metallic orange. Of the RAZR phones that have touch screens, 80 are lime green and the rest are metallic orange. If a RAZR phone is selected at random, find the probability that it will
    (a) Be lime green or have a digital camera.
    (b) Be metallic orange or have a touch screen.
19. BlueFly.com, an online designer clothing marketplace, purchases items from Kenneth Cole, Michael

Kors, and Vera Wang. The most recent purchases are shown here:

Product	Kenneth Cole	Michael Kors	Vera Wang
Dresses	24	18	12
Jeans	13	36	15

If one item is selected at random, find these probabilities:

(a) It was purchased from Kenneth Cole or is a dress.

(b) It was purchased from Michael Kors or Vera Wang.

(c) It is a pair of jeans or it was purchased from Kenneth Cole.

20. In a recent campus survey, the following data were obtained in response to the question "Do you think there should be harsher penalties for underage drinking on campus?"

	Yes	No	No opinion
Males	72	81	5
Females	103	68	7

If a person is selected at random, find these probabilities:

(a) The person has no opinion.
(b) The person is a male or is against the issue.
(c) The person is a female or favors the issue.

21. A grocery store employs cashiers, stock clerks, and deli personnel. The distribution of employees according to marital status is shown next.

Marital status	Cashiers	Stock clerks	Deli personnel
Married	8	12	3
Not married	5	15	2

If an employee is selected at random, find these probabilities:

(a) The employee is a stock clerk or married.
(b) The employee is not married.
(c) The employee is a cashier or is not married.

22. Students were surveyed on campus about their study habits. Some said they study in the morning, others study during the day between classes, and others study at night. Some students always study in a group and others always study alone. The distribution is shown below:

How students study	Morning	Between classes	Evening
Study in a group	2	3	1
Study alone	3	4	2

If a student who was surveyed is selected at random, find these probabilities:

(a) The student studies in the evening.
(b) The student studies in the morning or in a group.

(c) The student studies in the evening or studies alone.

23. Three cable channels (95, 97, and 103) air quiz shows, comedies, and dramas. The numbers of shows aired are shown here.

Type of show	Channel 95	Channel 97	Channel 103
Quiz show	5	2	1
Comedy	3	2	8
Drama	4	4	2

If a show is selected at random, find these probabilities:

(a) The show is a quiz show or it is shown on Channel 97.
(b) The show is a drama or a comedy.
(c) The show is shown on Channel 103 or it is a drama.

24. A local postal carrier distributed first-class letters, advertisements, and magazines. For a certain day, she distributed the following number of each type of item.

Delivered to	First-class letters	Ads	Magazines
Home	325	406	203
Business	732	1,021	97

If an item of mail is selected at random, find these probabilities:

(a) The item went to a home.
(b) The item was an ad or it went to a business.
(c) The item was a first-class letter or it went to a home.

25. As part of her major in microbiology, Juanita spent 3 weeks studying the spread of a disease in the jungles of South America. When she returned, she found that she had many e-mails sent to her home account and her school account, and that the e-mails were either spam, school announcements, or messages from friends as follows:

Delivered to	School announcements	Spam	Messages from friends
Home	325	406	203
School	732	1,021	97

If an e-mail is selected at random, find these probabilities:

(a) The e-mail was sent to her home.
(b) The e-mail was a school announcement or it was sent to her school account.
(c) The e-mail was spam or it was sent to her home account.

26. During a windstorm, the two large dice atop a new casino in Las Vegas crash into the pool below. Find the probabilities the dice landed with

(a) A sum of 6, 7, or 8.
(b) Doubles or a sum of 4 or 6.
(c) A sum greater than 9 or less than 4 or equal to 7.

27. Before a Walk for the Cure 10-mile walk, participants could choose a T-shirt from a box with six red shirts, two green shirts, one blue shirt, and one white shirt. When the first participant randomly selects a shirt from the box, what is the probability she will select a red shirt or a white shirt?

28. Colby tosses the contents of his jeans onto a table before putting them into the washer. Among the things thrown are three dice. Find the probability that the dice landed so that

   (a) All three have the same number showing.
   (b) The three numbers sum to 5.

Critical Thinking

29. The probability that a customer selects a pizza with mushrooms or pepperoni is 0.55, and the probability that the customer selects mushrooms only is 0.32. If the probability that he or she selects pepperoni only is 0.17, find the probability of the customer selecting both items.

30. In building new homes, a contractor finds that the probability of a buyer selecting a two-car garage is 0.70 and of selecting a one-car garage is 0.20. Find the probability that the buyer will select no garage. The builder does not build houses with garages for three or more cars.

31. In Exercise 30, find the probability that the buyer will not want a two-car garage.

32. In this exercise, we will attempt to justify addition rule 1. When two dice are rolled, we will find the probability of getting a sum of 5 or 10.

   (a) Explain why the two events are mutually exclusive.
   (b) How many total outcomes are possible when two dice are rolled?
   (c) How many outcomes result in a sum of either 5 or 10?
   (d) Find the probability of rolling a sum of 5 or 10 without the addition rule, using your answers from parts b and c.
   (e) Find the probability of rolling a sum of 5.
   (f) Find the probability of rolling a sum of 10.
   (g) Add your answers from parts e and f, then explain why the calculations from parts d and g will always be the same for any pair of mutually exclusive events.

Section 11-8 The Multiplication Rules and Conditional Probability

LEARNING OBJECTIVES

☐ 1. Find the probability of two or more independent events all occurring.

☐ 2. Find the probability of two or more dependent events all occurring.

☐ 3. Find conditional probabilities.

Based on data collected from 1960–2000, the probability of it raining on any given day during March in Daytona Beach, Florida, is about 1/5. So you head to Daytona for spring break, and you're more than a little disappointed when it rains the first 2 days. Trying to remain upbeat, you say "With only a $\frac{1}{5}$ chance of rain, what are the chances of it raining 3 days in a row?"

   That's actually a much more interesting question than you think. One reason is that many people would say that it's less likely to rain the third day because it already rained 2 days in a row, but that's not the case. Assuming that there's not a massive storm system lasting for 3 days, what happened on Saturday has no effect on whether or not it rains on Monday, so the probability of rain on the third day is $\frac{1}{5}$ regardless of what happened the first 2 days.

   Returning to the original question, the probability of it raining 3 days in a row, we see that a rule for finding the probability of consecutive events occurring would be helpful. As we will see, the probability of consecutive events depends on whether the first event affects the second.

Two events A and B are **independent** if the fact that A occurs has no effect on the probability of B occurring.

Based on our description above, rain on Saturday and rain on Monday are independent events.

Each day a professor selects a student at random to work out a problem from the homework. If the student is selected regardless of who already went, the events are independent. If the student is selected from the pool of students who haven't gone yet, the events are dependent.

Here are other examples of independent events:

Rolling a die and getting a 6, and then rolling a second die and getting a 3.

Drawing a card from a deck and getting a queen, replacing it, and drawing a second card and getting a queen.

On the other hand, when the occurrence of the first event changes the probability of the occurrence of the second event, the two events are said to be *dependent*. For example, suppose a card is drawn from a deck and *not* replaced, and then a second card is drawn. The probability for the second card is changed since the sample space contains only 51 cards when the first card is not replaced.

Two events A and B are **dependent** if the outcome of A has some effect on the probability of B occurring.

Here are some examples of dependent events:

Drawing a card from a deck, not replacing it, and then drawing a second card.

Selecting a lottery ball from a tumbler, not replacing it, and then drawing a second ball.

Parking in a no-parking zone and getting a parking ticket.

When a coin is flipped twice, the outcomes of the first and second flips are independent, and in each case, the probability of getting tails is $\frac{1}{2}$. The sample space for the two flips is {HH, TT, HT, TH}, and the probability of getting tails twice is $\frac{1}{4}$. Notice that $\frac{1}{4} = \frac{1}{2} \cdot \frac{1}{2}$. This shows that the probability of two consecutive tails is the product of the probabilities of getting tails in each individual trial. This result is our first *multiplication rule*.

Multiplication Rule 1

When two events A and B are independent, the probability of both occurring is

$$P(A \text{ and } B) = P(A) \cdot P(B)$$

EXAMPLE 1   Using Multiplication Rule 1

A coin is flipped and a die is rolled. Find the probability of getting heads on the coin and a 4 on the die.

SOLUTION

The two events, the coin landing on heads and the die showing 4, are independent. We know from earlier examples that the probability of heads is $\frac{1}{2}$ and the probability of getting 4 with one die is $\frac{1}{6}$. Using the multiplication rule:

$$P(\text{heads and } 4) = P(\text{heads}) \cdot P(4) = \frac{1}{2} \cdot \frac{1}{6} = \frac{1}{12}$$

Math Note

The problem in Example 1 could be solved using standard sample space methods, but as outcomes get more complicated, it can be extremely difficult to list sample spaces. That's why the multiplication rules are so helpful.

▼ Try This One 1

If the probability of your alarm not going off is $\frac{1}{20}$, and the probability of getting a ticket on your way to work is $\frac{1}{200}$, find the probability that both will happen.

EXAMPLE 2   **Using Multiplication Rule 1**

As part of a psychology experiment on perception and memory, colored balls are picked from an urn. The urn contains three red balls, two green balls, and five white balls. A ball is selected and its color is noted. Then it is replaced. A second ball is selected and its color is noted. Find the probability of each of these.

(a) Selecting two green balls.
(b) Selecting a green ball and then a white ball.
(c) Selecting a red ball and then a green ball.

SOLUTION

Remember, selection is done with replacement, which makes the events independent.
(a) The probability of selecting a green ball on each trial is $\frac{2}{10}$, so

$$P(\text{green and green}) = P(\text{green}) \cdot P(\text{green}) = \frac{2}{10} \cdot \frac{2}{10} = \frac{4}{100} = \frac{1}{25}$$

(b) The probability of selecting a green ball is $\frac{2}{10}$ and the probability of selecting a white ball is $\frac{5}{10}$, so

$$P(\text{green and white}) = P(\text{green}) \cdot P(\text{white}) = \frac{2}{10} \cdot \frac{5}{10} = \frac{10}{100} = \frac{1}{10}$$

(c) The probability of selecting a red ball is $\frac{3}{10}$ and the probability of selecting a green ball is $\frac{2}{10}$, so

$$P(\text{red and green}) = P(\text{red}) \cdot P(\text{green}) = \frac{3}{10} \cdot \frac{2}{10} = \frac{6}{100} = \frac{3}{50}$$

▼ **Try This One 2**

As part of a card trick, a card is drawn from a deck and replaced; then a second card is drawn. Find the probability of getting a queen and then an ace.

EXAMPLE 3   **Finding Probabilities for Three Independent Events**

Three cards are drawn from a deck. After each card is drawn, its denomination and suit are noted and it is replaced before the next card is drawn. Find the probability of getting

(a) Three kings.
(b) Three clubs.

Math Note

Multiplication rule 1 can be extended to three or more independent events using the formula

$P(A_1$ and A_2 and $A_3 \cdots$
and $A_n)$
$= P(A_1) \cdot P(A_2) \cdot P(A_3) \cdots$
$\cdot P(A_n)$

SOLUTION

(a) Since there are four kings, the probability of getting a king on each draw is $\frac{4}{52}$ or $\frac{1}{13}$. The probability of getting three kings is

$$\frac{1}{13} \cdot \frac{1}{13} \cdot \frac{1}{13} = \frac{1}{2,197}$$

(b) Since there are 13 clubs, the probability of getting a club is $\frac{13}{52}$ or $\frac{1}{4}$. The probability of getting three clubs in a row is

$$\frac{1}{4} \cdot \frac{1}{4} \cdot \frac{1}{4} = \frac{1}{64}$$

▼ Try This One 3

Given that the probability of rain on any given day in March in Daytona Beach is $\frac{1}{5}$, find the probability that

(a) *It rains three straight days in March.*
(b) *It rains on March 10 and 12, but not March 11.*

Assume that weather on any day is independent of the others.

When a few subjects are selected from a large number of subjects in a sample space, and the subjects are not replaced, the probability of the event occurring changes so slightly that, for the most part, it is considered to remain the same. Example 4 illustrates this concept.

EXAMPLE 4   Using Multiplication Rule 1 with Large Samples

According to a Gallup Poll in 2007, 47 percent of all parents in America with children under 18 feel frequent stress. If three parents are chosen randomly, find the probability that all three will say they feel frequent stress.

SOLUTION

Let S denote the event that the chosen parent feels stress.

$$P(S \text{ and } S \text{ and } S) = P(S) \cdot P(S) \cdot P(S) = (0.47)(0.47)(0.47) \approx 0.104$$

▼ Try This One 4

☑ 1. Find the probability of two or more independent events all occurring.

According to a report from the National Institute of Justice, 64% of males arrested for any reason in 2000 tested positive for illegal drugs. If four prisoners at random were chosen, find the probability that all four test positive.

CAUTION

Even though the three events in Example 4 are not independent, because parents were not replaced after being chosen, there are millions and millions of parents, so having one or two fewer in the sample has a negligible effect. Make sure to carefully consider the situation before using multiplication rule 1.

When we are interested in finding the probability of consecutive events that are dependent, we can still use the multiplication rule, but with a minor modification. For example, let's say we draw two cards at random from a standard deck. The probability of getting an ace on the first draw is $\frac{4}{52}$. But if the first card is not put back into the deck, that changes the probability of drawing another ace—it's now $\frac{3}{51}$. Using the multiplication rule, the probability of both events occurring is

$$\frac{4}{52} \cdot \frac{3}{51} = \frac{12}{2,652} = \frac{1}{221}.$$

We can summarize this procedure as multiplication rule 2.

Multiplication Rule 2

When two events are dependent, the probability of both occurring is

$$P(A \text{ and } B) = P(A) \cdot P(B \text{ given that } A \text{ has already occurred})$$

EXAMPLE 5 | **Using Multiplication Rule 2**

An appliance store gets a shipment of 25 plasma TVs, and 3 of them are defective. If two of the TVs are chosen at random, find the probability that both are defective. (The first TV is not replaced after it's tested.)

SOLUTION

Since there are 3 defective TVs out of a total of 25, the probability of the first being defective is $\frac{3}{25}$. After the first one is found to be defective and not replaced, there are 2 defective sets left out of 24, so the probability of the second being defective given that the first one is defective is $\frac{2}{24}$. Using multiplication rule 2, the probability that both are defective is

$$P(\text{1st defective and 2nd defective}) = P(\text{1st}) \cdot P(\text{2nd given 1st})$$

$$= \frac{3}{25} \cdot \frac{2}{24} = \frac{6}{600} = \frac{1}{100}$$

▼ **Try This One 5**

The 2009 NCAA men's basketball tournament field had (among 64 teams) 7 teams from the Big East conference, 7 from the Big Ten, 6 from the Big 12, and 3 from the Southeastern conference. If you were randomly assigned two teams in a dorm pool, find the probability that

(a) Both were from the Big East.
(b) The first was from the Southeastern conference and the second was from the Big 12.

Multiplication rule 2 can be extended to three or more events as shown in Example 6.

EXAMPLE 6 | **Using Multiplication Rule 2 with Three Events**

Three cards are drawn from an ordinary deck and not replaced. Find the probability of

(a) Getting three jacks.
(b) Getting an ace, a king, and a queen in order.
(c) Getting a club, a spade, and a heart in order.
(d) Getting three clubs.

SOLUTION

(a) $P(\text{three jacks}) = \frac{4}{52} \cdot \frac{3}{51} \cdot \frac{2}{50} = \frac{24}{132,600} = \frac{1}{5,525}$

(b) $P(\text{ace and king and queen}) = \frac{4}{52} \cdot \frac{4}{51} \cdot \frac{4}{50} = \frac{64}{132,600} = \frac{8}{16,575}$

(c) $P(\text{club and spade and heart}) = \frac{13}{52} \cdot \frac{13}{51} \cdot \frac{13}{50} = \frac{2,197}{132,600} = \frac{169}{10,200}$

(d) $P(\text{three clubs}) = \frac{13}{52} \cdot \frac{12}{51} \cdot \frac{11}{50} = \frac{1,716}{132,600} = \frac{11}{850}$

☑ 2. Find the probability of two or more dependent events all occurring.

▼ Try This One 6

When drawing four cards from a deck, what is the probability that

(a) All four are aces?   (b) All four are clubs?

Math Note

We use the term conditional probability because the condition that A has already occurred affects the probability of B.

Conditional Probability

We know that to find the probability of two dependent events occurring, it's important to find the probability of the second event occurring given that the first has already occurred. We call this the **conditional probability** of event B occurring given that event A has occurred, and denote it $P(B \mid A)$.

Now that we have a symbol to represent the probability of event B given that A has occurred, we can rewrite multiplication rule 2, and solve the equation for $P(B \mid A)$:

$$P(A \text{ and } B) = P(A) \cdot P(B \mid A)$$

$$P(B \mid A) = \frac{P(A \text{ and } B)}{P(A)}$$

This gives us a formula for conditional probability.

Formula for Conditional Probability

The probability that the second event B occurs given that the first event A has occurred can be found by dividing the probability that both events occurred by the probability that the first event has occurred. The formula is

$$P(B \mid A) = \frac{P(A \text{ and } B)}{P(A)}$$

Example 7 illustrates the use of this rule.

EXAMPLE 7   Finding a Conditional Probability

Military strategies (and other types of strategies) use conditional probability. If A occurs, how likely is B? How likely is B if A doesn't occur?

Suppose that your professor goes stark raving mad and chooses your final grade from A, B, C, D, F, or Incomplete totally at random. Find the probability of getting an A given that you get a letter grade higher than D.

SOLUTION

We are asked to find $P(A \mid \text{letter grade higher than D})$.

Method 1 Knowing that you got a letter grade higher than D reduces the sample space to {A, B, C}, which has three outcomes. One of them is an A, so $P(A \mid \text{letter grade higher than D}) = \frac{1}{3}$.

Method 2 With the full sample space of {A, B, C, D, F, I}, $P(A) = \frac{1}{6}$, and $P(\text{letter grade higher than D}) = \frac{3}{6}$. Using the formula for conditional probability,

$$P(A \mid \text{letter grade higher than D}) = \frac{\frac{1}{6}}{\frac{3}{6}} = \frac{1}{6} \cdot \frac{6}{3} = \frac{1}{3}$$

▼ Try This One 7

A group of buses is rented for an away game, and they are numbered from 1–8. All students are randomly assigned to a bus. What is the probability that you get an even–numbered bus given that your bus number is less than 6?

EXAMPLE 8 **Finding a Conditional Probability**

Hate crimes are defined to be crimes in which the victim is targeted because of one or more personal characteristics, such as race, religion, or sexual orientation. The table below lists the motivation for certain crimes as reported by the FBI for 2007.

Motivation	Crimes against persons	Crimes against property	Crimes against society
Race	3,031	1,686	7
Religion	421	1,054	2
Sexual orientation	1,039	418	3
Total	4,491	3,158	12

(a) Find the probability that a hate crime was racially motivated given that it was a crime against persons.
(b) Find the probability that a hate crime was against property given that it was motivated by the victim's sexual orientation.

SOLUTION

(a) Since we are interested only in crimes against persons, we only need to look at that column. There were 4,491 such crimes total, and 3,031 were racially motivated, so the probability is

$$\frac{3,031}{4,491} \approx 0.675$$

(b) This time we are given that the crime was motivated by sexual orientation, so we only need to look at that row. There were 1,460 such crimes total, and 418 were against property, so the probability is

$$\frac{418}{1,460} \approx 0.286$$

▼ Try This One 8

☑ 3. Find conditional probabilities.

Based on the data in the above table, find the probability that

(a) A crime was motivated by either race or religion given that it was a crime against society.
(b) A crime was against persons given that it was motivated by religion or sexual orientation.

Answers to Try This One

1 $\frac{1}{4,000}$

2 $\frac{1}{169}$

3 (a) $\frac{1}{125}$ (b) $\frac{4}{125}$

4 Approximately 0.168

5 (a) $\frac{1}{96}$ (b) $\frac{1}{224}$

6 (a) $\frac{1}{270,725}$ (b) $\frac{11}{4,165}$

7 $\frac{2}{5}$

8 (a) $\frac{3}{4}$ (b) $\frac{1,460}{2,937} \approx 0.497$

EXERCISE SET   11-8

Writing Exercises

1. What is the difference between independent and dependent events? Give an example of each.
2. What is meant by the term conditional probability?
3. Describe two methods for computing conditional probability.
4. Explain why the probability of two consecutive events occurring couldn't possibly be the sum of the two individual probabilities.

In Exercises 5–12, decide whether the events are independent or dependent, and explain your answer.

5. Tossing a coin and drawing a card from a deck.
6. Drawing a ball from an urn, not replacing it, and then drawing a second ball.
7. Getting a raise in salary and purchasing a new car.
8. Driving on ice and having an accident.
9. Having a large shoe size and having a high IQ.
10. A father being left-handed and a daughter being left-handed.
11. Smoking excessively and having lung cancer.
12. Eating an excessive amount of ice cream and smoking an excessive amount of cigarettes.

Real-World Applications

13. If 18% of students on campus said they were voting for Homer Simpson for the next President of the United States, find the probability that if three students were randomly selected on campus and asked whom they were voting for in the presidential election, all would say they were voting for Homer Simpson.
14. A national study of patients who were overweight found that 56% also have elevated blood pressure. If two overweight patients are selected, find the probability that both have elevated blood pressure.
15. According to the National Highway Traffic Safety Administration, 83% of Americans used seat belts regularly in 2008. If four people are selected at random, find the probability that all four regularly use seat belts.
16. A computer salesperson at Best Buy claims that she has a 20% chance of selling a computer when helping out a customer. If this is true and she talks to four customers before lunch, find the probability that all four will buy computers.
17. If 25% of Michael's graduating class are not U.S. citizens, find the probability that two randomly selected graduating students are not U.S. citizens.
18. If two people are selected at random, what is the probability that they were both born in December?
19. If two people are selected at random, find the probability that they were born in the same month.
20. If three people are selected, find the probability that all three were born in March.
21. If half of Americans believe that the federal government should take "primary responsibility" for eliminating poverty, find the probability that three randomly selected Americans will agree that it is the federal government's responsibility to eliminate poverty.
22. What is the probability that a husband, wife, and daughter have the same birthday?
23. A telecommunications company has six satellites, two of which are sending a weak signal. If two are selected at random without replacement find the probability that both are sending a weak signal.

24. In Exercise 23, find the probability that one satellite sends a strong signal and the other sends a weak signal.
25. The U.S. Department of Justice reported that in 2005, 50.8% of all murders are committed with a handgun. If three murder cases are selected at random, find the probability that a handgun was used in all three.
26. In a department store there are 120 customers, 90 of whom will buy at least one item. If five customers are selected at random, one by one, find the probability that all will buy at least one item.
27. During a game of online hearts, three cards are dealt, one at a time without replacement, from a shuffled, ordinary deck of cards. Find these probabilities:

    (a) All are jacks.
    (b) All are clubs.
    (c) All are red cards.

28. In a group of eight Olympic track stars, five are hurdlers. If three are selected at random without replacement, find the probability they are all hurdlers.
29. In Exercise 28, find the probability none of them are hurdlers.
30. In a class consisting of 15 men and 12 women, two different homework papers were selected at random. Find the probability that both papers belonged to women.
31. While practicing juggling with a die, a quarter, and a spoon, Ken drops the quarter first and then the die and is left holding the spoon. Find the probability of getting a 3 on the die given that the coin landed heads up.
32. Juan draws a black card from an ordinary deck as the first card for a game of Gin Rummy. What is the probability the card was a king?
33. At a carnival gambling booth, two dice are rolled, and a sum of seven wins double your money. Find the probability that the sum is 7 if it is given that one of the numbers was a 6.
34. Frank flips a coin to see who will pick up the pizza from Pizza Hut, and then Sun rolls a die to see how much the person picking up the pizza has to pay toward the meal. Find the probability that the coin landed on tails and the number on the die was odd.

35. A computer randomly deals an ordinary deck of cards for a game of FreeCell, and the first card dealt is a face card. Find the probability that the card was also a diamond.
36. During a backgammon game, Kelly rolled the two dice on the board. Find the probability that the sum obtained was greater than 8 given that the number on one die was a 6.

Use this information for Exercises 37–40.
Three red cards are numbered 1, 2, and 3. Three black cards are numbered 4, 5, and 6.
The cards are placed in a box and one card is selected at random.

37. Find the probability that a red card was selected given that the number on the card was an odd number.
38. Find the probability that a number less than 5 was selected given that the card was a black card.
39. Find the probability that a number less than 5 was selected given that the card was red.
40. Find the probability that a black card was selected given that the number on the card was an even number.

Use the following information for Exercises 41–44.
A survey of 200 college students shows the average number of minutes that people talk on their cell phones each month.

	Less than 600	600–799	800–999	1,000 or more
Men	56	18	10	16
Women	61	18	13	8

If a person is selected at random, find these probabilities:

41. The person talked less than 600 minutes if it is known that the person was a woman.
42. The person talked 1,000 or more minutes if it is known that the person was a man.
43. The person was a woman if it is known that the person talked between 600 and 799 minutes.
44. The person was a man if it is known that the person talked between 600 and 999 minutes.

Critical Thinking

45. A magician is carrying his box of tricks and out spill three dice. What is the probability that the three dice sum to 9?
46. In a rush to pay for her latte, Shelly dropped her change purse and five coins fell out. What is the probability that as the coins fell to the floor, there was at least one head?
47. During a comedy show, the comedian selected three people at random from the audience. What is the probability that the three people will have the same birthday? (Ignore the year.)
48. Suppose that I roll two dice and tell you that the result is definitely even, then offer you 3 to 1 odds that the total isn't 4. Draw a Venn diagram to illustrate the outcomes, then use the diagram to compute the conditional probability. Finally, decide if the given odds are in your favor or not.

Section 11-9 The Binomial Distribution

LEARNING OBJECTIVES

☐ 1. Identify binomial experiments.

☐ 2. Compute probabilities of outcomes in a binomial experiment.

☐ 3. Construct a probability distribution.

Many probability problems involve situations that have only two outcomes. When a baby is born, it will be either male or female. When a coin is tossed, it will land either heads or tails. When the New York Yankees play, they either win or they lose. That cute girl that sits behind you in class will either go out with you or she won't.

Other situations can be reduced to two outcomes. For example, medical procedures can be classified as either successful or unsuccessful. An answer to a multiple choice exam question can be classified as correct or incorrect even though there may be four answer choices.

Situations like these are called *binomial experiments*.

A **binomial experiment** is a probability experiment that satisfies the following requirements:

1. Each trial can have only two outcomes, or outcomes that can be reduced to two outcomes. These outcomes can be considered as either a success or a failure.
2. The outcomes must be independent of each other.
3. There must be a fixed number of trials.
4. The probability of a success must remain the same for all trials of the experiment.

EXAMPLE 1 **Deciding if an Experiment is Binomial**

Decide whether or not each is a binomial experiment.

(a) Drawing a card from a deck and seeing what suit it is
(b) Answering a question on a true-false test
(c) Asking 100 people whether or not they smoke
(d) Selecting cards at random from a deck without replacement and deciding if they are red or black cards

SOLUTION

(a) No, since there are four outcomes: heart, diamond, spade, or club.
(b) Yes, there are only two outcomes: correct and incorrect.
(c) Yes, there are only two outcomes: yes or no.
(d) No, since the cards are not being replaced, the probability changes on each draw.

☑ 1. Identify binomial experiments.

▼ Try This One 1

Decide whether or not each experiment is a binomial experiment.

(a) Selecting a colored ball with replacement from an urn with three balls, each of which is a different color
(b) Selecting a number from a bingo machine
(c) Selecting a card at random from a deck with replacement and noting its color, red or black
(d) Tossing a die and getting a 3

Consider the following experiment. A box contains four colored balls—one each of red, black, white, and green. A ball is randomly selected and its color is recorded. It is then replaced and a second ball is randomly selected and its color is recorded. The tree diagram for this experiment is shown in Figure 11-9.

The probability of selecting two green balls is $\frac{1}{16}$ since there is only one way to select two green balls, namely (G, G), and there are 16 total possible outcomes in the sample space. The probability of selecting exactly one green is $\frac{6}{16}$ or $\frac{3}{8}$ since there are 6 outcomes that contain one green ball: (R, G), (B, G), (W, G), (G, R), (G, B), and (G, W). The probability of selecting no green balls is $\frac{9}{16}$ since there are 9 outcomes that contain no green balls.

A table for the probabilities can be shown.

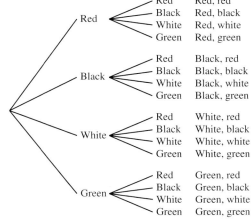

Outcome	Probability
0 green balls	$\frac{9}{16}$
1 green ball	$\frac{3}{8} = \frac{6}{16}$
2 green balls	$\frac{1}{16}$
Sum	$\frac{16}{16} = 1$

The experiment can be considered a binomial experiment since it meets the four conditions of a binomial experiment:

Figure 11-9

1. Each trial has only two outcomes. The ball chosen is either green or it is not green.

2. The outcomes are independent of each other: each ball is replaced before the second ball is selected.

3. There is a fixed number of trials. In this case, there are two draws.

4. The probability of a success remains the same in each case. In this case, since there is only one green ball and a total of four balls, $P(S) = \frac{1}{4}$ and $P(F) = 1 - \frac{1}{4} = \frac{3}{4}$. (Getting a green ball is considered a success. Getting any other colored ball is considered a failure.)

The probability of a given outcome for a binomial experiment can be found using the binomial probability formula.

The Binomial Probability Formula

The probability of exactly x successes in n trials is

$$P(x) = {}_nC_x \cdot p^x \cdot q^{n-x}$$

where p = the probability of a success

q = the probability of a failure ($q = 1 - p$)

Since p is the probability of success on any given trial, using the multiplication rule, p^x is the probability of x successes. The same reasoning shows that q^{n-x} is the probability of $n - x$ failures. We also need to multiply by the number of different ways we can get x successes in n trials, which is ${}_nC_x$: the number of combinations of n objects taken x at a time.

In our example of drawing balls from a box, let's find the probability of getting one green ball in two draws. In this case, $n = 2$, $x = 1$, and $n - x = 1$. The probability of success (p) is $\frac{1}{4}$, and the probability of failure (q) is $\frac{3}{4}$. Using the binomial probability formula,

$$P(1 \text{ green ball}) = {}_nC_x \cdot p^x \cdot q^{n-x}$$

$$= {}_2C_1 \cdot \left(\frac{1}{4}\right)^1 \cdot \left(\frac{3}{4}\right)^1$$

$$= \frac{2!}{(2-1)!\,1!} \cdot \frac{1}{4} \cdot \frac{3}{4}$$

$$= 2 \cdot \frac{3}{16} = \frac{3}{8}$$

This matches the probability found using a tree diagram.

EXAMPLE 2   Using the Binomial Probability Formula

Suppose that the morning after your birthday, you remember that you have a 20 question true or false quiz in your early class. Uh oh! Completely unprepared and a little woozy, you decide to guess on every question. What is the probability that you'll get 16 out of 20 right?

SOLUTION

Because the questions are true or false, and you're arbitrarily guessing, the probability of getting any given question right is $\frac{1}{2}$. The number of trials is $n = 20$, and the number of successes is $x = 16$. The probability of success is $p = \frac{1}{2}$, and the probability of failure is then $q = 1 - \frac{1}{2}$. Substituting these values into the binomial probability formula, we get

$$P(16 \text{ right}) = {}_nC_x \cdot p^x \cdot q^{n-x}$$

$$= {}_{20}C_{16} \cdot \left(\frac{1}{2}\right)^{16} \cdot \left(\frac{1}{2}\right)^{20-16}$$

$$= \frac{20!}{(20-16)!\,16!} \cdot \left(\frac{1}{2}\right)^{16} \cdot \left(\frac{1}{2}\right)^4$$

$$= 4{,}845 \cdot \frac{1}{1{,}048{,}576} \approx 0.0046$$

In short, your chances are not good.

> ### *Math Note*
>
> Notice that because there are 20 trials in Example 2, it would be cumbersome (to say the very least!) to use a tree diagram to find the probability.

▼ Try This One 2

What is the probability of getting exactly 6 questions right when guessing on a 10 question true or false quiz?

EXAMPLE 3   Using the Binomial Probability Formula

A box contains three red balls and two yellow balls. Five balls are selected with each ball being replaced before the next ball is selected. Find the probability of getting

(a) Exactly two yellow balls
(b) Fewer than two yellow balls

SOLUTION

(a) Use the binomial probability formula with $n = 5$, $x = 2$, $p = \frac{2}{5}$, and $q = \frac{3}{5}$.

$$P(2 \text{ yellow}) = {}_5C_2 \left(\frac{2}{5}\right)^2 \left(\frac{3}{5}\right)^3$$

$$= \frac{5!}{(5-2)!2!} \cdot \frac{4}{25} \cdot \frac{27}{125}$$

$$= 0.3456$$

(b) Fewer than two yellow balls means 0 or 1 yellow ball, so we will find each probability and add the answers.

$$P(0 \text{ yellow}) = {}_5C_0 \left(\frac{2}{5}\right)^0 \left(\frac{3}{5}\right)^5$$

$$= \frac{5!}{(5-0)!0!}(1)\left(\frac{243}{3,125}\right)$$

$$= 0.07776$$

$$P(1 \text{ yellow}) = {}_5C_1 \left(\frac{2}{5}\right)^1 \left(\frac{3}{5}\right)^4$$

$$= \frac{5!}{(5-1)!1!}\left(\frac{2}{5}\right)\left(\frac{81}{625}\right)$$

$$= 0.2592$$

$$P(0 \text{ or } 1 \text{ yellow}) = 0.07776 + 0.2592 = 0.33696$$

▼ Try This One 3

For the experiment in Example 3, find the probability of getting

(a) Exactly one red ball
(b) More than three red balls

When several subjects are selected without replacement from a large group of subjects, theoretically the selections are not independent and the binary probability formula doesn't apply. However, since the individual probabilities of a subject selected change only slightly, binomial probabilities can be used. This is shown in the next example.

EXAMPLE 4 Using the Binary Probability Formula with a Large Sample

Forty-two percent of individuals surveyed said that a man should always pay for the first date. If 10 people are randomly selected, find the probability that 3 randomly selected people will agree that a man should pay.

SOLUTION

Since the population is large, the binomial distribution can be used even though there's no replacement. In this case, $n = 10$, $x = 3$, $n - x = 7$, $p = 0.42$ and $q = 1 - 0.42 = 0.58$.

$$P(x) = {}_nC_x \cdot p^x \cdot q^{n-x}$$

$$P(3 \text{ people agree}) = {}_{10}C_3(0.42)^3(0.58)^7$$

$$= \frac{10!}{(10-7)!3!}(0.42)^3(0.58)^7$$

$$\approx 120(0.074)(0.022)$$

$$\approx 0.196$$

▼ **Try This One 4**

☑ 2. Compute probabilities of outcomes in a binomial experiment.

In a large community, it was determined that 44% of the residents use the public library at least once a year. If 10 people are selected, find the probability that exactly 2 people have used the library during the last year.

To describe all of the outcomes in a probability experiment, we can build a *probability distribution.*

A **probability distribution** consists of a list of all outcomes and the corresponding probabilities for a probability experiment.

EXAMPLE 5   Constructing a Probability Distribution

Figure 11-10

Construct a probability distribution for the possible number of tails when you flip two coins.

SOLUTION

When two coins are tossed, the outcomes can be shown using a tree diagram. See Figure 11-10.

The sample space is {HH, HT, TH, TT}. Each outcome has a probability of $\frac{1}{4}$. Notice that the outcome "No tails" is HH, and $P(HH) = \frac{1}{4}$. The outcome of one tail consists of HT and TH, and $P(HT, TH) = \frac{1}{4} + \frac{1}{4} = \frac{1}{2}$. The outcome of two tails is TT and $P(TT) = \frac{1}{4}$. Now a probability distribution can be constructed by considering the outcomes as the number of tails. The probability distribution is

Math Note

In Example 5, the number of trials was small enough that a tree diagram was more efficient than using the binomial probability formula three times.

Number of tails, x	0	1	2
Probability, $P(x)$	$\frac{1}{4}$	$\frac{1}{2}$	$\frac{1}{4}$

▼ **Try This One 5**

☑ 3. Construct a probability distribution.

Three cards are numbered 1, 2, 3 and placed into a bag. Another bag is set up the same way, then one card is drawn from each bag and the numbers are added. Find all possible totals, and construct a probability distribution for the experiment.

Answers to Try This One

1 (a) Yes   (b) No   (c) Yes   (d) Yes

2 $\frac{105}{512} \approx 0.205$

3 (a) 0.0768 (b) 0.33696

4 ≈ 0.084

5

Total	2	3	4	5	6
Probability	$\frac{1}{9}$	$\frac{2}{9}$	$\frac{1}{3}$	$\frac{2}{9}$	$\frac{1}{9}$

EXERCISE SET 11-9

Writing Exercises

1. What are the four requirements for a probability experiment to be a binomial experiment?
2. Give a brief description of how an experiment with several outcomes can be reduced to one with two outcomes.
3. What is a probability distribution?
4. In a binomial experiment, given the probability of any trial being a success, explain how to find the probability of a failure.

Computational Exercises

Find the probability of each using the binary probability formula.

5. $n = 3, p = 0.40, x = 2$
6. $n = 5, p = 0.80, x = 3$
7. $n = 10, p = 0.66, x = 4$
8. $n = 5, p = 0.20, x = 8$

9. $n = 20, p = 0.93, x = 12$
10. $n = 13, p = 0.16, x = 7$
11. $n = 9, p = 0.33, x = 5$
12. $n = 6, p = 0.58, x = 2$

13. $n = 4, p = 0.72, x = 0$
14. $n = 7, p = 0.25, x = 1$

Real-World Applications

15. During a game of Yahtzee, a player needs three sixes. She rolls the same die three times. What is the probability she got three sixes?

16. A cooler held three energy drinks. One was a Monster, another was a Red Bull, and the third was Atomic X. Simon selects an energy drink at random, puts it back, then selects another, puts it back and then selects a third drink. Find the probability that

    (a) No Red Bull drinks are selected.
    (b) Exactly one Atomic X drink is selected.
    (c) Exactly three Monster drinks are selected.

17. Of all identity thefts, 27% are solved in 1 day or less. If 10 cases are selected, find the probability that exactly 5 are solved in 1 day or less.

18. Of all people who do banking, 16% prefer to use ATMs. Of 20 people who are banking customers, find the probability that exactly 4 prefer to use the ATM.

19. According to the Bureau of Labor Statistics, among married-couple families where both the husband and wife have earnings, 26% of wives earned more than their husbands. If 18 wives are selected, find the probability that exactly 6 of them earn more than their husbands.

20. It is reported that 41% of people surveyed said that they eat meals while driving. If 12 drivers are selected, find the probability that exactly 6 will say that they eat meals while driving.

21. An instructor gives a 10-question true-false exam. If a student does not study and guesses, find the probability of getting exactly five correct answers.

22. A multiple-choice quiz consists of five questions. Each question has four responses, and only one of the answers is correct. Find the probability of guessing and getting exactly three correct answers.

23. Approximately 45% of people who eat at fast food places choose McDonald's. If 10 randomly selected people are surveyed, find the probability that 5 selected McDonald's.

24. About 30% of people who listen to commercial radio change the station in 1 to 2 minutes after the commercials begin. If six people are randomly selected, find the probability that two will change the station within 1 to 2 minutes after the commercials begin.

25. A survey shows that 65% of workers ages 42 to 60 would select excellent retirement benefits over a high salary when seeking a job. If 15 people are randomly selected, find the probability that 9 would select excellent benefits over a high salary.

26. About 22% of people selected Yahoo for instant messaging services during a selected year. If six randomly selected people are asked what instant messaging service they use, find the probability that one will say that he or she uses Yahoo. (Source: Nielson/net Ratings.)

27. A survey done by Zoomerang found that 30% of the people who were planning to remodel were planning to remodel the family room or den. If 12 people planning to remodel are selected, find the probability that 5 are planning to remodel the family room or den.

28. Approximately 20% of all college students in the United States do not have health insurance. If 10 college students are randomly selected in the United States, find the probability that 3 will not have health insurance.

29. A survey found that 55% of people said that a diet was harder to stick to than a budget. (Source: Kelton Research for Medifast.) If 20 people are randomly selected, find the probability that 10 will say that a diet is harder to stick to than a budget.

30. A survey done by Harris found that 40% of the people surveyed said that their children will have between $5,001 and $20,000 in debt when they graduate from college. If 25 people are selected, find the probability that 14 will say that their children will have a debt between $5,001 and $20,000 when they graduate from college.

31. A survey done by Harris International QUICK-QUERY found the 10% of women had a fear of flying. If 50 women are selected, find the probability that 6 will have a fear of flying.

32. In a Harris survey, 40% of the people surveyed said that they received error messages from doing online transactions. If 18 people are randomly selected, find the probability that 5 or 6 people would have received error messages while doing online transactions.

33. A survey found that 33% of people earning between $30,000 and $75,000 said that they were very happy. If 6 people are selected at random, find the probability that at most 2 people who earn between $30,000 and $75,000 would consider themselves very happy.

34. In a recent survey, 2% of the people selected stated that they would keep their current job if they won a multi-million-dollar lottery. If 20 people are selected, find the probability that 3, 4, or 5 of them would keep their job.

Critical Thinking

35. Using coins, cards, colored balls, etc., design a binomial experiment.

CHAPTER **11** **Summary**

Section	Important Terms	Important Ideas
11-1	Fundamental counting principle Factorial notation Permutation Permutation rule Tree diagram	**In order** to determine the total number of outcomes for a sequence of events, the fundamental counting rule or the permutation rule can be used. When the order or arrangement of the objects in a sequence of events is important, then the result is called a permutation of the objects.
11-2	Combination Combination rule	**When the** order of the objects is not important, then the result is called a combination.
11-3	Probability experiment Outcome Sample space Event Classical probability Empirical probability Observed frequency	**Flipping coins,** drawing cards from a deck, and rolling a die are examples of probability experiments. The set of all possible outcomes of a probability experiment is called a sample space. The two types of probability are classical and empirical. Classical probability uses sample spaces. Empirical probability uses frequency distributions and is based on observation. Probability is a number that represents how likely it is that something will occur. Probability can be zero, one, or any number in between. When the probability of an event is close to zero, the event is highly unlikely to occur. When the probability of an event is near one, the event is almost certain to occur.
11-4		**When sample** spaces are difficult to identify, it is often helpful to use tree diagrams or tables to identify all possible outcomes for a probability experiment.
11-5		**Probabilities** of events can be found by using the fundamental counting principle, the permutation rule, or the combination rule, depending on the situation.
11-6	Odds Expectation (expected value)	**In order** to determine payoffs, gambling establishments give odds. There are two ways to compute odds for a game of chance. They are "odds in favor of an event" and "odds against the event." Another concept related to probability and odds is the concept of expectation or expected value. Expected value is used to determine what happens over the long run. It is found by multiplying the outcomes of a probability experiment by their corresponding probabilities and then finding the sum of the products.
11-7	Mutually exclusive events Addition rules	**Two events** are said to be mutually exclusive if they cannot occur at the same time. To find the probability of one event or another event occurring, one of two addition rules can be used, depending on whether or not the events are mutually exclusive.

11-8	Multiplication rules Independent events Dependent events Conditional probability	**Events can** be classified as independent or dependent. Events are said to be independent if the occurrence of the first event does not affect the probability of the occurrence of the next event. If the probability of the second event occurring is changed by the occurrence of the first event, then the events are dependent. To find the probability of one event and another event occurring, one of the two multiplication rules can be used, depending on whether the two events are independent or dependent. If the probability of an event B occurring is affected by an event A occurring, then we say that a condition has been imposed on the event and the probability of event B occurring given that A has occurred is called a conditional probability.
11-9	Binomial experiment Probability distribution	**Many probability** experiments have two outcomes or can be reduced to two outcomes. If the trials are independent, fixed in number, and have the same probability of a success, then the experiment can be considered a binomial experiment. These problems can be solved using the binomial probability formula. For some probability experiments, a probability distribution can be constructed, listing all outcomes with the corresponding probabilities.

MATH IN Gambling REVISITED

1. Using the table for rolling two dice on page 601, the probability of rolling 2, 3, 11, or 12 is $\frac{1}{6}$, meaning the probability of losing is $\frac{5}{6}$. So the two outcomes are $+\$4$ with probability $\frac{1}{6}$, and $-\$1$ with probability $\frac{5}{6}$. The expected value of each trial is then

$$+4 \cdot \frac{1}{6} + (-1) \cdot \frac{5}{6} = -\frac{1}{6}$$

In 100 trials, you would be expected to lose $100\left(\frac{1}{6}\right)$, or $16.67.

2. The probability of winning $35 is $\frac{1}{38}$, and the probability of losing $1 is $\frac{37}{38}$. The expected value of each spin is

$$+35 \cdot \frac{1}{38} + (-1) \cdot \frac{37}{38} = -\frac{2}{38} = -\frac{1}{19}$$

In 100 trials, you would expect to lose $100\left(\frac{1}{19}\right)$, or $5.26.

3. Using the same idea as scenarios 1 and 2, the expected value of each ticket is

$$+20,000,000 \cdot \frac{1}{175,711,536} + (-1) \cdot \frac{175,711,535}{175,711,536}$$
$$\approx -\$0.8862$$

Buying 100 tickets, you would be expected to lose $100(-0.8862)$, or $88.62.

4. You would win $1 with probability $\frac{1}{2}$, and lose $1 with probability $\frac{1}{2}$, so the expected value of each flip is

$$1 \cdot \frac{1}{2} + (-1) \cdot \frac{1}{2} = 0$$

In 100 flips you would be expected to break even.

The best, by far is flipping a coin, followed by roulette, the church fair dice game, and, bringing up the rear by quite a bit, the multistate lottery. Notice that under the best of circumstances, you are likely to break even!

Review Exercises

Section 11-1

1. Compute $\frac{14!}{11!}$.
2. Compute $_{12}P_6$.
3. An automobile license plate consists of three letters followed by four digits. How many different plates can be made if repetitions are allowed? If repetitions are allowed in the letters but not in the digits?
4. How many different arrangements of the letters in the word *bread* are there?
5. How many different arrangements of the letters in the word *cheese* are there?
6. How many different three-digit odd numbers use only the digits 0, 1, 2, 3, 4?

Section 11-2

7. Compute $_9C_6$.
8. Find both the number of combinations and the number of permutations of 10 objects taken 4 at a time.
9. Describe the difference between combinations and permutations.
10. How many different three-digit combinations can be made by using the numbers 1, 3, 5, 7, and 9 without repetitions if the "right" combination can open a safe? Does a combination lock really use combinations?
11. How many two-card pairs (i.e., the same rank) are there in a standard deck?
12. How many ways can five different television programs be selected from 12 programs?
13. A quiz consists of six multiple-choice questions. Each question has three possible answer choices. How many different answer keys can be made?
14. How many different ways can a buyer select four television models from a possible choice of six models?

Section 11-3

15. Which of the following numbers could represent a probability?
    - (a) $\frac{3}{2}$
    - (b) $\frac{2}{3}$
    - (c) 0.1
    - (d) $-\frac{1}{2}$
    - (e) 80%

16. When a die is rolled, find the probability of getting
    - (a) A 5. (b) A 6. (c) A number less than 5.

17. When a card is drawn from a deck, find the probability of getting
    - (a) A heart.
    - (b) A 7 and a club.
    - (c) A 7 or a club.
    - (d) A jack.
    - (e) A black card.

18. In a survey conducted at the food court in the local mall, 20 people preferred Panda Express, 16 preferred Sbarro Pizza, and 9 preferred Subway for lunch. If a person is selected at random, find the probability that he or she prefers Sbarro Pizza.

19. If a die is rolled one time, find these probabilities:
    - (a) Getting a 7
    - (b) Getting an odd number
    - (c) Getting a number less than 3

20. In a recent survey in a college dorm that has 1,500 rooms, 850 have an Xbox 360. If a room in this dorm is randomly selected, find the probability that it has an Xbox 360.

21. During a Midnight Madness sale at Old Navy, 16 white cargo pants, 3 khaki cargo pants, 9 tan cargo pants, and 7 black cargo pants were sold. If a customer who made a purchase during the sale is selected at random, find the probability that he or she bought
    - (a) A pair of tan cargo pants.
    - (b) A pair of black cargo pants or a pair of white cargo pants.
    - (c) A pair of khaki, tan, or black cargo pants.
    - (d) A pair of cargo pants that was not white.

22. In a survey of college students who reported they used a search engine that day, 16 reported they used Google, 4 used MSN, 3 used Yahoo! Search, and 7 used Ask Jeeves. If a student from the survey is selected at random and the student used one search engine that day, find the probability he or she used
    - (a) Yahoo! Search.
    - (b) MSN or Ask Jeeves.
    - (c) Google or Yahoo! Search or Ask Jeeves.
    - (d) A search engine that was not MSN.

23. When two dice are rolled, find the probability of getting
    - (a) A sum of 5 or 6.
    - (b) A sum greater than 9.
    - (c) A sum less than 4 or greater than 9.
    - (d) A sum that is divisible by 4.
    - (e) A sum of 14.
    - (f) A sum less than 13.

24. Two dice are rolled. Find the probability of getting a sum of 8 if the number on one die is a 5.

Section 11-4

25. A person rolls an eight-sided die and then flips a coin. Draw a tree diagram and find the sample space.

26. A student can select one of three courses at 8:00 A.M.: English, mathematics, or chemistry. The student can select either psychology or sociology at 11:00 A.M. Finally, the student can select either world history or economics at 1:00 P.M. (a) Draw a tree diagram and find all the different ways the student can make a schedule. (b) Repeat part (a), but include the condition that the student will take classes only at 8 A.M. and 11 A.M. if his first class is chemistry.

27. As an experiment in probability, a two-question multiple choice quiz is given at the beginning of class, but the answers are all written in Hebrew, which none of the students can read. This forces everyone to guess. Each question has choices A, B, C, D, and E. Construct a table that displays the sample space, then use the table to find the probability that both questions in a randomly selected quiz were answered with D or E (either D-E, or E-D).

Section 11-5

28. A card is selected from a deck. Find the probability that it is a diamond given that it is a red card.

29. A person has six bond accounts, three stock accounts, and two mutual fund accounts. If three investments are selected at random, find the probability that one of each type of account is selected.

30. A newspaper advertises five different movies, three plays, and two baseball games. If a couple selects three activities at random, find the probability they will attend two plays and one movie.

31. In putting together the music lineup for an outdoor spring festival, Fast Eddie can choose from 4 student bands and 12 nonstudent bands. There are five time slots for bands; the first at 3 P.M., the others on the hour until 7 P.M. If Eddie chooses the bands randomly, find the probability that no student bands will be picked.

Section 11-6

32. Find the odds for an event E when $P(E) = \frac{1}{4}$.
33. Find the odds against an event E when $P(E) = \frac{5}{6}$.
34. Find the probability of an event when the odds for the event are 6:4.
35. The table lists five outcomes for a probability experiment with the corresponding probabilities. Find the expected value.

Outcome	5	10	15	20	25
Probability	0.5	0.2	0.1	0.1	0.1

36. Ishi has a penny, a nickel, a dime, a quarter, and a half-dollar in her wallet. One falls out onto the counter as she is paying for gas. Find the expected value of the event.

37. A person selects a card from a deck. If it is a red card, he wins $1. If it is a black card between and including 2 and 10, he wins $5. If it is a black face card, he wins $10, and if it is a black ace, he wins $100. Find the expectation of the game.

Section 11-7

In Exercises 38–40, decide if the two events are mutually exclusive.

38. You meet someone while out; she gives you her phone number or her email address.
39. You complete a course and either pass or fail.
40. You spend a weekend in Las Vegas; you either win money, lose money, or break even.
41. If one of the 50 states is selected at random to be the site of a new nuclear power plant,

   (a) Find the probability that the state either borders Canada or Mexico.
   (b) Find the probability that the state begins with either A or ends with S.

42. During Halloween, Seth collected six Snickers bars, three Twix bars, two packages of M&M's, and two boxes of Nerds while trick-or-treating in the dorm. If one candy is selected from his candy stash, find the probability of getting a package of M&M's or a Twix bar.

Section 11-8

In Exercises 43–46, decide if the two events are independent.

43. Missing 3 straight days of class and failing the next test.
44. Missing 3 straight days of class and getting overloaded with spam e-mails.
45. Drawing an ace from a standard deck, then drawing a second ace.
46. Drawing an ace from a standard deck, then replacing that card, shuffling, and drawing another ace.
47. In a family of three children, find the probability that all the children will be girls if it is known that at least one of the children is a girl.
48. A Gallup Poll found that 78% of Americans worry about the quality and healthfulness of their diet. If five people are selected at random, find the probability that all five worry about the quality and healthfulness of their diet.

Source: *The Book of Odds,* Michael D. Shook and Robert C. Shook (New York: Penguin Putnam, Inc., 1991), p. 33.

49. Twenty-five percent of the engineering graduates of a university received a starting salary of $50,000 or more. If three of the graduates are selected at random, find the probability that all have a starting salary of $50,000 or more.

50. Three cards are drawn from an ordinary deck *without* replacement. Find the probability of getting

    (a) All black cards.
    (b) All spades.
    (c) All queens.

51. A coin is tossed and a card is drawn from a deck. Find the probability of getting

    (a) A head and a 6.
    (b) A tail and a red card.
    (c) A head and a club.

52. The data in the table below are based on a nationwide exit poll taken on November 4, 2008. The numbers are based on an average sample of 1,000 voters. The rows represent the political affiliation of voters, and the columns represent how they voted.

	Obama	McCain	Other
Democrat	347	39	4
Republican	32	285	3
Independent	151	128	11

(a) Find the probability that a randomly selected person voted for Obama given that he or she was not Republican.
(b) Find the probability that a randomly selected person voted for either Obama or McCain given that he or she was Independent.
(c) Find the probability that a randomly selected person was a Republican given that he or she voted for McCain.

Section 11-9

53. Use the binomial probability formula to find the probability of five successes in six trials when the probability of success on each trial is 1/3.

54. A survey found that 24% of families eat at home as a family five times a week. If 10 families are selected, find the probability that exactly 3 will say that they eat at home as a family five times a week.

55. According to a survey, 45% of teenagers said that they have seen passengers in an automobile encouraging the driver to speed. If 16 teens are selected, find the probability that exactly 6 will say that they have seen passengers encouraging the driver to speed.

56. Construct a probability distribution for the possible number of heads when tossing a coin three times.

Chapter Test

In Exercises 1–4, compute the requested value.

1. $\frac{20!}{18!}$
2. $_7C_5$
3. $_{12}P_5$
4. The probability of 8 successes in 10 trials when the probability of success on each trial is $\frac{1}{4}$.
5. If someone saw the title of Chapter 11 in this book and asked you "What is probability?" what would you say?
6. Describe a situation where combinations would be used to count possibilities and one where permutations would be used.
7. One company's ID cards consist of five letters followed by two digits. How many cards can be made if repetitions are allowed? If repetitions are not allowed?
8. A physics test consists of 25 true-false questions. How many different possible answer keys can be made?
9. At Blockbuster Video, there are seven DVDs in a box. How many different ways can four DVDs be selected?

10. How many ways can five sopranos and four altos be chosen for the university chorus from seven sopranos and nine altos?
11. Eight students at graduation are in line to take their seats. How many ways can they be seated in a row?
12. A soda machine servicer must restock and collect money from 15 machines, each one at a different location. How many ways can she select four machines to service in one day?
13. How many different ways can three cell phone covers be drawn from a box containing four differently colored cell phone covers, if

    (a) Each cell phone cover is replaced after it has been drawn?
    (b) There is no replacement?

14. If a man can wear a shirt or a sweater and a pair of dress slacks or a pair of jeans, how many different outfits can he wear?
15. When a card is drawn from an ordinary deck, find the probability of getting

    (a) A jack.   (b) A 4.

(c) A card less than 6 (an ace is considered above 6).

16. When a card is drawn from a deck, find the probability of getting

   (a) A diamond.
   (b) A 5 or a heart.
   (c) A 5 and a heart.
   (d) A king.
   (e) A red card.

17. At a sporting goods store, 12 people purchased blue rollerblades, 8 purchased green rollerblades, 4 purchased gray rollerblades, and 7 bought black rollerblades. If a customer is selected at random, find the probability he or she purchased

   (a) A pair of blue rollerblades.
   (b) A pair of green or gray rollerblades.
   (c) A pair of green or black or blue rollerblades.
   (d) A pair of rollerblades that was not black.

18. When two dice are rolled, find the probability of getting

   (a) A sum of 6 or 7.
   (b) A sum greater than 3 or greater than 8.
   (c) A sum less than 3 or greater than 8.
   (d) A sum that is divisible by 3.
   (e) A sum of 16.
   (f) A sum less than 11.

19. There are six cards numbered 1, 2, 3, 4, 5, and 6. A person flips a coin. If it lands heads up, he will select a card with an odd number. If it lands tails up, he will select a card with an even number. Draw a tree diagram and find the sample space.

20. Of the physics graduates of a university, 30% received a starting salary of $60,000 or more. If five of the graduates are selected at random, find the probability that all had a starting salary of $60,000 or more.

21. Five cards are drawn from an ordinary deck *without* replacement. Find the probability of getting

   (a) All red cards.
   (b) All diamonds.
   (c) All aces.

22. Four coins are tossed. Find the probability of getting four heads if it is known that two of the four coins landed heads up.

23. A card is drawn from a deck. Find the probability of getting a club if it is known that the card selected was a black card.

24. A die is rolled. Find the probability of getting a four if it is known that the result of the roll was an even number.

25. A coin is tossed and a die is rolled. Find the probability of getting a head on the coin if it is known that the number on the die is even.

26. Nurses at one hospital can be classified according to gender (male, female), income (low, medium, high), and rank (staff nurse, charge nurse, head nurse). Draw a tree diagram and show all possible outcomes.

27. The National Gaming Association can select one of four cities for its Pac Man tournament next year. The cities are Miami, San Francisco, Philadelphia, and Houston. The following year, it can hold the tournament in Chicago or Indianapolis. How many different possibilities are there for the next 2 years? Draw a tree diagram and show all possibilities.

28. Find the odds in favor of an event E when $P(E) = \frac{3}{8}$.

29. Find the odds against an event E when $P(E) = \frac{4}{9}$.

30. Find the probability of an event when the odds against the event are 3:7.

31. There are six cards placed face down in a box. Each card has a number written on it. One is a 4, one is a 5, one is a 2, one is a 10, one is a 3, and one is a 7. A person selects a card. Find the expected value of the draw.

32. A person selects a card from an ordinary deck of cards. If it is a black card, she wins $2. If it is a red card between or including 3 and 7, she wins $10. If it is a red face card, she wins $25, and if it is a black jack, she wins an additional $100. If it is any other card, she wins nothing. Find the expectation of the game.

33. In a soda machine in the student union, there are five Diet Cokes, four Mountain Dews, and two Dr. Peppers. If a person selects three sodas at random, find the probability that the selection will include one Diet Coke, one Mountain Dew, and one Dr. Pepper.

34. At Sally's freshman orientation, there were six computer science majors, four electrical engineering majors, and three architecture majors in her group. If four students are selected at random to receive a free tote bag with the school's logo, find the probability that the selection will include two computer science majors, one electrical engineering major, and one architecture major.

35. The results of a survey revealed that 30% of the people surveyed said that they would buy home electronic equipment at post-holiday sales. If 20 people are selected, find the probability that exactly 8 will purchase home electronic equipment after the holidays.

Projects

1. Make a set of three cards—one with the word "heads" on both sides, one with the word "tails" on both sides, and one with "heads" on one side and "tails" on the other side. With a partner, play the game described in Exercise 23 of Section 11-6 (page 616) 100 times and record how many times your partner wins. (*Note:* Do not change options during the 100 trials.)

   (a) Do you think the game is fair (i.e., does one person win approximately 50% of the time)?

   (b) If you think the game is unfair, explain what the probabilities might be and why.

2. Take a coin and tape a small weight (e.g., part of a paper clip) to one side. Flip the coin 100 times and record the results. Do you think you have changed the probabilities of the results of flipping the coin?

3. This game is called "Diet Fractions." Roll two dice and use the numbers to make a fraction less than or equal to one. Player A wins if the fraction cannot be reduced; otherwise, player B wins.

   (a) Play the game 100 times and record the results.

   (b) Decide if the game is fair or not. Explain why or why not.

   (c) Using the sample space for two dice, compute the probabilities of player A winning and player B winning. Do these agree with the results obtained in part a?

   Source: George W. Bright, John G. Harvey, and Margariete Montaque Wheeler, "Fair Games, Unfair Games." Chapter 8, *Teaching Statistics and Probability. NCTM 1981 Yearbook.* Reston, Virginia: The National Council of Teachers of Mathematics, Inc., 1981, p. 49. Used with permission.

4. Remember looking through cereal boxes for toys when you were a kid? It always seemed like you didn't get the exact one you wanted. Let's say that there was a certain toy you wanted, and five others that you could take or leave, all packed one per box at random. About how may boxes would you expect to have to buy to get the toy you wanted? Of course, you might have gotten it in the first box. Or you might have exhausted mom and dad's savings without ever getting it. These are the extremes.

   (a) You can simulate this experience using a single die, and rolling until a particular number of your choice comes up. Keep track of how many rolls it took, then repeat 99 more times, and find the average number of times it took.

   (b) If there were 10 different choices, you could simulate that by using the ace through 10 of a certain suit. Pick a certain card, shuffle the deck, and start dealing out the cards, keeping track of how many it takes to get the one you picked. Repeat 99 times and find the average.

   (c) Summarize your findings for both experiments.

   (d) Call getting the number or card you wanted a value of 2, and not getting it a value of 1. Then find the probability of each on any given roll or draw, and find the expected value for each experiment. How does it compare to the experimental results?

CHAPTER 12

Statistics

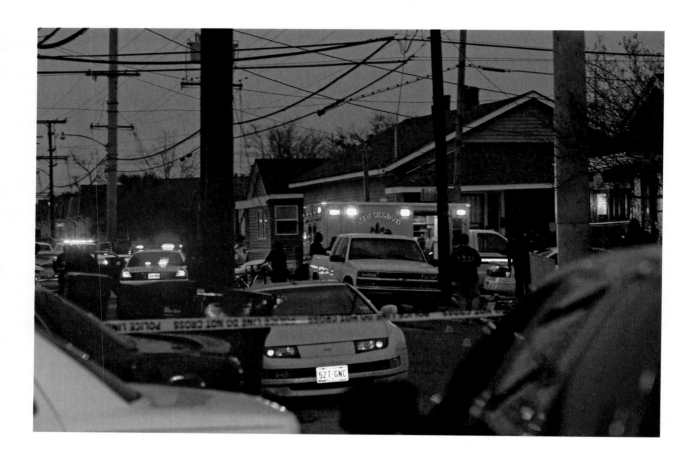

Outline

12-1 Gathering and Organizing Data
12-2 Picturing Data
12-3 Measures of Average
12-4 Measures of Variation
12-5 Measures of Position
12-6 The Normal Distribution

12-7 Applications of the Normal Distribution
12-8 Correlation and Regression Analysis
Summary

MATH IN Sociology

Broadly defined, sociology is the study of human behavior within society. One important branch is criminology. This is not about investigating crimes, but rather studying patterns of criminal behavior and their effect on society. One of the main tools used by sociologists is statistics. This important area of math allows researchers to study patterns of behavior objectively, by analyzing information gathered from a mathematical perspective, not a subjective one.

It all begins with the gathering of data. Data are measurements or observations that are gathered for a study of some sort. Let's look at an example. There is an old adage in police work that violent crime increases with the temperature. A statement like "My cousin Jed is a cop, and he told me that there are more violent crimes during the summer" is not evidence, nor is it data. It's the subjective opinion of one individual. In order to study whether this phenomenon is legitimate, we would need to gather information about the number of violent crimes at different times during the year, as well as temperature information, and study those numbers objectively to see if there appears to be a connection. This is one of the most important topics in this chapter.

Data on its own isn't good for very much unless we develop methods for organizing, studying, and displaying that data. These are the methods that make up the bulk of this chapter. After discussing methods of gathering data, we will learn effective methods for organizing and displaying data so that it can be presented in a meaningful, understandable way. We will then turn our attention to techniques of analyzing data that will help us to unlock the secrets of what sets of data may be trying to tell us.

As for math in sociology, in an attempt to study the phenomena of violent crime and temperature increase, the data below were gathered. The table shows the number of homicides committed in each month of 2008 in Columbus, Ohio, along with the average high temperature for each of those months.

Month	Avg. high temp.	Homicides
1	36	6
2	40	8
3	51	5
4	63	7
5	73	7
6	82	12
7	85	9
8	84	12
9	77	11
10	66	15
11	53	9
12	41	7

After you've finished this chapter, you should be able to answer the following questions.

1. Based on a graph of the data called a scatter plot, does there appear to be a relationship between temperature and homicide rate?

2. Can you conclude, using a measure called the correlation coefficient, with 95% certainty that there is in fact a relationship between the data sets? What about with 99% certainty?

3. Do the results indicate that warmer temperatures cause people to behave in a more violent manner?

For answers, see Math in Sociology Revisited on page 711

Section 12-1 Gathering and Organizing Data

LEARNING OBJECTIVES

☐ 1. Define data and statistics.

☐ 2. Explain the difference between a population and a sample.

☐ 3. Describe four basic methods of sampling.

☐ 4. Construct a frequency distribution for a data set.

☐ 5. Draw a stem and leaf plot for a data set.

One of the big issues being discussed over the last 10 years or so in higher education is grade inflation—the perception that college students in general are getting much higher grades than they used to. But perception and reality are often two different things, so how could we decide if this is actually taking place? And if so, what are some possible reasons? Are students just getting smarter? Are professors lowering their standards?

In order to examine questions like this, it would be very valuable to gather some *data*.

Data are measurements or observations that are gathered for an event under study.

Gathering data plays an important role in many different areas. In college sports, recruiters look at past performance to help them decide which high school players will be stars in college. In public health, administrators keep track of the number of residents in a certain area who contract a new strain of the flu. In education, researchers might try to determine if a new method of teaching is an improvement over traditional methods. Media outlets report the results of Nielsen, Harris, and Gallup polls. All of these studies begin with collecting data.

Once data have been collected, in order to get anything of value from it, the data need to be organized, summarized, and presented in a form that allows observers to draw conclusions. This is what the study of statistics is all about:

☑ 1. Define data and statistics.

Statistics is the branch of mathematics that involves collecting, organizing, summarizing, and presenting data and drawing general conclusions from that data.

Populations and Samples

In the case of grade inflation, relevant data might be average grade point averages for students in several different years. Table 12-1 shows some GPA data from the website Gradeinflation.com.

TABLE 12-1   **Average GPAs for the Years 1991–1992 to 2006–2007 at Some American Universities**

School Year	Average undergraduate GPA
1991–1992	2.93
1996–1997	2.99
2001–2002	3.07
2006–2007	3.11

The numbers certainly appear to indicate that grade inflation is real. But where did the data come from? Does this factor in *all* colleges, or just some?

When statistical studies are performed, we usually begin by identifying the *population* for the study.

A **population** consists of all subjects under study.

In our example, the population is all colleges in the United States. If you were interested in study habits of the students at your school, the population would be all of the students at the school. More often than not, it's not realistic to gather data from every member of a population. In that case, a smaller representative group of the population would be selected. This group is called a *sample*.

☑ 2. Explain the difference between a population and a sample.

A **sample** is a representative subgroup or subset of a population.

The GPA data in Table 12-1 were gathered from a sample of 70 schools. The reason the data are compelling is that the sample is *representative* of the population as a whole. The schools chosen vary in size, cost, and geographic location. Some are public, and some are private. In order to ensure that a sample is representative, researchers use a variety of methods. Four of these sampling methods are explained next.

Wildlife biologists capture and tag animals to study how they live in the wild. The population is all the animals of the species in this region. The tagged animals constitute the sample. If the sample is not representative of the species the data will be skewed, and possibly misleading.

Sampling Methods

We will study four basic sampling methods that can be used to obtain a representative sample: random, systematic, stratified, and cluster.

In order to obtain a **random sample,** each subject of the population must have an equal chance of being selected. The best way to obtain a random sample is to use a list of random numbers. Random numbers can be obtained from a table or from a computer or calculator. Subjects in the population are numbered, and then they are selected by using the corresponding random numbers.

Using a random number generator such as a calculator, computer, or table of random numbers is like selecting numbers out of a hat. The difference is that when random numbers are generated by a calculator, computer, or table, there is a better chance that every number has an equally likely chance of being selected. When numbers are placed in a hat and mixed, you can never be sure that they are thoroughly mixed so that each number has an equal chance of being chosen.

A **systematic sample** is taken by numbering each member of the population and then selecting every kth member, where k is a natural number. For example, the researcher from gradeinflation.com might have numbered all of the colleges in the country and chosen every tenth one. When using systematic sampling, it's important that the starting number is selected at random.

When a population is divided into groups where the members of each group have similar characteristics (like large public schools, large private schools, small public schools, and small private schools) and members from each group are chosen at random, the result is called a **stratified sample.** The grade inflation researcher might have decided to choose five schools from each of those groups. Since 20 is a relatively small sample, it's possible that 15 or more came from large public schools. This would jeopardize the study because it may be the case that grade inflation is more or less likely at large public schools than schools in the other categories. So the purpose of a stratified sample is to ensure that all groups will be properly represented.

When an existing group of subjects that represent the population is used for a sample, it is called a **cluster sample.** For example, an inspector may select at random one carton of calculators from a large shipment and examine each one to determine how many are defective. The group in this carton represents a cluster. In this case, the researcher assumes that the calculators in the carton represent the population of all calculators manufactured by the company.

Samples are used in the majority of statistical studies, and if they are selected properly, the results of a study can be generalized to the population.

EXAMPLE 1   Choosing a Sample

A student in an education class is given an assignment to find out how late typical students at his campus stay up to study. He decides to stop by the union before his 9 A.M. class and ask everyone sitting at a table how late they were up studying the night before.

(a) What method of sampling is he using?
(b) Do you think he's likely to get a representative sample?

SOLUTION

(a) Since he is choosing all students in a particular place at a particular time, he has chosen a cluster sample.
(b) The sample is unlikely to be representative. Since he's polling people early in the morning, those that tend to stay up very late studying are less likely to be included in the sample.

☑ 3. Describe four basic methods of sampling.

▼ Try This One 1

To study the number of credit hours taken by a typical student, Shawna asks the registrar to provide e-mail addresses for 10 freshmen, 10 sophomores, 10 juniors, and 10 seniors. From each group, she asks for one whose student ID ends in 0, one whose ends in 1, and so forth.

(a) What method of sampling did she use?
(b) Do you think the sample will be representative?

Descriptive and Inferential Statistics

There are two main branches of statistics: descriptive and inferential. Statistical techniques that are used to *describe* data are called **descriptive statistics.** For example, a researcher may wish to determine the average age of the full-time students enrolled in your college and the percentage who own automobiles.

Sidelight **MATH IN THE COURTROOM**

Mathematicians are often called on to testify in court, and often it's to interpret the statistical likelihood of some event. In one case in Los Angeles, a couple was convicted of robbery based almost entirely on statistics! There were witnesses who saw the robbers leaving the scene, but they could not positively identify the suspects: just certain characteristics, like race, hair color, facial hair, and type of vehicle. A mathematician calculated that there was just one chance in 12 million of a second couple with the exact characteristics as the suspects being in the same area at that time. Despite a lack of any hard evidence, the couple was convicted.

When the conviction was appealed, the appellate judge was somewhat less impressed by the statistical argument than the jury had been. The conviction was overturned based on faulty calculations and the lack of other evidence.

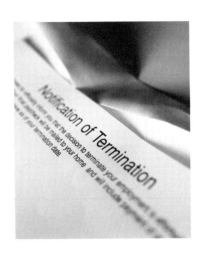

Statistical techniques used to make *inferences* are called **inferential statistics.** For example, every month the Bureau of Labor and Statistics estimates the number of people in the United States who are unemployed. Since it would be impossible to survey every adult resident of the United States, the Bureau selects a sample of adult individuals in the United States to see what percent are unemployed. In this case, the information obtained from a sample is used to estimate a population measure.

Another area of inferential statistics is called *hypothesis testing.* A researcher tries to test a hypothesis to see if there is enough evidence to support it. Here are some research questions that lend themselves to hypothesis testing:

Is one brand of aspirin better than another brand?
Does taking vitamin C prevent colds?
Are children more susceptible to ear infections than adults?

A third aspect of inferential statistics is determining whether or not a relationship exists between two or more variables. This area of statistics is called *correlation and regression;* for example:

Is caffeine related to heart trouble?
Is there a relationship between a person's age and his or her blood pressure?
Is these a connection between hours spent studying and grades on a final exam?

Frequency Distributions

The data collected for a statistical study are called **raw data.** In order to describe situations and draw conclusions, the researcher must organize the data in a meaningful way.

Two methods that we will use are *frequency distributions* and *stem and leaf plots.* There are two types of frequency distributions, the categorical frequency distribution and the grouped frequency distribution.

A categorical frequency distribution is used when the data are categorical rather than numerical. Example 2 shows how to construct a **categorical frequency distribution.**

EXAMPLE 2 Constructing a Frequency Distribution

Twenty-five volunteers for a medical research study were given a blood test to obtain their blood types. The data follow.

A	B	B	AB	O
O	O	B	AB	B
B	B	O	A	O
AB	A	O	B	A
A	O	O	O	AB

Construct a frequency distribution for the data.

SOLUTION

Step 1 Make a table as shown, with all categories represented.

Type	Tally	Frequency
A		
B		
O		
AB		

Step 2 Tally the data using the second column.

Step 3　Count the tallies and place the numbers in the third column. The completed frequency distribution is shown.

Type	Tally	Frequency
A	⳾	5
B	⳾ //	7
O	⳾ ////	9
AB	////	4

▼ Try This One 2

A health-food store recorded the type of vitamin pills 35 customers purchased during a 1-day sale. Construct a categorical frequency distribution for the data.

```
C   C   C   A   D   E   C
E   E   A   B   D   C   E
C   E   C   C   C   D   A
B   B   C   C   A   A   E
E   E   E   A   B   C   B
```

Another type of frequency distribution that can be constructed uses numerical data and is called a **grouped frequency distribution.** In a grouped frequency distribution, the numerical data are divided into classes. For example, if you gathered data on the weights of people in your class, there's a decent chance that no two people have the exact same weight. So it would be reasonable to group people into weight ranges, like 100–119 pounds, 120–139 pounds, and so forth. In the 100–119 pound class, we call 100 the lower limit and 119 the upper limit. When deciding on classes, here are some useful guidelines:

1. Try to keep the number of classes between 5 and 15.

2. Make sure the classes do not overlap.

3. Don't leave out any numbers between the lowest and highest, even if nothing falls into a particular class.

4. Make sure the range of numbers included in a class is the same for each one. (For example, don't have the first class go from 100–120 pounds and the second from 121–130 pounds.)

Example 3 demonstrates the steps for building a grouped frequency distribution.

EXAMPLE 3　Constructing a Frequency Distribution

These data represent the record high temperatures for each of the 50 states in degrees Fahrenheit. Construct a grouped frequency distribution for the data.

```
112   100   127   120   134   105   110   109   112   118
110   118   117   116   118   114   114   105   109   122
107   112   114   115   118   118   122   106   110   117
116   108   110   121   113   119   111   104   111   120
120   113   120   117   105   118   112   114   114   110
```

Source: *The World Almanac Book of Facts*

SOLUTION

Step 1 Subtract the lowest value from the highest value: $134 - 100 = 34$.

Step 2 If we use a range of 5 degrees, that will give us seven classes, since the entire range (34 degrees) divided by 5 is 6.8. This is certainly not the only choice for the number of classes: if we choose a range of 4 degrees, there will be 9 classes.

Step 3 Start with the lowest value and add 5 to get the lower class limits: 100, 105, 110, 115, 120, 125, 130, 135.

Step 4 Set up the classes by subtracting one from each lower class limit except the first lower class limit.

Step 5 Tally the data and record the frequencies as shown.

Class	Tally	Frequency
100–104	//	2
105–109	//// ///	8
110–114	//// //// //// ///	18
115–119	//// //// ///	13
120–124	//// //	7
125–129	/	1
130–134	/	1

☑ 4. Construct a frequency distribution for a data set.

▼ Try This One 3

In one math class, the data below represent the number of hours each student spends on homework in an average week. Construct a grouped frequency distribution for the data using six classes.

1	2	6	7	12	13	2	6	9	5
18	7	3	15	15	4	17	1	14	5
4	16	4	5	8	6	5	18	5	2
9	11	12	1	9	2	10	11	4	10
9	18	8	8	4	14	7	3	2	6

Stem and Leaf Plots

Another way to organize data is to use a **stem and leaf plot** (sometimes called a stem plot). Each data value or number is separated into two parts. For a two-digit number such as 53, the tens digit, 5, is called the *stem,* and the ones digit, 3, is called its *leaf.* For the number 72, the stem is 7, and the leaf is 2. For a three-digit number, say 138, the first two digits, 13, are used as the stem, and the third digit, 8, is used as the leaf. Example 4 shows how to construct a stem and leaf plot.

EXAMPLE 4 **Drawing a Stem and Leaf Plot**

The data below show the number of games won by the Chicago Cubs in each of the 21 seasons from 1988–2008, with the exception of 1994, which was a short season because of a player strike. Draw a stem and leaf plot for the data.

97	85	66	79	89	88	67	88	65	67	90	68
76	73	84	78	77	77	93	77				

SOLUTION

Notice that the first digit ranges from 6 to 9, so we set up a table with stems 6, 7, 8, 9:

Stems	Leaves
6	
7	
8	
9	

Now we go through the data one value at a time, putting the appropriate leaf next to the matching stem. For 97, we put a 7 under leaves, next to the stem 9 (shown in color below). For 85, we put a 5 under leaves, next to the stem 8, and so on, until all data values have been included.

The stem and leaf plot for number of wins by the Cubs is

Stems	Leaves
6	6 7 5 7 8
7	9 6 3 8 7 7 7
8	5 9 8 8 4
9	7 0 3

This is an efficient way of organizing the data. We can easily see that the most common class of wins is from 70–79, and the least common is 90–99. We can also see that 77 is the number of wins that occurred most often, three times.

☑ 5. Draw a stem and leaf plot for a data set.

Math Note

Remember, when drawing a stem and leaf plot with three-digit numbers, the first two digits are the stem. So for 119, the stem is 11 and the leaf is 9.

▼ **Try This One 4**

It's no secret that gas prices have fluctuated wildly in the last few years, but from 1980–1999, they were surprisingly stable. According to the Energy Information Administration, the data below represent the average price (in cents) per gallon of regular unleaded gas for those years. Draw a stem and leaf plot of the data.

| 119 | 131 | 122 | 113 | 112 | 86 | 90 | 90 | 100 | 115 |
| 114 | 113 | 111 | 111 | 115 | 123 | 123 | 123 | 106 | 117 |

Answers to Try This One

1 (a) Stratified sample
(b) The population is likely to be representative since the last digit of a student's ID number is likely to be completely random.

2

Type	Tally	Frequency
A	ⵜⵜⵜ /	6
B	ⵜⵜⵜ	5
C	ⵜⵜⵜ ⵜⵜⵜ //	12
D	///	3
E	ⵜⵜⵜ ////	9

3

Class	Tally	Frequency
1–3	卌 卌	10
4–6	卌 卌 ////	14
7–9	卌 卌	10
10–12	卌 /	6
13–15	卌	5
16–18	卌	5

4

8	6
9	0 0
10	0 6
11	9 3 2 5 4 3 1 1 5 7
12	2 3 3 3
13	1

EXERCISE SET 12-1

Writing Exercises

1. What are *data?*
2. Define *statistics.*
3. Explain the difference between a population and a sample.
4. How is a random sample selected?
5. How is a systematic sample selected?
6. How is a stratified sample selected?
7. How is a cluster sample selected?
8. What are the similarities between a grouped frequency distribution and a stem and leaf plot?

For Exercises 9–14, classify each sample as random, systematic, stratified, or cluster and explain your answer.

9. In a large school district, all teachers from two buildings are interviewed to determine whether they believe the students have less homework to do now than in previous years.

10. Every seventh customer entering a shopping mall is asked to select his or her favorite store.
11. Nursing supervisors are selected using random numbers in order to determine annual salaries.
12. Every hundredth hamburger manufactured is checked to determine its fat content.
13. Mail carriers of a large city are divided into four groups according to gender (male or female) and according to whether they walk or ride on their routes. Then 10 are selected from each group and interviewed to determine whether they have been bitten by a dog in the last year.
14. For the draft lottery that was conducted from 1969 to 1975, the days of the year were written on pieces of paper and put in plastic capsules. The capsules were then mixed in a barrel and drawn out one at a time, with the day recorded.

Real-World Applications

15. At a college financial aid office, students who applied for a scholarship were classified according to their class rank: Fr = freshman, So = sophomore, Jr = junior, Se = senior. Construct a frequency distribution for the data.

Fr	Fr	Fr	Fr	Fr
Jr	Fr	Fr	So	Fr
Fr	So	Jr	So	Fr
So	Fr	Fr	Fr	So
Se	Jr	Jr	So	Fr
Fr	Fr	Fr	Fr	So
Se	Se	Jr	Jr	Se
So	So	So	So	So

16. A questionnaire about how students primarily get news resulted in the following responses from 25 people. Construct a frequency distribution for the data. (I = Internet, N = newspaper, R = radio, T = TV.)

    T I N I I I N I R T N I
    I T R I I N I R T N I I

17. Twenty-five fans of reality TV were asked to rate four shows, and the data below reflect which one each rated highest. Construct a frequency distribution for the data. (S = *Survivor,* P = *Project Runway,* B = *Big Brother,* A = *The Amazing Race.*)

    S S B P P B S P A B A A S
    B A P B A S A P B B S A

18. The new rap artist, Funky Fido, has had some success, although not as much as he'd like. The number of downloads per week of his hit, "Bark Up My Tree," is listed below. Construct a frequency distribution for the data using six classes.

373	254	237	243	308	210	266	253	201	266
239	114	224	373	286	329	236	284	247	273
198	361	416	207	243	326	251	169	360	311
215	189	344	268	363	21	270	165	240	48
150	300	207	314	197	209	210	260	327	

19. The ages of the signers of the Declaration of Independence are shown here. (Age is approximate since only the birth year appeared in the source, and one has been omitted since his birth year is unknown.) Construct a frequency distribution for the data using seven classes.

41	54	47	40	39	35	50	37	49	42	70	32
44	52	39	50	40	30	34	69	39	45	33	52
44	62	60	27	42	34	50	42	52	38	36	45
35	43	48	46	31	27	55	63	46	33	60	62
35	46	45	34	53	50	50					

Source: *The Universal Almanac*

20. The percentage of people killed in car accidents who were not wearing seatbelts in 2006 is shown for 27 states. Construct a frequency distribution using five classes.

56.9	59.1	33.1	43.3	62.3	36.3	74.4	64.0	60.0
56.8	45.5	38.2	71.0	46.6	42.4	39.3	46.0	60.4
52.5	69.2	63.9	60.5	47.5	43.3	62.3	67.1	39.8

Source: *Statemaster.com*

21. The data (in cents) are the cigarette taxes per pack imposed by each state as of April 1, 2009. Construct a frequency distribution. Use 0–39, 40–79, 80–119, etc.

42.5	200	200	115	87	84	200	115	33.9	37
200	57	98	99.5	136	79	60	36	200	200
251	200	150.4	18	17	170	64	80	133	257.5
91	275	35	44	125	103	118	135	246	7
153	62	141	69.5	199	30	202.5	55	177	60

Source: *National Conference at State Legislatures*

22. The acreage (in thousands of acres) of the 39 U.S. National Parks is shown here. Construct a frequency distribution for the data using eight classes.

41	66	233	775	169
36	338	233	236	64
183	61	13	308	77
520	77	27	217	5
650	462	106	52	52
505	94	75	265	402
196	70	132	28	220
760	143	46	539	

Source: *The Universal Almanac*

23. The heights in feet above sea level of the major active volcanoes in Alaska are given here. Construct a frequency distribution for the data using 10 classes.

4,265	3,545	4,025	7,050	11,413
3,490	5,370	4,885	5,030	6,830
4,450	5,775	3,945	7,545	8,450
3,995	10,140	6,050	10,265	6,965
150	8,185	7,295	2,015	5,055
5,315	2,945	6,720	3,465	1,980
2,560	4,450	2,759	9,430	
7,985	7,540	3,540	11,070	
5,710	885	8,960	7,015	

Source: *The Universal Almanac*

24. During the 1998 baseball season, Mark McGwire and Sammy Sosa both broke Roger Maris's home run record of 61. The distances in feet for each home run follow. Construct a frequency distribution for each player using the same eight classes.

	McGwire				**Sosa**		
306	370	370	430	371	350	430	420
420	340	460	410	430	434	370	420
440	410	380	360	440	410	420	460
350	527	380	550	400	430	410	370
478	420	390	420	370	410	380	340
425	370	480	390	350	420	410	415
430	388	423	410	430	380	380	366
360	410	450	350	500	380	390	400
450	430	461	430	364	430	450	440
470	440	400	390	365	420	350	420
510	430	450	452	400	380	380	400
420	380	470	398	370	420	360	368
409	385	369	460	430	433	388	440
390	510	500	450	414	482	364	370
470	430	458	380	400	405	433	390
430	341	385	410	480	480	434	344
420	380	400	440	410	420		
377	370						

Source: *USA Today*

25. The data (in millions of dollars) are the values of the 32 National Football League franchises in 2009. Construct a frequency distribution for the data using seven classes.

937	1,178	872	1,064	1,076	941	1,116	1,612
861	1,035	929	1,040	1,016	888	876	1,010
994	839	1,125	1,044	1,170	865	885	1,324
1,061	1,015	1,053	1,538	914	917	1,023	1,062

26. Twenty-nine executives reported the number of telephone calls made during a randomly selected week as shown here. Construct a stem and leaf plot for the data and analyze the results.

22	14	12	9	54	12
16	12	14	49	10	14
8	21	37	28	36	22
9	33	58	31	41	19
3	18	25	28	52	

27. The National Insurance Crime Bureau reported that these data represent the number of registered

vehicles per car stolen for 35 selected cities in the United States. For example, in Miami, one automobile is stolen for every 38 registered vehicles in the city. Construct a stem and leaf plot for the data and analyze the distribution. (The data have been rounded to the nearest whole number.)

38	53	53	56	69	89	94
41	58	68	66	69	89	52
50	70	83	81	80	90	74
50	70	83	59	75	78	73
92	84	87	84	85	84	89

Source: *USA Today*

28. As an experiment in a botany class, 20 plants are placed in a greenhouse, and their growth in centimeters after 20 days is recorded, with the results shown below. Construct a stem and leaf plot for the data.

20	12	39	38
41	43	51	52
59	55	53	59
50	58	35	38
23	32	43	53

29. The data shown represent the percentage of unemployed males for a sample of countries of the world. Using whole numbers as stems and the decimals as leaves, construct a stem and leaf plot.

8.8	1.9	5.6	4.6	1.5
2.2	5.6	3.1	5.9	6.6
9.8	8.7	6.0	5.2	5.6
4.4	9.6	6.6	6.0	0.3
4.6	3.1	4.1	7.7	

Source: *The Time Almanac*

Critical Thinking

For Exercises 30–34, decide whether descriptive or inferential statistics is being used.

30. A recent study showed that eating garlic can lower blood pressure.
31. The average number of students in a class at White Oak University is 22.6.
32. It is predicted that the average number of automobiles each household owns will increase next year.
33. Last year's total attendance at Long Run High School's football games was 8,325.
34. The chance that a person will be robbed in a certain city is 15%.

35. In addition to the four basic sampling methods, other methods are also used. Some of these methods are *sequence sampling, double sampling,* and *multiple sampling.* Look up these methods on the Internet and explain the advantages and disadvantages of each method.
36. For the data in Exercise 25, draw a stem and leaf plot, and compare your result to the frequency distribution. Which do you think provides more useful information, and why? What are the strengths and weaknesses of each?

Section 12-2 Picturing Data

LEARNING OBJECTIVES

☐ 1. Draw bar graphs and pie charts.

☐ 2. Draw histograms and frequency polygons.

☐ 3. Draw time series graphs.

Now we've gathered some data, and we think maybe some of it has an interesting story to tell. How can we most effectively present that data? In Section 12-1, we displayed data in table form, using frequency distributions, and using stem and leaf plots. All are perfectly valid, but ... they don't exactly *pop.* The graphic on this page displays data related to identity theft complaints that could have been put in table form:

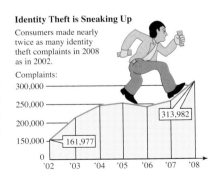

Source: Federal Trade Commission, February 2009

Year	2002	2003	2004	2005	2006	2007	2008
Complaints in thousands	162	215	247	256	246	258	314

The information is the same, but with the graph, just a quick glance is enough to see that identity theft rose sharply for a couple of years, then sort of leveled off, before another sharp rise. Simply put, if you want your data to really catch someone's eye, you can't do much better than a nice graphical representation. In this section, we'll study several methods for accomplishing this goal.

Bar Graphs and Pie Charts

The first type of frequency distribution we studied in Section 12-1 was the categorical frequency distribution. When data are representative of certain categories, rather than numerical, we often use bar graphs or circle graphs (commonly known as pie charts) to illustrate that data. We will start with a bar graph in Example 1.

EXAMPLE 1   Drawing a Bar Graph to Represent Data

The marketing firm Deloitte Retail conducted a survey in 2008 of grocery shoppers. The frequency distribution below represents the responses to the survey question "How often do you bring your own bags when grocery shopping?" Draw a vertical bar graph to represent the data.

Response	Frequency
Always	10
Never	39
Frequently	19
Occasionally	32

SOLUTION

Step 1 Draw and label the axes. We were asked for a vertical bar graph, so the responses go on the horizontal axis, and the frequencies on the vertical.

Step 2 Draw vertical bars with heights that correspond to the frequencies.

The completed graph is shown in Figure 12-1.

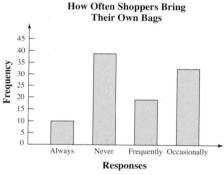

Figure 12-1

Math Note

For clarity, bar graphs are usually drawn with space between the bars.

▼ Try This One 1

The frequency distribution below represents responses to a survey on whether or not the posting of calorie information at fast food restaurants affects what customers order. Draw a vertical bar graph to illustrate the data.

Response	Frequency
Great impact	40
Some impact	42
Not much impact	11
None at all	7

CAUTION

In drawing a vertical bar graph, it's very important that the scale on the vertical axis begins at zero, and has consistent spacing. As you will see in the supplement on misuse of statistics, an improperly labeled axis can lead to a deceptive graph.

Another type of graph that can be drawn for the data that are categorical in nature is the **circle graph** or **pie chart.** A pie chart is a circle that is divided into sections in proportion to the frequencies corresponding to the categories. The purpose of a pie chart is to show the relationship of the parts to the whole by visually comparing the size of the sections. Example 2 shows the procedure for constructing a pie chart.

EXAMPLE 2 **Drawing a Pie Chart to Represent Data**

Math Note

Spreadsheet programs, like Microsoft Excel, have built-in commands that generate bar graphs and pie charts when you enter frequency distributions in table form.

Draw a pie chart for the frequency distribution from Example 1. The distribution is repeated below.

Response	Frequency
Always	10
Never	39
Frequently	19
Occasionally	32

SOLUTION

Step 1 Find the number of degrees corresponding to each slice using the formula

$$\text{Degrees} = \frac{f}{n} \cdot 360°$$

where f is the frequency for each class and n is the sum of the frequencies. In this case, $n = 100$, so the degree measures are:

Always $\quad \dfrac{10}{100} \cdot 360° = 36°$

Never $\quad \dfrac{39}{100} \cdot 360° = 140.4°$

Frequently $\quad \dfrac{19}{100} \cdot 360° = 68.4°$

Occasionally $\quad \dfrac{32}{100} \cdot 360° = 115.2°$

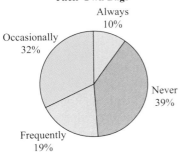

How Often Shoppers Bring Their Own Bags

Figure 12-2

Step 2 Using a protractor, graph each section on the circle using the calculated angles, as shown in Figure 12-2. Notice the labeling that makes it clear what each slice represents.

Step 3 Calculate the percent of the circle covered by each slice.

Always: $\dfrac{10}{100} = 10\%$ $\qquad$ Never: $\dfrac{39}{100} = 39\%$

Frequently: $\dfrac{19}{100} = 19\%$ $\qquad$ Occasionally: $\dfrac{32}{100} = 32\%$

Label each section with the percent, as shown in Figure 12-2.

▼ **Try This One 2**

Draw a pie chart that illustrates the frequency distribution from Try This One 1.

☑ 1. Draw bar graphs and pie charts.

Histograms and Frequency Polygons

When data are organized into grouped frequency distributions, two types of graphs are commonly used to represent them: *histograms* and *frequency polygons*.

A **histogram** is similar to a vertical bar graph in that the heights of the bars correspond to frequencies. The difference is that class limits are placed on the horizontal axis, rather than categories. The procedure is illustrated in Example 3.

EXAMPLE 3   **Drawing a Histogram**

The frequency distribution to the right is for the closing price of General Motors stock in dollars for each of the first 74 trading days of 2009. Draw a histogram for the data.

Class	Frequency	Class	Frequency
1.01–1.50	1	3.01–3.50	12
1.51–2.00	18	3.51–4.00	8
2.01–2.50	14	4.01–4.50	5
2.51–3.00	16		

SOLUTION

Step 1 Write the scale for the frequencies on the vertical axis and the class limits on the horizontal axis.

Step 2 Draw vertical bars with heights that correspond to the frequencies for each class. See Figure 12-3.

Figure 12-3

> **Math Note**
>
> When drawing a histogram, make sure that the bars touch (unlike a bar graph) and that every class is included, even if the frequency is zero.

▼ **Try This One 3**

Draw a histogram for the frequency distribution to the right, which represents the number of losses by the team that won the NCAA men's basketball championship for the years from 1939–2009.

Losses	Frequency	Losses	Frequency
0–1	13	6–7	9
2–3	27	8–9	2
4–5	17	10–11	3

A **frequency polygon** is similar to a histogram, but instead of bars, a series of line segments is drawn connecting the midpoints of the classes. The heights of those points match the heights of the bars in a histogram. In Example 4, we'll draw a frequency polygon for the frequency distribution from Example 3 so you can compare the two.

EXAMPLE 4   **Drawing a Frequency Polygon**

> **Math Note**
>
> Once you have the first midpoint, you can get all of the others by just adding the size of each class to the previous. For example, the second midpoint is the first, 1.255, plus the size of the classes, 0.50.

Draw a frequency polygon for the frequency distribution from Example 3. The distribution is repeated here.

Class	Frequency	Class	Frequency
1.01–1.50	1	3.01–3.50	12
1.51–2.00	18	3.51–4.00	8
2.01–2.50	14	4.01–4.50	5
2.51–3.00	16		

SOLUTION

Step 1 Find the midpoints for each class. This is accomplished by adding the upper and lower limits and dividing by 2. For the first two classes, we get:

$$\frac{1.50 + 1.01}{2} = 1.255$$

$$\frac{2.00 + 1.51}{2} = 1.755$$

The remaining midpoints are 2.255, 2.755, 3.255, 3.755, and 4.255.

Math Note

A frequency polygon should always touch the horizontal axis at both ends to indicate that the frequency is zero for any values not included on the graph.

Step 2 Write the scale for the frequencies on the vertical axis, and label a scale on the horizontal axis so that all midpoints will be included.

Step 3 Plot points at the midpoints with heights matching the frequencies for each class, then connect those points with straight lines.

Step 4 Finish the graph by drawing a line back to the horizontal axis at the beginning and end. The horizontal distance to the axis should equal the distance between the midpoints. In this case, that distance is 0.5, so we extend back to 0.755 and forward to 4.755. See Figure 12-4.

Figure 12-4

☑ 2. Draw histograms and frequency polygons.

▼ **Try This One 4**

Draw a frequency polygon for the frequency distribution from Try This One 3.

Time Series Graphs

A **time series graph** can be drawn for data collected over a period of time. This type of graph is used primarily to show trends, like prices rising or falling, for the time period. There are three types of trends. Secular trends are viewed over a long period of time, such as yearly. Cyclical trends show oscillating patterns. Seasonal trends show the values of a commodity for shorter periods of the year, such as fall, winter, spring, and summer. Example 5 shows how to draw a time series graph.

EXAMPLE 5 **Drawing a Time Series Graph**

Identity theft has increased as more people are shopping online. The table below shows the number of identify theft complaints made to the FTC in thousands between 2002 and 2008. Draw a time series graph for the data.

Year	2002	2003	2004	2005	2006	2007	2008
Complaints in thousands	162	215	247	256	246	258	314

Source: Federal Trade Commission

SOLUTION

Label the horizontal axis with years, and the vertical axis with the number of complaints in thousands, then plot the points from the table and connect them with line segments. See Figure 12-5.

Math Note

Notice how this time series graph matches the one at the beginning of this section.

Figure 12-5

☑ 3. Draw time series graphs.

Math Note

It's especially important to scale the vertical axis appropriately when drawing a time series graph. See Exercise 27 for some perspective on why.

▼ Try This One 5

The number of bankruptcy filings (in millions) in the United States from 2002 to 2008 is shown in the table. Draw a time series graph for the data.

Year	2002	2003	2004	2005	2006	2007	2008
Filings (millions)	1.58	1.66	1.60	2.08	0.62	0.85	1.12

This section provided just a sampling of the many types of charts and graphs used to picture data. A Google search for the string *picturing data* will help you find a more comprehensive list.

Answers to Try This One

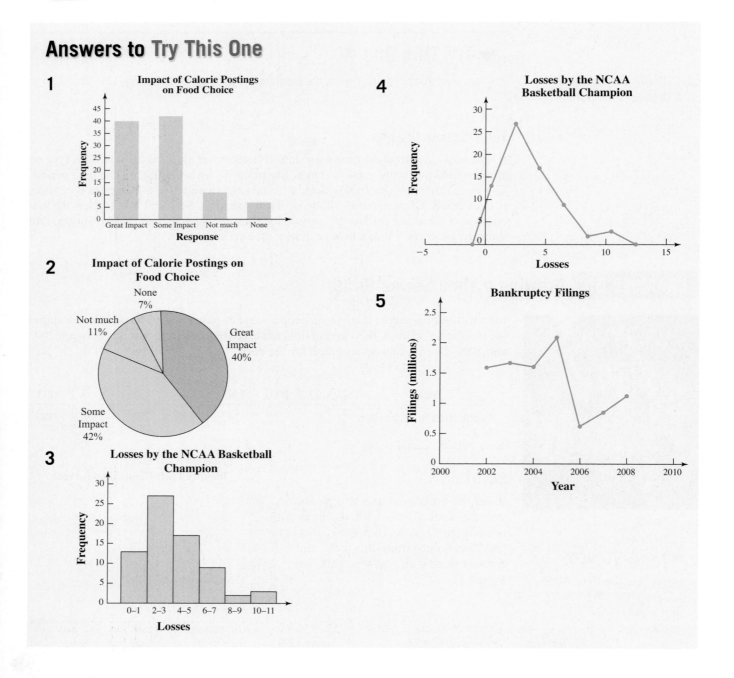

EXERCISE SET 12-2

Writing Exercises

1. Describe how to draw a bar graph and a pie chart given a frequency distribution.
2. Explain why bar graphs and pie charts are typically used for categorical frequency distributions, while histograms are used for grouped frequency distributions.
3. How are histograms and frequency polygons similar? How are they different?
4. Describe the purpose of a time series graph.

Real-World Applications

5. Draw a bar graph for the number of transplants of various types performed in the United States in 2008.

Type	Number
Kidney	13,743
Liver	5,273
Pancreas	370
Heart	1,802
Lung	1,221

Source: *Infoplease.com*

6. The data below show the number of students visiting a university health care center during finals week who suffered from certain conditions. Draw a bar graph to illustrate the data.

Condition	Number
Flu	48
Panic attack	36
Bronchitis	32
Headache	32
Broken bone	19
Cold/sniffles	17
Rash	16
Pneumonia	11
Ear infection	9

7. Draw a bar graph for the number of registered taxicabs in 2008 in the selected cities.

City	Number
New York	13,087
Washington, D.C.	7,000
Chicago	7,000
Los Angeles	2,300
Atlanta	1,600

Source: *Wikipedia*

8. Draw a bar graph for the number of unemployed people in the selected states for February 2009.

State	Number
Texas	772,000
New York	760,000
Pennsylvania	486,000
Florida	886,000
Ohio	567,000

Source: *Bureau of Employment Statistics*

9. The number of students at one campus who had a 4.0 GPA is shown below, organized by class. Draw a pie chart for the data.

Rank	Frequency
Freshman	12
Sophomore	25
Junior	36
Senior	17

10. In an insurance company study of the causes of 1,000 deaths, these data were obtained. Draw a pie chart to represent the data.

Cause of death	Number of deaths
Heart disease	432
Cancer	227
Stroke	93
Accidents	24
Other	224
	1,000

11. In a survey of 100 college students, the numbers shown here indicate the primary reason why the students selected their majors. Draw a pie chart for the data and analyze the results.

Reason	Number
Interest in subject	62
Future earning potential	18
Pressure from parents	12
Good job prospects	8

12. A survey of the students in the school of education at a large university obtained the following data for

students enrolled in specific fields. Draw a pie chart for the data and analyze the results.

Major field	Number
Preschool	893
Elementary	605
Middle	245
Secondary	1,096

13. For 108 randomly selected college applicants, the frequency distribution shown here for entrance exam scores was obtained. Draw a histogram and frequency polygon for the data.

Class	Frequency
90–98	6
99–107	22
108–116	43
117–125	28
126–134	9

14. For 75 employees of a large department store, the distribution shown here for years of service was obtained. Draw a histogram and frequency polygon for the data.

Class	Frequency
1–5	21
6–10	25
11–15	15
16–20	0
21–25	8
26–30	6

15. Thirty cars and trucks were tested by the EPA for fuel efficiency in miles per gallon (mpg). The frequency distribution shown here was obtained. Draw a histogram and frequency polygon for the data.

Class	Frequency
8–12	3
13–17	5
18–22	15
23–27	5
28–32	2

16. In a study of reaction times of dogs to a specific stimulus, an animal trainer obtained these data, given in seconds. Draw a histogram and frequency polygon for the data and analyze the results.

Class	Frequency
2.3–2.9	10
3.0–3.6	12
3.7–4.3	6
4.4–5.0	8
5.1–5.7	4
5.8–6.4	2

17. The data below represent the number of people admitted to graduate programs in mechanical engineering by year. Draw a time series graph for the data.

Year	2004	2005	2006	2007	2008
Number	1,981	2,895	3,027	1,651	1,432

18. The data below represent the number of laptops sold by a local computer store for the years listed. Draw a time series graph for the data.

Year	Number
1999	201
2000	256
2001	314
2002	379
2003	450
2004	576
2005	681
2006	799
2007	873
2008	1,012

19. The data below represent the number of downloads per year of a popular shareware program. Draw a time series graph for the data.

Year	2000	2002	2004	2006	2008
Downloads	12,413	15,160	18,201	20,206	19,143

Critical Thinking

In Exercises 20–25, state which type of graph (bar graph, pie chart, or time series graph) would most appropriately represent the given data.

20. The number of students enrolled at a local college each year for the last 5 years.

21. The budget for the student activities department at your college.

22. The number of students who get to school by automobile, bus, train, or by walking.

23. The record high temperatures of a city for the last 30 years.
24. The areas of the five lakes in the Great Lakes.
25. The amount of each dollar spent for wages, advertising, overhead, and profit by a corporation.
26. Use the Internet or a library to find a reference describing what a pictograph is, then describe its purpose.

27. Redraw the time series graph from Example 5, but make the scale on the vertical axis range from 150 to 350 rather than from 0 to 350. Why does this make the graph deceiving?

Section 12-3 Measures of Average

LEARNING OBJECTIVES

☐ 1. Compute the mean of a data set.

☐ 2. Compute the median of a data set.

☐ 3. Compute the mode of a data set.

☐ 4. Compute the midrange of a data set.

☐ 5. Compare the four measures of average.

Are you an average college student? What does that even mean? According to a variety of sources found on the Web, the average college student is 20 years old, lives on campus, and works off campus during the school year. She is female, talks to her parents every day, and comes from a family with an annual income between $50,000 and $100,000. She sleeps 6 hours a night, has $2,700 in credit card debt, and will leave college with $21,000 in total debt.

If this doesn't sound exactly like anyone you know, don't feel bad. As we will learn in this section, the word *average* is ambiguous—there are a variety of ways to describe an average. So what one source considers average might not match someone else's thoughts, and with so many different facets to a person, it's possible that nobody exactly meets all of the average criteria.

Our goal in Section 12-3 will be to understand the different measures of average. In casual terms, average means the most typical case, or the center of the distribution. Measures of average are also called *measures of central tendency,* and include the *mean, median, mode,* and *midrange.*

The Mean

The *mean,* also known as the arithmetic average, is found by adding the values of the data and dividing by the total number of values. The Greek letter Σ (sigma) is used to represent the sum of a list of numbers. If we use the letter $\overline{X}$ to represent data values, then ΣX means to find the sum of all values in a data set. Using this notation:

The **mean** is the sum of the values in a data set divided by the number of values. If $X_1, X_2, X_3, \ldots X_n$ are the data values, we use $\overline{X}$ to stand for the mean, and

$$\overline{X} = \frac{X_1 + X_2 + X_3 + \cdots + X_n}{n} = \frac{\sum X}{n}$$

EXAMPLE 1 **Finding the Mean of a Data Set**

In 2003, there were 12 inmates on death row who were proven innocent and freed. In the 5 years after that, there were 6, 2, 1, 3, and 4. Find the mean number of death row inmates proven innocent for the 6 years from 2003 to 2008.

SOLUTION

$$\overline{X} = \frac{\sum X}{n} = \frac{12 + 6 + 2 + 1 + 3 + 4}{6} = \frac{28}{6} \approx 4.7$$

The mean is about 4.7.

▼ **Try This One 1**

To test a customer's Internet connection, a tech records how long it takes for 10 different websites to load completely. The times in seconds are shown below. Find the mean time.

20.68   16.22   16.76   16.90   20.98   18.84   14.18   40.04   24.92   22.96

The procedure for finding the mean for grouped data uses the midpoints and the frequencies of the classes as shown in Example 2. This procedure will give only an approximate value for the mean, and it is used when the data set is very large or when the original raw data are unavailable but have been grouped by someone else.

Formula for Finding the Mean for Grouped Data:

$$\overline{X} = \frac{\sum (f \cdot X_m)}{n}$$

where f = frequency

X_m = midpoint of each class

$n = \sum f$ or sum of the frequencies

EXAMPLE 2   **Finding the Mean for Grouped Data**

Find the mean for the price of GM stock for the first 74 days of trading in 2009. The frequency distribution is below.

Class	Frequency	Class	Frequency
1.01–1.50	1	3.01–3.50	12
1.51–2.00	18	3.51–4.00	8
2.01–2.50	14	4.01–4.50	5
2.51–3.00	16		

SOLUTION

We found the midpoint of each class in Example 4 of Section 12-2: the midpoints are 1.255, 1.755, 2.255, 2.755, 3.255, 3.755, and 4.255. Now we multiply each midpoint by the frequency:

Midpoint (X_m)	Frequency (f)	$f \cdot X_m$
1.255	1	1.255
1.755	18	31.59
2.255	14	31.57
2.755	16	44.08
3.255	12	39.06
3.755	8	30.04
4.255	5	21.275
Sums	74	198.87

Now we divide $\Sigma(f \cdot X_m)$ by the sum of the frequencies to get the mean:

$$\overline{X} = \frac{198.87}{74} \approx 2.69$$

The mean closing price was $2.69.

▼ Try This One 2

☑ 1. Compute the mean of a data set.

Find the mean for the number of losses by the NCAA men's basketball champion for the years from 1939–2009. The frequency distribution is below.

Losses	Frequency	Losses	Frequency
0–1	13	6–7	9
2–3	27	8–9	2
4–5	17	10–11	3

The Median

According to payscale.com, the *median* salary for all federal government employees as of early 2009 was $60,680. This measure of average means that half of all government employees made less than $60,680, and half made more.

Simply put, the **median** is the halfway point of a data set when it is arranged in order. When a data set is ordered, it is called a **data array.** The median will either be a specific value in the data set, or will fall between two values, as shown in Examples 3 and 4.

Steps in Computing the Median of a Data Set

Step 1 Arrange the data in order, from smallest to largest.

Step 2 Select the middle value. If the number of data values is odd, the median is the value in the exact middle of the list. If the number of data values is even, the median is the mean of the two middle data values.

EXAMPLE 3 Finding the Median of a Data Set

The mean and median age for this group are different. The grandfather's age pulls up the mean, while the four children bring down the median.

The weights of the five starting offensive linemen for the Pittsburgh Steelers in Super Bowl XLIII were 345, 340, 315, 285, and 317. Find the median weight.

SOLUTION

Step 1 Arrange the data in order.

285   315   317   340   345

Step 2 Select the middle value.

The median weight was 317 pounds.

▼ Try This One 3

The high temperatures for seven consecutive days in April, 2009 in Cincinnati were 60°, 49°, 67°, 73°, 76°, 59°, and 59°. Find the median temperature.

EXAMPLE 4   Finding the Median of a Data Set

One of the authors of this book conducts a campus food drive at the end of each semester. The amount of food in pounds gathered over the last eight semesters is shown below. Find the median weight.

1,675   1,209   1,751   1,700   1,532   2,171   2,292   3,211

SOLUTION

Step 1 Arrange the data in order.

1,209   1,532   1,675   1,700   1,751   2,171   2,292   3,211

Step 2 Find the middle value: in this case, it is in between 1,700 and 1,751, so we find the mean of those two values.

$$\frac{1,700 + 1,751}{2} = 1,725.5$$

The median weight is 1,725.5 pounds.

▼ Try This One 4

The data below are the number of fatalities in the United States caused by tornadoes for the years 1999–2008. Find the median number of fatalities.

125   81   67   39   66   54   55   44   41   94

CAUTION   When finding the median of a data set, make sure the data values are arranged in order!

☑ 2. Compute the median of a data set.

The Mode

The third measure of average is called the *mode.* The mode is sometimes said to be the most typical case.

> The value that occurs most often in a data set is called the **mode.**

A data set can have more than one mode or no mode at all. These situations will be shown in some of the examples that follow.

EXAMPLE 5   Finding the Mode of a Data Set

These data represent the duration (in days) of U.S. space shuttle voyages for the years 2002–2008. Find the mode.

10   10   13   10   13   15   13   12   11   12   13   12   15   12   15   13   15

Source: Wikipedia

SOLUTION

If we construct a frequency distribution, it will be easy to find the mode—it's simply the value with the greatest frequency. The frequency distribution for the data is shown to the right, and the mode is 13.

Days	Frequency	Days	Frequency
10	3	13	5
11	1	15	4
12	4		

▼ Try This One 5

The data below represent the number of fatal commercial airline incidents in the United States for each year from 1998–2008. Find the mode.

1 2 3 6 0 2 2 3 2 1 2

EXAMPLE 6 **Finding the Mode of a Data Set**

Math Note

When there is no mode, don't say that the mode is zero. That would be incorrect because for some data, such as temperature, zero can be an actual value.

Six strains of bacteria were tested by the Centers for Disease Control to see how long they could remain alive outside their normal environment. The time, in minutes, is recorded below. Find the mode.

2 3 5 7 8 10

SOLUTION

Since each value occurs only once, there is no mode.

▼ Try This One 6

The final exam scores for 10 students in a seminar course are listed below. Find the mode.

91 74 66 93 76 85 86 90 71 89

EXAMPLE 7 **Finding the Mode of a Data Set**

Math Note

When a data set has two modes, it is called *bimodal*.

The number of wins in a 16-game season for the Cincinnati Bengals from 1997–2008 is listed below. Find the mode.

7 3 4 4 6 2 8 8 11 8 7 4

SOLUTION

There are two numbers that occur three times: 4 and 8. No number occurs more than three times, so the data set has two modes, 4 and 8.

▼ Try This One 7

The table below lists the average high temperature in degrees Fahrenheit for each month of the year on the island of Antigua. Find the mode.

Month	Jan	Feb	Mar	Apr	May	Jun	Jul	Aug	Sep	Oct	Nov	Dec
High	81	82	82	83	85	86	87	87	87	86	84	82

The mode is the only measure of central tendency that can be used in finding the most typical case when the data are classified by groups or categories, like those shown in Example 8.

EXAMPLE 8   Finding the Mode for Categorical Data

The winner of an election by popular vote is the mode.

☑ 3. Compute the mode of a data set.

A survey of the junior class at Fiesta State University shows the following number of students majoring in each field. Find the mode.

Business	1,425
Liberal arts	878
Computer science	632
Education	471
General studies	95

SOLUTION

The values here are not the numbers, but the categories: business, liberal arts, computer science, education, and general studies. The value that appears most often is business, so that is the mode.

▼ Try This One 8

Five hundred college graduates were asked how much they donate to their alma mater on an annual basis. Find the mode of their responses, summarized below.

$500 or more	45
Between 0 and $500	150
Nothing	275
Refused to answer	30

The Midrange

The midrange is a very quick and rough estimate of the middle of a data set. It is found by adding the lowest and highest values and dividing by 2.

Finding the Midrange for a Data Set

$$\text{Midrange} = \frac{\text{Lowest value} + \text{highest value}}{2}$$

The midrange is not terribly reliable since it can be greatly affected by just one extremely high or low data value.

EXAMPLE 9   Finding the Midrange

In Example 1, we saw that the number of death row inmates proven innocent for the years 2003–2008 was 12, 6, 2, 1, 3, and 4. Find the midrange.

SOLUTION

The lowest value is 1 and the highest is 12, so the midrange is

$$\text{Midrange} = \frac{12 + 1}{2} = 6.5.$$

▼ **Try This One 9**

☑ 4. Compute the midrange of a data set.

The number of earthquakes worldwide measuring at least 6.0 on the Richter scale from 2000–2008 is shown below. Find the midrange.

173   142   143   155   157   151   153   200   178

In Example 1, we found that the mean for the data set in Example 9 is 4.7. The midrange is much higher because the data value 12 is so much higher than the rest. This brings up an interesting question: how do our four measures of average compare for a data set?

EXAMPLE 10 **Comparing the Four Measures of Average**

The table below lists the number of golfers who finished the Masters tournament with a better score than Tiger Woods between 1997 and 2009.

Year	Number	Year	Number
1997	0	2004	21
1998	7	2005	0
1999	17	2006	2
2000	4	2007	1
2001	0	2008	1
2002	0	2009	5
2003	14		

Find the mean, median, mode, and midrange for the data.

SOLUTION

It will be helpful to arrange the numbers in order:

0   0   0   0   1   1   2   4   5   7   14   17   21

$$\text{Mean} = \frac{\sum X}{n} = \frac{0 + 0 + 0 + 0 + 1 + 1 + 2 + 4 + 5 + 7 + 14 + 17 + 21}{13} \approx 5.54$$

$$\text{Median} = 2$$

$$\text{Mode} = 0$$

$$\text{Midrange} = \frac{21 + 0}{2} = 10.5$$

So which is the best indicator of average performance? That's open to interpretation, but all four measures of average are very different.

▼ **Try This One 10**

☑ 5. Compare the four measures of average.

Tiger's final scores in relation to par for the 13 Masters tournaments from 1997 to 2009 are listed below. Find the mean, median, mode, and midrange.

−18   −3   +1   −4   −16   −12   +2   +2   −12   −4   +3   −5   −8

To conclude the section, Table 12-2 summarizes some of the strengths and weaknesses of each measure of average.

TABLE 12-2 A Comparison of Measures of Average

Measure	Strengths	Weaknesses
Mean	• Unique—there's exactly one mean for any data set • Factors in all values in the set • Easy to understand	• Can be adversely affected by one or two unusually high or low values • Can be time-consuming to calculate for large data sets
Median	• Divides a data set neatly into two groups • Not affected by one or two extreme values	• Can ignore the effects of large or small values even if they are important to consider
Mode	• Very easy to find • Describes the most typical case • Can be used with categorical data like candidate preference, choice of major, etc.	• May not exist for a data set • May not be unique • Can be very different from mean and median if the most typical case happens to be near the low or high end of the range
Midrange	• Very quick and easy to compute • Provides a simple look at average	• Dramatically affected by extremely high or low values in the data set • Ignores all but two values in the set

Sidelight THE BIRTH OF STATISTICS

The study of statistics has its origin in censuses taken by the Babylonians and Egyptians almost 6,000 years ago. "Birth" is an appropriate word to use in describing the beginning of statistics, since it started with birth records. The infancy of statistics occurred much later, some time around 27 BCE, when the Roman emperor Augustus conducted surveys on births and deaths of citizens, as well as the amount of livestock each owned and the crops each had harvested. Suddenly, a large amount of data was wanted, and methods had to be developed to collect, organize, and summarize that data.

The adolescence of statistics is probably sometime around the 14th century, when people began keeping detailed records of births, deaths, and accidents in order to determine insurance rates. Over the next 600 years or so, statistics grew up, with a wide variety of methods developed to fill needs in biology, physics, astronomy, commerce, and many other areas.

The true adulthood of statistics coincides with the rise of computer technology. Today, with just a few clicks of a mouse, statisticians can process and analyze amounts of data that would have taken the pioneers in the field centuries.

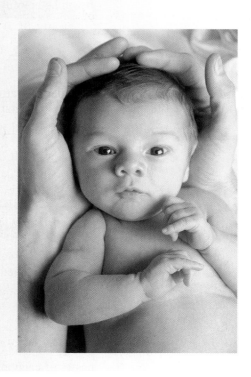

Answers to Try This One

1 21.248 seconds

2 3.63 losses

3 60°

4 60.5 fatalities

5 2 incidents

6 There is no mode.

7 The modes are 82° and 87°.

8 The mode is donating nothing.

9 171 earthquakes

10 Mean: -5.69; median: -4; mode: $-12, -4, +2$; midrange: -7.5

EXERCISE SET 12-3

Writing Exercises

1. If someone asked you before covering this section what the word "average" meant, what would you have said? What would your response be now?
2. Describe how to find the mean of a data set.
3. Describe how to find the median of a data set.
4. What is meant by the term *mode of a data set?*
5. Describe how to find the midrange of a data set.
6. Which of the measures of average can be used to describe the average for categorical data? Why?

Real-World Applications

For exercises 7–18, find the mean, median, mode, and midrange.

7. These data are the number of on-campus burglaries reported in 2008 for nine western Pennsylvania universities.

   61 11 1 3 2 30 18 3 7

8. The data below show the number of attorneys employed by the ten largest law firms in Pittsburgh.

   87 109 57 221 175 123 170 80 66 80

9. A graduate student in social work surveyed students at 10 colleges in a Midwestern state to find how many are single parents. The results are the data below.

   700 298 638 260 1,380 280 270 1,350 380 570

10. The number of wins for the teams that won college football bowl games at the end of the 2008 season is

    8 7 8 8 7 11 7 7 9 9 9 8 8 10
    8 10 10 8 9 7 8 8 9 8 10 9 7
    8 11 12 10 13 12 13

11. The average number of cigarettes smoked per person in a year in the top ten countries for smoking are shown next.

Greece	4,313	Malta	2,668
Hungary	3,265	Bulgaria	2,574
Kuwait	3,062	Belarus	2,571
Japan	3,023	Belgium	2,428
Spain	2,779	Turkey	2,394

12. The number of existing home sales in millions for the months from August 2007 to February 2009 are shown below.

    5.5 5.1 5.1 5.0 4.9 4.9 5.0 4.9 4.9 5.0
    4.9 5.0 4.9 5.1 4.9 4.5 4.7 4.5 4.7

13. The number of bids for the five most popular products under concert tickets on eBay for a day in April is shown below.

    340 75 123 259 151

14. The number of sales of single-family homes in the largest metropolitan areas of Florida in 2008 was

    321 307 338 200 141 115 518 185 258
    276 31 116 881 72 181 175 490 162
    1,235 369

15. From 1992 to 2004, the number of violent crimes committed per 1,000 students in U.S. schools each year was

    10 12 13 9 9 8 9 7 5 6 6 5

16. The average amount of tuition, fees, room and board for full-time students at public 4-year institutions in 2005–2006 in states starting with "M" was

$12,865 $15,253 $15,199 $14,519 $13,719
$10,040 $12,588 $11,292

17. The annual number of murders in the United States from 1995 to 2007 was as follows:

Year	Murders	Year	Murders
1995	21,610	2002	16,229
1996	19,650	2003	16,528
1997	18,208	2004	16,148
1998	16,914	2005	16,740
1999	15,522	2006	17,030
2000	15,586	2007	16,929
2001	16,037		

18. The 10 states with the highest unemployment rates in February 2009 and their rates of unemployment are given below:

State	Rate
Michigan	12.0
South Carolina	11.0
Oregon	10.8
Rhode Island	10.5
Nevada	10.1
North Carolina	10.7
California	10.5
District of Columbia	9.9
Florida	9.4
Indiana	9.4

For Exercises 19–26, find the mean of the data set.

19. For 50 students in the student union at one campus, the distribution of the students' ages was obtained as shown.

Class	Frequency	Class	Frequency
18–20	20	24–26	8
21–23	18	27–29	4

20. Thirty new automobiles were tested for fuel efficiency by the EPA (in miles per gallon). This frequency distribution was obtained:

Class	Frequency	Class	Frequency
8–12	3	23–27	5
13–17	5	28–32	2
18–22	15		

21. In a study of the time it takes an untrained mouse to run a maze, a researcher recorded these data in seconds.

Class	Frequency
2.1–2.7	5
2.8–3.4	7
3.5–4.1	12
4.2–4.8	14
4.9–5.5	16
5.6–6.2	8

22. Eighty randomly selected lightbulbs were tested to determine their lifetimes (in hours). The frequency distribution was obtained as shown.

Class	Frequency
53–63	6
64–74	12
75–85	25
86–96	18
97–107	14
108–118	5

23. These data represent the net worth (in millions of dollars) of 45 national corporations.

Class	Frequency
10–20	2
21–31	8
32–42	15
43–53	7
54–64	10
65–75	3

24. The cost per load (in cents) of 35 laundry detergents tested by *Consumer Reports* is shown here.

Class	Frequency
13–19	2
20–26	7
27–33	12
34–40	5
41–47	6
48–54	1
55–61	0
62–68	2

25. The frequency distribution shown represents the commission earned (in dollars) by 100 salespeople employed at several branches of a large chain store.

Class	Frequency	Class	Frequency
150–158	5	186–194	20
159–167	16	195–203	15
168–176	20	204–212	3
177–185	21		

26. This frequency distribution represents the data obtained from a sample of 75 copy machine service technicians. The values represent the days between service calls for various copy machines.

Class	Frequency	Class	Frequency
16–18	14	25–27	10
19–21	12	28–30	15
22–24	18	31–33	6

Critical Thinking

27. For each of the characteristics of the average college student listed on page 665, decide which measure of average you think was used, and explain your choices.

28. For these situations, state which measure of average—mean, median, or mode—should be used.

   (a) The most typical case is desired.
   (b) The data are categorical.
   (c) The values are to be divided into two approximately equal groups, one group containing the larger and one containing the smaller values.

For Exercises 29–34, describe which measure of average—mean, median, or mode—was probably used in each situation.

29. Half of the factory workers make more than $5.37 per hour and half make less than $5.37 per hour.
30. The average number of children per family in the Plaza Heights is 1.8.
31. Most people prefer red convertibles to any other color.
32. The average person cuts the lawn once a week.
33. The most common fear today is fear of speaking in public.
34. The average age of college professors is 42.3 years.

Section 12-4 Measures of Variation

LEARNING OBJECTIVES

☐ 1. Find the range of a data set.

☐ 2. Find the variance and standard deviation of a data set.

☐ 3. Interpret standard deviation.

Now that we know about measures of average, we'll consider the fact that there's more to the story told by a data set than just the average. For an example, consider the two pictures of dogs on this page.

If we look only at measures of average, particularly the mean, we might be fooled into thinking that the two groups are very similar, when clearly they are not. The difference, of course, is that all of the dogs in the first picture are of similar size, while those in the second picture have many different weights. Because there are some small dogs and one very large one, the mean weight in both groups is probably similar.

In this section we will study *measures of variation,* which will help to describe how the data within a set vary. The three most commonly used measures of variation are *range, variance,* and *standard deviation.*

The two groups of dogs have about the same mean size, but the range of sizes is quite different.

Range

The *range* is the simplest of the three measures of variation that we will study.

The **range** of a data set is the difference between the highest and lowest values in the set.

$$\text{Range} = \text{Highest value} - \text{lowest value}$$

EXAMPLE 1   **Finding the Range of a Data Set**

The first list below is the weights of the dogs in the first picture, and the second is the weights of the dogs in the second picture. Find the mean and range for each list.

70   73   58   60
30   85   40   125   42   75   60   55

SOLUTION

For the first list,

$$\text{Mean} = \frac{70 + 73 + 58 + 60}{4} = 65.25 \text{ lb}$$

$$\text{Range} = 73 - 58 = 15 \text{ lb}$$

For the second list,

$$\text{Mean} = \frac{30 + 85 + 40 + 125 + 42 + 75 + 60 + 55}{8} = 64 \text{ lb}$$

$$\text{Range} = 125 - 30 = 95 \text{ lb}$$

As we suspected, the means are very close, but the ranges are very different.

▼ **Try This One 1**

1. Find the range of a data set.

The monthly average high temperatures from January to December in Aruba are shown below. Find the range.

85   85   86   87   88   89   88   89   89   89   87   85

Variance and Standard Deviation

The range is a limited measure of variation because it ignores all the data except the highest and lowest values. If most of the values are similar, but there's just one unusually high value, the range will make it look like there's a lot more variation than there actually is. For this reason, we will next define *variance* and *standard deviation,* which are much more reliable measures of variation.

Variance and standard deviation are a little tricky to compute. In the box below, we'll explain how to find them. Later in the section, we'll discuss their significance.

Procedure for Finding the Variance and Standard Deviation

Step 1   Find the mean.

Step 2   Subtract the mean from each data value in the data set.

Step 3   Square the differences.

Step 4   Find the sum of the squares.

Step 5   Divide the sum by $n - 1$ to get the variance, where n is the number of data values.

Step 6   Take the square root of the variance to get the standard deviation.

EXAMPLE 2 **Finding Variance and Standard Deviation**

The heights in inches of the top six scorers for the Cleveland Cavaliers during the 2008–2009 season are listed below. Find the variance and standard deviation.

80 73 87 74 83 74

SOLUTION

Step 1 Find the mean height.

$$\text{Mean} = \frac{\sum X}{n} = \frac{80 + 73 + 87 + 74 + 83 + 74}{6} = 78.5 \text{ inches}$$

Step 2 Subtract the mean from each data value.

$80 - 78.5 = 1.5$ $87 - 78.5 = 8.5$ $83 - 78.5 = 4.5$

$73 - 78.5 = -5.5$ $74 - 78.5 = -4.5$ $74 - 78.5 = -4.5$

Step 3 Square each result.

$(1.5)^2 = 2.25$ $(8.5)^2 = 72.25$ $(4.5)^2 = 20.25$

$(-5.5)^2 = 30.25$ $(-4.5)^2 = 20.25$ $(-4.5)^2 = 20.25$

Step 4 Find the sum of the squares.

$2.25 + 30.25 + 72.25 + 20.25 + 20.25 + 20.25 = 165.5$

Step 5 Divide the sum by $n - 1$ to get the variance, where n is the sample size. In this case, n is 6, so $n - 1 = 5$.

$$\text{Variance} = \frac{165.5}{5} = 33.1$$

Step 6 Take the square root of the variance to get standard deviation.

$$\text{Standard deviation} = \sqrt{33.1} \approx 5.75 \text{ inches}$$

To organize the steps, you might find it helpful to make a table with three columns: The original data, the difference between each data value and the mean, and their squares. Then you just add the entries in the last column and divide by $n - 1$ to get the variance.

Data (X)	$X - $ mean	$(X - $ mean$)^2$
80	1.5	2.25
73	-5.5	30.25
87	8.5	72.25
74	-4.5	20.25
83	4.5	20.25
74	-4.5	20.25
		165.5

▼ Try This One 2

The heights in inches for the eight nonpitchers in the starting lineup for the New York Mets on opening day 2008 are listed below. Find the variance and standard deviation.

73 74 72 75 73 74 73 71

To understand the significance of standard deviation, we'll look at the process one step at a time.

Step 1 *Compute the mean.*   Variation is a measure of how far the data vary from the mean, so it makes sense to begin there.

Step 2 *Subtract the mean from each data value.*   In this step, we are literally calculating how far away from the mean each data value is. The problem is that since some are greater than the mean and some less, their sum will always add up to zero. (Try it!) So that doesn't help much.

Step 3 *Square the differences.*   This solves the problem of those differences adding to zero—when we square, they're all positive.

Step 4 *Add the squares.*   In the next two steps, we're getting an approximate average of the squares of the individual variations from the mean. First we add them, then . . .

Step 5 *Divide the sum by $n - 1$.*   It's a bit technical to explain why we divide by $n - 1$ rather than n, but in any case we now have the approximate average of the squares of the individual variations from the mean.

Step 6 *Take the square root of the sum.*   This "undoes" the square we did in step 3. It will return the units of our answer to the units of the original data, giving us a good measure of how far the typical data value varies from the mean.

Now we'll formally define these two key measures of variation.

2. Find the variance and standard deviation of a data set.

The **variance** for a data set is an approximate average of the square of the distance between each value and the mean. If X represents individual values, $\overline{X}$ is the mean and n is the number of values:

$$\text{Variance} = \frac{\sum(X - \overline{X})^2}{n - 1}$$

The **standard deviation** is the square root of the variance.

Interpreting Standard Deviation

Since standard deviation measures how far typical values are from the mean, its size tells us how spread out the data are. We'll examine this idea in Example 3.

EXAMPLE 3   **Interpreting Standard Deviation**

A professor has two sections of Math 115 this semester. The 8:30 A.M. class has a mean score of 74% with a standard deviation of 3.6%. The 2 P.M. class also has a mean score of 74%, but a standard deviation of 9.2%. What can we conclude about the students' averages in these two sections?

SOLUTION

In relative terms, the morning class has a small standard deviation and the afternoon class has a large one. So even though they have the same mean, the classes are quite different. In the morning class, most of the students probably have scores relatively close to the mean, with few very high or very low scores. In the afternoon class, the scores vary more widely, with a lot of high scores and a lot of low scores that average out to a mean of 74%.

▼ **Try This One 3**

☑ 3. Interpret standard
deviation.

For the dogs in the two pictures on page 675, discuss what you think the standard deviations might be in comparison to one another, then check your answer by computing the standard deviation for each group.

Answers to Try This One

1 4°

2 Variance ≈ 1.55 inches;
standard deviation ≈ 1.25 inches

3 The second group should have a much larger standard deviation than the first since the weights are more spread out. The actual standard deviation for the first group is 7.37 lb and for the second group it is 30.7 lb.

EXERCISE SET 12-4

Writing Exercises

1. Name three measures of variation.
2. What is the range?
3. Why is the range not usually the best measure of variation?
4. What is the relationship between the variance and standard deviation?
5. Explain the procedure for finding the standard deviation for data.
6. Explain how the variation of two data sets can be compared by using the standard deviations.

For Exercises 7–10, discuss the relative sizes of the standard deviations for the two data sets.

7. Data set 1: 12 15 13 10 16 13 12 13
   Data set 2: 5 26 31 2 10 25 6 33

8. Data set 1: 40-yard dash times for starting running backs in the National Football League
   Data set 2: 40-yard dash times for every student in your math class
9. Data set 1: Average monthly high temperature in Chicago
   Data set 2: Average monthly high temperature in Los Angeles
10. Data set 1: Weights of all the dogs at a golden retriever rescue shelter
    Data set 2: Weights of all the dogs for sale in a pet store

Real-World Applications

For Exercises 11-26, find the range, variance, and standard deviation.

11. These data are the number of junk e-mails Lena received for 9 consecutive days.

    61 1 1 3 2 30 18 3 7

12. The number of hospitals in the five largest hospital systems is shown here.

    340 75 123 259 151

    Source: USA Today

13. Ten used trail bikes are randomly selected from a bike shop, and the odometer reading of each is recorded as follows.

    1,902 103 653 1,901 788 361 216 363 223 656

14. Fifteen students were selected and asked how many hours each studied for the final exam in statistics. Their answers are recorded here.

    8 6 3 0 0 5 9 2 1 3 7 10 0 3 6

15. The weights of nine players from a college football team are recorded as follows.

    206   215   305   297   265   282   301   255   261

16. Shown here are the numbers of stories in the 11 tallest buildings in St. Paul, Minnesota.

    37   46   32   32   33   25   17   27   21   25   33
    Source: The World Almanac and Book of Facts

17. The heights (in inches) of nine male army recruits are shown here.

    78   72   68   73   75   69   74   73   72

18. The number of calories in 12 randomly selected microwave dinners is shown here.

    560   832   780   650   470   920   1,090   970
    495   550   605   735

19. The table below shows the average price of a gallon of regular unleaded gas in U.S. dollars for various cities in June 2007.

City	Price
Chicago	2.69
Paris	6.52
Toronto	3.28
Moscow	2.89
São Paulo	4.89
Seoul	6.06

20. The number of attorneys in 10 law firms in Pittsburgh is 87, 109, 57, 221, 175, 123, 170, 80, 66, and 80.
    Source: *Pittsburgh Tribune Review*

21. The stock prices for eight major grocery store chains in early 2009 were: $18.28, $20.32, $9.34, $11.57, $15.21, $48.04, $48.84, and $28.23.

22. The table reflects consumer priorities worldwide for a variety of expenditures:

Global Priority	U.S. Currency (in billions)
Cosmetics in the United States	8
Ice cream in Europe	11
Perfumes in Europe and the United States	12
Pet foods in Europe and the United States	17
Business entertainment in Japan	35
Cigarettes in Europe	50
Alcoholic drinks in Europe	105
Narcotic drugs in the world	400
Military spending in the world	780

Source: www.globalissues.org

23. The number of flu breakouts in 2009 in various regions of the U.S. were

    429   690   884   827   914   176   565   479   569
    Source: cdc.gov

24. The five teams in baseball's National League eastern division had the following number of wins in 2008: 92, 89, 84, 72, 59.

25. The number of workplace fatalities in the United States from 2000 to 2007 were as follows:

Year	Fatalities	Year	Fatalities
2000	5,920	2004	5,764
2001	5,915	2005	5,734
2002	5,534	2006	5,840
2003	5,575	2007	5,488

Source: *bls.gov*

26. From 1992 to 2004, the number of violent crimes committed per 1,000 students in U.S. schools each year was

    10   12   13   9   9   8   9   7   5   6   6   5

Critical Thinking

27. The three data sets have the same mean and range, but is the variation the same? Explain your answer.

    (a) 5   7   9   11   13   15   17
    (b) 5   6   7   11   15   16   17
    (c) 5   5   5   11   17   17   17

28. Using this set—10, 20, 30, 40, and 50,
    (a) Find the standard deviation.
    (b) Add 5 to each value and then find the standard deviation.
    (c) Subtract 5 from each value and then find the standard deviation.
    (d) Multiply each value by 5 and then find the standard deviation.
    (e) Divide each value by 5 and then find the standard deviation.
    (f) Generalize the results of (a)–(e).

Section 12-5 Measures of Position

LEARNING OBJECTIVES

☐ 1. Compute the percentile rank for a data value.

☐ 2. Find a data value corresponding to a given percentile.

☐ 3. Use percentile rank to compare values from different data sets.

☐ 4. Compute quartiles for a data set.

So you managed to survive 4 years of college and escape with that long-awaited diploma. But maybe the thought of entering the real world starts to look a little less appealing, and you realize that a couple more years of college might suit you. Next step: take the GRE (Graduate Record Examination), which is like the SAT for grad school.

When you get your score back, you see that it's 1120. How do you know if that's a good score? The quickest way is to look at the *percentile rank* on the report, which in this case would probably be 60%. Does this mean that you only got 60% of the questions right? That wouldn't be a very good score! In fact, that's not at all what it means, and you did just fine.

The term percentile is used in statistics to measure the position of a data value in a data set.

A **percentile,** or percentile rank, of a data value indicates the percent of data values in a set that are below that particular value.

In this case, your percentile rank of 60% means that 60% of all students who took the GRE scored lower than you did. Not bad! Scores on standardized tests are one of the most common uses for percentiles because they help you to put a raw score like 1120 into context.

Percentiles are also used very commonly in health care, especially pediatrics. To monitor a child's development, doctors compare the child's height, weight, and head size at a certain age to measurements of other children at the same age. If a child's percentiles suddenly change radically, the doctor might suspect a problem in his or her development.

Percentiles were originally used to analyze data sets with 100 or more values. But when statistical techniques were developed for smaller data sets, the percentile concept came into use for those sets as well. There are several methods that can be used for computing percentiles, and sometimes the answers vary slightly, especially with small data sets. In this section, we will use a basic method that works well for smaller data sets.

EXAMPLE 1   Finding the Percentile Rank of a Data Value

Math Note

In order to keep our study of percentiles relatively simple, we'll work with data sets with no repeated values. More complicated techniques are used to find percentiles for data sets with repeated values.

Suppose you score 77 on a test in a class of 10 people, with the 10 scores listed below. What was your percentile rank?

93   82   64   75   98   52   77   88   90   71

SOLUTION

Step 1 Arrange the scores in order.

52   64   71   75   77   82   88   90   93   98

Step 2 Find the number of data values below 77. There are 4 values below 77.

Step 3 Divide the number below the score by the total number of data values and change the answer to a percent.

$$\frac{4}{10} = 0.40 = 40\%$$

A test score of 77 is equivalent to the 40th percentile.

1. Compute the percentile rank for a data value.

▼ Try This One 1

The weights in pounds for the 12 members of a college gymnastics team are below. Find the percentile rank of the gymnast who weighs 97 pounds.

101   120   88   72   75   80   98   91   105   97   78   85

In Example 1, we saw how to find the percentile rank for a given data value. In Example 2, we'll examine the opposite question—finding the data value that corresponds to a given percentile.

EXAMPLE 2   Finding a Data Value Corresponding to a Given Percentile

The number of words in each of the last 10 presidential inaugural addresses is listed below. Find the length that corresponds to the 30th percentile.

2,406   2,073   1,571   2,170   1,507   2,283   2,546   2,463   1,087   1,668

SOLUTION

Step 1 We are asked to find the number on the list that has 30% of the numbers below it. There are 10 numbers, and 30% of 10 is 3.

Step 2 Arrange the data in order from smallest to largest, and find the value that has 3 values below it.

1,087   1,507   1,571   1,668   2,073   2,170   2,283   2,406   2,463   2,546

The 30th percentile is the speech that consisted of 1,668 words.

▼ Try This One 2

The average monthly rainfall in inches for St. Petersburg, Florida, is shown in the chart below. Which month is at the 75th percentile?

Jan	Feb	Mar	Apr	May	Jun	Jul	Aug	Sep	Oct	Nov	Dec
2.3	2.8	3.4	1.6	2.6	5.7	7.0	7.8	6.1	2.5	1.9	2.2

2. Find a data value corresponding to a given percentile.

Percentile ranks are particularly useful in comparing data that come from two different sets, as shown in Example 3.

EXAMPLE 3   Using Percentiles to Compare Data from Different Sets

Two students are competing for one remaining spot in a law school class. Miguel ranked 51st in a graduating class of 1,700, while Dustin ranked 27th in a class of 540. Which student's position was higher in his class?

SOLUTION

This is an ideal application of percentile rank. Miguel ranked 51st out of 1,700, so there were $1,700 - 51 = 1,649$ students ranked below him. His percentile rank is

$$\frac{1,649}{1,700} = 0.97 \text{ or } 97\%$$

Dustin had $540 - 27 = 513$ students ranked below him, so his percentile rank is

$$\frac{513}{540} = 0.95 \text{ or } 95\%$$

Both are excellent students, but Miguel's ranking is higher.

▼ Try This One 3

3. Use percentile rank to compare values from different data sets.

In the 2007–2008 school year, West Virginia University finished the season ranked sixth out of 119 Division IA football teams, and ranked 17th out of 346 Division I basketball teams. Which team had the higher percentile rank?

In Section 12-3, we saw that the median of a data set divides the set into equal halves. Another statistical measure we will study is the **quartile,** which divides a data set into quarters. The second quartile is the same as the median, and divides a data set into an upper half and a lower half. The first quartile is the median of the lower half, and the third quartile is the median of the upper half. We use the symbols Q_1, Q_2, and Q_3 for the first, second, and third quartiles respectively.

EXAMPLE 4 Finding Quartiles for a Data Set

Find Q_1, Q_2, and Q_3 for the number of aircraft stolen during a recent 8-year period.

    14   11   20   21   42   24   36   35

Source: USA Today

SOLUTION

Step 1 Arrange the data in order.

    11   14   20   21   24   35   36   42

Step 2 Find the median. This is Q_2.

    11   14   20   21   24   35   36   42
                       ↑
                   $Q_2 = 22.5$

Step 3 Find the median of the data values less than Q_2. This is Q_1.

    11   14   20   21
              ↑
          $Q_1 = 17$

Step 4 Find the median of the data values above Q_2. This is Q_3.

    24   35   36   42
              ↑
          $Q_3 = 35.5$

In summary, $Q_1 = 17$, $Q_2 = 22.5$, and $Q_3 = 35.5$.

▼ **Try This One 4**

☑ 4. Compute quartiles for a data set.

Find Q_1, Q_2, and Q_3 for the data shown.

18 32 54 36 27 42 31 15 60 25

In this section, we studied two measures of position, percentile and quartile. In Section 12-6, the concept of position plays a very important role when we study a third measure of position, the z score.

Answers to Try This One

1 58th percentile

2 September

3 Basketball

4 $Q_1 = 25$, $Q_2 = 31.5$, $Q_3 = 42$

EXERCISE SET 12-5

Writing Exercises

1. If your score in your math class puts you in the 60th percentile, what exactly does that mean?
2. Does a score in the 90th percentile mean that you got 90% of the questions right on a test? Explain.
3. Explain what quartiles are.
4. What is the connection between the second quartile and the median for a data set? Explain.

Real-World Applications

5. The scores for 20 students on a 50-point math test are 42, 48, 50, 36, 35, 27, 47, 38, 32, 43, 24, 33, 39, 49, 44, 40, 29, 30, 41, and 37.

   (a) Find the percentile rank for a score of 32.
   (b) Find the percentile rank for a score of 44.
   (c) Find the percentile rank for a score of 36.
   (d) Find the percentile rank for a score of 27.
   (e) Find the percentile rank for a score of 49.

6. The heights (in inches) of the 12 students in a seminar course are 73, 68, 64, 63, 71, 70, 65, 67, 72, 66, 60, and 61.

   (a) Find the percentile rank for a height of 67 in.
   (b) Find the percentile rank for a height of 70 in.
   (c) Find the percentile rank for a height of 63 in.
   (d) Find the percentile rank for a height of 68 in.
   (e) Find the percentile rank for a height of 66 in.

7. In a class of 500 students, Carveta's rank was 125. Find her percentile rank.

8. In a class of 400 students, John's rank was 80. Find his percentile rank.
9. In a charity marathon to raise money for AIDS research, Chen finished 43rd out of 200 entrants. Find her percentile rank.
10. In a speed boat race, there were 25 participants. Nate came in 4th place. What is his percentile rank?
11. On an exam, Angela scored in the 20th percentile. If there were 50 students in the class, how many students scored lower than she did?
12. Out of 600 applicants to a graduate program at an Ivy League school, Marissa's GRE score was in the 25th percentile. How many applicants scored lower than she did?
13. Lea's percentile rank on an exam in a class of 600 students is 60. Maurice's class rank is 220. Who is ranked higher?
14. In an English class of 30 students, Audrelia's percentile rank is 20. Maranda's class rank is 20. Whose rank is higher?

15. In an evening statistics class, the ages of 20 students are as follows.

    18 24 19 20 33 42 43 27 31 39
    21 44 26 32 37 34 23 35 28 25

    (a) What is the percentile rank of 33?
    (b) What is the rank (from the top) of 33?
    (c) What age corresponds to the 20th percentile?

16. Twenty subjects in a psychology class experiment scored the following on an IQ test.

    95 107 110 101 122 96 94 104 131 90
    111 103 97 100 119 85 108 120 130 88

    (a) What is the percentile rank of 96?
    (b) What is the rank (from the top) of 96?
    (c) What score corresponds to the 40th percentile?

For Exercises 17–22, find the values for Q_1, Q_2, and Q_3.

17. Number of drive-in theaters in nine selected states:

    59 20 21 34 52 48 24 29 55

    Source: National Association of Theater Owners

18. Average cost in cents per kilowatt hour of producing electricity using nuclear energy for the past 8 years:

    1.83 2.18 2.36 2.04 2.10 2.25 2.48 2.57

    Source: Nuclear Energy Institute

19. The costs of a 1-hour massage in 10 large cities are:

    $75 $77 $78 $90 $87 $93 $89 $93 $95 $88

20. Number of passengers (in millions) at 10 selected airports in the United States:

    32.6 28.9 15.5 16.6 19.4 15.9 31.6 15.4 29.1 15.7

    Source: Aviation Statistics

21. The annual number of homicides in Milwaukee for a 10-year period is shown.

    122 111 124 121 127 108 107 88 122 103

22. Below are the market caps in billions of dollars of nine of the largest companies that are 30 years old or younger.

Google	$140.6	Yahoo	$40.2
Home Depot	$85.2	EMC	$31.9
Apple	$73.0	Starbucks	$24.5
Dell	$53.4	Staples	$19.4
eBay	$45.8		

    Source: *USA Today*

Critical Thinking

23. Is it possible to score 90% on a test and have a percentile rank less than 90th? Is it possible to score 90% and have a percentile rank of exactly 90?

24. What would you have to do in order to rank in the 100th percentile in your college graduating class?

Section 12-6 The Normal Distribution

LEARNING OBJECTIVES

☐ 1. Identify characteristics of a data set that is normally distributed.

☐ 2. Apply the empirical rule.

☐ 3. Compute *z* scores.

☐ 4. Use a table and *z* scores to find areas under the standard normal distribution.

If you grew up anywhere near maple trees, you're probably familiar with the seed pods they drop by the thousands in the spring. Like almost all living things, the individual pods vary in size—on any given tree, there's a typical size, with some pods bigger and some smaller.

On a beautiful spring day, I gathered 100 pods from the maple in my back yard, measured each, then grouped them according to their length. The

smallest was 42 mm, the largest 59 mm, and in the photo they're grouped in classes 42–43, 44–45, 46–47, etc. An interesting thing happened—we see that the largest number of pods have lengths somewhere in the middle of the range, and the classes further away from the center have less pods.

A wide variety of quantities in the real world, like sizes of individuals in a population, IQ scores, life spans for batteries of a certain brand, and many others, tend to exhibit this same phenomenon. In fact, it's so common that frequency distributions of this type came to be known as *normal distributions.*

Suppose a researcher selects a random sample of 100 adult women, measures their heights, and constructs a histogram. The researcher would probably get a graph similar to the one shown in Figure 12-6a. If the researcher increases the sample size and decreases the width of the classes, the histograms will look like the ones shown in Figures 12-6b and 12-6c. Finally, if it were possible to measure the exact heights of all adult females in the United States and plot them, the histogram would approach what is called the *normal distribution,* shown in Figure 12-6d. This distribution is also known as a *bell curve* or a *Gaussian distribution,* named for the German mathematician Carl Friedrich Gauss (1777–1855) who derived its equation.

A normal distribution is defined formally as follows.

A **normal distribution** is a continuous, symmetric, bell-shaped distribution.

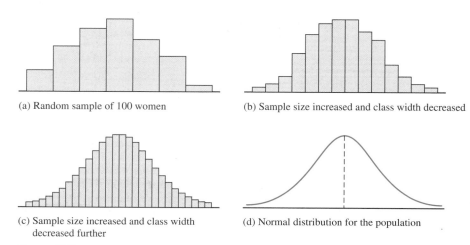

(a) Random sample of 100 women

(b) Sample size increased and class width decreased

(c) Sample size increased and class width decreased further

(d) Normal distribution for the population

Figure 12-6

Some properties of a normal distribution, including those mentioned in the definition, are explained next.

In a normal distribution, values cluster around a central value and fall off in both directions. Waiting times can be normally distributed.

☑ 1. Identify characteristics of a data set that is normally distributed.

Some Properties of a Normal Distribution

1. It is bell-shaped.

2. The mean, median, and mode are equal and located at the center of the distribution.

3. It is unimodal (i.e., it has only one mode).

4. It is symmetrical about the mean, which is equivalent to saying that its shape is the same on both sides of a vertical line passing through the center.

5. It is continuous—i.e., there are no gaps or holes.

6. The area under a portion of a normal curve is the percentage (in decimal form) of the data that falls between the data values that begin and end that region. (We will use this property extensively in Section 12-7.)

7. The total area under a normal curve is exactly 1. This makes sense based on property 6, since the area under the whole curve encompasses all data values.

The Empirical Rule

When data values are normally distributed, there is a rule that allows us to quickly determine a range in which most of the data values fall. It is known as the *empirical rule.*

The Empirical Rule

When data are normally distributed, approximately 68% of the values are within 1 standard deviation of the mean, approximately 95% are within 2 standard deviations of the mean, and approximately 99.7% are within 3 standard deviations of the mean (see Figure 12-7).

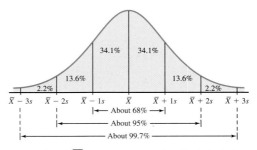

Figure 12-7 $\overline{X}$ = mean, s = standard deviation

EXAMPLE 1   Using the Empirical Rule

According to the website answerbag.com, the mean height for male humans is 5 feet 9.3 inches, with a standard deviation of 2.8 inches. If this is accurate, out of 1,000 randomly selected men, how many would you expect to be between 5 feet 6.5 inches and 6 feet 0.1 inch?

SOLUTION

The given range of heights corresponds to those within 1 standard deviation of the mean, so we would expect about 68% of men to fall in that range. In this case, we expect about 680 men to be between 5 feet 6.5 inches and 6 feet 0.1 inch.

☑ 2. Apply the empirical rule.

▼ Try This One 1

A standard test of intelligence is scaled so that the mean IQ is 100, and the standard deviation is 15. If there are 40,000 people in a stadium, how many would you expect to have an IQ between 70 and 130?

The Standard Normal Distribution

Any set of data that is normally distributed has its own mean and standard deviation, so the exact shape and location of the associated normal curve varies accordingly. This presents a problem: to answer questions related to the number of data values that are likely to fall into a given range, we need a method for finding the area under the curve for each specific case. This is not an easy problem to solve. Instead, statisticians developed a way to standardize the normal curves for different data sets by using the *standard normal distribution.*

The **standard normal distribution** is a normal distribution with mean 0 and standard deviation 1.

The standard normal distribution is shown in Figure 12-8. The values under the curve shown in Figure 12-8 indicate the proportion of area in each section. For example, the area between the mean and 1 standard deviation above or below the mean is about 0.341, or 34.1%.

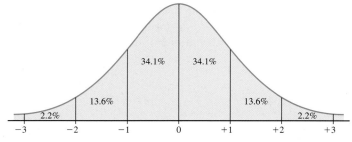

Figure 12-8

Tables have been compiled that help us to find the area under certain portions of a standard normal curve. In order to apply them to any data that are normally distributed, those data have to be altered to make the distribution have mean 0 and standard deviation 1. To accomplish that, we will use *z scores*.

For a given data value from a data set that is normally distributed, we define that value's **z score** to be

$$z = \frac{\text{Data value} - \text{mean}}{\text{Standard deviation}}$$

The z score is a measure of position: it describes how many standard deviations a data value lies above (if positive) or below (if negative) the mean.

EXAMPLE 2   Computing a *z* Score

Math Note

Notice that the units divide out, so z scores have no units.

Based on the information in Example 1, find the z score for a man who is 6 feet 4 inches tall.

SOLUTION

Using the formula for z scores with mean 5 feet 9.3 inches and standard deviation 2.8 inches:

$$z = \frac{76 \text{ in.} - 69.3 \text{ in.}}{2.8 \text{ in.}} \approx 2.4$$

☑ 3. Compute *z* scores.

▼ Try This One 2

Using the information in Try This One 1, find the z score for a person with an IQ of 91.

The value of z scores is that they will allow us to find areas under a normal curve using only areas under a standard normal curve, which can be read from a table, like Table 12-3.

TABLE 12-3 **Area Under a Normal Distribution Curve Between $z = 0$ and a Positive Value of z**

Math Note

An area table with more values can be found in Appendix A. If you need the area for a z score between two values in Table 12-3, you can get an approximate area by choosing an area between areas in the table, or use the more extensive table in the appendix.

z	A	z	A	z	A
0.00	0.000	1.10	0.364	2.20	0.486
0.05	0.020	1.15	0.375	2.25	0.488
0.10	0.040	1.20	0.385	2.30	0.489
0.15	0.060	1.25	0.394	2.35	0.491
0.20	0.079	1.30	0.403	2.40	0.492
0.25	0.099	1.35	0.412	2.45	0.493
0.30	0.118	1.40	0.419	2.50	0.494
0.35	0.137	1.45	0.427	2.55	0.495
0.40	0.155	1.50	0.433	2.60	0.495
0.45	0.174	1.55	0.439	2.65	0.496
0.50	0.192	1.60	0.445	2.70	0.497
0.55	0.209	1.65	0.451	2.75	0.497
0.60	0.226	1.70	0.455	2.80	0.497
0.65	0.242	1.75	0.460	2.85	0.498
0.70	0.258	1.80	0.464	2.90	0.498
0.75	0.273	1.85	0.468	2.95	0.498
0.80	0.288	1.90	0.471	3.00	0.499
0.85	0.302	1.95	0.474	3.05	0.499
0.90	0.316	2.00	0.477	3.10	0.499
0.95	0.329	2.05	0.480	3.15	0.499
1.00	0.341	2.10	0.482	3.20	0.499
1.05	0.353	2.15	0.484	3.25*	0.499

*For z scores greater than 3.25, use $A = 0.500$

Finding Areas under the Standard Normal Distribution

Section 12-7 is entirely devoted to solving real-world problems that use areas under a normal distribution. In the remainder of this section, we will focus on simply finding those areas. We will find areas corresponding to z scores using Table 12-3 and the following key facts.

Two Important Facts about the Standard Normal Curve

1. The area under any normal curve is divided into two equal halves at the mean. Each of the halves has area 0.500.
2. The area between $z = 0$ and a positive z score is the same as the area between $z = 0$ and the negative of that z score.

Each of the facts in the colored box is a consequence of the fact that normal distributions are symmetric about the mean. Examples 3, 4, and 5 will illustrate how to find areas under a normal curve.

EXAMPLE 3   **Finding the Area between Two z Scores**

Math Note

Remember that the area under any portion of a normal distribution has to be non-negative and less than or equal to 1. If you don't get an area in that range, you must have made a mistake.

Find the area under the standard normal distribution

(a) Between $z = 1.55$ and $z = 2.25$.
(b) Between $z = -0.60$ and $z = -1.35$.
(c) Between $z = 1.50$ and $z = -1.75$.

SOLUTION

(a) Draw the picture, label z scores, and shade the requested area. See Figure 12-9.

Using Table 12-3, the area between $z = 0$ and $z = 2.25$ is 0.488, and the area between $z = 0$ and $z = 1.55$ is 0.439. The area we are looking for is the larger area minus the smaller:

$$0.488 - 0.439 = 0.049.$$

Shaded area = 0.488 − 0.439 = 0.049

Figure 12-9

The area between $z = 1.55$ and $z = 2.25$ is 0.049.

(b) Draw the picture, label z scores, and shade the requested area. See Figure 12-10.

Using key fact 2, we can find the area between $z = 0$ and the two given negative z scores by finding the corresponding positive z scores in the table. The areas are 0.226 for $z = -0.60$, and 0.412 for $z = -1.35$. Again, the area we're looking for is the larger area minus the smaller:

$$0.412 - 0.226 = 0.186$$

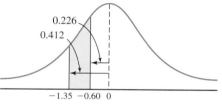

Shaded area = 0.412 − 0.226 = 0.186

Figure 12-10

The area between $z = -0.60$ and $z = -1.35$ is 0.186.

(c) Draw the picture, label the z scores, and shade the requested area. See Figure 12-11.

Since the z values are on opposite sides of the mean, the areas corresponding to the z values are added. The area corresponding to $z = -1.75$ is 0.460, and the area corresponding to $z = 1.50$ is 0.433.

$$0.460 + 0.433 = 0.893$$

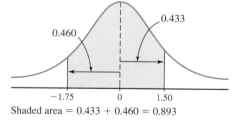

Shaded area = 0.433 + 0.460 = 0.893

Figure 12-11

The area between $z = 1.50$ and $z = -1.75$ is 0.893.

▼ Try This One 3

Find the area under the standard normal distribution

(a) Between $z = 2.05$ and $z = 2.40$.   (b) Between $z = -3.2$ and $z = -2.0$.
(c) Between $z = -0.55$ and $z = 1.6$.

When we want to find the area to the right or left of a single z score, we will use the fact that the area under half of the curve is exactly 0.500, as in Examples 4 and 5.

EXAMPLE 4 **Finding the Area to the Right of a *z* Score**

Find the area under the standard normal distribution

(a) To the right of $z = 1.70$. (b) To the right of $z = -0.95$.

Math Note

Using a sketch and the two important facts on page 689 allows us to find areas without having to learn a variety of rules and formulas for the different possible situations.

SOLUTION

(a) Draw the picture, label the z scores, and shade the area. See Figure 12-12.

The area of the entire portion to the right of $z = 0$ is 0.500. According to the table, the area of the portion between $z = 0$ and $z = 1.70$ is 0.455. So the shaded portion is the difference between 0.500 and 0.455:

$$0.500 - 0.455 = 0.045$$

The area to the right of $z = 1.70$ is 0.045.

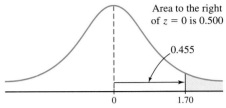

Shaded area = $0.500 - 0.455 = 0.045$

Figure 12-12

(b) Draw the picture, label the z scores, and shade the area. See Figure 12-13.

This time, the area is the sum of 0.500 (the entire right half of the distribution) and the area between $z = 0$ and $= -0.95$, which we find to be 0.329 using Table 12-3.

$$0.500 + 0.329 = 0.829$$

The area to the right of $z = -0.95$ is 0.829.

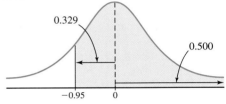

Shaded area = $0.500 + 0.329 = 0.829$

Figure 12-13

▼ **Try This One 4**

Find the area under the standard normal distribution

(a) To the right of $z = -2.40$. (b) To the right of $z = 0.25$.

EXAMPLE 5 **Finding the Area to the Left of a *z* Score**

Find the area under the standard normal distribution

(a) To the left of $z = 2.20$. (b) To the left of $z = -1.95$.

SOLUTION

(a) Draw the picture, label the z scores, and shade the area. See Figure 12-14.

The shaded area is the entire left half (0.500) minus the area between $z = 0$ and $z = -2.2$, which is 0.486 according to Table 12-3.

$$0.500 - 0.486 = 0.014$$

The area to the left of $z = -2.2$ is 0.014.

Shaded area = $0.500 - 0.486 = 0.014$

Figure 12-14

(b) Draw the picture, label the z scores, and shade the area. See Figure 12-15.

Table 12-3 gives us an area of 0.474 between $z = 0$ and $z = 1.95$. Adding to the area of the left half (0.500), we get

$$0.500 + 0.474 = 0.974$$

The area to the left of $z = 1.95$ is 0.974.

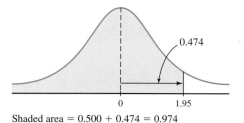

Shaded area = 0.500 + 0.474 = 0.974

Figure 12-15

CAUTION

Don't ignore your graph when writing your final answer! As long as you keep in mind that the total area under the distribution is 1, you can visually check if your answer is reasonable. In Example 5b, just from a quick glance at the graph you can see that most of the distribution is shaded, so your answer should be close to 1.

▼ Try This One 5

4. Use a table and z scores to find areas under the standard normal distribution.

Find the area under the standard normal distribution

(a) To the left of $z = -1.05$.

(b) To the left of $z = 0.1$.

To close the section, we should point out that no data set fits the normal distribution perfectly, since the normal curve is a theoretical distribution that would come from infinitely many data values. But there are many, many quantities that vary from a true normal distribution so slightly that the normal curve can be used to study those quantities very effectively.

Answers to Try This One

1 About 38,000

2 −0.6

3 (a) 0.012
(b) 0.022
(c) 0.654

4 (a) 0.992
(b) 0.401

5 (a) 0.147
(b) 0.540

EXERCISE SET 12-6

Writing Exercises

1. What is the distinguishing characteristic of a quantity that is normally distributed?
2. Write as many properties of a normal curve as you can think of.
3. What does the area under a portion of a normal curve tell you about the data in the associated distribution?

4. Explain what the empirical rule says.
5. What percentage of the area under a normal curve falls to the right of the mean? To the left? Explain.
6. Why does it make sense that the total area under a normal curve is 1?

Computational Exercises

For Exercises 7–10, assume that the data set described is normally distributed with the given mean and standard deviation, and with n total values. Find the approximate number of data values that will fall in the given range.

7. Mean $= 12$, standard deviation $= 1.5$, $n = 50$.
   Range: 10.5 to 13.5

8. Mean $= 100$, standard deviation $= 8$, $n = 200$.
   Range: 84 to 116

9. Mean $= 400$, standard deviation $= 25$, $n = 500$.
   Range: 325 to 475

10. Mean $= -14.2$, standard deviation $= 1.6$, $n = 120$.
    Range: -17.4 to -11

For Exercises 11–28, find the area under the standard normal distribution curve

11. Between $z = 0$ and $z = 1.95$.

12. Between $z = 0$ and $z = 0.55$.

13. Between $z = 0$ and $z = -0.5$. 0.192

14. Between $z = 0$ and $z = -2.05$.

15. To the right of $z = 1.0$.

16. To the right of $z = 0.25$.

17. To the left of $z = -0.40$.

18. To the left of $z = -1.45$.

19. Between $z = 1.25$ and $z = 1.90$.

20. Between $z = 0.8$ and $z = 1.3$.

21. Between $z = -0.85$ and $z = -0.20$.

22. Between $z = -1.55$ and $z = -1.85$.

23. Between $z = 0.25$ and $z = -1.10$.

24. Between $z = 2.45$ and $z = -1.05$.

25. To the left of $z = 1.20$.

26. To the left of $z = 2.15$.

27. To the right of $z = -1.90$.

28. To the right of $z = -0.20$.

Critical Thinking

29. Find a z value to the right of the mean so that 67.4% of the distribution lies to the left of it.

30. Find a z value to the left of the mean so that 98.6% of the area lies to the right of it.

31. Find two z values, one positive and one negative but having the same absolute value, so that the areas in the two tails (ends) total these values.
    (a) 4%
    (b) 8%
    (c) 1.6%

Section 12-7 Applications of the Normal Distribution

LEARNING OBJECTIVES

☐ 1. Use the normal distribution to find percentages.

☐ 2. Use the normal distribution to find probabilities.

☐ 3. Use the normal distribution to find percentile ranks.

Surely there must be someone out there who doesn't like Oreos, but I haven't met him or her. A standard package of America's favorite cookie contains 510 grams of sweet temptation. Of course, when you buy a package, you expect every one of those 510 grams. But there's variation in just about everything, so some packages will have more than the intended weight, and some will have less. The folks running Nabisco aren't dummies, though—they know that if someone decides to check the weight and finds it to be less than 510 grams, they won't be a very happy customer. So what to do?

This is exactly the sort of situation where weights tend to be normally distributed. The company would likely design its production and packaging process so that the mean is somewhat larger than 510 grams, with a standard deviation that assures that the vast majority of packages will weigh at least 510 grams.

In this section, we will see how the area calculations we practiced in Section 12-6 can be used to solve real-world problems for data that are normally distributed. Our general strategy will be to transform specific data into z scores, then use Table 12-3 to find areas. Finally, we'll interpret the area as it applies to the given data.

The reason this works is indicated by Figure 12-16. Suppose that the weight of Oreos in a package is normally distributed with mean 518 grams and standard deviation 4 grams. The distribution would look like Figure 12-16a. After using the z score formula to standardize, we get the graph in Figure 12-16b; now we can apply our area calculations.

Figure 12-16

EXAMPLE 1   Solving a Problem Using the Normal Distribution

If the weights of Oreos in a package are normally distributed with mean 518 grams and standard deviation 4 grams, find the percentage of packages that will weigh less than 510 grams.

SOLUTION

Step 1 Draw the figure and represent the area, as shown in Figure 12-17.

Step 2 Find the z score for data value 510.

$$z = \frac{\text{value} - \text{mean}}{\text{standard deviation}}$$

$$= \frac{510 - 518}{4} = -2$$

Figure 12-17

This tells us that 510 grams is 2 standard deviations below the mean.

Step 3 Find the shaded area using Table 12-3. The shaded area is the area of the left half (0.5) minus the area between $z = 0$ and $z = -2$. The area between $z = 0$ and $z = -2$ is 0.477 (using $z = +2$ from the table).

$$\text{Area} = 0.5 - 0.477 = 0.023$$

Step 4 Interpret the area. In this case, an area of 0.023 tells us that only 2.3% of packages will have weights less than 510 grams.

Math Note

It's typical for manufacturers to make sure that the listed weight for products packaged by weight is at least two standard deviations below the mean, ensuring that over 97% of the packages have the listed weight or more.

☑ 1. Use the normal distribution to find percentages.

▼ Try This One 1

Based on data compiled by the World Health Organization, the mean systolic blood pressure in the United States is 120, the standard deviation is 16, and the pressures are normally distributed. Find each.

(a) The percent of individuals who have a blood pressure between 120 and 128
(b) The percent of individuals who have a blood pressure above 132
(c) The percent of individuals who have a blood pressure between 112 and 116
(d) The percent of individuals who have a blood pressure between 124 and 144
(e) The percent of individuals who have a blood pressure lower than 104

Our next interpretation for area under a normal distribution is tremendously important because it ties our study of statistics to the main topic of Chapter 11, probability.

Probability and Area under a Normal Distribution

The area under a normal distribution between two data values is the probability that a randomly selected data value is between those two values.

Example 2 illustrates the use of area to find probability.

EXAMPLE 2   **Using Area under a Normal Distribution to Find Probabilities**

Based on data in the 2009 *Statistical Abstract of the United States,* the average *American* generates 1,679 pounds of garbage per year. Let's assume that the number of pounds generated per person is approximately normally distributed with standard deviation 200 pounds. Find the probability that a randomly selected person generates

(a) Between 1,300 and 2,000 pounds of garbage per year.
(b) More than 2,000 pounds of garbage per year.

SOLUTION

(a) **Step 1** Draw the figure and represent the area. See Figure 12-18 below.

Step 2 Find the z scores for the two given weights.

$$1{,}300 \text{ pounds: } z = \frac{1{,}300 - 1{,}679}{200} \approx -1.9$$

$$2{,}000 \text{ pounds: } z = \frac{2{,}000 - 1{,}679}{200} \approx 1.6$$

Step 3 Find the shaded area. Using Table 12-3, the area between $z = 0$ and $z = 1.6$ is 0.445, and the area between $z = 0$ and $z = -1.9$ is 0.471. So the shaded area is

$$0.471 + 0.445 = 0.916$$

Step 4 Interpret the area. This tells us that if a person is selected at random, the probability that he or she generates between 1,300 and 2,000 pounds of garbage per year is 0.916, or 91.6%.

Figure 12-18

(b) Most of the work was already done in part a. We can adapt the graph a bit (Figure 12-19).

The shaded area is the area between $z = 0$ and $z = 1.6$ subtracted from the area of the entire right half (0.5).

$$0.5 - 0.445 = 0.055$$

Figure 12-19

The probability that a randomly selected person generates more than 2,000 pounds of garbage per year is 0.055, or 5.5%.

Math Note

The probability that a randomly selected value from a normal distribution is less than some value is the area to the left of that value. The probability of a randomly selected value being greater than some value is the area to the right of that value.

☑ 2. Use the normal distribution to find probabilities.

▼ Try This One 2

The *Statistical Abstract* also indicates that of the 1,679 pounds of garbage generated by the average individual, 913 pounds will end up in a landfill. If these amounts are approximately normally distributed with standard deviation 160 pounds, find the probability that a randomly selected person generates

(a) Less than 600 pounds that end up in a landfill.
(b) Between 600 and 1,000 pounds that end up in a landfill.

Normal distributions can also be used to find percentiles, and answer questions of "how many?" Example 3 illustrates these types of questions.

EXAMPLE 3   Finding Number in a Sample and Percentile Rank

The American Automobile Association reports that the average time it takes to respond to an emergency call is 25 minutes. Assume the response time is approximately normally distributed and the standard deviation is 4.5 minutes.

(a) If 80 calls are randomly selected, approximately how many will have response times less than 15 minutes?
(b) In what percentile is a response time of 30 minutes?

SOLUTION

(a) **Step 1** Draw a figure and represent the area as shown in Figure 12-20.

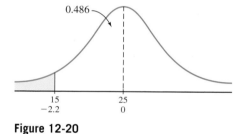

Figure 12-20

Step 2 Find the z value for 15.

$$z = \frac{\text{Value} - \text{mean}}{\text{Standard deviation}}$$

$$= \frac{15 - 25}{4.5} \approx -2.2$$

Step 3 Find the shaded area. Using Table 12-3, we find that the area between $z = 0$ and $z = -2.2$ is 0.486. The shaded area is the difference of the entire left half (0.5) and 0.486.

$$\text{Area} = 0.5 - 0.486 = 0.014.$$

Step 4 Interpret the area. An area of 0.014 tells us that 1.4% of calls will have a response time of less than 15 minutes. Multiply the percentage by the number of calls in our sample:

$$1.4\% \text{ of } 80 \text{ calls} = (0.014)(80) = 1.12$$

Approximately one call in 80 will have response time less than 15 minutes.

Math Note

Notice that in this case (number of calls), an answer of 1.12 doesn't make sense. We need to round to the nearest whole number.

(b) **Step 1** Draw a figure and represent the area as shown in Figure 12-21. Remember that to find the percentile, we are interested in the percentage of times that are less than 30 minutes.

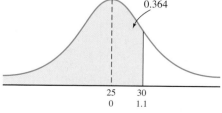

Figure 12-21

Step 2 Find the z score for a response time of 30 minutes.

$$z = \frac{30 - 25}{4.5} \approx 1.1$$

Step 3 Find the shaded area. The area to the left of $z = 1.1$ is the area of the left half (0.5) plus the area between $z = 0$ and $z = 1.1$ (0.364 according to Table 12-3).

$$\text{Area} = 0.5 + 0.364 = 0.864$$

Step 4 Interpret the area. An area of 0.864 means that 86.4% of calls will get a response time of less than 30 minutes, so the time of 30 minutes is in the 86th percentile.

▼ Try This One 3

The mean for a reading test given nationwide is 80, and the standard deviation is 8. The variable is normally distributed. If 10,000 students take the test, find each.

☑ 3. Use the normal distribution to find percentile ranks.

(a) The number of students who will score above 90
(b) The number of students who will score between 78 and 88
(c) The percentile of a student who scores 94
(d) The number of students who will score below 76

Answers to Try This One

1 (a) 19.2%
(b) 22.7%
(c) 9.3%
(d) 33.4%
(e) 15.9%

2 (a) 0.026 or 2.6%
(b) 0.683 or 68.3%

3 (a) 1,060
(b) 4,400
(c) 96th percentile
(d) 3,080

EXERCISE SET 12-7

Writing Exercises

1. Explain why the normal distribution can be used to solve many real-life problems.

2. Given a data set, how could you decide if the distribution of the data was approximately normal?

Real-World Applications

3. The average hourly wage of production workers in manufacturing in 2007 was $17.41. Assume the variable is normally distributed. If the standard deviation of earning is $3.72, find these probabilities for a randomly selected production worker.

   (a) The production worker earns more than $18.55.
   (b) The production worker earns less than $14.00.
   Source: Statistical Abstract of the United States

4. The average cost for two people to go to a movie is $22. The standard deviation is $3. Assume the cost is normally distributed. Find the probability that at any given theater, the cost will be more than $26 for two people to go to a movie.

5. If the mean salary of public school teachers in the United States in 2007 was $49,294 and the standard deviation was $9,000, find these probabilities for a randomly selected teacher. Assume the variable is normally distributed.

   (a) The teacher earns more than $55,000.
   (b) The teacher earns less than $45,000.

6. Average sales for an online textbook distributor were $71.12 per customer per purchase. Assume the sales are normally distributed. If the standard deviation of the amount spent on textbooks is $8.42, find these probabilities for a randomly selected customer of the online textbook distributor.

   (a) He or she spent more than $60 per purchase.
   (b) He or she spent less than $80 per purchase.

7. A survey found that people keep their television sets an average of 4.8 years. The standard deviation is 0.89 year. If a person decides to buy a new TV set,

find the probability that he or she has owned the old set for the given amount of time. Assume the variable is normally distributed.

(a) Less than 2.5 years   (b) Between 3 and 4 years
(c) More than 4.2 years

8. The average age of CEOs is 56 years. Assume the variable is normally distributed. If the standard deviation is 4 years, find the probability that the age of a randomly selected CEO will be in the given range.

(a) Between 53 and 59 years old
(b) Between 58 and 63 years old
(c) Between 50 and 55 years old

9. The average life of a brand of automobile tires is 30,000 miles, with a standard deviation of 2,000 miles. If a tire is selected and tested, find the probability that it will have the given lifetime. Assume the variable is normally distributed.

(a) Between 25,000 and 28,000 miles
(b) Between 27,000 and 32,000 miles
(c) Between 31,500 and 33,500 miles

10. The average time a person spends in each visit to an online social networking service is 62 minutes. The standard deviation is 12 minutes. If a visitor is selected at random, find the probability that he or she will spend the time shown on the networking service. Assume the times are normally distributed.

(a) At least 180 minutes   (b) At least 50 minutes

11. The average amount of snow per season in Trafford is 44 inches. The standard deviation is 6 inches. Find the probability that next year Trafford will receive the given amount of snowfall. Assume the variable is normally distributed.

(a) At most 50 inches of snow
(b) At least 53 inches of snow

12. The average waiting time for a drive-in window at a local bank is 9.2 minutes, with a standard deviation of 2.6 minutes. When a customer arrives at the bank, find the probability that the customer will have to wait the given time. Assume the variable is normally distributed.

(a) Between 5 and 10 minutes
(b) Less than 6 minutes or more than 9 minutes

13. The average time it takes college freshmen to complete the Mason Basic Reasoning Test is 24.6 minutes. The standard deviation is 5.8 minutes. Find these probabilities. Assume the variable is normally distributed.

(a) It will take a student between 15 and 30 minutes to complete the test.
(b) It will take a student less than 18 minutes or more than 28 minutes to complete the test.

14. A brisk walk at 4 miles per hour burns an average of 300 calories per hour. If the standard deviation of the distribution is 8 calories, find the probability that a person who walks 1 hour at the rate of 4 miles per hour will burn the given number of calories. Assume the variable is normally distributed.

(a) More than 280 calories
(b) Less than 293 calories
(c) Between 285 and 320 calories

15. During September, the average temperature of Laurel Lake is 64.2° and the standard deviation is 3.2°. Assume the variable is normally distributed. For a randomly selected day in September, find the probability that the temperature will be

(a) Above 62°.   (c) Between 65° and 68°.
(b) Below 67°.

16. If the systolic blood pressure for a certain group of people has a mean of 132 and a standard deviation of 8, find the probability that a randomly selected person in the group will have the given systolic blood pressure. Assume the variable is normally distributed.

(a) Above 130   (c) Between 131 and 136
(b) Below 140

17. An IQ test has a mean of 100 and a standard deviation of 15. The test scores are normally distributed. If 2,000 people take the test, find the number of people who will score

(a) Below 93.   (c) Between 80 and 105.
(b) Above 120.   (d) Between 75 and 82.

18. The average size (in square feet) of homes built in the United States in the fourth quarter of 2008 was 2,343. Assume the variable is normally distributed and the standard deviation is 152 square feet. In a sample of 500 recently built homes, find the number of homes that will

(a) Have between 1,900 and 2,000 square feet.
(b) Have more than 3,000 square feet.
(c) Have less than 2,000 square feet.
(d) Have more than 1,600 square feet.

Source: National Association of Homebuilders

19. According to the National Association of Realtors, the mean sale price for existing homes in the United States in 2008 was $242,700. Assume that sale prices are normally distributed with a standard deviation of $41,000. If 800 home sales are selected at random, find the number of homes that cost

(a) More than $300,000.
(b) Between $200,000 and $300,000.
(c) Less than $150,000.

20. The average price of Stephen King paperbacks sold at bookstores across the country is $9.52, and the standard deviation is $1.02. Assume the price is normally distributed. If a national bookstore sells 1,000 Stephen King paperbacks during August,

find the number of Stephen King paperbacks that were sold

(a) For less than $8.00.
(b) For more than $10.00.
(c) Between $9.50 and $10.50.
(d) Between $9.80 and $10.05.

21. Refer to Exercise 3. If your buddy Earl gets a job as a manufacturing production worker making $15.20 per hour, what percentile is he in?

22. Refer to Exercise 7. If you buy a TV for your dorm and keep it for your 4 years of school then sell it, what percentile does that put you in?

23. Refer to Exercise 10. Suppose that your grades have been slipping, and you impose a new rule on yourself: no more than 20 minutes at a time on social networking sites. What percentile would that put you in?

24. Refer to Exercise 18. When the one-hit wonder band The Flaming Rogers falls off the charts, their singer is forced to downsize from the 5,000 square foot home he built earlier in the year to a more modest 2,000 square foot model. What was his change in percentile rank?

Critical Thinking

25. If a distribution of raw scores were plotted and then the scores were transformed into z scores, would the shape of the distribution change?

26. An instructor gives a 100-point examination in which the grades are normally distributed. The mean is 60 and the standard deviation is 10. If there are 5% A's and 5% F's, 15% B's and 15% D's, and 60% C's, find the scores that divide the distribution into those categories.

27. A researcher who is in charge of an educational study wants subjects to perform some special skill. Fearing that people who are unusually talented or unusually untalented could distort the results, he decides to use people who scored in the middle 50% on

a certain test. If the mean for the population is 100 and the standard deviation is 15, find the two limits (upper and lower) for the scores that would enable a volunteer to participate in the study. Assume the scores are normally distributed.

28. While preparing for their comeback tour, The Flaming Rogers find that the average time it takes their sound tech to set up for a show is 58.6 minutes, with a standard deviation of 4.3 minutes. If the band manager decides to include only the fastest 20% of sound techs on the tour, what should the cutoff time be for concert setup? Assume the times are normally distributed.

Section 12-8 Correlation and Regression Analysis

LEARNING OBJECTIVES

☐ 1. Construct scatter plots for two data sets.

☐ 2. Calculate correlation coefficients.

☐ 3. Determine if correlation coefficients are significant.

☐ 4. Find a regression line for two data sets.

☐ 5. Use regression lines to make predictions.

The Business Insider blog posted an article in November 2008 with the headline "Proof of a Correlation between MySpace Usage and Illiteracy." It certainly seems to imply that MySpace users tend to be illiterate. On what data were these claims based?

The key word in the claim is *correlation*. In statistics, that term describes an attempt to determine if a relationship exists between two sets of data, like literacy rates and MySpace usage.

In order to decide if a relationship exists between two data sets, we have to first gather data in such a way that values from each set can be paired together. In this case, the literacy rate for each state was recorded, as well as data from Google on how likely Internet users from each state were to search for the term "MySpace." We can then plot a graph designating one set of data as the *x variable* or **independent variable** and the other as the *y variable* or **dependent variable.** This graph is called a *scatter plot*.

A **scatter plot** is a graph of the ordered pairs (x, y) consisting of data from two data sets.

After the scatter plot is drawn, we can analyze the graph to see if there is a pattern. If there is a noticeable pattern, such as the points falling in an approximately straight line, then a possible relationship between the two variables may exist.

If a strong relationship appears to exist between two data sets, we might further analyze the relationship by trying to find an equation relating the variables. This is known as *regression analysis,* which we will learn about later in the section. For now, we'll focus on scatter plots.

EXAMPLE 1   **Constructing a Scatter Plot**

A medical researcher selects a sample of small hospitals in his state and hopes to discover if there is a relationship between the number of beds and the number of personnel employed by the hospital. Construct a scatter plot for the data shown.

No. of beds (x)	28	56	34	42	45	78	84	36	74	95
Personnel (y)	72	195	74	211	145	139	184	131	233	366

SOLUTION

Step 1 Draw and label the x and y axes, as shown.

Step 2 Plot the data pairs. See Figure 12-22.

Figure 12-22

▼ Try This One 1

The data below represent the heights in feet and the number of stories of the tallest buildings in Pittsburgh. Draw a scatter plot for the data and describe the relationship.

Height (x)	485	511	520	535	582	615	616	635	728	841
No. of stories (y)	40	37	41	42	38	45	31	40	54	64

Source: *The World Almanac and Book of Facts*

Analyzing the Scatter Plot

There are several types of relationships that can exist between the x values and the y values in a scatter plot. These relationships can be identified by looking at the pattern of the points on the graphs. The types of patterns and corresponding relationships are:

1. *A positive linear relationship* exists when the points fall approximately in an ascending straight line from left to right, and both the x and y values increase at the same time. See Figure 12-23a on the next page.
2. *A negative linear relationship* exists when the points fall approximately in a descending straight line from left to right. See Figure 12-23b on the next page. The relationship then is as the x values are increasing, the y values are decreasing.

3. *A nonlinear relationship* exists when the points fall in a curved line. See Figure 12-23c. The relationship is described by the nature of the curve.
4. *No relationship* exists when there is no discernible pattern to the points. See Figure 12-23d.

☑ 1. Construct scatter plots for two data sets.

The relationship between the variables in Example 1 might be a positive linear relationship. It looks like as the size of the hospital based on the number of beds increases, the number of personnel also increases.

(a) Positive linear relationship

(b) Negative linear relationship

(c) Nonlinear relationship

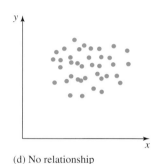
(d) No relationship

Figure 12-23

The Correlation Coefficient

Deciding whether or not two data sets are related by simply looking at a scatter plot is a pretty subjective process, so it would be nice to have a way to quantify how strongly connected data sets are.

The **correlation coefficient** is a number that describes how close to a linear relationship there is between two data sets. Correlation coefficients range from -1 (perfect negative linear relationship) to $+1$ (perfect positive linear relationship). The closer this number is to one in absolute value, the more likely it is that the data sets are related. A correlation coefficient close to zero indicates that the data are most likely not related at all (see Figure 12-24). We use the letter r to represent the correlation coefficient. It doesn't depend on the units for the two data sets, and it also doesn't depend on which set you choose for the x variable.

Figure 12-24

Calculating the Value of the Correlation Coefficient

In order to find the value of the correlation coefficient, we will use the following formula:

Math Note

The sign of r will indicate the nature of the relationship if one exists. That is, if r is positive, the linear relationship will be positive. If r is negative, the linear relationship will be negative. Looking at the scatter plots in Figure 12-23, for (a) r would be close to $+1$; for (b), r would be close to -1; for (c) and (d), r would be close to zero.

Formula for Finding the Value of r:

$$r = \frac{n(\Sigma xy) - (\Sigma x)(\Sigma y)}{\sqrt{[n(\Sigma x^2) - (\Sigma x)^2][n(\Sigma y^2) - (\Sigma y)^2]}}$$

where
n = the number of data pairs
Σx = the sum of the x values
Σy = the sum of the y values
Σxy = the sum of the products of the x and y values for each pair
Σx^2 = the sum of the squares of the x values
Σy^2 = the sum of the squares of the y values

When calculating the value of r, it is helpful to make a table, as shown in Example 2.

EXAMPLE 2   Calculating a Correlation Coefficient

Find the correlation coefficient for the data in Example 1.

SOLUTION

Step 1 Make a table as shown with the following headings: x, y, xy, x^2, and y^2.

Step 2 Find the values for the product xy, the values for x^2, the values for y^2, and place them in the columns as shown. Then find the sums of the columns.

x	y	xy	x^2	y^2
28	72	2,016	784	5,184
56	195	10,920	3,136	38,025
34	74	2,516	1,156	5,476
42	211	8,862	1,764	44,521
45	145	6,525	2,025	21,025
78	139	10,842	6,084	19,321
84	184	15,456	7,056	33,856
36	131	4,716	1,296	17,161
74	233	17,242	5,476	54,289
95	366	34,770	9,025	133,956
$\sum x = 572$	$\sum y = 1{,}750$	$\sum xy = 113{,}865$	$\sum x^2 = 37{,}802$	$\sum y^2 = 372{,}814$

Step 3 Substitute into the formula and evaluate (note that there are 10 data pairs):

$$r = \frac{n(\Sigma xy) - (\Sigma x)(\Sigma y)}{\sqrt{[n(\Sigma x^2) - (\Sigma x)^2][n(\Sigma y^2) - (\Sigma y)^2]}}$$

$$= \frac{10(113{,}865) - (572)(1{,}750)}{\sqrt{[10(37{,}802) - (572)^2][10(372{,}814) - (1{,}750)^2]}}$$

$$= \frac{137{,}650}{\sqrt{(50{,}836)(665{,}640)}}$$

$$\approx 0.748$$

The correlation coefficient for the two data sets is 0.748. This appears to confirm what our eyes tell us about the scatter plot in Example 1—it's certainly not a perfect linear relationship, but does tend to indicate that as bed space goes up, the number of personnel does as well.

▼ Try This One 2

2. Calculate correlation coefficients.

Find the correlation coefficient for the data in Try This One 1.

Next we will tackle the issue of how to interpret the correlation coefficient. In Example 2, the value of r was based on a sample of data. The population is all hospitals in a certain state with fewer than 100 beds, and a sample of such hospitals was chosen. When data from a sample is used, we can't be positive that it represents the entire population. So conclusions drawn, like the conclusion that there's a connection between numbers of beds and personnel, may not be correct.

Sidelight TECHNOLOGY AND THE CORRELATION COEFFICIENT

If there's just one thing you learned from Example 2, it's probably that finding a correlation coefficient is not exactly simple. Even for a reasonably small data set, the calculations involved are a little cumbersome. You can imagine how much worse it would be for larger data sets.

(a) (b) (c)

Figure 12-25

Fortunately, most graphing calculators and spreadsheets have built-in commands to compute correlation coefficients. In Microsoft Excel, enter the two data sets in two columns. Then choose another blank cell to enter the correlation coefficient. Next, choose Function . . . from the Insert menu: in the category dialog box choose Statistical, from the list of functions choose CORREL. You will then be prompted to choose the range of cells that make up each data set, and presto! The correlation coefficient appears in the chosen cell.

Using a standard graphing calculator, the data are entered on the list editing screen (STAT 1). This is shown in

Figure 12-25a with the data from Example 1 entered. Next, push STAT   right Arrow   8 as shown in Figure 12-25b, then ENTER. The resulting screen shows the correlation coefficient at the bottom, as well as the regression line for the data, which we will learn about shortly (see Figure 12-25c). If your calculator doesn't display r, push CATALOG, which is 2nd   0 , then scroll down and choose DiagnosticOn.

Statisticians have traditionally agreed that when we conclude that two data sets have a relationship, we can be satisfied with that conclusion if there is either a 95% or 99% chance that we're correct. This corresponds to a 5% or 1% chance of being wrong. These percentages are called **significance levels.**

We know that the more data we have, the more likely that data are representative of the population. Not surprisingly, the value of r needed to be reasonably sure that two data sets are correlated is higher for small sample sizes, and lower for large sample sizes. In Table 12-4, we see the minimum r values needed to have a 5% and 1% chance of being wrong when we conclude that two data sets are related.

TABLE 12-4 Significant Values for the Correlation Coefficient

Sample Size	5%	1%	Sample Size	5%	1%
4	.950	.990	17	.482	.606
5	.878	.959	18	.468	.590
6	.811	.917	19	.456	.575
7	.754	.875	20	.444	.561
8	.707	.834	21	.433	.549
9	.666	.798	22	.423	.537
10	.632	.765	23	.412	.526
11	.602	.735	24	.403	.515
12	.576	.708	25	.396	.505
13	.553	.684	30	.361	.463
14	.532	.661	40	.312	.402
15	.514	.641	60	.254	.330
16	.497	.623	120	.179	.234

Using Significant Values for the Correlation Coefficient

If $|r|$ is greater than or equal to the value given in Table 12-4 for either the 5% or 1% significance level, then we can reasonably conclude that the two data sets are related.

The use of Table 12-4 is illustrated in Example 3.

EXAMPLE 3 Deciding if a Correlation Coefficient is Significant

Researchers could use correlation and regression analysis to find out if there is a correlation between the size of a family's home and the number of children in the family.

Determine if the correlation coefficient $r = 0.748$ found in Example 2 is significant at the 5% level.

SOLUTION

Since the sample size is $n = 10$ and the 5% significance level is used, the value of $|r|$ must be greater than or equal to the number found in Table 12-4 to be significant. In this case, $|r| = 0.748$, which is greater than or equal to 0.632 obtained from the table. We can conclude that there is a significant relationship between the data sets.

However, we can't conclude that there is a relationship between the data sets at the 1% significance level since r would need to be greater than or equal to 0.765. In this example, $r = 0.748$, which is less than 0.765.

▼ Try This One 3

Test the significance of the correlation coefficient obtained from Try This One 2. Use 5%, and then 1%.

CAUTION

Remember, the result of Example 3 doesn't guarantee that the data sets are actually related—there's still a 5% chance that they're not related at all.

Multi-symptom cold and cough relief without drowsiness

INDICATIONS: For the temporary relief of nasal congestion, minor aches, pains, headache, muscular aches, sore throat, and fever associated with the common cold. Temporarily relieves cough occurring with a cold. Helps loosen phlegm (mucus) and thin bronchial secretions to drain bronchial tubes and make coughs more productive.

DIRECTIONS: Adults and children 12 years of age and over, 2 liquid caps every 4 hours, while symptoms persist, not to exceed 8 liquid caps in 24 hours, or as directed by a doctor. Not recommended for children under 12 years of age.

WARNINGS: **Do not exceed recommended dosage.** If nervousness, dizziness, or sleeplessness occur, discontinue use and consult a doctor. Do not take this product for more than 10 days. A persistent cough may be a sign of a serious condition. If symptoms do not improve or if cough persists for more than 7 days, tends to recur, or is accompanied by rash, persistent headache, fever that lasts for more than 3 days, or if new symptoms occur, consult a doctor. Do not take this product for persistent or chronic cough such as occurs with smoking, asthma, chronic bronchitis, or emphysema, or where cough is accompanied by excessive phlegm (mucus) unless directed by a doctor. If sore throat is severe, persists for more than 2 days, is accompanied or followed by fever, headache, rash, nausea, or vomiting, consult a doctor promptly. Do not take this product if you have heart disease, high blood pressure, thyroid disease, diabetes, or difficulty in urination due to enlargement of the prostate gland unless directed by a doctor. As with any drug, if you are pregnant or nursing

Medication labels help users to become aware of the effects of taking medications.

☑ 3. Determine if correlation coefficients are significant.

How should we choose whether to use the 5% or 1% significance level in a given situation? It depends on the seriousness of the situation and the importance of drawing a correct conclusion. Suppose that researchers think that a new medication helps patients with asthma to breathe easier, but that some patients have experienced side effects. A correlation study would probably be done to decide if there is a relationship between the medication and these particular side effects. If the potential side effects are serious, like heart attacks or strokes, the 1% significance level would be used. If the side effects are mild, like headache or nausea, the 5% significance level would probably be considered sufficient, since the consequences of being wrong are not as dire as in the first case.

Regression

Once we have concluded that there is a significant relationship between the two variables, the next step is to find the *equation* of the **regression line** through the data points.

The regression line is a line that best fits the data. Broadly speaking, we say it is the line that passes through the points in such a way that the overall distance each point is from the line is at a minimum. The regression line is also called the *line of best fit*.

Recall from algebra that the equation of a line in the slope-intercept form is $y = mx + b$, where m is the slope and b is the y intercept. (See Section 7-1.) In statistics, the equation of the regression line is written as $y = a + bn$, where a is the y intercept and b is the slope. This is the equation that will be used here. In order to find the values for a and b, two formulas are used.

Formulas for Finding the Values of *a* and *b* for the Equation of the Regression Line

$$b = \frac{n(\Sigma xy) - (\Sigma x)(\Sigma y)}{n(\Sigma x^2) - (\Sigma x)^2} \quad \text{slope}$$

$$a = \frac{\Sigma y - b(\Sigma x)}{n} \quad y \text{ intercept}$$

EXAMPLE 4   Finding a Regression Line

Find the equation of the regression line for the data in Example 1.

SOLUTION

We already calculated the values needed for each formula in Example 2. Substitute into the first formula to find the value for the slope, b.

$$b = \frac{n(\Sigma xy) - (\Sigma x)\Sigma y}{n(\Sigma x^2) - (\Sigma x)^2} = \frac{10(113,865) - (572)(1,750)}{10(37,802) - (572)^2} = \frac{137,650}{50,836} \approx 2.7077$$

Substitute into the second formula to find the value for the y intercept, a, when $b = 2.7077$.

$$a = \frac{\Sigma y - b(\Sigma x)}{n} = \frac{(1,750) - 2.7077(572)}{10} = \frac{201.20}{10} = 20.120$$

The equation of the regression line is $y = 20.120 + 2.7077x$.

Math Note

The procedure outlined in the Sidelight on page 703 is a great way to find regression lines using a graphing calculator. Because of potential rounding error, the answer may be a bit different than the one obtained using the procedure in Example 4. This procedure is very sensitive to rounding error, so using at least three decimal places is a good idea.

☑ 4. Find a regression line for two data sets.

Try This One 4

Find the equation of the regression line for the data in Try This One 1.

After the equation of the regression line is found, it can be drawn on the scatter plot using one of the methods shown in Chapter 7. For example, you can find the coordinates of two points on the line by selecting two values for x, then substituting each into the regression line equation, and finding the corresponding values for y.

In the first case, let $x = 30$; then

$$y = 19.988 + 2.71x$$
$$= 19.988 + 2.71(30)$$
$$= 101.288$$

In the second case, let $x = 70$; then

$$y = 19.988 + 2.71x$$
$$= 19.988 + 2.71(70)$$
$$= 209.688$$

The coordinates of the first point are (30, 101), and the coordinates of the second point are (70, 210) (the y values have been rounded). Next, plot the two points and draw a line through each point. See Figure 12-26.

Figure 12-26

The Relationship between r and the Regression Line

Two things should be noted about the relationship between the value of r and the regression line. First, the value of r and the value of the slope, b, always have the same sign. Second, the closer the value of r is to $+1$ or -1, the better the points will fit the line. In other words, the stronger the relationship, the better the fit. Figure 12-27 shows the relationship between the correlation coefficient and the regression line.

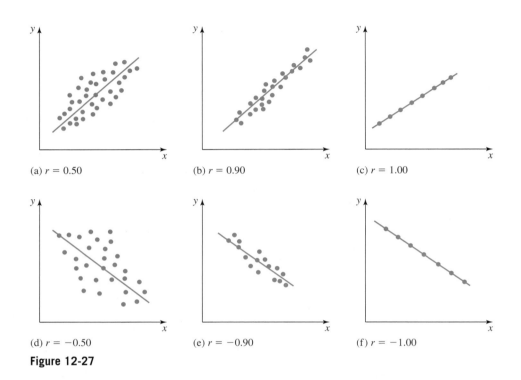

(a) $r = 0.50$　　(b) $r = 0.90$　　(c) $r = 1.00$

(d) $r = -0.50$　　(e) $r = -0.90$　　(f) $r = -1.00$

Figure 12-27

Once we have the equation of a regression line for two data sets, we can use it to predict a value for y given a particular value for x, as we will see in Example 5.

EXAMPLE 5　Using a Regression Line to Make a Prediction

Use the equation of the regression line found in Example 4 to predict the approximate number of personnel for a hospital with 65 beds.

SOLUTION

Substitute 65 for x into the equation $y = 20.120 + 2.7077x$ and find the value for y.

$$y = 20.120 + 2.7077(65) = 196.12 \text{ (which can be rounded to 196)}$$

We predict that a hospital with 65 beds will have approximately 196 personnel.

▼ Try This One 5

☑ 5. Use regression lines to make predictions.

Use the equation of the regression line found in Try This One 4 to predict the number of stories for a 670-foot building.

CAUTION

Never use a regression line to predict anything unless you've already checked that the correlation is significant! If it isn't significant, the regression line is meaningless.

Correlation and Causation

As you will see in the Sidelight below, there's more to the story of a relationship between two data sets than simply finding out that they're related. The nature of the relationship then needs to be further explored. The following is a list of possibilities to consider.

Possible Relationships between Data Sets

1. *There is a direct cause-and-effect relationship between two variables.* That is, x causes y. For example, water causes plants to grow, poison causes death, and heat causes ice to melt.

2. *There is a reverse cause-and-effect relationship between the variables.* That is, y causes x. Suppose that we find a correlation between excessive coffee consumption and nervousness. It would be tempting to conclude that drinking too much coffee causes nervousness. But it might actually be the case that nervous people drink a lot of coffee because they think it calms their nerves.

3. *The relationship between the variables may be caused by a third variable.* You could probably find a positive correlation between the amount of ice cream consumed per week and the number of drowning deaths for each week of the year. But this doesn't mean that eating ice cream causes you to drown. Both eating ice cream and swimming are more common during the summer months, and it stands to reason that more people will drown when more people are swimming. In this case, a third variable (seasonal weather) is affecting each of the original two variables.

Sidelight DOES MYSPACE CAUSE ILLITERACY?

At the beginning of this section, we looked at a claim that there's a correlation between using MySpace and illiteracy. How strong is that connection? And what does it mean?

A scatter plot of the data for all 50 states is shown in Figure 12-28. The x variable is the percent of the adult population that lacks basic literacy as measured by the National Assessment of Adult Literacy. The y variable is a scaled score that indicates how often Internet users from each state searched for the term MySpace on Google. The scatter plot looks like there is a positive linear correlation, and the correlation coefficient bears that out: it is almost exactly 0.6, which is well above the 1% significance level for a sample size of 50. So we can definitely conclude that the two data sets are related. (Note that $n = 50$ is not in Table 12-4, but we can see that 0.6 is within the 1% confidence interval for any sample size greater than 17.)

Then the most important question should be asked: what does it mean? This is the key point about correlation—there is a big difference between *correlation* and *causation*. When two data sets are related, that tells us nothing about *why* they are related. In this case, it would be inappropriate to conclude that being illiterate causes people to use MySpace, and it would be just plain silly to conclude that using MySpace

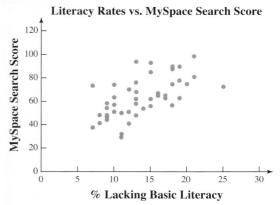

Figure 12.28

causes people to be illiterate. There may be some other combination of factors that keep literacy rates low in certain states and make people more likely to search for the term MySpace. Or (and this is my best guess) it might just be one big, amazing coincidence. In any case, it's important to understand that correlation between data sets by itself never tells us anything about *how* or *why* two sets are related.

4. *There may be a complexity of interrelationships among many variables.* For example, a researcher may find a significant relationship between students' high school grades and college grades. But there probably are many other variables involved, such as IQ, hours of study, influence of parents, motivation, age, and instructors.

5. *The relationship might simply be coincidental.* For example, historians have noticed that there is a very strong correlation between the party that wins a presidential election and the result of the Washington Redskins' final game before the election. But common sense dictates that any such relationship has to be coincidental.

Answers to Try This One

1

Scatter Plot for the Heights and Number of Stories in the Tallest Buildings in Pittsburgh

2 $r \approx 0.798$

3   Significant at both levels

4 $y = 1.634 + 0.0685x$

5   47 stories

EXERCISE SET   12-8

Writing Exercises

1. Describe what a scatter plot is and how one is used.
2. Explain what is meant when two variables are positively linearly related. What would the scatter plot look like?
3. Explain what is meant when two variables are negatively linearly related. What would the scatter plot look like?

4. Explain what the value of the correlation coefficient tells you about the relationship between two data sets.
5. What is a regression line for two data sets?
6. Describe how regression lines can be used to make predictions about situations.

Computational Exercises

For the data sets in Exercises 7–12,

(a) Draw a scatter plot.
(b) Find the value for r.
(c) Test the significance of r at the 5% level and at the 1% level.
(d) Find the equation of the regression line and draw the line on the scatter plot, but only if r is significant.
(e) Describe the nature of the relationship if one exists.

7.

x	1	4	6	2	3	5	7
y	8	15	20	10	11	16	25

8.

x	21	25	24	30	36	40
y	12	8	9	5	3	2

9.

x	75	80	85	90
y	10	5	11	4

10.

x	9	12	15	11	10	13
y	50	60	71	55	53	60

11.

x	27	35	48	43	32
y	19	13	8	10	15

12.

x	31	34	37	40	46
y	3	15	2	13	5

Real-World Applications

For the data sets in Exercises 13–18,

(a) Draw a scatter plot. (b) Find the value for r.
(c) Test the significance of r at the 5% level and at the 1% level.
(d) Find the equation of the regression line and draw the line on the scatter plot, but only if r is significant.
(e) Describe the nature of the relationship if one exists.
(f) Make the requested prediction using your regression line.

13. The data represent the heights in feet and the number of stories of the tallest buildings in Cleveland.

Height, x	947	708	658	529	450	446	430	420	419
Stories, y	57	52	46	40	31	28	24	26	32

Source: *The World Almanac and Book of Facts*

Predict the number of stories in a 500-foot building.

14. A researcher hopes to determine whether the number of hours a person jogs per week is related to the person's age.

Age, x	34	22	48	56	62
Hours, y	3.5	7	3.5	3	1

Predict the number of hours for a 35-year-old.

15. A study was conducted to determine if the amount a college student spends per month on recreation is related to the student's income.

Monthly income, x	Amount, y	Monthly income, x	Amount, y
$800	$160	$850	$145
$1,200	$300	$907	$190
$1,000	$260	$1,100	$250
$900	$235		

Predict the amount spent by a student with an income of $925.

16. A researcher hopes to determine if there is a relationship between the number of days an employee missed a year and the person's age.

Age, x	22	30	25	35	65	50	27	53	42	58
Days missed, y	0	4	1	2	14	7	3	8	6	4

Predict the number of days missed by a 56-year-old employee.

17. A statistics instructor plans to see it there's a relationship between the final exam score in Statistics 102 and the final exam scores of the same students who took Statistics 101.

Stat 101, x	87	92	68	72	95	78	83	98
Stat 102, y	83	88	70	74	90	74	83	99

Predict the stat 102 score for a student who got 90 on the stat 101 final.

18. The data shown indicate the number of wins and the number of goals scored for teams in the National Hockey League after the first month of the season.

No. of wins, x	No. of goals, y	No. of wins, x	No. of goals, y
10	23	7	21
9	22	5	16
6	15	9	12
5	15	8	19
4	10	6	16
12	26	6	16
11	26	4	11
8	26		

Source: *USA Today*

Predict the number of goals for a team with 8 wins.

Critical Thinking

19. Explain why when r is significant, you can't conclude that x causes y.

20. Find the value for r, then interchange the values for x and y and find the value of r. Explain the results.

x	1	2	3	4	5
y	3	5	7	9	11

21. Draw a scatter plot and determine if the variables are related. Explain the results. Then find the value for r for the data shown.

x	−3	−2	−1	0	1	2	3
y	9	4	1	0	1	4	9

22. Design your own correlation problem. Think of two quantities that you think might be correlated, then gather some data, and use the techniques of this section to decide if the data sets are correlated.

CHAPTER **12 Summary**

Section	Important Terms	Important Ideas

12-1	Data
	Statistics
	Population
	Sample
	Random sample
	Systematic sample
	Stratified sample
	Cluster sample
	Descriptive statistics
	Inferential statistics
	Raw data
	Categorical frequency
	  distribution
	Grouped frequency
	  distribution
	Stem and leaf plot
		Statistics is the branch of mathematics that involves the collection, organization, summarization, and presentation of data. In addition, researchers use statistics to make general conclusions from the data. When a study is conducted, the researcher defines a population, which consists of all subjects under study. Since populations are usually large, the researcher will select a representative subgroup of the population, called a sample, to study. There are four basic sampling methods. They are random, systematic, stratified, and cluster. Once the data are collected, they are organized into a frequency distribution. There are two types of frequency distributions. They are categorical and grouped. When the data set consists of a small number of values, a stem and leaf plot can be constructed. This plot shows the nature of the data while retaining the original data values.

12-2	Bar graph Pie chart Histogram Frequency polygon Time series graph	**In order** to represent data pictorially, graphs can be drawn. From a categorical frequency distribution, a bar graph and a pie chart can be drawn. From a grouped frequency distribution, a histogram and a frequency polygon can be drawn to represent the data. To show how data vary over time, a time series graph can be drawn.
12-3	Mean Data array Median Mode Midrange	**In addition** to collecting data, organizing data, and representing data using graphs, various summary statistics can be found to describe the data. There are four measures of average. They are the mean, median, mode, and midrange. The mean is found by adding all of the data values and dividing the sum by the number of data values. The median is the middle point of the data set. The mode is the most frequent data value. The midrange is found by adding the lowest and the highest data values and dividing by two.
12-4	Range Variance Standard deviation	**There are** three commonly used measures of variation. They are the range, variance, and standard deviation. The range is found by subtracting the lowest data value from the highest data value. The standard deviation measures the spread of the data values. When the standard deviation is small, most data values are close to the mean. When the standard deviation is large, the data values are spread out farther away from the mean.
12-5	Percentile Quartile	**The position** of a data value in a data set can be determined by its percentile rank. The percentile rank of a specific data value gives the percent of data values that fall below the specific value. Quartiles divide a distribution into quarters.

12-6	Normal distribution Empirical rule Standard normal distribution z score	**Many variables** have a distribution that is bell-shaped. These variables are said to be approximately normally distributed. Statisticians use the standard normal distribution to describe these variables. The standard normal distribution has a mean of zero and a standard deviation of 1. A variable can be transformed into a standard normal variable by finding its corresponding z score. A table showing the area under the standard normal distribution can be used to find areas for various z scores.
12-7		**Since many** real-world variables are approximately normally distributed, the standard normal distribution can be used to solve many real-world applications.
12-8	Correlation Independent variable Dependent variable Scatter plot Correlation coefficient Significance levels Regression line	**Statisticians** are also interested in determining whether or not two variables are related. In order to determine this, they draw and analyze a scatter plot. After the scatter plot is drawn, the value of the correlation coefficient is computed. If the correlation coefficient is significant, the equation of the regression line is found. Then a prediction for y can be obtained given a specific value of x.

MATH IN Sociology REVISITED

1. The scatter plot is shown below, with temperature as the x variable. While it's not at all clear whether there is a real correlation, it looks like there's at least a chance that the two data sets have a positive linear relationship.

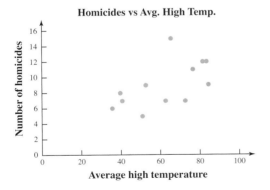

2. The correlation coefficient is about 0.584. According to the significance table, for a sample size of 12 this is significant at the 5% level (just barely), but not at the 1% level. So we can say with 95% confidence that the two data sets are related.

3. Absolutely not. In fact, no matter how strongly the data sets are related, we can't draw any conclusions about whether one causes the other. All we know is that for some reason, they appear to be related. There are a wide variety of theories trying to account for this phenomenon, but none have been proven or even widely accepted.

Review Exercises

Section 12-1

1. A sporting goods store kept a record of sales of five items for one randomly selected hour during a recent sale. Construct a frequency distribution for the data (B = baseballs, G = golf balls, T = tennis balls, S = soccer balls, F = footballs).

F	B	B	B	G	T	F
G	G	F	S	G	T	
F	T	T	T	S	T	
F	S	S	G	S	B	

2. The data set shown below represents the number of hours 25 part-time employees worked at the Sea Side Amusement Park during a randomly selected week in June. Construct a stem and leaf plot for the data and analyze the results.

16	25	18	39	25	17	29	14	37
22	18	12	23	32	35	24	26	
20	19	25	26	38	38	33	29	

3. During June, a local theater company recorded the given number of patrons per day. Construct a grouped frequency distribution for the data. Use six classes.

102	116	113	132	128	117
156	182	183	171	168	179
170	160	163	187	185	158
163	167	168	186	117	108
171	173	161	163	168	182

Section 12-2

4. Construct a bar graph for the number of homicides reported for these cities.

City	Number
New Orleans	179
Washington, D.C.	186
Chicago	509
Baltimore	234
Atlanta	105

Source: FBI

5. The data set shown below represents the time in minutes spent using a computer at Kinko's Copy Center by 25 customers on a randomly selected day. Construct a stem and leaf plot for the data and analyze the results.

16	25	18	39	25	17	29	14	37
22	18	12	23	32	35	24	26	
20	19	25	26	38	38	33	29	

6. Draw a histogram and frequency polygon for the frequency distribution obtained from the data in Exercise 3.

7. The data set shown below indicates how much Janine earned each year from her part-time job at the Otherworld Internet Cafe during the 5 years that she attended college. Draw a time series graph for the data.

Year	Amount
2005	$8,973
2006	$9,388
2007	$11,271
2008	$13,877
2009	$19,203

Section 12-3

8. These data represent the number of deer killed by motor vehicles for eight counties in Southwestern Pennsylvania.

2,343 1,240 1,088 600 497 1,925 1,480 458

Source: *Pittsburgh Post-Gazette*

Find each of these.

(a) Mean   (c) Mode
(b) Median   (d) Midrange

9. Twelve batteries were tested to see how many hours they would last. The frequency distribution is shown here.

Hours	Frequency
1–3	1
4–6	4
7–9	5
10–12	1
13–15	1

Find the mean.

10. In your own words, explain the difference between mean, median, mode, and midrange. Include an explanation of why each is considered a measure of average.

Section 12-4

11. Find the range, variance, and standard deviation for the data in Exercise 8.

12. Which data set do you think would have a greater standard deviation: the ages of everyone currently working out in the gym on your campus, or the ages of everyone currently shopping at the nearest off-campus grocery store? Explain your answer.

Section 12-5

13. The number of previous jobs held by each of six applicants is shown here.

    2 4 5 6 8 9

    (a) Find the percentile for each value.
    (b) What value corresponds to the 30th percentile?

14. The data shown represent the number of days' inventory eight high-tech firms have on hand. Find the values for Q_1, Q_2, and Q_3.

    158 151 91 45 74 118 285 29

Section 12-6

15. Find the area under the standard normal distribution curve.

    (a) Between $z = 0$ and $z = 1.95$
    (b) Between $z = 0$ and $z = 0.40$
    (c) Between $z = 1.30$ and $z = 1.80$
    (d) Between $z = -1.05$ and $z = 2.05$
    (e) Between $z = -0.05$ and $z = 0.55$
    (f) Between $z = 1.10$ and $z = -1.80$
    (g) To the right of $z = 2.00$
    (h) To the right of $z = -1.35$
    (i) To the left of $z = -2.10$
    (j) To the left of $z = 1.70$

16. The weights of players on one college rugby team are normally distributed with mean 210 pounds and standard deviation 12 pounds. Use the empirical rule to estimate the number of players out of 35 that weigh between 186 and 234 pounds.

17. For a data set with 90 values that is normally distributed with mean 200 and standard deviation 25, approximately how many data values will fall in each range?

    (a) The range from 190 to 210.
    (b) The range of values greater than 240.

Section 12-7

18. The average number of years a person takes to complete a graduate degree program is 3. The standard deviation is 4 months or $\frac{1}{3}$ of a year. Assume the data are normally distributed. If an individual enrolls in the program, find the probability that it will take

    (a) More than 4 years to complete the program.
    (b) Less than 3 years to complete the program.
    (c) Between 3.8 and 4.5 years to complete the program.
    (d) Between 2.5 and 3.1 years to complete the program.

19. On the daily run of an express bus, the average number of passengers is 48. The standard deviation is 3. Assume the data are normally distributed. Find the probability that the bus will have

    (a) Between 36 and 40 passengers.
    (b) Fewer than 42 passengers.
    (c) More than 48 passengers.
    (d) Between 43 and 48 passengers.

20. The average weight of an airline passenger's suitcase is 45 pounds. The standard deviation is 2 pounds. Assume the weights are normally distributed. If an airline handles 2,000 suitcases in one day, find the number that will weigh less than 43.5 pounds.

21. The average cost of Cheetah brand running shoes is $83.00 per pair, with a standard deviation of $8.00. If 90 pairs of shoes are sold, how many will cost between $80.00 and $85.00? Assume the cost is normally distributed.

Section 12-8

22. A study is done to see whether there is a relationship between a student's grade point average and the number of hours the students watches television each week. The data are shown here.

Hours, x	10	6	8	15	5	6	12
GPA, y	2.4	4	3.2	1.6	3.7	3.7	3.0

    Draw a scatter plot for the data and describe the relationship. Find the value for r and determine whether or not it is significant at the 5% significance level. If yes, find the equation of the regression line, and predict y when $x = 9$.

23. The table below displays the number of homicides committed in Chicago, and the number of wins by the Chicago Bears of the NFL for each year from 2000 to 2008.

Homicides	Wins	Homicides	Wins
628	5	449	11
666	13	452	13
647	4	442	7
598	7	509	9
448	4		

    (a) Without doing any calculations, discuss whether or not you think the two data sets should be related.
    (b) Find the correlation coefficient for the data sets, and then see if it is significant at the 5% level. Was your prediction from part (a) right or wrong?

Chapter Test

1. A questionnaire about the last 25 peripheral devices purchased at a computer store is shown below. Construct a frequency distribution (L = laser mouse, E = external hard drive, K = wireless keyboard, W = webcam)

   ```
   L  L  K  E  E  K  L  E  W  K
   W  W  L  K  W  E  K  W  L  W
   E  K  K  L  L
   ```

2. Draw a bar graph for the frequency distribution obtained in Exercise 1.
3. Draw a pie chart for the data found in Exercise 2.
4. The data (in millions of dollars) are the values of the 30 Major League baseball franchises. Construct a frequency distribution for the data using eight classes.

   ```
   1,500  912  320  700  356  277  347  722
    401   314  496  390  833  509  450  342
    373   486  400  353  319  288  405  445
    399   471  426  371  446  406
   ```

   Source: *Forbes Magazine*

5. Draw a histogram and frequency polygon using the frequency distribution for the data in Exercise 4.
6. A special aptitude test is given to job applicants. The data shown here represent the scores of 30 applicants. Construct a stem and leaf plot for the data and summarize the results.

   ```
   204  210  227  218  254
   256  238  242  253  227
   251  243  233  251  241
   237  247  211  222  231
   218  212  217  227  209
   260  230  228  242  200
   ```

7. The given data represent the federal minimum hourly wage in the years shown. Draw a time series graph to represent the data and analyze the results.

Year	Wage	Year	Wage
1960	$1.00	1990	3.80
1965	1.25	1995	4.25
1970	1.60	2000	5.15
1975	2.10	2005	5.15
1980	3.10	2009	7.25
1985	3.35		

8. These temperatures were recorded in Pasadena for a week in April.

   ```
   87  85  80  78  83  86  90
   ```

   Find each of these.
   (a) Mean   (c) Mode
   (b) Median   (d) Midrange
   (e) Range   (g) Standard deviation
   (f) Variance

9. The distribution of the number of errors 10 students made on a typing test is shown.

Errors	Frequency
0–2	1
3–5	3
6–8	4
9–11	1
12–14	1

   Find the mean.

10. The number of credits in business courses eight job applicants had is shown here.

    ```
    9  12  15  27  33  45  63  72
    ```

    (a) Find the percentile for each value.
    (b) What value corresponds to the 40th percentile?

11. Find the area under the standard normal distribution for each.

    (a) Between 0 and 1.50
    (b) Between 0 and -1.25
    (c) Between 1.56 and 1.96
    (d) Between -1.20 and -2.25
    (e) Between -0.06 and 0.73
    (f) Between 1.10 and -1.80
    (g) To the right of $z = 1.75$
    (h) To the right of $z = -1.28$
    (i) To the left of $z = -2.12$
    (j) To the left of $z = 1.36$

12. The mean time it takes for a certain pain reliever to begin to reduce symptoms is 30 minutes, with a standard deviation of 4 minutes. Assuming the time is normally distributed, find the probability that it will take the medication

    (a) Between 34 and 35 minutes to begin to work.
    (b) More than 35 minutes to begin to work.
    (c) Less than 25 minutes to begin to work.
    (d) Between 35 and 40 minutes to begin to work.

13. The average height of a certain age group of people is 53 inches. The standard deviation is 4 inches. If the heights are normally distributed, find the probability that a selected individual's height will be

    (a) Greater than 59 inches.
    (b) Less than 45 inches.
    (c) Between 50 and 55 inches.
    (d) Between 58 and 62 inches.

14. The average cost of a skateboard at Sk8 Gr8, a local skate shop, is $55.00, with a standard deviation of $8.00. The prices are normally distributed. If 200 skateboards are purchased, how many of them cost more than $60.00?

15. A study is conducted to determine the relationship between a driver's age at the beginning of the study and the number of accidents he or she has over a 1-year period. The data are shown here. Draw a scatter plot for the data and explain the nature of the relationship. Find the value for r and determine whether or not it is significant at the 5% significance level. If r is significant, find the equation of the regression line, and predict y when x is 61.

Age, x	No. of accidents, y
32	1
20	1
55	0
16	3
19	2
17	1
45	0
26	0
32	1
61	0

Projects

1. Survey at least 30 students on your campus to find out how many miles away from the campus they live. Construct a frequency distribution with at least five classes from the data. Draw a histogram and frequency polygon for your data, then compute the mean, median, mode, midrange, and standard deviation for the data. Write a report summarizing the results of your study, including a discussion of whether or not the data appear to be approximately normally distributed.

2. Survey at least 30 students on your campus to find out how many credit hours each is taking, and the estimated number of hours per week that they spend on schoolwork outside of class. Draw a scatter plot for the data. Then find the correlation coefficient and decide if it is significant at the 5% level and at the 1% level. Write a report summarizing your findings. Include a discussion of whether or not you were surprised by the results and why.

APPENDIX A

Area Under the Standard Normal Distribution

The area in the A column is the area under the normal distribution between $z = 0$ and the positive value of z found in the z column.

z	A	z	A	z	A	z	A	z	A	z	A	z	A
.00	.000	.25	.099	.50	.192	.75	.273	1.00	.341	1.25	.394	1.50	.433
.01	.004	.26	.103	.51	.195	.76	.276	1.01	.344	1.26	.396	1.51	.435
.02	.008	.27	.106	.52	.199	.77	.279	1.02	.346	1.27	.398	1.52	.436
.03	.012	.28	.110	.53	.202	.78	.282	1.03	.349	1.28	.400	1.53	.437
.04	.016	.29	.114	.54	.205	.79	.285	1.04	.351	1.29	.402	1.54	.438
.05	.020	.30	.118	.55	.209	.80	.288	1.05	.353	1.30	.403	1.55	.439
.06	.024	.31	.122	.56	.212	.81	.291	1.06	.355	1.31	.405	1.56	.441
.07	.028	.32	.126	.57	.216	.82	.294	1.07	.358	1.32	.407	1.57	.442
.08	.032	.33	.129	.58	.219	.83	.297	1.08	.360	1.33	.408	1.58	.443
.09	.036	.34	.133	.59	.222	.84	.300	1.09	.362	1.34	.410	1.59	.444
.10	.040	.35	.137	.60	.226	.85	.302	1.10	.364	1.35	.412	1.60	.445
.11	.044	.36	.141	.61	.229	.86	.305	1.11	.367	1.36	.413	1.61	.446
.12	.048	.37	.144	.62	.232	.87	.308	1.12	.369	1.37	.415	1.62	.447
.13	.052	.38	.148	.63	.236	.88	.311	1.13	.371	1.38	.416	1.63	.449
.14	.056	.39	.152	.64	.239	.89	.313	1.14	.373	1.39	.418	1.64	.450
.15	.060	.40	.155	.65	.242	.90	.316	1.15	.375	1.40	.419	1.65	.451
.16	.064	.41	.159	.66	.245	.91	.319	1.16	.377	1.41	.421	1.66	.452
.17	.068	.42	.163	.67	.249	.92	.321	1.17	.379	1.42	.422	1.67	.453
.18	.071	.43	.166	.68	.252	.93	.324	1.18	.381	1.43	.424	1.68	.454
.19	.075	.44	.170	.69	.255	.94	.326	1.19	.383	1.44	.425	1.69	.455
.20	.079	.45	.174	.70	.258	.95	.329	1.20	.385	1.45	.427	1.70	.455
.21	.083	.46	.177	.71	.261	.96	.332	1.21	.387	1.46	.428	1.71	.456
.22	.087	.47	.181	.72	.264	.97	.334	1.22	.389	1.47	.429	1.72	.457
.23	.091	.48	.184	.73	.267	.98	.337	1.23	.391	1.48	.431	1.73	.458
.24	.095	.49	.188	.74	.270	.99	.339	1.24	.393	1.49	.432	1.74	.459

Continued

A-1

z	A	z	A	z	A	z	A	z	A	z	A	z	A
1.75	.460	1.97	.476	2.19	.486	2.41	.492	2.63	.496	2.85	.498	3.07	.499
1.76	.461	1.98	.476	2.20	.486	2.42	.492	2.64	.496	2.86	.498	3.08	.499
1.77	.462	1.99	.477	2.21	.487	2.43	.493	2.65	.496	2.87	.498	3.09	.499
1.78	.463	2.00	.477	2.22	.487	2.44	.493	2.66	.496	2.88	.498	3.10	.499
1.79	.463	2.01	.478	2.23	.487	2.45	.493	2.67	.496	2.89	.498	3.11	.499
1.80	.464	2.02	.478	2.24	.488	2.46	.493	2.68	.496	2.90	.498	3.12	.499
1.81	.465	2.03	.479	2.25	.488	2.47	.493	2.69	.496	2.91	.498	3.13	.499
1.82	.466	2.04	.479	2.26	.488	2.48	.493	2.70	.497	2.92	.498	3.14	.499
1.83	.466	2.05	.480	2.27	.488	2.49	.494	2.71	.497	2.93	.498	3.15	.499
1.84	.467	2.06	.480	2.28	.489	2.50	.494	2.72	.497	2.94	.498	3.16	.499
1.85	.468	2.07	.481	2.29	.489	2.51	.494	2.73	.497	2.95	.498	3.17	.499
1.86	.469	2.08	.481	2.30	.489	2.52	.494	2.74	.497	2.96	.499	3.18	.499
1.87	.469	2.09	.482	2.31	.490	2.53	.494	2.75	.497	2.97	.499	3.19	.499
1.88	.470	2.10	.482	2.32	.490	2.54	.495	2.76	.497	2.98	.499	3.20	.499
1.89	.471	2.11	.483	2.33	.490	2.55	.495	2.77	.497	2.99	.499	3.21	.499
1.90	.471	2.12	.483	2.34	.490	2.56	.495	2.78	.497	3.00	.499	3.22	.499
1.91	.472	2.13	.483	2.35	.491	2.57	.495	2.79	.497	3.01	.499	3.23	.499
1.92	.473	2.14	.484	2.36	.491	2.58	.495	2.80	.497	3.02	.499	3.24	.499
1.93	.473	2.15	.484	2.37	.491	2.59	.495	2.81	.498	3.03	.499	3.25	.499
1.94	.474	2.16	.485	2.38	.491	2.60	.495	2.82	.498	3.04	.499		*
1.95	.474	2.17	.485	2.39	.492	2.61	.496	2.83	.498	3.05	.499		
1.96	.475	2.18	.485	2.40	.492	2.62	.496	2.84	.498	3.06	.499		

*For z values beyond 3.25 use $A = 0.500$.

SELECTED ANSWERS

CHAPTER 1: PROBLEM SOLVING

Exercise Set 1-1

7. 37 9. 10 11. 72 13.

15. $5 + 13 + 17 = 35$, which is odd. 17. $5^2 \div 2 = 12.5$
19. Conjecture: The final answer is -10.
21. Conjecture: The final answer is 20.
23. $12,345,679 \times 72 = 12,345,679 \times 9(8) = 888,888,888$
25. $999,999 \times 9 = 8,999,991$ 27. $99,999 \times 99,999 = 9,999,800,001$
29. $11,111 \times 11,111 = 123,454,321$
31. When multiplied by the numbers 1–6 the digits in the answer are a permutation of the original number. But the hypothesis fails when the number is multiplied by 7 and 8.
33. The result will always be 9. 35. The next three sums are $\frac{9}{5}$, $\frac{11}{6}$, and $\frac{13}{7}$.
37. $5 + 10 + 15 + 20 + 25 = \frac{25(6)}{2}$ 39. $37,037 \times 15 = 555,555$
41. Inductive 43. Inductive 45. Deductive 47. Inductive
49. Inductive 51. Deductive 53. Deductive 55. Inductive
57. Deductive 59. Inductive 61. Inductive 63. Inductive
65. It is not possible. 67. 1 6 15 20 15 6 1
69. (a) 21, 28, 36 (b) 36, 49, 64 (c) 35, 51, 70 (d) 1, 6, 15, 28

Exercise Set 1-2

7. 2,900 9. 3,260,000 11. 63 13. 200,000 15. 3.67 17. 327.1
19. 5,460,000 21. 300,000 23. 264.9735 25. 563.27 27. $136
29. 6 hours 31. $72 33. $6.50 35. 9 hours 37. $18,000 per year
39. $54 41. $25 43. 3,200 acres 45. 4,400 acres 47. 490 people
49. 65% 51. 350 billion 53. 1,940 55. 99 miles 57. 28%
59. 48% 61. 25% 63. $15 billion
65. The difference between the cost of milk in 1988 and the cost in 2006 is exaggerated by the fact that the picture changed in all three dimensions, rather than just vertically. 67. Answers vary

Exercise Set 1-3

5. 8 and 14 7. 43 9. Mark is 7 years old.
11. 16 inches and 32 inches 13. 13 quarters and 18 dimes
15. 35 girls 17. Four $15 cards and six $20 cards
19. 28 feet 21. 143 inches or about 12 feet 23. 50 feet
25. 38 windows 27. Sam earned $45 and Pete earned $15.
29. 84 pounds 31. $1,093 33. 42,900 calories 35. $206.35
37. $420 39. $49.29 41. $465.50 43. 2 hours
45. Fill the 3-gallon container; pour it into the 5-gallon container. Fill the 3-gallon container again and pour into the 5-gallon container until it's full. There will then be one gallon left in the 3-gallon container. 47. $8,000

Review Exercises

1. 18, 19, 21 3. q, 1,024, n 5.

7. $5(7)(11) = 385$, which is odd. 9. Conjecture: The final answer is 13 more than $\frac{1}{2}$ of the original even number.
11. $337 \times 12 = 4,044$
    $337 \times 15 = 5,055$
13. 9 15. Inductive 17. Deductive 19. 132,000 21. 14.6316

23. 3,730 25. $340 27. $340 29. 13 DVDs
31. 254 million pounds 33. $520 35. 9 37. 110 pounds
39. 30 years old 41. $40 43. 20 years old 45. Debbie is 3 years old.
47. Joe has done 2 problems and Tina has done 3. 49. 13 triangles
51. 7.5 and 12.5 53. Mr. Taylor invested $800 at 8% and $200 at 6%.

Chapter 1 Test

* When using estimation, other correct answers are possible.
1. 13, 12, 18 3. 8,888,888
5. The final answer is equal to the original number plus 13. 7. Eighth
9. Move the last coin on the right on top of another coin. 11. 84
13. 13 15. First person earns $36; second person earns $24. 17. 93%
19. 65,400 feet 21. Mark is 17 years old and his mother is 49.
23. $1.3\overline{8}$ 25. Number of hours per week in 1980 was about 35.5 hours. Number of hours per week in 2005 was about 33.8 hours. 27. 310

CHAPTER 2: SETS

Exercise Set 2-1

7. $S = \{s, t, r, e\}$ 9. $P = \{51, 52, 53, 54, 55, 56, 57, 58, 59\}$
11. $Q = \{1, 3, 5, 7, 9, 11, 13\}$ 13. $G = \{11, 12, 13, \dots\}$
15. $Y = \{2,001, 2,002, 2,003, \dots, 2,999\}$
17. $W = \{$Sunday, Monday, Tuesday, Wednesday, Thursday, Friday, Saturday$\}$
19. $D = \{$hearts, diamonds, spades, clubs$\}$
21. The set of even natural numbers.
23. The set of the first four multiples of 9.
25. The set of letters in Mary.
27. The set of natural numbers from 100 to 199.
29. $\{x \mid x$ is a multiple of $10\}$ 31. $X = \{x \mid x \in N$ and $x > 20\}$
33. $\{x \mid x$ is an odd natural number less than $10\}$
35. There are no natural numbers less than zero so $H = \varnothing$
37. $\{7, 14, 21, 28, 35, 42, 49, 56, 63\}$
39. $\{102, 104, 106, 108, 110, 112, 114, 116, 118\}$
41. Well-defined 43. Not well-defined 45. Well-defined
47. Not well-defined 49. True 51. True 53. True
55. Infinite 57. Finite 59. Infinite 61. Finite
63. Equal and equivalent 65. Neither 67. Equivalent 69. Neither
71. $\{10, 20, 30, 40\}$ 73. $\{1, 2, 3, \dots, 25, 26\}$
    $\updownarrow \updownarrow \updownarrow \updownarrow$ $\updownarrow \updownarrow \updownarrow \quad \updownarrow \updownarrow$
    $\{40, 10, 20, 30\}$ $\{a, b, c, \dots, y, \ z\}$
75. $n(A) = 5$ 77. $n(C) = 7$ 79. $n(E) = 1$ 81. $n(G) = 0$ 83. True
85. True 87. False 89. False
91. (a) {California, New York, Florida}
    (b) {Virginia, Massachusetts, Georgia, Maryland}
    (c) {California, New York, Florida, Texas, New Jersey}
    (d) {Texas, New Jersey, Illinois}
93. (a) {Drunk driving, Injury, Assault}
    (b) {Injury, Health problems}
    (c) {Injury, Assault, Drunk driving}
    (d) {97,000, 1,700, 150,000}
    (e) Answers vary
95. (a) {Employment fraud, Bank fraud}
    (b) {18–29, 30–39, 40–49}
    (c) {Utilities/phone fraud, Credit card fraud, Other}
    (d) {20, 13, 9}
    (e) {Employment fraud, Bank fraud, Utilities/phone fraud}

97. (a) {2000, 2001, 2002}
(b) {2002, 2003, 2004, 2005}
(c) {2002, 2003, 2004, 2005, 2006}
(d) {2000, 2001, 2002}
99. Yes   **101.** Answers vary   **103.** Answers vary

Exercise Set 2-2

11. $A' = \{2, 3, 17, 19\}$ **13.** $C' = \{2, 3, 5, 7, 11\}$
15. $\varnothing$; {r}; {s}; {t}; {r, s}; {r, t}; {s, t}; {r, s, t}
17. $\varnothing$; {1}; {3}; {1, 3}   **19.** { } or $\varnothing$
21. $\varnothing$; {5}; {12}; {13}; {14}; {5, 12}; {5, 13}; {5, 14}; {12, 13};
{12, 14}; {13, 14}, {5, 12, 13}; {5, 12, 14}; {5, 13, 14}; {12, 13, 14};
{5, 12, 13, 14}
23. $\varnothing$; {1}; {10}; {20}; {1, 10}; {1, 20}; {10, 20}   **25.** $\varnothing$ **27.** None
29. True   **31.** False   **33.** False   **35.** False   **37.** True   **39.** $2^3 = 8$
41. $2^0 = 1$ **43.** $2^2 = 4$ **45.** $U = \{1, 2, 3, 4, 5, 6, 7, 8, 9\}$
47. $B = \{5, 6, 7, 8, 9\}$ **49.** $A \cup B = \{2, 3, 5, 6, 7, 8, 9\}$
51. $B' = \{1, 2, 3, 4\}$ **53.** $(A \cap B)' = \{1, 2, 3, 4, 6, 7, 8\}$
55. $A \cup C = \{10, 30, 40, 50, 60, 70, 90\}$
57. $A' = \{20, 40, 60, 80, 100\}$ **59.** $A' \cap (B \cup C) = \{20, 40, 60, 80, 100\}$
61. $(A \cup B)' \cap C = \varnothing$ **63.** $(B \cup C) \cap A' = \{20, 40, 60, 80, 100\}$
65. $P \cap Q = \{b, d\}$ **67.** $P' = \{a, c, e, h\}$ **69.** $R' \cap P' = \{a, c, h\}$
71. $(Q \cup P)' \cap R = \{e\}$ **73.** $(P \cup Q) \cap (P \cup R) = \{b, d, f, g\}$
75. $W \cap Y = \{2, 4, 6\}$ **77.** $W \cup X =$ the universal set
79. $W \cap X = \varnothing$ **81.** $(X \cup Y) \cap Z = \{2, 5, 6, 11\}$ **83.** $W' \cap X' = \varnothing$
85. $A \cap B = B$
87. $A \cap (B \cup C') = \{x \mid x$ is an odd multiple of 3 or an even
multiple of 9}
$= \{3, 9, 15, 18, 21, 27, 33, 36, 39, \ldots\}$
89. $A - B = \{20, 110\}$ **91.** $B - C = \{60\}$ **93.** $C \cap B' = \{110\}$
95. $C - B = \{p\}$ **97.** $B - C = \{s, u\}$ **99.** $B \cap C' = \{s, u\}$
101. $A \times B = \{(9, 1), (9, 2), (9, 3), (12, 1), (12, 2), (12, 3), (18, 1), (18, 2), (18, 3)\}$
103. $A \times A = \{(9, 9), (9, 12), (9, 18), (12, 9), (12, 12), (12, 18), (18, 9), (18, 12), (18, 18)\}$
105. $A \times B = \{(1, 1), (1, 3), (2, 1), (2, 3), (4, 1), (4, 3), (8, 1), (8, 3)\}$
107. $B \times B = \{(1, 1), (1, 3), (3, 1), (3, 3)\}$
109. {cell phone, laptop, iPod}, {cell phone, laptop}, {cell phone, iPod}, {laptop, iPod}, {cell phone}, {laptop}, {iPod}, $\varnothing$
111. $2^7 - 1 = 127$ **113.** $2^4 = 16$ **115.** Answers vary
117. Answers vary

Exercise Set 2-3

5.

7.

9.

11.

13.

15.

17.

19.

21.

23.

25.

27.

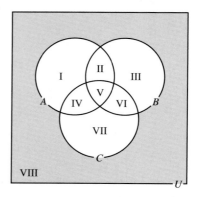

29. equal   **31.** equal   **33.** not equal   **35.** not equal   **37.** $n(A) = 6$
39. $n(A \cap B) = 2$ **41.** $n(A') = 6$ **43.** $n(A' \cap B') = 3$
45. $n(A - B) = 4$ **47.** $n(A) = 6$ **49.** $n(A \cap B) = 4$
51. $n(A \cap B') = 1$ **53.** $n(A') = 6$ **55.** $n(A - B) = 2$
57. People who drive an SUV or a hybrid vehicle.

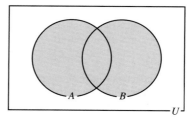

59. People who do not drive an SUV.

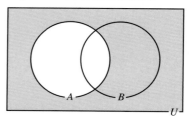

61. Students in online courses and blended or traditional courses.

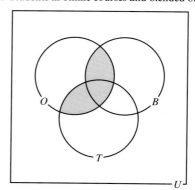

63. Students who are in blended, online, and traditional courses.

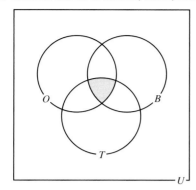

65. Students not voting democrat or voting republican.

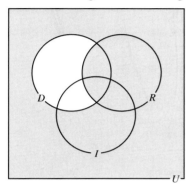

67. Students voting democrat or republican but not independent.

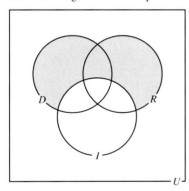

69. People who regularly use Google but not Yahoo!.

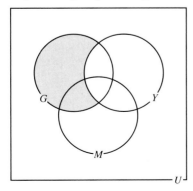

71. People who do not regularly use Google, Yahoo!, or MSN Live.

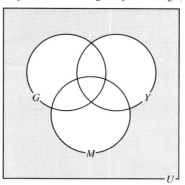

73. Region IV   **75.** Region VII   **77.** Region V   **79.** No; Answers vary

Exercise Set 2-4

1. (a) 13	(b) 18	(c) 2	
3. (a) 8	(b) 5	(c) 0	
5. (a) 2	(b) 9	(c) 35	
7. (a) 16	(b) 7	(c) 14	(d) 9
9. (a) 37	(b) 2	(c) 37	
11. (a) 22	(b) 3	(c) 15	
13. (a) 32	(b) 37	(c) 58	

15. 6   **17.** The total of the eight regions is 39 but the researcher surveyed 40 people.

Exercise Set 2-5

5. $7n$ **7.** 4^n **9.** $-3n$ **11.** $\dfrac{1}{n+1}$ **13.** $4n-2$ **15.** $\dfrac{n+1}{n+2}$

17. $100n$ **19.** $-3n-1$

For 21 through 30 we will show each set is infinite by putting it into a one-to-one correspondence with a proper subset of itself.

21. $\{3,\ 6,\ 9,\ 12,\ 15,\ \dots,\ 3n,\ \dots\}$
$\updownarrow\ \updownarrow\ \updownarrow\ \updownarrow\ \updownarrow\qquad\updownarrow$
$\{6,\ 12,\ 18,\ 24,\ 30,\ \dots,\ 6n,\ \dots\}$

23. $\{9,\ 18,\ 27,\ 36,\ 45,\ \dots,\ 9n,\ \dots\}$
$\updownarrow\ \updownarrow\ \updownarrow\ \updownarrow\ \updownarrow\qquad\updownarrow$
$\{18,\ 36,\ 54,\ 72,\ 90,\ \dots,\ 18n,\ \dots\}$

25. $\{2,\ 5,\ 8,\ 11,\ \dots,\ 3n-1,\ \dots\}$
$\updownarrow\ \updownarrow\ \updownarrow\ \updownarrow\qquad\updownarrow$
$\{5,\ 11,\ 17,\ 23,\ \dots,\ 6n-1,\ \dots\}$

27. $\{10,\ \ 100,\ \dots,\ 10^n,\ \dots\}$
$\ \ \updownarrow\qquad\updownarrow\qquad\updownarrow$
$\{100,\ 10{,}000,\ \dots,\ 10^{2n},\ \dots\}$

29. $\left\{\dfrac{5}{1},\dfrac{5}{2},\dfrac{5}{3},\dots,\ \ \dfrac{5}{n},\dots\right\}$
$\ \ \updownarrow\ \updownarrow\ \updownarrow\qquad\updownarrow$
$\left\{\dfrac{5}{2},\dfrac{5}{3},\dfrac{5}{4},\dots,\ \dfrac{5}{n+1},\dots\right\}$

31. $\aleph_0+1 = \aleph_0$ and $\aleph_0 + \aleph_0 = \aleph_0$

33. The rational numbers can be put into a one-to-one correspondence with the natural numbers.

Review Exercises

1. $D = \{52, 54, 56, 58\}$ **3.** $L = \{l, e, t, r\}$

5. $B = \{501, 502, 503, \dots\}$ **7.** $M = \varnothing$

9. $\{x \mid x$ is even and $16 < x < 26\}$

11. $\{x \mid x$ is an odd natural number greater than $100\}$

13. Infinite   **15.** Finite   **17.** Finite   **19.** False   **21.** False

23. $\varnothing$; {r}; {s}; {t}; {r, s}; {r, t}; {s, t}; {r, s, t}

25. $2^5 = 32$ subsets; 31 proper subsets

27. $A \cap B = \{t, u, v\}$ **29.** $(A \cap B) \cap C = \varnothing$ **31.** $A - B = \{p, r\}$

33. $(A \cup B)' \cap C = \{s, w, z\}$ **35.** $(B \cup C) \cap A' = \{s, w, x, y, z\}$

37. $(B' \cap C') \cup A' = \{p, q, r, s, w, x, y, z\}$

39. $M \times N = \{(s, v), (s, w), (s, x), (t, v), (t, w), (t, x), (u, v), (u, w), (u, x)\}$

41. $M \times M = \{(s, s), (s, t), (s, u), (t, s), (t, t), (t, u), (u, s), (u, t), (u, u)\}$
43. $A - B$ **45.** $B - A$ **47.** $(A \cup B) - (A \cap B)$
49.

51.

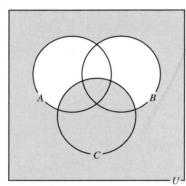

53. 20   **55.** Region V   **57.** Region II   **59.** (a) 12   (b) 3
61. (a) 3   (b) 5   (c) 6   **63.** $-3 - 2n$

Chapter 2 Test

1. $P = \{92, 94, 96, 98\}$ **3.** $K = \{e, n, v, l, o, p\}$
5. $X = \{1, 2, 3, 4, \ldots, 79\}$ **7.** $J = \{$January, June, July$\}$
9. $\{x \mid x \in E$ and $10 < x < 20\}$
11. $\{x \mid x$ is an odd natural number greater than 200$\}$
13. Infinite   **15.** Finite   **17.** Finite
19. $\varnothing$; $\{p\}$; $\{q\}$; $\{r\}$; $\{p, q\}$; $\{p, r\}$; $\{q, r\}$; $\{p, q, r\}$
21. $A \cap B = \{a\}$ **23.** $B' = \{b, c, d, e, f, h\}$
25. $(A \cap B') \cup C' = \{a, b, c, d, e, f, g, i, k\}$
27. $B - C = \{a, g, i, k\}$ **29.** $A - C = \{a, b, d, f\}$
31. $A \times B = \{(@, \pi), (@, \#), (!, \pi), (!, \#), (\alpha, \pi), (\alpha, \#)\}$
33. $B \times B = \{(\pi, \pi), (\pi, \#), (\#, \pi), (\#, \#)\}$
35.

37.

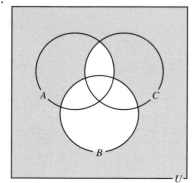

39. (a) 11   (b) 4
41. $\{1, -1, 2, -2, 3, -3, \ldots, n, \quad -n, \ldots\}$
$\{1, \quad 2, 3, \quad 4, 5, \quad 6, \ldots, 2n - 1, 2n, \ldots\}$
43. True   **45.** True   **47.** True   **49.** False   **51.** True   **53.** False

CHAPTER 3: LOGIC
Exercise Set 3-1
5. Not a statement   **7.** Statement   **9.** Not a statement
11. Not a statement   **13.** Not a statement   **15.** Compound statement
17. Compound statement   **19.** Simple statement
21. Compound statement   **23.** Simple statement   **25.** Conjunction
27. Biconditional   **29.** Disjunction   **31.** Biconditional
33. The sky is not blue.   **35.** The dorm room is large.
37. You will fail this class.   **39.** Universal   **41.** Existential
43. Universal   **45.** Existential   **47.** Universal   **49.** Existential
51. Not all fish swim in water; Some fish do not swim in water.
53. No people who live in glass houses throw stones.
55. Not every happy dog wags its tail; Some happy dog does not wag
its tail.   **57.** There is no four leaf clover.
59. Someone with green eyes wears glasses.
61. None of my friends have an iPhone.
63. $p \wedge q$ **65.** $\sim q \rightarrow p$ **67.** $\sim q$ **69.** $q \vee \sim p$ **71.** $q \leftrightarrow p$
73. $\sim q$ **75.** $q \rightarrow p$ **77.** $\sim q \vee p$ **79.** $q \leftrightarrow p$ **81.** $\sim q \rightarrow p$
83. The plane is on time and the sky is clear.
85. If the sky is clear, then the plane is on time.
87. The plane is not on time and the sky is not clear.
89. The plane is on time or the sky is not clear.
91. If the sky is clear, then the plane is or is not on time.
93. Trudy does not live off campus.
95. Mark lives on campus or Trudy does not live off campus.
97. If Mark does not live on campus, then Trudy does not live off
campus.   **99.** Mark lives on campus or Trudy lives off campus.
101. Trudy lives off campus or Mark lives on campus.
103. It cannot be classified as true or false.

Exercise Set 3-2
5. FFFT   **7.** FFTF   **9.** FTTF   **11.** TTFF   **13.** TFTT   **15.** TTFF
17. TTFF   **19.** TTFFTFFF   **21.** TTTTTTTT   **23.** TFFFTFTF
25. TTTFFFTF   **27.** FTFTFTTT   **29.** FFFTTTTT
31. FFFFTFFF   **33.** TFTFFFFF   **35.** False   **37.** True   **39.** True
41. Let p be "if you take their daily product," q be "you cut your calories intake by 10%, and r be "you lose at least 10 pounds in the next
4 months."   **43.** TFTTTTTT   **45.** True
47. Let p be "the attendance for the following season is over 2 million,"
q be "he will add 20 million dollars to the payroll," and r be "the
team will make the playoffs the following year."   **49.** TFFFTTTT
51. True   **53.** The statements are equivalent.   **55.** False

Exercise Set 3-3
7. Tautology   **9.** Self-contradiction   **11.** Tautology   **13.** Neither
15. Neither   **17.** Equivalent   **19.** Neither   **21.** Neither
23. Negations   **25.** Neither   **27.** $q \rightarrow p$; $\sim p \rightarrow \sim q$; $\sim q \rightarrow \sim p$
29. $p \rightarrow \sim q$; $q \rightarrow \sim p$; $\sim p \rightarrow q$ **31.** $\sim q \rightarrow p$; $\sim p \rightarrow q$; $q \rightarrow \sim p$
33. The concert is not long and it is not fun.
35. It is cold or I am not soaked.
37. I will not go to the beach or I will get sunburned.
39. The student is not a girl and the professor is a man.
41. It is not right and it is not wrong.   **43.** $p \rightarrow q$ **45.** $p \rightarrow q$
47. $p \rightarrow q$ **49.** $\sim p \rightarrow \sim q$
51. *Converse*: If he did get a good job, then he graduated with a Bachelor's degree in Management Information Systems.
Inverse: If he did not graduate with a Bachelor's degree in
Management Information Systems, then he will not get a good job.
Contrapositive: If he did not get a good job, he did not graduate
with a Bachelor's degree in Management Information Systems.

53. *Converse*: If I host a party in my dorm room, then the *American Idol* finale is today.
Inverse: If the *American Idol* finale is not today, then I will not host a party in my dorm room.
Contrapositive: If I do not host a party in my dorm room, then the *American Idol* finale is not today.

55. *Converse*: If I go to Nassau for spring break then I will lose 10 pounds by March 1.
Inverse: If I do not lose 10 pounds by March 1 then I will not go to Nassau for spring break.
Contrapositive: If I do not go to Nassau for spring break then I did not lose 10 pounds by March 1.

57. $\sim(p \to q) \equiv p \wedge \sim q$ 59. Answers vary   61. Equivalent

Exercise Set 3-4

7. Valid   9. Invalid   11. Invalid   13. Valid   15. Invalid
17. Valid   19. Valid   21. Invalid   23. Valid   25. Invalid
27. Valid   29. Invalid   31. Invalid   33. Invalid   35. Invalid
37. Valid   39. Invalid   41. Valid   43. Invalid   45. Valid
47. Invalid   49. Valid   51. Valid   53. Answers vary

Exercise Set 3-5

5.

7.

9.

11.

13.

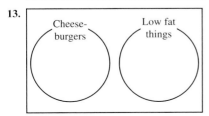

15. Invalid   17. Valid   19. Invalid   21. Valid   23. Invalid
25. Invalid   27. Invalid   29. Valid   31. Invalid   33. Invalid
35. Valid   37. Invalid   39. All A is C.
41. No calculators can make breakfast.

Review Exercises

1. Not a statement   3. Not a statement   5. Not a Statement
7. Simple   9. Compound   11. It is not scary.
13. The popsicle is not green.
15. No failing students can learn new study methods.
17. All printers have ink.
19. None of the contestants will be voted off the island.
21. Conjunction   23. Disjunction   25. Conditional
27. $q \to p$ 29. $q \wedge \sim p$ 31. $\sim(q \wedge p)$ 33. $\sim q \leftrightarrow \sim p$
35. $\sim p \wedge \sim q$ 37. If it is cloudy, then it is cool.
39. If it is cool or cloudy, then it is cool.   41. FTTT
43. FFFT   45. FFFT   47. TFTFFFTF   49. False   51. True
53. Tautology   55. Neither   57. Neither   59. Not equivalent
61. The internet connection is not dial-up and it's not DSL.
63. The signature is authentic or the check is valid.
65. Let p be the statement "I will be happy" and q be the statement "I get rich." The compound statement is $p \to q$.
67. *Converse:* If I start riding my bike to work, gas prices will go higher.
Inverse: If gas prices do not go any higher, I will not start riding my bike to work.
Contrapositive: If I do not start riding my bike to work, then gas prices will not go any higher.
69. *Converse:* If it rains, the festival will move inside the student center.
Inverse: If the festival did not move inside the student center, then it did not rain.
Contrapositive: If it does not rain, then the festival will not move inside the student center.
71. Invalid   73. Invalid   75. Invalid   77. Invalid   79. Invalid
81. Valid   83. Invalid   85. Invalid

Chapter 3 Test

1. Statement   3. Not a statement
5. The image is not uploading to my online bio.
7. No students ride a bike to school.   9. $p \wedge q$ 11. $p \leftrightarrow q$
13. $\sim(\sim p \wedge q)$ 15. It is sunny or not warm.
17. It is sunny if and only if it is warm.
19. It is not the case that it is not sunny or it is warm.
21. FFTFTFTF   23. TTFF   25. Self-contradiction
27. Neither   29. Tautology   31. Equivalent
33. It is cold or it is not snowing.   35. Invalid   37. Valid
39. Invalid   41. Valid   43. Invalid   45. Valid

CHAPTER 4: NUMERATION SYSTEMS

Exercise Set 4-1

7. 35   9. 20,225   11. 30,163   13. 20,314   15. 1,112,010

17. ||||||| 19. ∩∩∩|||||||

21. ⟃∩∩∩∩∩||||||||

23. ⟃⟃⟃⟃⟃⟃⟃⟃⟃|

25. ⌐⟃⟃∩∩∩∩∩||||||

27. ⟃∩|||||||

29. ⊲⊲⊲∤∤∤∤∤∩∩∩|||||

31. ⌐⌐⌐⌐⌐⌐⌐⌐⌐⟃⟃⟃⟃⟃⟃⟃⟃⟃
∩∩∩∩∩∩∩∩∩||||||||||

33. 189   35. 52   37. 713

39. **41.** 二百八十四 **43.** 二千三百五十六

45. hundreds **47.** ten thousands **49.** ones **51.** $8 \times 10^1 + 6$
53. $1 \times 10^3 + 8 \times 10^2 + 1 \times 10^1 + 2$ **55.** $6 \times 10^3 + 2$
57. $1 \times 10^5 + 6 \times 10^4 + 2 \times 10^3 + 8 \times 10^2 + 7 \times 10^1 + 3$
59. $1 \times 10^7 + 7 \times 10^6 + 5 \times 10^5 + 3 \times 10^4 + 1 \times 10^3 + 8 \times 10^2 + 1$
61. 12 **63.** 51 **65.** 40,871 **67.** 109,284 **69.** 792
71. ⟨⟨⟨ ▼▼ **73.** ▼ ⟨▼▼▼▼▼▼▼
75. ▼▼▼▼ ⟨⟨⟨⟨⟨▼▼ **77.** ⟨▼▼▼▼▼▼ ▼▼▼
79. ▼ ⟨⟨▼▼▼▼▼▼ ⟨⟨⟨⟨⟨▼▼▼▼▼
81. 17 **83.** 43 **85.** 86 **87.** 418 **89.** 490 **91.** XXXIX
93. DLXVII **95.** MCCLVIII **97.** MCDLXII **99.** MMM
101. 1939 **103.** 1978 **105.** 2005 **107.** Answers vary
109. Because the Babylonian system is an ancient number system which is not in use today.

Exercise Set 4-2

3. 252 **5.** 391 **7.** 3,740 **9.** 448 **11.** 216 **13.** 253 **15.** 368
17. 374 **19.** 392 **21.** 270 **23.** 10,488 **25.** 166,786 **27.** 791,028
29. 58,625 **31.** 203,912 **33.** 4,707 **35.** 1,035 **37.** 5,781
39. 36,344 **41.** Answers vary **43.** Answers vary

Exercise Set 4-3

3. 11 **5.** 33 **7.** 108 **9.** 106 **11.** 311 **13.** 69 **15.** 359 **17.** 184
19. 37,406 **21.** 1,166 **23.** 11111_{two} **25.** 1333_{six} **27.** 22_{seven}
29. 1017_{nine} **31.** 10110_{two} **33.** 33_{five} **35.** $939_{sixteen}$ **37.** 1042212_{five}
39. 44_{seven} **41.** 100000000_{two} **43.** 111010_{two} **45.** 81_{twelve}
47. 310_{four} **49.** $1B6_{twelve}$ **51.** 3665_{seven}
53. (a) 3272_{eight} **57.** (a) 2731_{eight} **61.** (a) 6553_{eight}
    (b) $6BA_{sixteen}$ (b) $5D9_{sixteen}$ (b) $D6B_{sixteen}$
55. (a) 637_{eight} **59.** (a) 3775_{eight}
    (b) $19F_{sixteen}$ (b) $7FD_{sixteen}$
63. 1101111000_{two} **65.** 110101000100_{two} **67.** 110010000_{two}
69. 110001_{two} **71.** 111010001110101_{two} **73.** 110101000101011_{two}
75. 1010101_{two} **77.** 1101100010_{two} **79.** 101001011101_{two}
81. 110010101001011_{two} **83.** 5 lb 7 oz **85.** 34 yd 2 ft 8 in.
87. STOP **89.** CLASSISOVER **91.** ITISRAINING
93. 13256 **95.** 67138 **97.** 44501
99. |||⌐|||||⌐|||||⌐|||||⌐||| **101.** ||||||||⌐||||⌐|||⌐||⌐||
103. ||||||⌐||||⌐||⌐||⌐||||⌐|||
105. one symbol; same as tally system **107.** 6; manufacturer's
109. 0; product

Exercise Set 4-4

3.

+	0	1	2
0	0	1	2
1	1	2	10
2	2	10	11

5.

×	0	1	2	3
0	0	0	0	0
1	0	1	2	3
2	0	2	10	12
3	0	3	12	21

7. 32_{five} **9.** 11212_{four} **11.** 2020_{six} **13.** 6657_{nine} **15.** 31_{five} **17.** 101_{seven}
19. 40040_{nine} **21.** 571_{twelve} **23.** 332_{six} **25.** 56067_{nine} **27.** $3976A_{twelve}$
29. 482_{nine} remainder 2_{nine} **31.** 230_{five} remainder 3_{five} **33.** 10000_{two}
35. $403_{sixteen}$ **37.** 1001_{two} **39.** $4DCA_{sixteen}$ **41.** 110010_{two}
43. $2894_{sixteen}$ **45.** 11_{two} remainder 10_{two}
47. $B23_{sixteen}$ remainder $2_{sixteen}$ **49.** base 8 **51.** L
53. G **55.** 01000100 01001111 01010010 01001101
57. 01010101 01001110 01001001 01001111 01001110

Review Exercises

1. 1,000,221 **3.** 681 **5.** 419 **7.** 2,604
9. ⌐⌐⌐⌐⌐||||||||| **11.** ▼ ⟨⟨▼▼▼▼▼▼▼
13. DIII **15.** ▼▼ ⟨⟨⟨⟨▼▼▼▼▼
17.
19. 276 **21.** 147 **23.** 330 **25.** 156 **27.** 1,955 **29.** 365,687
31. 2,542 **33.** 13,965 **35.** 119 **37.** 17,327 **39.** 1,246
41. 2,058 **43.** 215 **45.** 52_{six} **47.** 2663_{nine} **49.** 101011_{two}
51. 103_{four} **53.** 1000_{seven} **55.** (a) 733_{eight} (b) $1DB_{sixteen}$
57. (a) 1547_{eight} (b) $367_{sixteen}$ **59.** 111011010100_{two}
61. 1010010110110011_{two} **63.** 251_{nine} **65.** 111011_{two}
67. $15AB6_{twelve}$ **69.** 101100_{two} **71.** 331_{four} **73.** 21331_{nine}
75. 1011011_{two} **77.** 230_{five} remainder 2_{five} **79.** 342_{eight} remainder 6_{eight}

Chapter 4 Test

1. 2,000,312 **3.** 1,271 **5.** 426
7. ⌐⌐⌐⌐⌐⌐⌐⌐||||
9. ⟨⟨⟨⟨⟨▼▼▼▼▼ **11.** DCV **13.** 221 **15.** 267,904
17. 96 **19.** 17,375 **21.** 1,231 **23.** 500 **25.** 241 **27.** 133_{five}
29. 6362_{nine} **31.** 10001_{two} **33.** 1123_{four} **35.** 1160_{seven}
37. (a) 731_{eight} (b) $1D9_{sixteen}$ **39.** 111011010100_{two} **41.** 282_{nine}
43. 1000111_{two} **45.** $14B25_{twelve}$ **47.** 10010111_{two} **49.** 1030_{four}
51. 1250_{six} **53.** 151_{eight} remainder 3_{eight}

CHAPTER 5: THE REAL NUMBER SYSTEM

Exercise Set 5-1

7. 1, 2, 4, 8, 16 **9.** 1, 2, 3, 6, 7, 9, 14, 18, 21, 42, 63, 126
11. 1, 2, 4, 8, 16, 32 **13.** 1, 3, 9 **15.** 1, 2, 3, 4, 6, 8, 12, 16, 24, 32, 48, 96
17. 1, 17 **19.** 1, 2, 4, 8, 16, 32, 64 **21.** 1, 3, 5, 7, 15, 21, 35, 105
23. 1, 2, 7, 14, 49, 98 **25.** 1, 71 **27.** 3, 6, 9, 12, 15
29. 10, 20, 30, 40, 50 **31.** 15, 30, 45, 60, 75 **33.** 17, 34, 51, 68, 85
35. 1, 2, 3, 4, 5 **37.** 2^4 **39.** $2^4 \times 3^4$ **41.** 17 is prime **43.** 2×5^2
45. 2^7 **47.** $2^2 \times 3 \times 5^2$ **49.** $5^2 \times 19$ **51.** 7×2^6 **53.** 13×19
55. $2 \times 3 \times 5^3$ **57.** 3 **59.** 1 **61.** 6 **63.** 21 **65.** 25 **67.** 12
69. 6 **71.** 12 **73.** 25 **75.** 10 **77.** 35 **79.** 126 **81.** 150
83. 630 **85.** 308 **87.** 60 **89.** 36 **91.** 840 **93.** 4 students
95. 72 minutes **97.** 6 members per team; 5 female teams, 6 male teams
99. noon **101.** 4 groups of Republicans, 5 groups of Democrats, 7 groups of Independents **103.** 221 years
105. The only even prime number is 2.
107. 3 + 1 = 4   7 + 7 = 14
    3 + 3 = 6   3 + 13 = 16
    3 + 5 = 8   5 + 13 = 18
    5 + 5 = 10   3 + 17 = 20
    5 + 7 = 12
109. Answers vary, 13.

Exercise Set 5-2

7. 8 **9.** 10 **11.** 8 **13.** −10 **15.** 0 **17.** < **19.** > **21.** >
23. < **25.** < **27.** −1 **29.** 9 **31.** −11 **33.** −12 **35.** −13
37. 14 **39.** −5 **41.** 1 **43.** −5 **45.** −70 **47.** 45 **49.** −24
51. −36 **53.** 42 **55.** 0 **57.** 8 **59.** −5 **61.** −4 **63.** 7 **65.** 1

67. 0 **69.** 0 **71.** 11 **73.** 51 **75.** 36 **77.** 6 **79.** -758
81. -56 **83.** 59 **85.** -492 **87.** \$1,180 **89.** 1,399 rats
91. Flagler, FL: 24,002, Sumter, FL: 18,797: Paulding, GA: 21,082, Kendall, IL: 13,877, Pinal, AZ: 56,264. **93.** 8 inches
95. 7,000 pounds **97.** No general statements can be made.
99. Answers vary

Exercise Set 5-3

9. $\frac{1}{6}$ **11.** $\frac{7}{10}$ **13.** $\frac{5}{6}$ **15.** $\frac{7}{8}$ **17.** $\frac{5}{9}$ **19.** $\frac{15}{48}$ **21.** $\frac{43}{49}$ **23.** $\frac{35}{45}$ **25.** $\frac{55}{80}$
27. $\frac{6}{30}$ **29.** $-\frac{1}{6}$ **31.** $-\frac{37}{24}$ or $-1\frac{13}{24}$ **33.** $\frac{7}{24}$ **35.** $\frac{7}{6}$ or $1\frac{1}{6}$ **37.** $\frac{7}{10}$
39. $-\frac{1}{16}$ **41.** $\frac{11}{12}$ **43.** $\frac{6}{5}$ or $1\frac{1}{5}$ **45.** $\frac{3}{4}$ **47.** $\frac{7}{36}$ **49.** 0.2
51. $0.66\ldots$ or $0.\overline{6}$ **53.** 2.25 **55.** $0.3055\ldots$ or $0.30\overline{5}$ **57.** 0.75
59. 0.9411764705882352 **61.** $\frac{4}{25}$ **63.** $\frac{3}{8}$ **65.** $\frac{7}{9}$ **67.** $\frac{6}{11}$ **69.** $\frac{34}{75}$
71. 171 miles **73.** 1/7 **75.** 935 people **77.** 935 people **79.** 12 feet
81. $\frac{3}{8}$ **83.** $1\frac{1}{4}$ cups of flour and $\frac{1}{3}$ cup of sugar **85.** $\frac{7}{500}$ **87.** $\frac{13}{100}$
89. $\frac{45}{100}$ **91.** Any common denominator will do.
93. This question is a paradox, an answer of yes or no leads to a contradiction. **95.** Add the fractions and divide by two.

Exercise Set 5-4

7. rational **9.** irrational **11.** irrational **13.** 3 and 4 **15.** 9 and 11
17. 14 and 15 **19.** $2\sqrt{6}$ **21.** $4\sqrt{5}$ **23.** $\sqrt{30}$ **25.** $20\sqrt{5}$ **27.** $30\sqrt{7}$
29. $2\sqrt{5}$ **31.** $3\sqrt{30}$ **33.** $24\sqrt{3}$ **35.** $\sqrt{30}$ **37.** $2\sqrt{2}$ **39.** $12\sqrt{7}$
41. $-7\sqrt{3}$ **43.** $-2\sqrt{3}$ **45.** $4\sqrt{5}$ **47.** $-6\sqrt{5}$ **49.** $18\sqrt{2}$
51. $\sqrt{2}+8\sqrt{3}$ **53.** $10\sqrt{10}-4\sqrt{2}$ **55.** $7\sqrt{15}$ **57.** $\frac{\sqrt{5}}{5}$ **59.** $\frac{\sqrt{6}}{2}$ **61.** $\frac{\sqrt{21}}{14}$
63. $\frac{\sqrt{6}}{3}$ **65.** $\sqrt{9}+\sqrt{16}=3+4\neq 5=\sqrt{25}$
67. $\sqrt{40}+\sqrt{40}\approx 6.32+6.32\neq 8.94\approx\sqrt{80}$
69. 3 seconds **71.** 9.2 seconds
73. 3.5 seconds, 2.5 seconds, the difference is 1 second.
75. 20 volts **77.** 141.4 volts **79.** 4π seconds **81.** 0.8 foot
83. The irrational numbers are not closed under multiplication. The rational numbers are closed under multiplication.
85. You cannot compute the square root of a negative number because there is no number, that when squared, is negative.
87. Yes, $\sqrt{3+0}=\sqrt{3}+\sqrt{0}$. The conjecture will be true when one of a or b is zero.

Exercise Set 5-5

7. Integer, rational, real **9.** Rational, real **11.** Rational, real
13. Irrational, real **15.** Irrational, real **17.** Rational, real
19. Natural, whole, integer, rational, real
21. Natural, whole, integer, rational, real
23. Closure property of addition
25. Commutative property of addition
27. Commutative property of multiplication
29. Distributive property **31.** Inverse property of multiplication
33. Commutative property of addition
35. Identity property of addition
37. Commutative property of multiplication
39. Addition, multiplication **41.** Addition, subtraction, multiplication
43. None **45.** 27.46, overweight **47.** 23.73, normal
49. 17.53, underweight **51.** 38.51, obese **53.** not commutative
55. commutative **57.** associative **59.** associative
61. The results are not the same, subtraction is not associative.
63. The results are not the same, addition does not distribute over multiplication.

Exercise Set 5-6

7. 243 **9.** 1 **11.** 1 **13.** $\frac{1}{243}$ **15.** $\frac{1}{64}$ **17.** $3^6=729$
19. $4^7=16,384$ **21.** $3^2=9$ **23.** 2^1 or 2 **25.** $5^6=15,625$
27. $\frac{1}{3^2}=\frac{1}{9}$ **29.** $\frac{1}{5^5}=\frac{1}{3,125}$ **31.** $\frac{1}{2^2}=\frac{1}{4}$ **33.** $\frac{1}{4^3}=\frac{1}{64}$ **35.** $\frac{1}{7}$
37. 6.25×10^8 **39.** 7.3×10^{-3} **41.** 5.28×10^{11} **43.** 6.18×10^{-6}
45. 4.32×10^4 **47.** 8.14×10^{-2} **49.** 3.2×10^{13} **51.** 59,000

53. 0.0000375 **55.** 2,400 **57.** 0.000003 **59.** 1,000
61. 8,020,000,000 **63.** 7,000,000,000,000
65. $6\times 10^{10}=60,000,000,000$ **67.** $2.67\times 10^{-7}=0.000000267$
69. $8.8\times 10^{-3}=0.0088$ **71.** $1.5\times 10^{-9}=0.0000000015$
73. $2\times 10^2=200$ **75.** $6\times 10^0=6$ **77.** $6\times 10^{-2}=0.06$
79. 2.58×10^{15} **81.** 2.4×10^1 **83.** 1×10^{-12} **85.** 1.116×10^8 miles
87. 56% **89.** 2.4696×10^{13} miles **91.** 7.96×10^{-4} light years
93. 10 billion **95.** 421 million miles **97.** \$111,000,000 a day
99. 5.7 million tickets
101. Each entry is half the previous entry so the last three entries are 1, ½, and ¼. **103.** Answers vary

Exercise Set 5-7

7. (a) 1, 7, 13, 19, 25 (b) 6 (c) 67 (d) 408
9. (a) $-9, -12, -15, -18, -21$ (b) -3 (c) -42 (d) -306
11. (a) $\frac{1}{4}, \frac{5}{8}, 1, \frac{11}{8}, \frac{7}{4}$ (b) $\frac{3}{8}$ (c) $\frac{35}{8}$ (d) $\frac{111}{4}$
13. (a) 4, $\frac{11}{3}, \frac{10}{3}$, 3, $\frac{8}{3}$ (b) $-\frac{1}{3}$ (c) $\frac{1}{3}$ (d) 26
15. (a) 5, 13, 21, 29, 37 (b) 8 (c) 93 (d) 588
17. (a) 50, 48, 46, 44, 42 (b) -2 (c) 28 (d) 468
19. (a) $\frac{1}{8}, \frac{19}{24}, \frac{35}{24}, \frac{17}{8}, \frac{67}{24}$ (b) $\frac{2}{3}$ (c) $\frac{179}{24}$ (d) $\frac{91}{2}$
21. (a) 0.6, 1.6, 2.6, 3.6, 4.6 (b) 1 (c) 11.6 (d) 73.2
23. (a) 12, 24, 48, 96, 192 (b) 2 (c) 24,576 (d) 49,140
25. (a) $-5, -\frac{5}{4}, -\frac{5}{16}, -\frac{5}{64}, -\frac{5}{256}$ (b) $\frac{1}{4}$ (c) $-\frac{5}{4,194,304}$ (d) ≈ -6.7
27. (a) $\frac{1}{6}, -1, 6, -36, 216$ (b) -6 (c) 60,466,176 (d) $-\frac{15,237,476,345}{6}$
29. (a) 100, $-25, \frac{25}{4}, -\frac{25}{16}, \frac{25}{64}$ (b) $-\frac{1}{4}$ (c) $-\frac{25}{1,048,576}$ (d) ≈ 80
31. (a) 4, 12, 36, 108, 324 (b) 3 (c) 708,588 (d) 1,062,880
33. (a) $\frac{1}{2}, \frac{1}{4}, \frac{1}{8}, \frac{1}{16}, \frac{1}{32}$ (b) 1/2 (c) ≈ 0.000244 (d) ≈ 0.9998
35. (a) $-3, 15, -75, 375, -1875$ (b) -5 (c) 146,484,375 (d) 122,070,312
37. (a) 1, 3, 9, 27, 81 (b) 3 (c) 177,147 (d) 265,720
39. geometric **41.** neither **43.** arithmetic **45.** arithmetic
47. (a) \$500 (b) \$13,000 **49.** no **51.** \$18,000 **53.** 160 ft
55. \$3,766.11 **57.** 8 questions
59. First job pays \$5,300.65 more in ten years.
61. $a_1=\frac{3}{10}$ and $r=\frac{1}{10}$. The sum is $\frac{1}{3}$. **63.** Answers vary

Review Exercises

1. 1, 2, 3, 6, 13, 26, 39, 78 **3.** 1, 3, 5, 9, 15, 45
5. 1, 2, 4, 5, 7, 10, 14, 20, 28, 35, 70, 140 **7.** 4, 8, 12, 16, 20
9. 9, 18, 27, 36, 45 **11.** $2^5\times 3$ **13.** 2×5^3 **15.** $2^3\times 3\times 5^2$
17. 2; 30 **19.** 5; 280 **21.** 20; 1,200 **23.** 198 months, or 16.5 years
25. -14 **27.** -4 **29.** 44 **31.** 89 **33.** -157 **35.** $\frac{15}{19}$
37. $\frac{4}{5}$ **39.** $\frac{23}{24}$ **41.** $\frac{5}{21}$ **43.** $\frac{6}{17}$ **45.** $\frac{13}{18}$ **47.** $-\frac{17}{7}$ or $-2\frac{3}{7}$
49. $\frac{41}{40}$ or $1\frac{1}{40}$ **51.** 0.9 **53.** $0.\overline{857142}$ **55.** $\frac{11}{16}$ **57.** $\frac{23}{90}$
59. NFL: 12; MLB: 8; NBA and NHL: 16 **61.** $4\sqrt{7}$
63. $\frac{\sqrt{5}}{2}$ **65.** $\frac{\sqrt{15}}{6}$ **67.** $22\sqrt{2}$ **69.** $20\sqrt{3}$ **71.** $\sqrt{6}$ **73.** $14\sqrt{3}-6\sqrt{7}$
75. Rational, real **77.** Irrational, real
79. Natural, whole, integer, rational, real
81. Commutative property of addition **83.** Distributive property
85. 1 **87.** 1/81 **89.** 117,649 **91.** 6,561 **93.** 1/7,776
95. 2.59×10^{10} **97.** 4.8×10^{-4} **99.** 2,330,000,000 **101.** 0.0000088
103. 2.848×10^{-11} **105.** 6×10^{-8}
107. 1.41×10^4 seconds or about 3.9 hours
109. 4, 1, $-2, -5, -8, -11$; $a_9=-20$, $S_9=-72$
111. $-\frac{1}{5}, \frac{3}{10}, \frac{4}{5}, \frac{13}{10}, \frac{9}{5}, \frac{23}{10}$; $a_9=\frac{19}{5}$, $S_9=\frac{81}{5}$
113. $-3, -9, -27, -81, -243, -729$; $a_9=-19,683$, $S_9=-29,523$
115. $-\frac{2}{5}, \frac{1}{5}, -\frac{1}{10}, \frac{1}{20}, -\frac{1}{40}, \frac{1}{80}$; $a_9=-\frac{1}{640}$, $S_9=-\frac{171}{640}$
117. The profit for the sixth year is \$25,525.63, and the total earnings for the six years are \$136,038.26

Chapter 5 Test

1. Integer, rational, real   3. Rational, real   5. Irrational, real
7. Whole, integer, rational, real   9. Integer, rational, real
11. 14; 168   13. 25; 4,200   15. $\frac{3}{7}$ 17. $\frac{16}{25}$ 19. $\frac{7}{10}$ 21. $4\sqrt{3}$ 23. 36
25. $\frac{15}{16}$ 27. $\frac{27}{8}$ or $3\frac{3}{8}$ 29. $2(\sqrt{3} + \sqrt{6})$ 31. 3   33. $\frac{7}{8}$ 35. $\frac{2}{9}$
37. Commutative property of addition.
39. Identity property of addition
41. Associative property of multiplication   43. 4,096   45. 1
47. $\frac{1}{3,125}$ 49. 2.36×10^{-3} 51. -0.00006 53. 3×10^3
55. $\frac{3}{4}, -\frac{1}{8}, \frac{1}{48}, -\frac{1}{288}, \frac{1}{1,728}, -\frac{1}{10,368}, \frac{1}{62,208}$ 57. $320; $620
$a_{15} \approx 9.57 \times 10^{-12}, S_{15} \approx 0.643$

CHAPTER 6: TOPICS IN ALGEBRA

Exercise Set 6-1

7. $11x$ 9. $-18y$ 11. $9p - q - 17$ 13. $11x^2 - x + 5$
15. $30x - 35$ 17. $-48x + 40$ 19. $x + 27$ 21. $-26x - 50$
23. $8x - 23$ 25. $-x + 13$ 27. $3x - 5$ 29. $-2x^2 - 10x - 2$
31. $-4x^2y + 18xy^2 - 9$ 33. $13m - 9$ 35. $\frac{7}{2}yz + \frac{3}{4}$ 37. $-3.9x + 10$
39. $0.75tz$ 41. 83   43. 16   45. 79   47. 466   49. 104   51. 136
53. 997   55. 205   57. 17   59. $127\frac{7}{12}$ 61. -5.2 63. -27.5
65. 376.8 sq in.   67. $6,050   69. 267.95 mm³   71. $31,876.96
73. 678.24   75. $100   77. 3 defective items   79. 10°C
81. 600,000 ergs   83. $\frac{8}{9}$ 85. $14,281.87   87. $\sqrt{13}$ 89. 1,340 feet
91. 183 mg

Exercise Set 6-2

7. not linear   9. linear   11. not linear   13. linear   15. yes   17. no
19. yes   21. {26}   23. {59}   25. {−3}   27. {3}   29. {−12}
31. {6}   33. {16}   35. {20}   37. {11}   39. {5}   41. {4}   43. {12}
45. $\left\{\frac{20}{3}\right\}$ 47. {3}   49. {5}   51. {54}   53. {3}   55. {36}
57. {64}   59. $\left\{\frac{76}{3}\right\}$ 61. $\left\{\frac{180}{7}\right\}$ 63. $\left\{\frac{84}{13}\right\}$ 65. $\left\{\frac{30}{11}\right\}$ 67. $\left\{\frac{4}{9}\right\}$
69. $\left\{-\frac{9}{53}\right\}$ 71. $\left\{-\frac{40}{9}\right\}$ 73. $\left\{\frac{16}{13}\right\}$ 75. $y = \frac{3x + 4}{2}$ 77. $x = \frac{7y + 16}{5}$
79. $y = \frac{9 - 7x}{2}$ 81. identity; $\{x \mid x \text{ is a real number}\}$
83. contradiction; $\varnothing$ 85. contradiction; $\varnothing$
87. identity; $\{x \mid x \text{ is a real number}\}$ 89. $L = \frac{Rd^2}{k}$ 91. $h = \frac{v}{\pi r^2}$
93. $h = \frac{V}{lw}$ 95. $a = \frac{2d}{t^2}$ 97. $H = \frac{AP - S - 2D - 3T}{4}$ 99. $b = 2a - c$
101. 5 m/s²   103. 4 kg   105. $55.50   107. about 1,571 minutes
109. 2,720 kg·m/s   111. about 1.47 m/s   113. 81.7
115. 65   117. 62.5 watts   119. 9 ohms
121. Dividing is the same as multiplying by the reciprocal and subtracting is the same as adding the opposite.
123. This could introduce solutions that weren't solutions before, or eliminate solutions that were solutions before.   125. Answers vary

Exercise Set 6-3

5. $x - 3$ 7. $x + 9$ 9. $11 - x$ 11. $x - 9$ 13. $7 - x$ 15. $8 \cdot x$
17. $3x + 5$ 19. $5x + 3$ 21. $2x$ 23. $\frac{x}{14}$ or $x \div 14$ 25. 8   27. 16
29. 17 and 11   31. 12   33. 28   35. There are 27 students in one section and 30 students in the other section.   37. $15,713
39. The bill was $58.62 in September and $60.94 in October.
41. 18 games   43. $270
45. $1.25 billion on costumes and $1.93 billion on candy
47. 8 feet   49. $36,000   51. $40   53. No   55. $563.20
57. The losing candidate received 206 votes and the winning candidate received 281 votes.
59. wind chill = temperature − 1.5 × wind speed

Exercise Set 6-4

5. $\frac{18}{28} = \frac{9}{14}$ 7. $\frac{14}{32} = \frac{7}{16}$ 9. $\frac{12}{15} = \frac{4}{5}$ 11. $\frac{3}{8}$ 13. $\frac{60}{30} = \frac{2}{1}$ 15. $x = \frac{135}{14}$
17. $x = 35$ 19. $x = 10$ 21. $x = \frac{31}{3}$ 23. $x = \frac{21}{4}$ 25. 15 cones
27. $\frac{14}{3}$ inches   29. 4 gallons   31. 99   33. 40 iPods

35. 8 sections   37. 20 professors   39. 4 cans   41. $1,200
43. 298 lb   45. 117 lb   47. 24 lb   49. 3 lb   51. 9 more students
55. 25 pounds for $7.49 is a better buy.   57. 7 ounces for $1.99 is a better buy.   59. 34.5 ounces for $7.49 is a better buy.

Exercise Set 6-5

5. (number line, point at 3)   7. (number line, open at −4)
9. (number line, point at −9)   11. (number line, −3 open, 7 open)
13. (number line, open at 2, point at 5)   15. $\{x \mid x < 5\}$ (number line, open at 5)
17. $\{x \mid x \leq 30\}$ (number line, point at 30)
19. $\{y \mid y \geq 6\}$ (number line, point at 6)
21. $\{x \mid x < -35\}$ (number line, open at −35)
23. $\{x \mid x < 27\}$ (number line, open at 27)
25. $\{t \mid t > -3\}$ (number line, open at −3)
27. $\{z \mid z \geq 12\}$ (number line, point at 12)
29. $\{x \mid x \geq -8\}$ (number line, point at −8)
31. $\{x \mid x \leq 21\}$ (number line, point at 21)
33. $\left\{y \mid y \leq 8\frac{2}{5}\right\}$ (number line, point at $8\frac{2}{5}$)
35. $\left\{x \mid x \leq -\frac{6}{5}\right\}$ (number line, point at $-\frac{6}{5}$)
37. $\{x \mid x < 14\}$ (number line, open at 14)
39. $\left\{n \mid n \leq -10\frac{3}{5}\right\}$ (number line, point at $-10\frac{3}{5}$)
41. $\left\{x \mid x \geq -46\frac{1}{2}\right\}$ (number line, point at $-46\frac{1}{2}$)
43. $\{x \mid x \geq -20\}$ (number line, point at −20)
45. $\left\{x \mid x \leq -\frac{13}{45}\right\}$ (number line, point at $-\frac{13}{45}$)
47. $\left\{t \mid t \geq -\frac{46}{65}\right\}$ (number line, point at $-\frac{46}{65}$)
49. $\{x \mid -7 \leq x < 8\}$ (number line, point at −7, open at 8)
51. $\{y \mid -3 < y < 3\}$ (number line, open at −3, open at 3)
53. $\left\{z \mid -5 \leq z < \frac{5}{4}\right\}$ (number line, point at −5, open at $\frac{5}{4}$)
55. $\left\{x \mid -1 < x < \frac{3}{2}\right\}$ (number line, open at −1, open at $\frac{3}{2}$)
57. Texas, Florida, Kansas, Colorado   59. Missouri, West Virginia
61. Maryland, California, Pennsylvania, Missouri, West Virginia
63. at most $7,364.48   65. 64% or greater   67. at most $18.86
69. at least 312.5 miles   71. no more than 944 minutes
73. at most $76,923.08   75. at most 4 feet tall   77. 88% to 100%
79. between 20 and 30 hours   81. You can always move the variables to the side of the inequality that will leave the coefficient positive.

Exercise Set 6-6

7. $3x^2 + 2x - 5 = 0; a = 3, b = 2, c = -5$
9. $30x^2 - 10 = 0; a = 30, b = 0, c = -10$
11. $2x^2 + 5x = 0; a = 2, b = 5, c = 0$ **13.** $x^2 + 16x + 63$
15. $y^2 - 17y + 70$ **17.** $x^2 - 7x - 120$ **19.** $14x^2 - 67x + 63$
21. $15z^2 - 19z - 56$ **23.** $\{-2, -3\}$ **25.** $\{-4, 3\}$ **27.** $\{-3, 17\}$
29. $\{-27, 3\}$ **31.** $\{3, 5\}$ **33.** $\left\{-3, \frac{7}{2}\right\}$ **35.** $\left\{-\frac{4}{3}, \frac{3}{2}\right\}$ **37.** $\left\{-\frac{4}{3}, \frac{3}{2}\right\}$
39. $\left\{-2, \frac{3}{5}\right\}$ **41.** $\left\{-\frac{3}{2}, \frac{4}{3}\right\}$ **43.** $\{-3, 2\}$ **45.** $\left\{-\frac{1}{2}, -4\right\}$
47. $\left\{\frac{-1 + \sqrt{13}}{6}, \frac{-1 - \sqrt{13}}{6}\right\}$ **49.** $\left\{-\frac{3}{2}, 4\right\}$ **51.** $\left\{\frac{-5 + \sqrt{13}}{6}, \frac{-5 - \sqrt{13}}{6}\right\}$
53. $\{-1, 9\}$ **55.** $\left\{\frac{-5 + \sqrt{37}}{2}, \frac{-5 - \sqrt{37}}{2}\right\}$ **57.** $\left\{\frac{21 + \sqrt{321}}{2}, \frac{21 - \sqrt{321}}{2}\right\}$
59. $\left\{\frac{7 + \sqrt{199}}{5}, \frac{7 - \sqrt{199}}{5}\right\}$ **61.** $\left\{\frac{-13 + \sqrt{73}}{4}, \frac{-13 - \sqrt{73}}{4}\right\}$
63. $\left\{\frac{-8 + 7\sqrt{6}}{10}, \frac{-8 - 7\sqrt{6}}{10}\right\}$ **65.** 16 and 18 or -18 and -16
67. 9 seconds   **69.** 4 inches and 10 inches   **71.** 9 square feet
73. 40 gift baskets   **75.** width 8 feet and length 24 feet
77. 6 feet   **79.** 19.7 mph   **81.** 5 hours
83. horizontal distance 407 feet and vertical distance 419 feet
85. Since $x = 1$, $x - 1 = 0$. Division by 0 is undefined.
87. Answers vary

Review Exercises

1. $-2x + 5y - 7$ **3.** $7x - 36$ **5.** $13x - 21$ **7.** $x + 1$ **9.** 99
11. -70 **13.** 120   **15.** $\{-10\}$ **17.** $\{20\}$ **19.** $\{-13\}$ **21.** $\{67\}$
23. $\{-4\}$ **25.** $\{12\}$ **27.** $\left\{\frac{8}{5}\right\}$ **29.** $x = \frac{y+2}{3}$ **31.** $r = \frac{1}{pt}$
33. $r = \frac{C}{2\pi}$ **35.** $h = \frac{2A}{b}$ **37.** $6 \cdot 2n$ or $12n$ **39.** $n + 5$
41. 6 pounds of mixed soy nuts and 8 pounds of Asian trail mix.
43. 270 adults   **45.** 5 nickels, 20 dimes, 10 quarters
47. $\frac{82 \text{ miles}}{15 \text{ gallons}}$ **49.** $\frac{4 \text{ months}}{24 \text{ months}} = \frac{1}{6}$ **51.** $x = 9$ **53.** $x = 72$
55. 750 calories   **57.** wife \$10,800; son \$7,200   **59.** \$4,320
61. 4.44 amps   **63.** $x > 10$ **65.** $y > 7$ **67.** $t \le -\frac{93}{4}$
69. up to 28 months   **71.** $\{-2, 3\}$ **73.** $\{-3, 7\}$ **75.** $\left\{-1, \frac{2}{3}\right\}$
77. $\left\{\frac{5 + \sqrt{53}}{2}, \frac{5 - \sqrt{53}}{2}\right\}$ **79.** $\left\{\frac{-7 + \sqrt{17}}{8}, \frac{-7 + \sqrt{17}}{8}\right\}$ **81.** $\left\{\frac{-7 + \sqrt{69}}{4}, \frac{-7 - \sqrt{69}}{4}\right\}$
83. -12 and -11 or 11 and 12

Chapter 6 Test

1. $5x - 10y + 5$ **3.** 91   **5.** $\left\{\frac{9}{7}\right\}$ **7.** $r = \frac{mv^2}{F}$ **9.** $\left\{x \mid x \le -\frac{3}{2}\right\}$
11. $x = 4$ **13.** $2x^2 - 13x - 24$ **15.** $\{-3, 17\}$ **17.** $\left\{-\frac{3}{2}, \frac{4}{3}\right\}$
19. $\left\{-1, \frac{3}{5}\right\}$ **21.** \$2,500 was invested at 6% and \$500 was invested at 8%
23. 21.9 hours   **25.** 12 hours
27. The width is 8 inches and the length is 12 inches.

CHAPTER 7: ADDITIONAL TOPICS IN ALGEBRA

Exercise Set 7-1

7.

9.

11.

13.

15.

17.

19.

21.

23.

25.

27.

29.

31. 1   **33.** -0.5 **35.** $-\frac{3}{5}$ **37.** $\frac{33}{14}$
39. x intercept $= (8, 0)$; y intercept $= (0, 6)$
41. x intercept $= (-6, 0)$; y intercept $= (0, -5)$
43. x intercept $= (9, 0)$; y intercept $= (0, -18)$
45. x intercept $= (3, 0)$; y intercept $= (0, -7.5)$
47. $y = -\frac{7}{5}x + 7$ **49.** $y = \frac{1}{4}x - 4$

51. $y = \frac{8}{3}x - 8$ **53.** $y = 2x - 19$

55.

57.

13.

15.

59. (a) $69.50　(b) $82.50　(c) $115　**61.** (a) $109.30　(b) $86.20
(c) $179.70　**63.** 31.5 thousand or 31,500　**65.** 37.8 million
67. $14.64　**69.** (a) $39.97　(b) $54.94　(c) $144.76
71. $y = 40 + 20x$; 23 hours　**73.** $w = 160 - 3x$; 10 months
75. $y = 350 - 5x$; 70 years
77. The denominator of the fraction for the slope will always be zero.

Exercise Set 7-2

7. (3, 4) is a solution; (5, 10) is not a solution
9. (11, −6) is not a solution; (1/2, 3) is a solution
11. (−10, 25) is a solution; (5, 35) is not a solution　**13.** (7, 0)
15. (−2, 0)　**17.** (2, −2)　**19.** (6, −2)　**21.** (−3, 3)
23. (4, −1)　**25.** $\left(\frac{51}{11}, \frac{16}{11}\right)$　**27.** (5, 3)　**29.** $\left(\frac{76}{21}, \frac{3}{7}\right)$　**31.** (2, −1)
33. The system is dependent. The solution set is
$\{(x, y) \mid 5x - 2y = 11\}$.　**35.** (4, 2)　**37.** consistent; (1, −2)
39. consistent; (7, −2)　**41.** consistent; $\left(-\frac{5}{2}, -\frac{11}{2}\right)$
43. consistent; $\left(\frac{41}{19}, -\frac{45}{19}\right)$
45. $220 a week at Job A and $350 a week at Job B; $259 into checking
47. 25 adults and 15 children　**49.** about 10.2 pounds of chicken and
about 11.9 pounds of filet mignon　**51.** sandwich $2.19, fries $1.15
53. 322 students attending, 178 general admission　**55.** The tops cost $4
and the pants cost $6.　**57.** $22　**59.** 200 carnations and 600 bagels
61. paperbacks $7.22; hard cover books $15.15　**63.** Answers vary
65. Substitution: You have to divide by coefficients to solve and are
more likely to end up with fractions.

Exercise Set 7-3

5. row echelon form　**7.** not in row echelon form
9. row echelon form　**11.** not in row echelon form
13. (2, 1)　**15.** (3, 7)　**17.** (2, −1, 1)　**19.** (−1, 5, 3)
21. $\left\{\left(\frac{3t + 1}{13}, \frac{11t + 21}{13}, t\right)\right\}$ where t is any real number　**23.** (1, 1, −1)
25. 10 adult tickets, 22 child tickets, 7 senior citizen tickets
27. lawn tickets cost $40, general admission costs $80 and ground floor
seating costs $150　**29.** $500 in Fund A, $1,200 in Fund B, and
$300 in Fund C　**31.** won 9 games, lost 5 games, tied 2 games
33. 100 watched beam, 300 watched floor, 250 watched uneven bars
35. Answers vary

Exercise Set 7-4

5.

7.

9.

11.

17.

19.

21.

23.

25. x = number of computational problems, y = number of word
problems.

27. L = tubes of body lotion, S = number of sponges.

29. g = number of graduate classes, u = number of undergraduate
classes.

31. x = number of workers at first factory, y = number of workers at second factory.

33. C = number of civil suits, M = number of malpractice suits.

35. When the signs of both inequalities are a combination of $\geq$ or $\leq$.
37. The solution is $\varnothing$.

Exercise Set 7-5

5. $x \leq 50$; x = number of calculators
7. $x = 2y$; x = number of pens and y = number of pencils
9. $P = 85d + 130l$; d = number of desktop computers sold and l = number of laptop computers sold
11. $P = 4t + 3h$; t = number of turkeys sold and h = number of hams sold
13. $2v + 3c \leq 6$; v = number of VCRs assembled and c = number of CD players assembled
15. (5, 6) gives a maximum profit of $390
17. (7, 0) gives a maximum profit of $105
19. (0, 62) gives a maximum profit of $21,080
21. 20 television sets and 10 VCRs   **23.** 50 hats and 0 scarves
25. 18 square feet of tomatoes and 12 square feet of squash
27. 4 cats and 26 dogs   **29.** 100 laptops and 200 desktops
31. Answers vary

Exercise Set 7-6

7. Function   **9.** Function   **11.** Function   **13.** Function
15. Function   **17.** $f(3) = 17$; $f(-2) = 2$
19. $f(10) = 32$; $f(-10) = -48$ **21.** $f(0) = 0$; $f(6) = 306$
23. $f(-3.6) = 5.56$; $f(4.5) = 45.25$
25. Domain $\{x \mid -\infty \leq x < \infty\}$; Range $\{y \mid y \geq 0\}$
27. Domain $\{x \mid x \neq 2\}$; Range $\{y \mid y \neq 1\}$
29. Domain $\{x \mid x \geq 0\}$; Range $\{y \mid y \geq 3\}$
31. Domain: $\{x \mid -\infty \leq x < \infty\}$; Range: $\{y \mid -\infty \leq y < \infty\}$
33. Domain $\{x \mid x \geq -1\}$; Range $\{y \mid y \leq -1\}$
35. Function   **37.** Not a function
39. $88.08 for a 4-hour shift and $98.16 for an 8-hour shift
41. No, they lose $128; $2,422   **43.** $c(x) = 20x$; $100
45. $z(m) = 3m - 10$; $125   **47.** $d(t) = 80 + 65t$; three more hours
49. $n(r) = 3r$; 135 minutes, or 2 hours and 15 minutes
51. $B(W) = 2W + 4$; 4 games   **53.** $s(p) = 0.8p$; $95.82
55. $n(x) = \frac{2}{3}x + 4$; 24 cookies   **57.** $d(x) = 48 + 7.5x$; $20
59. $f(3) = 19$; $f(-3) = 1$;
   $f(x + 3) = x^2 + 9x + 19$;
   $f(x - 3) = x^2 - 3x + 1$

Exercise Set 7-7

9.

11.

13.

15.

17.

19.

21.

23.

25.

27.

29.

31. a) $C = -20p + 1,000$
b)

(c) 100 customers
(d) $35
(e) The p intercept is $(50, 0)$. It is the price of a ticket that would attract 0 customers.
(f) The C intercept is $(0, 1,000)$. It is the number of customers that a price of $0 would attract.

33. (a) $D(t) = 70t$
(b)

(c) 560 miles   (d) 3 hours
35. 62.25 feet; about 3.85 seconds   **37.** 144 feet
39. (a) June   (b) $3,600   (c) $2,700   (d) April and August
41. (a) $A = \frac{5}{2}W^2$ (b) $A = 250$ square inches and $l = 25$ inches
(c) width 4 inches; length 10 inches   (d) $A = 5w^2$
43. 4,732,864   **45.** $699.21   **47.** about 13 pounds
49. 0.217 is the rate at which unemployment is increasing per month and 4.40 is the unemployment rate at the beginning of 2008.
51. The graph is a sideways parabola opening to the right.

Review Exercises

1.

3.

5.

7. $-\frac{1}{4}$ **9.** 7   **11.** 0

13. $y = -3x + 12; m = -3$

15. $y = \frac{4}{7}x - 4; m = \frac{4}{7}$

17. Betty collected $7.64 and Mary collected $24.36.
19. $(10, 2)$ **21.** $(5, 2)$ **23.** $(10, -1)$ **25.** $(6, 3)$ **27.** $(4, 0)$
29. $\left(\frac{3}{2}, -\frac{5}{2}\right)$ **31.** coffee $2.50 per pound ; tea $1.75 per pound

33. $\begin{bmatrix} 2 & -1 & 4 & | & 10 \\ -3 & -4 & -5 & | & 8 \\ 1 & 1 & 1 & | & -8 \end{bmatrix}$ **35.** $(-8, 3)$ **37.** $(13, 1, 5)$

39.

41.

43.

45.

47. 26 of model A and 0 of model B
49. Domain $= \{2, 5, 6\}$; range $= \{5, -7, -10\}$; function
51. Domain $= \{x \mid x \le 3\}$; range $= \{y \mid y \ge 0\}$; function
53. Domain $= \{x \mid x \ne 3\}$; range $= \{y \mid y \ne 0\}$; function
55. $f(5) = 13$ **57.** $f(-10) = 40$

59.

61.

63.

65.

67.

69.

71. 104 feet

Chapter 7 Test

1.

3.

5.

7. $\frac{17}{7}$

9. $y = -\frac{x}{5} + 4$; $m = -\frac{1}{5}$

11. $(3, -1)$ **13.** The system is dependent. The solution set is $\{(x, y) \mid 3x + 4y = 19\}$.

15.

17. $(2, -3, 5)$ **19.** Domain $= \{-4, -10, 12\}$; range $= \{6, 18, 5\}$; function.   **21.** $f(-15) = 55$

23.

25.

27. 26 and 31 students
29. The cooks earn $7.50 per hour and the servers earn $5.50 per hour.
31. base width 12 inches and sides height 6 inches

CHAPTER 8: CONSUMER MATHEMATICS
Exercise Set 8-1
7. 63%   **9.** 2.5%   **11.** 156%   **13.** 20%   **15.** $66.\overline{6}\%$ **17.** 125%
19. 0.18   **21.** 0.06   **23.** 0.625   **25.** 3.2   **27.** $\frac{6}{25}$ **29.** $\frac{9}{100}$ **31.** $2\frac{9}{25}$
33. $\frac{1}{200}$ **35.** $\frac{1}{6}$ **37.** $15; $314.99   **39.** $9.00; $158.99   **41.** 60%
43. 24%   **45.** $95.99   **47.** $149.99   **49.** $1,256   **51.** About 2,446
53. 8.5%   **55.** 60%   **57.** 52.8%   **59.** No; the total discount is 44%.
61. Total discount will be 75%, not 100%

Exercise Set 8-2
7. $1,440   **9.** 2 years   **11.** 5%   **13.** $985   **15.** 3.2%   **17.** $128.25
19. 6.5 years   **21.** 10%   **23.** 6%   **25.** 3 years   **27.** $960
29. $1,120   **31.** $490.44   **33.** $1.65   **35.** $35   **37.** $26.47
39. (a) $720   (b) $2,280   (c) 10.5%   **41.** (a) $4,400   (b) $17,600
(c) 6.25%   **43.** (a) $421.20   (b) $358.80   (c) 13%   **45.** 8.43%
47. $141,509.43   **49.** 3 years   **51.** 4.25 years or 51 months
53. $2,096.25   **55.** $7,316   **57.** $6   **59.** (a) $5,400   (b) $12,600
(c) 7.1%   **61.** The personal loan   **63.** The repair loan
65. They are the same regardless of principal.

Exercise Set 8-3
5. $I = $396.20 and $A = $1,221.20   **7.** $I = $14.67 and $A = $89.67
9. $I = $991.92 and $A = $1,616.92   **11.** $I = $688.05 and $A = $2,683.05
13. $I = $70.62 and $A = $820.62   **15.** $2,604.21   **17.** $8,167.15
19. $58,541.39   **21.** $18,072.57   **23.** $7,710.98   **25.** 6.14%
27. 6.66%   **29.** 4.5% compounded semiannually
31. 3.1% compounded quarterly   **33.** $12,175.94   **35.** $335,095.61
37. $20,548.25   **39.** $27,223.76   **41.** $24,664.64   **43.** $59,556.16
45. $2,095.18   **47.** $114,717.32   **49.** $8,347.30   **51.** $1,235.34

Exercise Set 8-4
7. $480
9. Down payment: $56.25; Installment Price: $383.25;
Monthly payment: $27.25
11. $43.17   **13.** 8.5%   **15.** 12%   **17.** 9.5%
19. $u = $709.50; payoff amount: $10,956.50
21. $u = $14.54; payoff amount: $482.81
23. $u = $14.66; payoff amount: $615.34
25. $180.13   **27.** $8.22   **29.** $5.18   **31.** $16.65; $1,124.15
33. $39.49; $3,368.60   **35.** $13.32; $411.35
37. (a) $602.14   (b) $7.23   (c) $669.15
39. (a) $370.55   (b) $5.19   (c) $350.76
41. (a) $370.92   (b) $4.08   (c) $533.30   **43.** $3,636.36

Exercise Set 8-5
5. (a) $21,750   (b) $123,250   (c) $871.38   (d) $138,161
7. (a) $80,000   (b) $120,000   (c) $720.00   (d) $139,200
9. (a) $32,500   (b) $292,500   (c) $1,924.65   (d) $631,332
11. (a) $360,000   (b) $840,000   (c) $5,779.20   (d) $547,008
13. $1,499.44   **15.** $1,148.90   **17.** $4,215.22   **19.** $3,746.38

21.

Payment number	Interest	Payment on Principal	Balance of Loan
1	$718.96	$152.42	$123,097.58
2	$718.07	$153.31	$122,944.27
3	$717.17	$154.21	$122,790.06

23.

Payment number	Interest	Payment on Principal	Balance of Loan
1	$3,850	$1,929.20	$838,070.80
2	$3,841.16	$1,938.04	$836,132.76
3	$3,832.28	$1,946.92	$834,185.84

Exercise Set 8-6

7. $97.25 per share **9.** $1.23 per share **11.** 4,626,000 shares
13. $8.87 per share **15.** $766.29 **17.** $40.08 per share **19.** $0.04
21. 345,000 shares **23.** $1.49 per share **25.** $156.20
27. $50.87 per share **29.** $0.67 **31.** 9,662,000 shares
33. $2.53 per share **35.** $820.75 **37.** 24.91
39. 15.02 **41.** $0.34 per share **43.** $1.98 per share
45. lost $432.48 **47.** lost $2,022.63
49. The second investment would be the better choice.

Review Exercises

1. $0.875; 87.5\%$ **3.** $\frac{4}{5}; 0.8$ **5.** $\frac{37}{20}; 1.85$ **7.** $5.75; 575\%$
9. $\frac{91}{200}; 0.445$ **11.** 69.12 **13.** 1,100 **15.** $60 **17.** 73.5\%
19. $2,322 **21.** 2.5 years **23.** 7\% **25.** $1,375
27. $I = \$1,800$ and $A = \$7,800$ **29.** 1.4\% **31.** $25.56
33. Discount: $1,080; David received $4,920
35. $I = \$603.67$ and $A = \$2,378.67$ **37.** $I = \$12.07$ and $A = \$57.07$
39. 12.55\% **41.** $8,129.93
43. Total installment price: $788.25
    Monthly payment: $84.47
45. 10.5\% **47.** $u = \$156.44$; payoff amount $= \$3,873.56$
49. $15.24 **51.** $124.13; $7,424.53 **53.** $1,827.94
55. $342 **57.** $33.04 **59.** She earned $203.94

Chapter 8 Test

1. 31.25\% **3.** $\frac{7}{25}$ **5.** 80\% **7.** 300 **9.** $2,568 **11.** $486
13. $I = \$8.16$, $A = \$443.16$. The monthly payment is $73.86.
15. $I = \$216$, $A = \$2,016$. The monthly payment is $168.
17. Discount: $5,692.50; Latoya received $6,957.50
19. $I = \$7,885.08$ and $A = \$17,635.08$ **21.** 8.16\%
23. Total installment price: $1,000.45; Monthly payment: $166.74
25. The unearned interest is $438.36 and the payoff amount is $7,186.64.
27. The finance charge is $20.
    The new balance is $1,030.
29. 11\% **31.** $2,834.66 **33.** $60 **35.** $27.37

CHAPTER 9: MEASUREMENT

Exercise Set 9-1

5. 4 yd **7.** $5\frac{2}{3}$ yd **9.** 18 ft **11.** $1\frac{3}{4}$ ft **13.** $\frac{1}{2}$ yd **15.** $24\frac{1}{3}$ yd
17. 800 cm **19.** 120 m **21.** 6 hm **23.** 900 dm **25.** 3.756 m
27. 0.4053 km **29.** 1,200,000 cm **31.** 1,850,000 mm
33. 126,200 dm **35.** 0.8 km **37.** $\approx$196.85 in. **39.** 406.4 mm
41. $\approx$7.16 dam **43.** $\approx$4,429.08 ft **45.** 15.24 mm **47.** $\approx$19.68 ft
49. 4,099.56 dm **51.** $\approx$1.46 mi **53.** $\approx$4.59 yd **55.** $\approx$8.46 m
57. 15 ft **59.** 60 yd **61.** $\approx$0.85 mi **63.** $3\frac{1}{2}$ yd **65.** 2,300 mg
67. 14 km **69.** $\approx$103.04 km per hour **71.** $\approx$19.16 m
73. 38.1 mm by 76.2 mm **75.** 7.92×10^9 ft **77.** 573 boards
79. 20 g **81.** 488 Canadian dollars **83.** 37.85 francs
85. the first runner **87.** millimeters

Exercise Set 9-2

Note: Answers can vary, depending on rounding and on the conversion
    factors used.
7. 24 ft^2 **9.** $\approx$7.3 mi^2 **11.** 108 ft^2 **13.** $\approx$0.07 acre **15.** $\approx$505 yd^2
17. $\approx$116.1 cm^2 **19.** $\approx$47.85 yd^2 **21.** $\approx$0.13 km^2 **23.** $\approx$167.4 dm^2
25. $\approx$250.8 dm^2 **27.** $\approx$25,451.74 acres **29.** $\approx$650.32 in.^{2}
31. $\approx$120.94 dm^2 **33.** $\approx$8.26 in.^{2} **35.** $\approx$83.55 ft^2
37. $\approx$2,872.32 fluid oz **39.** $\approx$53.48 ft^3 **41.** $\approx$98.13 gal
43. $\approx$164,560 gal **45.** $\approx$1,616 gal **47.** 4,500 cm^3 **49.** 28.5 mL
51. 433 cm^3 **53.** 32,000 cm^3 **55.** 0.00032 m^3 **57.** 0.5 L
59. 920 dL **61.** 80 cL **63.** 67 daL **65.** $\approx$45.28 L **67.** $\approx$5.035 gal
69. $\approx$17,924.53 mL **71.** $\approx$22.31 qt **73.** $\approx$46,375 gal **75.** $\approx$0.34 kL
77. $\approx$31,250 lb **79.** $\approx$3.2 ft^3 **81.** 2 gallons **83.** 7.4 cubic yards
85. 1.56 mi^2 **87.** $\approx$0.67 ft^3 **89.** 576 tiles **91.** 520 lb
93. 5 bikers **95.** $\approx15\frac{1}{2}$ km^2 **97.** 9 trips **99.** Answers vary

Exercise Set 9-3

3. 2.0625 lb **5.** 36.8 oz **7.** 8,400 lb **9.** 1.75 T **11.** $\approx$1.08 T
13. 90 cg **15.** 440 hg **17.** 180 cg **19.** 7.1 dg **21.** 50 dg
23. 325 mg **25.** 4,325,000 g **27.** 0.086 g **29.** 0.4 kg **31.** 56.32 hg
33. $\approx$4.29 oz **35.** $\approx$0.106 lb **37.** $\approx$27,272.73 hg **39.** $\approx$162.36 t
41. $\approx$5.23 t **43.** $\approx$59,640 dg **45.** $\approx$291.07 oz **47.** $\approx$51,240 dg
49. $\approx$122,727.27 dg **51.** $\approx$18,636.36 g **53.** 57.2°F **55.** 131°F
57. 302°F **59.** −0.4°F **61.** −27.4°F **63.** −15°C **65.** 0°C
67. $\approx$37.78°C **69.** $\approx$−23.33°C **71.** $\approx$−25.56°C
73. Juan's parents are not correct, a 6.25 lb baby is average.
75. The elevator is more than able to hold their weight.
77. She will not pack a coat. **79.** The cars are too heavy.
81. 68°F **83.** He has plenty of solution.
85. The truck poured too much sand into the foundation.
87. They ate 5.5 lb of steak.
89. Her heating element will not be hot enough.
91. $\approx$1,545.5 kg **93.** There is not enough to fill 50 bags.

Review Exercises

1. 12 ft **3.** 1.75 ft **5.** $\approx$130.13 mi **7.** 3.6 dm **9.** 34.5 m
11. $\approx$275.59 in. **13.** $\approx$33.46 in. **15.** 1,051.56 dm **17.** 91.44 m
19. $\approx$330 km/h; $\approx$300.67 ft/sec **21.** The Eiffel Tower
23. $\approx$0.11 acre **25.** $\approx$352.10 yd^2 **27.** $\approx$148.35 cm^2 **29.** $\approx$0.50 km^2
31. $\approx$3,483,870,968 ft^2 **33.** 72,576,000 in.^{3} **35.** 3,500 cm^3
37. 300,000 mL **39.** 0.054457 kL **41.** 0.45672 kL **43.** 85 drops
45. The second is cheaper. **47.** 4.0625 lb **49.** 17.25 T **51.** $\approx$18 T
53. 457 mg **55.** 0.04 kg **57.** $\approx$4.576 oz **59.** $\approx$1,292.61 g
61. $\approx$0.05 lb **63.** 55.4°F **65.** 23°F **67.** $\approx$19.44°C
69. $\approx$−29.44°C **71.** $\approx$7.04 lb **73.** 66.4°F
75. It appears the deal on the Canadian side is better, but only if
    they're both using the same currency!

Chapter 9 Test

1. $\approx$3.67 yd **3.** 12.3 cm **5.** $\approx$13.39 in. **7.** $\approx$24.13 ft^2
9. $\approx$1.55 in.^{2} **11.** $\approx$6.10 in.^{3} **13.** $\approx$606 gal **15.** 22.8125 lb
17. $\approx$7.66 T **19.** $\approx$8.8 oz **21.** 55.4°F **23.** $\approx$41.86 km
25. The first at $1.39 per square foot is cheaper.
27. $\approx$ 3.37 hours **29.** $\approx$0.093 yd^2 per min
31. The agent is wasting her time. **33.** 15.12°F

CHAPTER 10: GEOMETRY

Exercise Set 10-1

7. Ray; $\overrightarrow{AB}$ **9.** Line; l **11.** Segment; $\overline{TU}$
13. $\angle RST$; $\angle TSR$; $\angle S$; $\angle 3$ **15.** straight **17.** obtuse
19. vertical angles **21.** corresponding angles
23. corresponding angles **25.** alternate exterior angles
27. 82° **29.** 58° **31.** 12° **33.** 24° **35.** 118° **37.** 60°
39. $m\angle 1 = 37°$; $m\angle 2 = 143°$; $m\angle 3 = 37°$
41. $m\angle 1 = 90°$; $m\angle 2 = 90°$; $m\angle 3 = 90°$
43. $m\angle 1 = m\angle 3 = m\angle 5 = m\angle 7 = 15°$
    $m\angle 2 = m\angle 4 = m\angle 6 = 165°$
45. 90° **47.** 60° **49.** 104° **51.** 104° **53.** 104° **55.** 104°
57. $m\angle 3 = 55°$; $m\angle 4 = 125°$

Exercise Set 10-2

9. Isosceles; acute **11.** Obtuse **13.** Scalene triangle; acute
15. 70° **17.** 15° **19.** 40° **21.** 34 ft **23.** 560 cm **25.** 810 yd
27. 12 ft **29.** 30 in. **31.** $21\frac{9}{11}$ in. **33.** 17 m **35.** 11 ft
37. $\approx$84.9 ft **39.** 14 mi **41.** 270 ft **43.** 10 ft **45.** $\approx$212.2 mi
47. 180° since the three angles form a straight angle
49. $m\angle 1 = m\angle 4$ since they are alternate interior angles between two
    parallel lines
51. This proves the result for every triangle.

Exercise Set 10-3

7. Octagon, 1,080° 9. Triangle, 180° 11. Hexagon, 720°
13. Rectangle 15. Trapezoid 17. 76 yd 19. 28 ft 21. 44 in.
23. 42 ft 25. 42 mi 27. 360 ft 29. 241 ft 31. 66 in.
33. 5.08 times 35. $392 37. ≈1.74 mph

Exercise Set 10-4

5. 289 in.^{2} 7. 450 yd^2 9. 400 m^2 11. 105 mi^2 13. 467.5 in.^{2}
15. 72 in.^{2} 17. $C \approx 50.27$ in.; $A \approx 201.06$ in.^{2}
19. $C \approx 50.27$ m; $A \approx 201.06$ m^2
21. $C \approx 131.95$ km; $A \approx 1,385.44$ km^2 23. 11.11 yd^2 25. 40 images
27. $1,620 29. 7.5 ft^2 31. $188.55 33. 11,309.73 mi^2 35. 16.28 ft^2
37. When the radius is 2. 39. Answers vary 41. 30 in.^{2}

Exercise Set 10-5

7. 125 in.^{3} 9. 210 m^3 11. 48 m^3 13. 19,704.07 cm^3
15. 1,005.31 ft^3 17. 33,510.32 in.^{3} 19. 461.81 cm^3 21. 150 in.^{2}
23. 214 m^2 25. 4,046.37 cm^2 27. 5,026.55 in.^{2} 29. 648 ft^3
31. 190,228,656 ft^3 33. 13,684.78 in.^{3} 35. 141.11 in.^{3}
37. 55,417,694.41 mi^2 39. 2,304 in.^{3} 41. 1,080 in.^{2} 43. 3.4 in.
45. two 5-gallon cans 47. 1 1-gallon can 49. 154 in.^{3}
51. 96 m^2 53. 2,262 ft^2

Exercise Set 10-6

5. $\cos A = \frac{3}{5}$; $\sin A = \frac{4}{5}$; $\tan A = \frac{4}{3}$
7. $\cos A = \frac{15}{17}$; $\sin A = \frac{8}{17}$; $\tan A = \frac{8}{15}$
9. $\cos A = \frac{\sqrt{51}}{10}$; $\sin A = \frac{7}{10}$; $\tan A = \frac{7}{\sqrt{51}}$
11. 92.71 cm 13. 76.88 in. 15. 1.39 mm 17. 122.98 in.
19. 1,857.41 ft 21. 77.47 mi 23. $\approx 48°$ 25. 60° 27. $\approx 29°$
29. $\approx 45°$ 31. 23,644.67 ft 33. 4,980.76 m 35. 1,218.93 ft
37. 68° 39. 352.50 ft 41. 3,932.92 ft 43. 1.2° 45. 6.9°
47. $h = 737.6$ ft and $d = 673.8$ ft
49. Use the cosine then use the Pythagorean Theorem.

Exercise Set 10-7

9. Answers vary 11. Answers vary 15. A regular polygon will tessellate only if the measure of its angle is a divisor of 360°.

Review Exercises

1. line 3. line segment 5. trapezoid 7. triangle 9. hexagon
11. obtuse 13. vertical angles 15. alternate exterior angles
17. (a) 63° (b) 2° 19. $m \angle 2 = 163°$; $m \angle 3 = m \angle 1 = 17°$
21. 43° 23. 72 ft 25. obtuse and scalene 27. acute and equilateral
29. 6 units 31. $a = 15$ and $b = 18$ 33. 15.8 ft 35. 166.4 ft
37. decagon; 1,440° 39. 16 ft 41. 28 m 43. 1,376 cm^2
45. 9,160.88 km^2 47. $C = 51.84$ yd; $A = 213.82$ yd^2 49. $199.74
51. 24,429.02 cm^3 53. 84.82 yd^3 55. 5,736 in.^{2}
57. 775.71 revolutions 59. 38.79 cm^3
61. $\sin B = \frac{3}{\sqrt{34}}$; $\cos B = \frac{5}{\sqrt{34}}$; $\tan B = \frac{3}{5}$ 63. ≈ 2.33 yd
65. $\approx 51.8°$ 67. 33.04 ft 69. 9 minutes

Chapter 10 Test

1. 17° 3. $m \angle 2 = 28°$; $m \angle 3 = m \angle 1 = 152°$ 5. 48° 7. 2.5 ft
9. 1,080° 11. 18 in.^{2} 13. 432 yd^2 15. 345.96 mi^2 17. 884.36 in.^{3}
19. 100 ft^3 21. 150 ft^3 23. 552.96 in.^{2} 25. 346.36 in.^{2}
27. A brick wall is a tessellation. 29. 24.49 mi
31. 0.21 pound 33. 33.3°

CHAPTER 11: PROBABILITY AND COUNTING TECHNIQUES

Exercise Set 11-1

5. 3,628,800 7. 362,880 9. 1 11. 12 13. 336 15. 420
17. 22,350 19. 56 21. 479,001,600 23. 720 25. 1 27. 990
29. 840 31. 151,200 33. 5,527,200 35. 300 37. 210 39. 720
41. 57,120 43. 120 45. 210 47. 210 49. 2,520 51. 43,680
53. $\approx 5.1988 \times 10^{35}$ 55. 362,880; 40,320

Exercise Set 11-2

5. 10 7. 35 9. 15 11. 1 13. 66
15. $_8C_5 = 56$ 17. $_6C_2 = 15$ 19. $_9C_9 = 1$
    $_8P_5 = 6,720$ $_6P_2 = 30$ $_9P_9 = 362,880$
21. Combination 23. Permutation 25. Permutation
27. Combination 29. 2,598,960 31. 126; 35 33. 120
35. 462 37. 166,320 39. 14,400 41. 67,200 43. 53,130
45. 126 47. 30,045,015

Exercise Set 11-3

9. Yes 11. No 13. No 15. Yes 17. Empirical 19. Classical
21. (a) $\frac{1}{6}$ (b) $\frac{1}{2}$ (c) $\frac{1}{3}$ (d) 1 (e) 1 (f) $\frac{5}{6}$ (g) $\frac{1}{6}$
23. (a) $\frac{1}{7}$ (b) $\frac{3}{7}$ (c) $\frac{3}{7}$ (d) 1 (e) 0 25. $\frac{4}{9}$ 27. $\frac{9}{16}$
29. 0.91 31. 0.84 33. $\frac{3}{13}$ 35. $\frac{5}{11}$ 37. $\frac{17}{25}$ 39. $\frac{13}{35}$ 41. 0
43. (a) ≈ 0.26 (b) ≈ 0.96 45. (a) 0.42 (b) 90%
47. It is likely that the penny is unbalanced.
49. (a) $\frac{6}{25}$ (b) $\frac{2}{5}$ (c) $\frac{9}{25}$ (d) $\frac{12}{25}$ (e) $\frac{1}{5}$

Exercise Set 11-4

3. (a) $\frac{3}{8}$ (b) $\frac{1}{8}$ (c) $\frac{7}{8}$ 5. (a) $\frac{5}{12}$ (b) $\frac{1}{4}$ (c) $\frac{1}{6}$
7. (a) $\frac{1}{3}$ (b) $\frac{1}{3}$ (c) $\frac{1}{9}$ (d) $\frac{4}{9}$ (e) $\frac{1}{3}$
9. (a) $\frac{1}{4}$ (b) $\frac{3}{4}$ (c) $\frac{1}{4}$ (d) $\frac{1}{8}$ 11. (a) $\frac{3}{5}$ (b) $\frac{1}{2}$ (c) $\frac{4}{5}$
13. (a) $\frac{1}{2}$ (b) $\frac{1}{6}$ (c) $\frac{1}{4}$
15. (a) $\frac{1}{13}$ (b) $\frac{1}{4}$ (c) $\frac{1}{52}$ (d) $\frac{2}{13}$ (e) $\frac{4}{13}$ (f) $\frac{4}{13}$ (g) $\frac{1}{2}$ (h) $\frac{1}{26}$
    (i) $\frac{7}{13}$ (j) $\frac{1}{26}$
17. (a) $\frac{1}{9}$ (b) $\frac{2}{9}$ (c) $\frac{1}{6}$ (d) $\frac{5}{18}$ (e) $\frac{11}{36}$ (f) $\frac{1}{2}$ (g) $\frac{3}{4}$ (h) 1
19. The outcomes are not equally likely because there is a $\frac{1}{4}$ probability of getting WW; each of the other six outcomes has a probability of $\frac{1}{8}$.
21. 216 23. $\frac{5}{108}$

Exercise Set 11-5

3. (a) 0.0004 (b) 0.15 (c) 0.383 (d) 0.45
5. (a) 0.033 (b) 0.0083 (c) $\frac{3}{10}$ (d) $\frac{3}{40}$ (e) $\frac{3}{20}$
7. (a) 0 (b) 0.51 (c) 0.018
9. (a) 0.07 (b) 0.42 (c) 0.015 (d) 0.16 (e) 0.336
11. 0.01 13. 0.42 15. 0.476 17. 0.00144 19. 0.0226
21. 0.0000015 23. 0.0000628

Exercise Set 11-6

7. (a) 1:11 (b) 1:35 (c) 5:1 (d) 17:1 (e) 1:5
9. (a) 1:12 (b) 3:10 (c) 3:1 (d) 1:12 (e) 1:1
11. (a) $\frac{7}{11}$ (b) $\frac{5}{7}$ (c) $\frac{3}{4}$ (d) $\frac{4}{5}$ 13. $\frac{5}{14}$ 15. −$3.00
17. $0.83 19. −$1.00 21. −$0.50; −$0.52

Exercise Set 11-7

3. No 5. No 7. Yes 9. $\frac{1}{6}$ 11. $\frac{11}{19}$ 13. (a) $\frac{17}{20}$ (b) $\frac{11}{20}$ (c) $\frac{3}{5}$
15. (a) $\frac{8}{17}$ (b) $\frac{6}{17}$ (c) $\frac{9}{17}$ (d) $\frac{12}{17}$ 17. (a) $\frac{6}{7}$ (b) $\frac{4}{7}$ (c) 1
19. (a) $\frac{67}{118}$ (b) $\frac{81}{118}$ (c) $\frac{44}{59}$ 21. (a) $\frac{38}{45}$ (b) $\frac{22}{45}$ (c) $\frac{2}{3}$
23. (a) $\frac{14}{31}$ (b) $\frac{23}{31}$ (c) $\frac{19}{31}$ 25. (a) $\frac{467}{1,392}$ (b) $\frac{25}{32}$ (c) $\frac{1,955}{2,784}$
27. $\frac{7}{10}$ 29. 0.06 31. 0.30

Exercise Set 11-8

5. Independent 7. Dependent 9. Independent 11. Dependent
13. 0.0058 15. 0.4746 17. 0.0625 19. $\frac{1}{12}$ 21. $\frac{1}{8}$ 23. $\frac{1}{15}$
25. 0.1311 27. (a) 0.00018 (b) 0.0129 (c) 0.1176
29. 0.0179 31. $\frac{1}{6}$ 33. $\frac{2}{11}$ 35. $\frac{1}{4}$ 37. $\frac{2}{3}$ 39. 1 41. 0.61
43. $\frac{1}{2}$ 45. $\frac{25}{216}$ 47. $\frac{1}{133,225}$

Exercise Set 11-9

5. 0.288 **7.** 0.0616 **9.** 0.0000304 **11.** 0.0994 **13.** 0.00615
15. 0.00463 **17.** 0.0750 **19.** 0.1546 **21.** 0.2461 **23.** 0.2340
25. 0.1906 **27.** 0.1585 **29.** 0.1593 **31.** 0.1541 **33.** 0.6870
35. Answers vary

Review Exercises

1. 2,184 **3.** 175,760,000; 88,583,040 **5.** 120 **7.** 84
9. In a permutation order matters, in a combination order does not
matter. **11.** 78 **13.** 729 **15.** b, c, and e

17. (a) $\frac{1}{4}$ (b) $\frac{1}{52}$ (c) $\frac{4}{13}$ (d) $\frac{1}{13}$ (e) $\frac{1}{2}$

19. (a) 0 (b) $\frac{1}{2}$ (c) $\frac{1}{3}$ **21.** (a) $\frac{9}{35}$ (b) $\frac{23}{35}$ (c) $\frac{19}{35}$ (d) $\frac{19}{35}$

23. (a) $\frac{1}{4}$ (b) $\frac{1}{6}$ (c) $\frac{1}{4}$ (d) $\frac{1}{4}$ (e) 0 (f) 1

25. $S = \{$1H, 1T, 2H, 2T, 3H, 3T, 4H, 4T, 5H, 5T, 6H, 6T, 7H, 7T,
8H, 8T$\}$

27. $\frac{2}{25}$ **29.** $\frac{12}{55}$ **31.** $\frac{33}{182}$ **33.** 1:5

35. 10.5 **37.** \$7.23

39. Mutually exclusive

41. (a) $\frac{17}{50}$ (b) $\frac{3}{25}$ **43.** Dependent

45. Dependent **47.** $\frac{1}{7}$ **49.** 0.016

51. (a) $\frac{1}{26}$ (b) $\frac{1}{4}$ (c) $\frac{1}{8}$

53. 0.0165 **55.** 0.1684

Chapter 11 Test

1. 380 **3.** 95,040
5. Probability is a number that represents the likelihood of an event.
7. 1,188,137,600; 710,424,000 **9.** 35 **11.** 40,320

13. (a) 64 (b) 24 **15.** (a) $\frac{1}{13}$ (b) $\frac{1}{13}$ (c) $\frac{4}{13}$

17. (a) $\frac{12}{31}$ (b) $\frac{12}{31}$ (c) $\frac{27}{31}$ (d) $\frac{24}{31}$ **19.** $S = \{$H1, H3, H5, T2, T4, T6$\}$

21. (a) 0.025 (b) 0.000495 (c) 0 **23.** $\frac{1}{2}$ **25.** $\frac{1}{2}$

27. $S = \{$M,CH; M,IN; SF,CH; SF,IN; P,CH; P,IN; H,CH; H,IN$\}$

29. 5:4 **31.** $5\frac{1}{6}$ **33.** $\frac{8}{33}$ **35.** 0.1144

CHAPTER 12: STATISTICS

Exercise Set 12-1

9. Cluster **11.** Random **13.** Stratified

15.
Rank	Frequency
Fr	18
So	12
Jr	6
Se	4

17.
Show	Frequency
S	6
P	5
B	7
A	7

19.
Class	Frequency
27–33	7
34–40	14
41–47	14
48–54	12
55–61	3
62–68	3
69–75	2

21.
Class	Frequency
0–39	8
40–79	10
80–119	10
120–159	7
160–199	3
200–239	8
240–279	4

23.
Class	Frequency
150–1,276	2
1,277–2,403	2
2,404–3,530	5
3,531–4,657	8
4,658–5,784	7
5,785–6,911	3
6,912–8,038	7
8,039–9,165	3
9,166–10,292	3
10,293–11,419	2

25.
Class	Frequency
839–949	12
950–1,060	9
1,061–1,171	7
1,172–1,282	1
1,283–1,393	1
1,394–1,504	0
1,505–1,615	2

27.
Stems	Leaves
3	8
4	1
5	0 0 2 3 3 6 8 9
6	6 8 9 9
7	0 0 3 4 5 8
8	0 1 3 3 4 4 4 5 7 9 9 9
9	0 2 4

29.
Stems	Leaves
0	3
1	5 9
2	2
3	1 1
4	1 4 6 6
5	2 6 6 6 9
6	0 0 6 6
7	7
8	7 8
9	6 8

31. Descriptive **33.** Descriptive **35.** Answers vary

Exercise Set 12-2

5.

7.

9.

11.

13.

15.

17.

19.

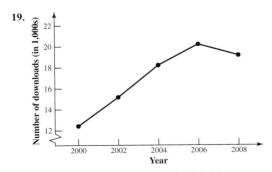

21. Pie chart   **23.** Time series graph   **25.** Pie chart
27. The scale makes the increase look greater.

Exercise Set 12-3
7. mean ≈ 15.11, median $= 7$, mode $= 3$, midrange $= 31$
9. mean $= 612.6$, median $= 475$, no mode, midrange $= 820$
11. mean $= 2{,}907.7$, median $= 2{,}723.5$, no mode, midrange $= 3{,}353.5$
13. mean $= 189.6$, median $= 151$, no mode, midrange $= 219.5$
15. mean $= 8.25$, median $= 8.5$, mode $= 9$, midrange $= 9$
17. mean $\approx 17{,}163.9$, median $= 16{,}740$, no mode, midrange $= 18{,}566$
19. mean $= 21.76$ **21.** mean ≈ 4.4 seconds
23. mean ≈ 42.87 or 42.87 million   **25.** mean $= \$180.28$
27. Answers vary   **29.** Median   **31.** Mode   **33.** Mode

Exercise Set 12-4
7. $s_1 < s_2$ **9.** $s_1 > s_2$
11. $R = 60$, variance $= 406.75$, $s \approx 20.17$
13. $R = 1{,}799$, variance $= 438{,}113.6$, $s \approx 661.90$
15. $R = 99$, variance $\approx 1{,}288.19$, $s \approx 35.89$
17. $R = 10$, variance $= 9$, $s = 3$
19. $R = \$3.83$, variance ≈ 2.79, $s \approx 1.67$
21. $R = \$39.50$, variance ≈ 242.59, $s \approx 15.58$
23. $R = 738$, variance $\approx 57{,}844.95$, $s \approx 240.5$
25. $R = 432$, variance $\approx 29{,}141.36$, $s \approx 170.7$
27. The variation is not the same

Exercise Set 12-5
5. (a) 20th percentile   (b) 75th percentile   (c) 35th percentile
   (d) 5th percentile   (e) 90th percentile
7. 75th percentile   **9.** 79th percentile
11. 10   **13.** Maurice is ranked higher.
15. (a) 60th percentile   (b) 8   (c) 23 years
17. $Q_1 = 22.5$, $Q_2 = 34$, $Q_3 = 53.5$ **19.** $Q_1 = 78$, $Q_2 = 88.5$, $Q_3 = 93$
21. $Q_1 = 107$, $Q_2 = 116$, $Q_3 = 122$ **23.** yes; yes

Exercise Set 12-6
7. 34   **9.** 499   **11.** 0.474   **13.** 0.192   **15.** 0.159   **17.** 0.345
19. 0.077   **21.** 0.223   **23.** 0.463   **25.** 0.885   **27.** 0.971
29. $z = +0.45$ **31.** (a) $z = \pm 2.05$ (b) $z = \pm 1.75$ (c) $z = \pm 2.40$

Exercise Set 12-7
3. (a) 0.378   (b) 0.179   **5.** (a) 0.264   (b) 0.316
7. (a) 0.005   (b) 0.162   (c) 0.749
9. (a) 0.153   (b) 0.774   (c) 0.187
11. (a) 0.841   (b) 0.067   **13.** (a) 0.776   (b) 0.405
15. (a) 0.758   (b) 0.816   (c) 0.286
17. (a) 638   (b) 184   (c) 1,074   (d) 136
19. (a) 65   (b) 616   (c) 10   **21.** 28th percentile   **23.** 0th percentile
25. No   **27.** 90, 110

Exercise Set 12-8
7. (a)

(b) $r \approx 0.977$
(c) r is significant at the 5% and the 1% level
(d) $y = 4.1 + 2.7x$
(e)   There is a positive linear relationship.

9. (a)

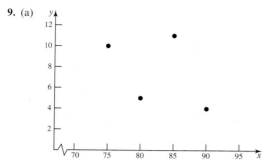

(b) $r \approx -0.441$
(c) r is not significant at 5% nor at 1% level.
(d) no regression line
(e) No relationship exists.

11. (a)

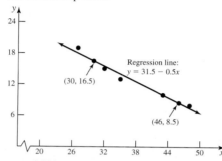

(b) $r \approx -0.983$
(c) r is significant at the 5% and 1% level.
(d) $y = 31.5 - 0.5x$
(e) There is a negative linear relationship.

13. (a)

(b) $r \approx 0.942$
(c) r is significant at the 5% and 1% level.
(d) $y = 2.76 + 0.06x$
(e) There is a positive linear relationship.   (f) 33 Stories

15. (a)

(b) $r \approx 0.896$
(c) r is significant at the 5% and 1% level.
(d) $y = -122.5 + 0.355x$
(e) There is a positive linear relationship.   (f) \$205.88

17. (a)

(b) $r \approx 0.963$ (c) r is significant at the 5% and 1% level.
(d) $y = 10.25 + 0.86x$
(e) There is a positive linear relationship.   (f) 88

19. Answers vary
21. Non-linear relationship; $r = 0$

Review Exercises

1.

Item	Frequency
B	4
F	5
G	5
S	5
T	6

3.

Rank	Frequency
102–116	4
117–131	3
132–146	1
147–161	4
162–176	11
177–191	7

5.

Stems	Leaves
1	2 4 6 7 8 8 9
2	0 2 3 4 5 5 5 6 6 9 9
3	2 3 5 7 8 8 9

7.

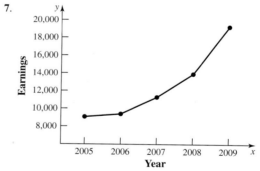

9. mean $= 7.25$ **11.** $R = 1,885$, variance $\approx 475,610.1$, $s \approx 689.6$

13. (a)

Value	Percentile
2	0th
4	17th
5	33rd
6	50th
8	67th
9	83rd

(b) 5

15. (a) 0.474   (f) 0.828
(b) 0.155   (g) 0.023
(c) 0.061   (h) 0.912
(d) 0.833   (i) 0.018
(e) 0.229   (j) 0.955

17. (a) 28   (b) 5   **19.** (a) 0.004   (b) 0.023   (c) 0.5   (d) 0.324
21. 22
23. (a) Answers vary
(b) $r \approx -0.144$; answers vary

Chapter 12 Test

1.

Source	Frequency
W	6
L	7
K	7
E	5

3.

5.

7.

9. mean = 6.4

11. (a) 0.433 (f) 0.828
(b) 0.394 (g) 0.040
(c) 0.035 (h) 0.903
(d) 0.103 (i) 0.016
(e) 0.293 (j) 0.912

13. (a) 0.067 (b) 0.023
(c) 0.465 (d) 0.094

15.

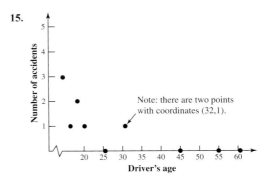

$r \approx -0.714$, r is significant at the 5% level.
$y = 2.31 - 0.04x$
$y \approx 0$ when $x = 61$

CHAPTER 13: OTHER MATHEMATICAL SYSTEMS

Exercise Set 13-1

7. C **9.** E **11.** E **13.** D **15.** D
17. Yes   **19.** Yes   **21.** D **23.** ☆   **25.** □
27. △   **29.** ☆   **31.** □   **33.** Yes   **35.** No
37. closure, associative
39. closure, commutative, identity
41. closure
43. closure, commutative, identity, inverse
45. closure, commutative, identity, inverse, associative; Abelian group
47. Abelian group   **49.** not a group   **51.** not a group
53. not a group   **55.** not a group
57.

*	0	1	2	3
0	0	1	2	3
1	1	2	3	0
2	2	3	0	1
3	3	0	1	2

59. yes
61. yes, 0 is its own inverse, 2 is its own inverse, and 1 and 3 are inverses.
63.

Ⓜ	R	B	Y
R	R	P	O
B	P	B	G
Y	O	G	Y

65. no   **67.** no
71.

→	T	F	Closure
T	T	F	
F	T	T	

Exercise Set 13-2

5. (a) 3 (b) 3 (c) 3   **7.** (a) 11 (b) 5 (c) 3
9. (a) 6 (b) 0 (c) 2   **11.** (a) 7 (b) 1 (c) 3
13. (a) 7 (b) 1 (c) 3   **15.** (a) 9 (b) 3 (c) 5
17. 2   **19.** 10   **21.** 3   **23.** 6   **25.** 11   **27.** 10   **29.** 2   **31.** 10
33. 6   **35.** 3   **37.** 11   **39.** 4   **41.** 6   **43.** 12   **45.** 10   **47.** 9
49. 6   **51.** 12   **53.** 2   **55.** 0   **57.** 5   **59.** 3   **61.** 2   **63.** 0
65. 12   **67.** 7   **69.** 10   **71.** 5   **73.** 5   **75.** None   **77.** None
79. 1   **81.** Answers vary   **83.** Answers vary   **85.** Answers vary
87. $y = 10$ **89.** $y = 1$ **91.** $y = 11, 2, 5$ and 8   **93.** $y = 6$
95. $y = 6$ **97.** 5:00 P.M.   **99.** 9:48 A.M.   **101.** 5:00 A.M.
103. 7:38 P.M.   **105.** 8:00 P.M.   **107.** 0352   **109.** 1156   **111.** 2006
113. 2136   **115.** 10:09 A.M.   **117.** 2:36 P.M.   **119.** The property holds.

Exercise Set 13-3

5. 2   **7.** 2   **9.** 7   **11.** 2   **13.** 3   **15.** 2   **17.** 2   **19.** 4   **21.** 1
23. 4   **25.** 3   **27.** 3   **29.** 2   **31.** 0   **33.** 6   **35.** 6   **37.** 6   **39.** 4
41. 3   **43.** 11   **45.** {4, 10, 16, 22, 28, . . . }
47. {3, 11, 19, 27, 35, . . . }   **49.** {2, 10, 18, 26, 34, . . . }

51. {2, 7, 12, 17, 22, . . . }   **53.** {5, 12, 19, 26, 33, . . . }
55. Tuesday **57.** Friday **59.** Tuesday **61.** Valid **63.** Invalid
65. 6 cans **67.** Friday **69.** It's April 22nd, 10 P.M. **71.** south
73. 17 tables; one empty space **75.** 10 oz **77.** Answers vary
79. You did not take your second dose.

Review Exercises

1. C **3.** B **5.** C **7.** yes **9.** yes
11. yes; A and C are inverses, B is its own inverse.
13. no **15.** no **17.** Abelian group **19.** not a group **21.** 3
23. 12 **25.** 6 **27.** 2 **29.** 6 **31.** 17 **33.** Friday at 3 P.M.
35. 2 **37.** 4 **39.** 2 **41.** 7 **43.** 2 **45.** 2 **47.** 0 **49.** 0
51. 1 **53.** 4 **55.** 3 **57.** 1 **59.** 4 **61.** 1 **63.** 2 **65.** 4
67. 2 **69.** 5 **71.** 2 **73.** 6 **75.** {4, 12, 20, 28, 36, . . . }
77. {3, 12, 21, 30, 39, . . . } **79.** {1, 7, 13, 19, 25, . . . }
81. {11, 23, 35, 47, 59, . . . } **83.** $y = 1$ **85.** 4 cookies **87.** no

Chapter 13 Test

1. z **3.** s **5.** z **7.** Yes **9.** -1 **11.** a **13.** -1 **15.** $-a$
17. $y = -1$ **19.** Yes **21.** Yes **23.** $-a$ is the inverse of a
25. 4 **27.** 4 **29.** 2 **31.** 1 **33.** 2 **35.** 4 **37.** 5 **39.** 1
41. {2, 8, 14, 20, 26, . . . } **43.** {0, 4, 8, 12, 16, . . . } **45.** 4 A.M.
47. 8 P.M. the following day

CHAPTER 14: VOTING METHODS

Exercise Set 14-1

5. (a) 22 (b) 4 (c) 8 (d) X
7. (a) 18 (b) 9 (c) 4 (d) Philadelphia
9. (a) 208 (b) Swimming pool
11. (a) 20 (b) Carnations **13.** No **15.** No **17.** 9
19. No **21.** Yes **23.** Answers vary

Exercise Set 14-2

5. role-playing (R) **7.** *Anatomy of a Murder* (A)
9. (a) swimming pool (S) (b) Yes **11.** Yes **13.** No
15. No **17.** Professor Donovan (D)
19. (a) carnations (C) (b) Yes **21.** Yes **23.** No
25. Answers vary **27.** Answers vary **29.** Yes

Exercise Set 14-3

7. 6 **9.** 45 **11.** Steel Center (S)
13. (a) There is a three-way tie. (b) The results are different.
15. (a) Rosa's Restaurant (R) (b) Yes **17.** No **19.** No
21. Dr. Zhang **23.** green **25.** inmate Z **27.** Answers vary
29. Using pairwise comparison puts the candidates head-to-head against each other.

Exercise Set 14-4

7. a) 32
  b) South: 1.9375
    Central: 4.625
    North: 3.4375

  c)
Campus	South	Central	North
Lower	1	4	3
Upper	2	5	4

  d)
Campus	South	Central	North
Promotions	2	5	3

9. a) 64,444
  b) District 1: 3.755
    District 2: 2.374
    District 3: 2.871

  c)
District	1	2	3
Lower	3	2	2
Upper	4	3	3

  d)
District	1	2	3
Representatives	4	2	3

11. a) 14.6
  b) Terminal A: 3.493
    Terminal B: 2.534
    Terminal C: 4.542
    Terminal D: 1.507

  c)
Terminal	A	B	C	D
Lower	3	2	4	1
Upper	4	3	5	2

  d) Jefferson's Method:
Terminal	A	B	C	D
Trucks	4	2	5	1

    Adams' Method:
Terminal	A	B	C	D
Trucks	3	3	4	2

  e) 12.7; 17.1
13. a) 54
  b) Store 1: 2.204
    Store 2: 1.833
    Store 3: 3.444
    Store 4: 2.519

  c)
Store	1	2	3	4
Lower	2	1	3	2
Upper	3	2	4	3

  d)
Store	1	2	3	4
Computers	2	2	3	3

  e) None
15. a) 1,217.875
  b) Precinct 1: 2.925
    Precinct 2: 6.956
    Precinct 3: 1.762
    Precinct 4: 4.358

  c)
Precinct	1	2	3	4
Lower	2	6	1	4
Upper	3	7	2	5

  d)
Precinct	1	2	3	4
Officers	3	7	2	4

  e) None
17. a) 1,098
  b) Office 1: 2.032
    Office 2: 0.907
    Office 3: 1.424
    Office 4: 1.638

  c)
Office	1	2	3	4
Lower	2	0	1	1
Upper	3	1	2	2

  d)
Office	1	2	3	4
Therapists	2	1	1	2

  e) 1,106
19. Answers vary

Exercise Set 14-5

7. Alabama paradox occurred **9.** Alabama paradox occurred
11. population paradox did not occur

13. a)
Campus	North	South
Podiums	9	52

  b)
Campus	North	South	Campus 3
Podiums	8	53	7

  c) new states paradox occurred
15. a)
State	A	B	C
Seats	11	46	40

  b)
State	A	B	C	D
Seats	10	47	40	13

  c) the new states paradox occurred

Review Exercises

1.

Number of votes	5	5	5
First choice	Q	P	R
Second choice	R	Q	P
Third choice	P	R	Q

3. 5

5.

Number of votes	6	4	10
First choice	C	P	H
Second choice	P	C	P
Third choice	H	H	C

7. 6 **9.** 58 **11.** Style A **13.** Style A **15.** No
17. No **19.** 47 **21.** *Music Man* (M) **23.** *Music Man* (M)
25. Yes **27.** No **29.** comedian

31.

Location	A	B	C	D
Asst. Pastors	5	1	1	3

33.

Location	A	B	C	D
Asst. Pastors	5	2	1	2

35.

Location	A	B	C	D
Asst. Pastors	5	1	1	3

37.

Location	A	B	C	D
Asst. Pastors	5	2	1	2

39. Alabama paradox occurred
41. population paradox did not occur
43. new states paradox did not occur

Chapter 14 Test

1.

Number of votes	1	7	4
First choice	A	B	C
Second choice	B	A	B
Third choice	C	C	A

3. 7 **5.** 100 **7.** Pittsburgh (P)
9. Pittsburgh (P)
11. No **13.** No
15. *Big Brother Nursing Home*

17.

Flight	A	B	C
Flight Attendants	4	6	2

19.

Flight	A	B	C
Flight Attendants	4	6	2

21.

Flight	A	B	C
Flight Attendants	4	6	2

23. population paradox did not occur

CHAPTER 15: GRAPH THEORY

Exercise Set 15-1

9. A, B, C, D, E, F, G **11.** B, G, F
13. B and E **15.** Answers vary; one such path is A, B, E, F
17. G **19.** There is no edge connecting E and D.

33. Answers vary

35.

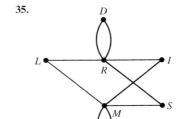

Exercise Set 15-2

7. Euler circuit **9.** Neither
11. (a) Euler path (b) $A, B, C, A, I, C, D, G, I, H, G, F, E, D, F$
13. (a) Euler circuit (b) $A, B, D, H, I, G, D, C, G, F, E, C, A$
15. (a) Neither **17.** (a) Euler circuit (b) A, B, A, C, B, C, A
19. (a) Neither

21. Euler circuit: A, B, C, D, C, A

23. Euler path: A, B, C, A, D, B

25. Euler path: A, B, E, D, A, C, D

27. Neither

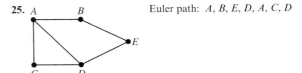

29. Euler path: $A, B, E, D, C, F, A, G, E$

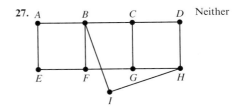

31. Euler circuit: WY, ID, MT, ND, SD, MT, WY, NE, SD, WY

33.

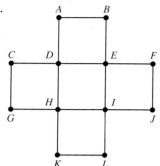

Euler circuit: $A, B, E, F, J, I,$
$L, K, H, I, E, D, H, G, C, D, A$

35. There would be no way to traverse every edge if the graph was not connected.
37. Answers vary

Exercise Set 15-3

9. Answers vary, two possibilities are: A, B, C, D, E, F and $A, C, D,$
$E, F, B.$
11. Answers vary, two possibilities are: $A, B, E, F, J, I, L, K, H, G, C, D$
and $A, B, E, D, C, G, H, K, L, I, J, F.$
13. Answers vary, two possibilities are: A, B, E, C, D and $A, B, E, D, C.$
15. Answers vary, two possibilities are: A, B, D, E, C, F, G, H and $A,$
$B, D, E, C, F, H, G.$
17. Answers vary, two possibilities are: A, B, C, E, D, A and $C, B, A,$
$D, E, C.$
19. Answers vary, two possibilities are: $A, B, D, G, F, E, H, I, C, A$ and
$D, B, A, C, I, H, E, F, G, D.$
21. Answers vary, two possibilities are: A, B, C, D, E, A and $A, D, B,$
$E, C, A.$
23. 2　**25.** 40,320　**27.** P, Q, R, S, P and $P, S, R, Q, P;$ 200
29. $A, F, B, C, E, D, A;$ 109
31. Let $T = $ Pitt, $L = $ Phil, $B = $ Balt and $W = $ Wash.

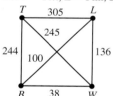

33. $T, B, W, L, T;$ 723 miles
35. Let $N = $ New York, $D = $ Cleveland, $O = $ Chicago and $B = $ Baltimore.

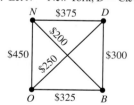

37. $O, D, B, N, O;$ $1,200　**39.** Answers vary　**41.** Answers vary

Exercise Set 15-4

7. The graph is not a tree because it contains a circuit.
9. The graph is a tree.
11. The graph is not a tree because it is disconnected.
13. The graph is a tree.
15. The graph is not a tree because it contains a circuit.
17.

19.

21.

23. 260;

25. 360;

27. 633;

29. 89;

31. 28 feet;

33. 162 feet;

35. Answers vary　**37.** Answers vary

Review Exercises

1. A, B, C, D, E, F **3.** Even **5.** E
7. Yes **9.**

11.

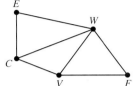

13. Answers vary; one Euler circuit is $D, C, A, B, C, E, B, G, F, E, D$.
15. Answers vary; one Hamilton circuit is A, B, C, D, E, H, F, A.
17. A, D, C, B, E, A for a total of 125
19. $C, D, F, E, C;$ $1,415
21.

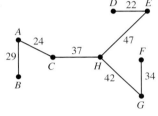

Chapter 15 Test

1. 4 **3.** Answers vary; one possible path is A, B, C, E, D, F.
5. A, B, D, E **7.** Answers vary
9.

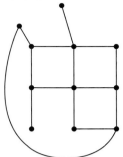

11. Answers vary; one Hamilton path is A, B, C, D, E, F.
13.

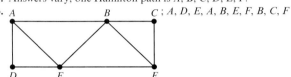

$; A, D, E, A, B, E, F, B, C, F$

15. 64 miles **17.** Euler path
19. Hamilton path **21.** Euler path

PHOTO CREDITS

Design Elements

(Pizza for Learning Objectives): MBPHOTO/iStock photo; (Silver pan under pizza): Laurent Renault/iStock Photo; (Calculator): iStock Photo.

Chapter 1

Opener: © Robert Voets/CBS Photo Archive via Getty Images; p. 4: © The McGraw-Hill Companies, Inc./C.P. Hammond, photographer; p. 5: © Photodisc/Getty RF; p. 8: © Mark Burnett/Stock Boston/PictureQuest; p. 16: © Photodisc/Alamy RF; p. 19: © JupiterImages RF; p. 28(top): © ETH-Bibliothek Zurich, Image Archive; p. 28(bottom): © Alinari Archives/Corbis; p. 30: © Thinkstock Images/JupiterImages RF; p. 31(top): © De Agostini/Getty Images; p. 31(bottom): © Bruce Laurance/ Getty Images; p. 35: © Robert Voets/CBS Photo Archive via Getty Images.

Chapter 2

Opener: © Lester Cohen/WireImage/Getty Images; p. 42: © PhotoLink/Getty Images RF; p. 43: © Phil Walter/ Getty Images; p. 48: © Royalty-Free/Corbis; p. 55: © The McGraw-Hill Companies, Inc./Barry Barker, photographer; p. 61: © Momentum Creative Group/Alamy RF; p. 71: © Digital Vision/Getty Images RF; p. 74: © Digital Vision Ltd./SuperStock RF; p. 76: © Digital Vision RF; p. 77: © BananaStock Ltd. RF; p. 82: © Royalty-Free/ Corbis; p. 84: © IMS Communications Ltd./Capstone Design/FlatEarth Images RF; p. 87: © Lester Cohen/ WireImage/Getty Images.

Chapter 3

Opener 3a: © Muskopf Photography, LLC/Alamy; Opener 3b: © Gino's Premium Images/Alamy; p. 92: © The McGraw-Hill Companies, Inc./Jill Braaten, photographer RF; p. 94: National Library of Medicine, #81192; p. 97: © Life File/Getty Images RF; p. 98: © Cat Sobecki; p. 101: © The McGraw-Hill Companies, Inc./John Flournoy, photographer; p. 104: © Comstock Images/Alamy RF; p. 105: © Photodisc/Getty Images RF; p. 106: © Creatas/PictureQuest RF; p. 107: © Getty Images RF; p. 111: © Robert Landau/Corbis; p. 115: © The McGraw-Hill Companies, Inc./Jill Braaten, photographer RF; p. 116, 119: © Cat Sobecki; p. 121: © Getty Images RF; p. 124: © Christina Lane; p. 126: © Royalty-Free/Corbis; p. 128: © StockTrek/Getty

Images RF; p. 129: © Liquidlibrary/PictureQuest RF; p. 134: Library of Congress, Prints and Photographs Division [LC-USZ62-13016]; p. 135: © Royalty-Free/ Corbis; p. 141(left): © Muskopf Photography, LLC/ Alamy; p. 141(right): © Gino's Premium Images/Alamy.

Chapter 4

Opener: © Spencer Platt/Getty Images; p. 148: © The Studio Dog/Getty Images RF; p. 157: © Scala/Art Resource, NY. Iraq Museum, Baghdad, Iraq; p. 159(top): © ThinkStock/JupiterImages RF; p. 159(bottom), 163: © Digital Vision/Getty Images RF; p. 167: © SSPL/The Image Works; p. 169: © Hulton Archive/Getty Images; p. 172: National Radio Astronomy Observatory; p. 176: © Kevin Winter/Getty Images; p. 178: © Getty Images RF; p. 180: © The McGraw-Hill Companies, Inc./Jill Braaten, photographer; p. 190: Courtesy, Naval Historical Center; p. 193: © Spencer Platt/Getty Images.

Chapter 5

Opener: © Brand X Pictures/PunchStock RF; p. 198: © Photodisc/Getty Images RF; p. 206: © Granger Collection; p. 210: © Steve Bronstein/Getty Images; p. 211: © Christina Lane; p. 216: © Creatas/PunchStock RF; p. 218: © C Squared Studios/Getty Images RF; p. 221(top): © Jamie Squire/Getty Images; p. 221(bottom): © David Young-Wolff/PhotoEdit; p. 228(top): © Cat Sobecki; p. 228(bottom): © Royalty-Free/Corbis; p. 236: © Hulton Archive/Getty Images; p. 244: © Stockdisc/ Getty Images RF; p. 247: © Getty Images RF; p. 251: © Nick Laham/Getty Images; p. 258(top): © Digital Vision/Getty Images RF; p. 258(bottom), 261: © Getty Images RF; p. 263: © Thinkstock Images/JupiterImages RF; p. 264: © Getty Images RF; p. 272: © Brand X Pictures/PunchStock RF.

Chapter 6

Opener: © Scott Olson/Getty Images; p. 278: © Getty Images RF; p. 282: © The Trustees of the British Museum; p. 283: © Blend Images/Getty Images RF; p. 296(top): © Digital Vision/Getty Images RF; p. 296(bottom): © The McGraw-Hill Companies, Inc./Ken Cavanagh, photographer; p. 304: © Royalty-Free/Corbis; p. 305(top): © Getty Images RF; p. 305(bottom): © Royalty-Free/ Corbis; p. 311: © 1999 Copyright IMS Communications Ltd./Capstone Design. All Rights Reserved. RF;

p. 312: © PhotoLink/Getty Images RF; p. 313(top): USDA; p. 313(bottom), 314: © Life File/Getty Images RF; p. 315: © Photodisc/PunchStock RF; p. 319: © Stockbyte/Getty Images RF; p. 324: © Getty Images RF; p. 325: © The McGraw-Hill Companies, Inc./Christopher Kerrigan, photographer RF; p. 326: © Getty Images RF; p. 328: © Brand X Pictures/JupiterImages RF; p. 341: © Scott Olson/Getty Images.

Chapter 7

Page 349: © Lowell Georgia/Corbis; p. 350: © C Squared Studios/Getty Images RF; p. 353, 356(top): © Getty Images RF; p. 356(bottom): © liquidlibrary/Dynamic Graphics/JupiterImages RF; p. 363: © PhotoLink/Getty Images RF; p. 370: © Getty Images RF; p. 374: © StockTrek/Getty Images RF; p. 380: © Digital Vision/Getty Images RF; p. 389: © Royalty-Free/Corbis; p. 390: © Susan Van Etten/PhotoEdit; p. 391: © PhotoLink/Getty Images RF; p. 394: © Royalty-Free/Corbis; p. 401: © Getty Images RF; p. 402: © Joel Gordon; p. 404: © Comstock Images/Corbis; p. 405: © Comstock Images/Alamy RF; p. 408(top,bottom): © Getty Images RF; p. 409: © James L. Amos/Photo Researchers, Inc.

Chapter 8

Opener: © Royalty-Free/Corbis; p. 420: © PhotoLink/Getty Images RF; p. 423: © Photodisc/Getty Images RF; p. 424: © Royalty-Free/Corbis; p. 425: © Getty Images RF; p. 429: © Stockbyte/PunchStock RF; p. 430–431: © PhotoLink/Getty Images RF; p. 432: © Royalty-Free/Corbis; p. 435: © Beathan/Corbis RF; p. 439: © Jeff Greenberg/PhotoEdit; p. 446: © SW Productions/Getty Images RF; p. 447(top): © Cat Sobecki; p. 447(bottom): © Getty Images RF; p. 453(top): © Royalty-Free/Corbis; p. 453(bottom): © Getty Images RF; p. 458: © Brand X Pictures RF; p. 460: © PhotoLink/Getty Images RF; p. 461: © Getty Images RF; p. 462: © Photodisc/Getty Images RF; p. 465: © Comstock Images RF; p. 467: © Royalty-Free/Corbis; p. 470: © The McGraw-Hill Companies, Inc./Jill Braaten, photographer; p. 475: © Royalty-Free/Corbis.

Chapter 9

Opener: © Panoramic Images/Getty Images; p. 482: © Stockbyte/PunchStock RF; p. 483: © Pixtal/SuperStock RF; p. 484: © PhotoLink/Getty Images RF; p. 485, 486: © Brand X Pictures RF; p. 487: © Cat Sobecki; p. 490, 491: © Royalty-Free/Corbis; p. 492: © Getty Images RF; p. 494: © Erica S. Leeds RF; p. 499(top): © AFP/Getty Images; p. 499(bottom): © Creatas/PictureQuest RF; p. 500–501: © Royalty-Free/Corbis; p. 502(top): © Creatas/PunchStock RF; p. 502(bottom): © The McGraw-Hill Companies, Inc./Ken Cavanagh, photographer; p. 506: © Panoramic Images/Getty Images.

Chapter 10

Opener 10a–d, p. 512(top): © Cat Sobecki; p. 512(bottom): © Getty Images RF; p. 516: © Hulton Archive/Getty Images; p. 521: © Life File/Getty Images RF; p. 524: © Royalty-Free/Corbis; p. 525: © Brand X Pictures RF; p. 527: © Brand X Pictures/PunchStock RF; p. 531: © Digital Vision/Getty Images RF; p. 532(left): © Ingram Publishing/Alamy RF; p. 532(middle): © Image Club RF; p. 532(right): © Stockbyte/Getty Images RF; p. 534: © Digital Vision RF; p. 536: © Comstock Images/PunchStock RF; p. 539(top, bottom): © Getty Images RF; p. 541: NASA; p. 544: © Comstock Images/JupiterImages/Alamy RF; p. 548: © Cat Sobecki; p. 549(left): © The McGraw-Hill Companies, Inc./Ken Cavanagh, photographer; p. 549(right): © Getty Images RF; p. 552: © Brand X Pictures RF; p. 556: © Purestock/Alamy RF; p. 557: © Royalty-Free/Corbis; p. 559: © Photodisc/Getty Images RF; p. 563: M.C. Escher's "Symmetry Drawing E110" © 2009 The M.C. Escher Company-Holland. All rights reserved. www.mcescher.com; p. 566 (1–4): © Cat Sobecki.

Chapter 11

Opener 11a: © Royalty-Free/Corbis; Opener 11b: © Mark Steinmetz/Amanita Pictures RF; Opener 11c: © Photodisc/Getty Images RF; Opener 11d: © Stockbyte/PunchStock RF; Opener 11e: © Royalty-Free/Corbis; p. 574: © Corbis/agefotostock RF; p. 575(top): © C Squared Studios/Getty Images RF; p. 577: © MedioImages RF; p. 580: © PhotoLink/Getty Images RF; p. 582, p. 584: © Christina Lane; p. 587: © Royalty-Free/Corbis; p. 588: © Photodisc/Getty Images RF; p. 589: © Getty Images RF; p. 590: © Stockbyte/Alamy RF; p. 591, 592: © Getty Images RF; p. 593: © The McGraw-Hill Companies, Inc./C.P. Hammond, photographer; p. 597: © MedioImages RF; p. 599: © Bettmann/Corbis; p. 600: © Royalty-Free/Corbis; p. 601: © The McGraw-Hill Companies, Inc./C.P. Hammond, photographer; p. 605(top): © Stockbyte/PunchStock RF; p. 605(bottom): © BananaStock/JupiterImages RF; p. 606: © F Schussler/PhotoLink/Getty Images RF; p. 609: © Rob Carr/AP Photo; p. 613: © PhotoLink/Getty Images RF; p. 614: © STAN HONDA/AFP/Getty Images; p. 616: Courtesy of the Office of the Historian, U.S. House of Representatives; p. 620: © Getty Images RF; p. 623: © The McGraw-Hill Companies, Inc./Barry Barker, photographer; p. 624: © moodboard/agefotostock RF; p. 627: © Digital Vision/SuperStock RF; p. 628: © Royalty-Free/Corbis; p. 632: © Veer RF; p. 635: © BananaStock/agefotostock RF; p. 640a: © Royalty-Free/Corbis; p. 640b: © Amanita Pictures RF; p. 640c: © PhotoDisc/Getty Images RF; p. 640d: © Stockbyte/PunchStock RF; p. 640e: © Royalty-Free/Corbis.

Chapter 12

Opener: © Julie Dermansky/Photo Researchers, Inc.; p. 648: © Royalty-FreeCorbis; p. 649: U.S. Fish & Wildlife

Service/Mike Lockhart; p. 650: © Brand X Pictures RF; p. 651: © Getty Images RF; p. 653: © Digital Vision/ Getty Images RF; p. 658: © Getty Images RF; p. 660: © Digital Vision/Getty Images RF; p. 661, 665, 666: © Getty Images RF; p. 667: © Purestock/PunchStock RF; p. 668(top): © Getty Images RF; p. 668(bottom): NASA; p. 670: © Image Source/PunchStock RF; p. 671: © Wire-Image/Getty Images; p. 672: © Frare/Brand X Pictures/ Corbis RF; p. 675(top): © Tim Davis/Corbis; p. 675(bottom): © Chris Collins/Corbis; p. 681(top): © Comstock Images/JupiterImages RF; p. 681(bottom): © Getty Images RF; p. 682(top): United States Navy; p. 682(bottom): © Comstock Images/JupiterImages RF; p. 685: © Cat Sobecki; p. 686: © Getty Images RF; p. 693: © The McGraw-Hill Companies, Inc./John Flournoy, photographer; p. 694: © PhotoLink/Getty Images RF; p. 695: © PhotoDisc/Getty Images RF; p. 696: © Life File/Getty Images RF; p. 699: © The McGraw-Hill Companies, Inc./ John Flournoy, photographer; p. 700(top): © Digital/ SuperStock RF; p. 700(bottom): © Royalty-Free/Corbis; p. 704(top): © Getty Images RF; p. 704 (bottom): © The McGraw-Hill Companies, Inc./C.P. Hammond, photographer; p. 707: © The McGraw-Hill Companies, Inc./ John Flournoy, photographer; p. 711: © Julie Dermansky/ Photo Researchers, Inc.; p. S1: © Tracy Kahn/Corbis RF; p. S2 (top): © Stockbyte/Getty Images RF; p. S2 (center): © Jim Bourg/Reuters; p. S2 (bottom): © The McGraw-Hill Companies, Inc./C.P. Hammond, photographer; p. S4: © SuperStock RF.

Chapter 13

Opener: © Chad Baker/Getty Images RF; p. 725: © Royalty Free/Corbis; p. 729: http://commons.wikimedia.org/wiki/ File:Evariste_galois.jpg#filelinks; p. 732: © Royalty Free/ Corbis; p. 733: © Getty Images RF; p. 735: © Photodisc/ Getty Images RF; p. 738: © Chad Baker/Getty Images RF.

Chapter 14

Opener: © Nick Laham/Getty Images; p. 744: © Comstock Images/PunchStock RF; p. 745: © Digital Vision Ltd./SuperStock RF; p. 747: © The McGraw-Hill Companies, Inc./Jill Braaten, photographer; p. 751: © Doug Benc/Getty Images; p. 755: © The McGraw-Hill Companies, Inc./Lars A. Niki, photographer; p. 759: © The McGraw-Hill Companies, Inc./John Flournoy, photographer; p. 761: © Royalty-Free/Corbis; p. 763: © Kenneth J. Arrow; p. 764: © Visions of America/Corbis RF; p. 767(top): © Getty Images RF; p. 767(bottom): © Royalty-Free/Corbis; p. 770: © BananaStock Ltd. RF; p. 774: © Comstock Images/Alamy RF; p. 778: The Library of Congress, Prints and Photographs Division [LC-USZC4-422]; p. 779: © Creatas/PunchStock RF; p. 782: © IT Stock/Alamy RF; p. 785: © Nick Laham/ Getty Images.

Chapter 15

Opener: © Digital Vision RF; p. 792: © Stockdisc/Digital Vision RF; p. 800: © Design Pics Inc./Alamy RF; p. 806: © Getty Images RF; p. 807: © Digital Vision RF; p. 814: © Comstock Images/Alamy RF; p. 817: © PhotoLink/ Getty Images RF; p. 823: © Digital Vision RF.

INDEX